Textbook of Applied Anatomy for Nurses - Volume 1

Textbook of Applied Anatomy for Nurses - Volume 1

3rd edition

Nachiket Shankar

MBBS, MS (Anatomy)
Professor, Department of Anatomy and
Medical Education
St. John's Medical College, Bangalore

ELSEVIER

ELSEVIER

RELX India Pvt. Ltd.
Registered Office: 818, Indraprakash Building, 8th Floor, 21, Barakhamba Road, New Delhi-110001
Corporate Office: 14th Floor, Building No. 10B, DLF Cyber City, Phase II, Gurgaon-122002, Haryana, India

Textbook of Applied Anatomy for Nurses, 3rd edition, Nachiket Shankar

ISBN: 978-81-312-6926-8
e-Book ISBN: 978-81-312-6927-5

ISBN (Set): 978-81-312-6924-4

Content Strategist: Deepti Damodaran
Content Project Manager: Shivani Pal
Sr Production Executive: Dhan Singh
Sr Cover Designer: Milind Majgaonkar

Typeset by GW Tech India

Printed in India by Rajkamal Electric Press, Kundli, Haryana.

Preface

The 3rd edition of this textbook has been divided into two volumes. Volume 1 deals with human anatomy, whereas Volume 2 relates to human physiology. This ensures that each volume is of a more manageable size, making it handy for students to refer to.

Volume 1 of the current edition has been improved, while retaining the strengths of the previous edition. The language has been further simplified to improve readability. Many figures have been edited to ensure that they are better aligned with the accompanying text. The content and order of the chapters have been modified, wherever required, to comply with the latest syllabus in anatomy prescribed by the Indian Nursing Council. The layout of the chapters has been improved to highlight the nursing applications. The accompanying workbook has also been revised to make it more user friendly.

It is hoped that this edition will enable readers to acquire a sound grasp of the subjects of anatomy and physiology, from an examination viewpoint, and as a solid foundation for their future work as healthcare professionals.

Preface to the Second Edition

A book is only useful when it serves the needs of its users. At the outset we would like to acknowledge the various reviewers and people who sent us feedback of the first edition. We continue to encourage feedback on the book so that we can address the continued needs of students and teachers.

This edition has been extensively revised in keeping with the revised INC curriculum. New chapters have been written, and old chapters have been updated with new material including tables and diagrams.

Given the rightful need for early clinical exposure, applied aspects of the basic concepts in anatomy and physiology have been addressed at the end of each chapter. These have been written keeping in mind that students are in the first year of their course. In the Physiology section, there are dedicated chapters on Applied aspects of an entire system. These chapters outline common conditions that the students will encounter in their clinical training. Case studies have also been provided that require the student to synthesise learning across chapters of an entire system. Simple suggested activities during hospital visits reinforce the need for early clinical exposure and the integration of the basic medical sciences with clinical medicine.

Nurses, like all other health professionals require to be self-learners. In order to facilitate this, the applied chapters in Physiology have topics for self-directed learning which are not covered in the book, but which encourage students to widen their reading. These topics could be the basis of assignments or student seminars.

This is a combined book of anatomy and physiology. This allows students to better understand structure-function relationships. We have opted to keep the anatomy and physiology sections separate as this is how the subjects are commonly taught and assessed. However, students are encouraged to use the readily available material in this book to cross reference chapters in anatomy and physiology. This will allow for more integrated learning. In order to facilitate this, a ready reckoner of chapter linkages on structure and function is provided.

Students coming into the nursing curriculum often grapple with the new nomenclature and the vast subject material. In order to help students deal with these problems, every chapter has specific learning objectives, a glossary of key terms and a summary at the end of each chapter.

Students are also acutely aware that they have the hurdles of examinations to overcome. In order to address this student need, we have created a workbook that helps students to review and revise the subject matter of the main textbook. This workbook, thus, complements the main textbook and contains short answer questions for rapid review and short and long essay questions. Answer keys to these questions have been provided or in the case of longer questions, references to the main textbook.

We would like to acknowledge the feedback from our own colleagues and students. In particular, we would like to acknowledge Dr Yogitha Ravindran (Anatomy) and Dr Savitha D (Physiology), both of St. John's Medical College for their comments and review.

We trust that this revised edition meets the needs of the students and teachers alike and strongly elicit your comments and feedback to improve the book.

Nachiket Shankar
Mario Vaz

Preface to 1st Edition

Over the years, as teachers, we have seen our nursing students struggle to find an appropriate textbook of Anatomy and Physiology that meets their needs. This book is intended to fulfil that need. In drafting the contents of the book, we paid close attention to the curriculum of the Nursing Council of India, which has prescribed the structure of the book and the chapters. One of the challenges in writing this book was the decision on the 'depth' of the material. We were aware that to write a book that was too sketchy would, in effect, be undermining the worth of nurses. Too detailed a book and the very purpose that we undertook this project would be defeated. We hope that we have provided a 'middle' ground: we are aware that some students may wish to explore the subject matter in greater detail from other reference books. In such a situation we trust that the book provides a solid foundation on which to build on.

We have written the chapters under several headings. Each chapter has specific learning objectives which allow the student to know what they should be able to learn on reading the chapter. A glossary of terms is provided so that students can come to grips with the nomenclature or vocabulary of a new subject. The main body of the chapter addresses the specific learning objectives that have been outlined and is followed by a summary. We have also provided Applications in Nursing, which have been restricted to things that we believe a first-year student would be reasonably expected to understand. Clearly, there are many more applications which the student will appreciate as they move on in the nursing course. Finally, there are review questions which allow the student to quiz themselves on what they have read.

Although primarily written for nurses, this book will also likely serve the needs of those who are enrolled in the allied health sciences.

A textbook is only useful if it meets the needs of students and teachers. We, therefore, would welcome feedback that will allow us to better address these needs in future editions.

Contributor

Yogitha Ravindranath
Department of Anatomy, St. John's Medical College, Bangalore

Contents

SECTION 1
Introduction to Anatomical Terms and Organization of the Human Body

SECTION 2
The Respiratory System

SECTION 3
The Digestive System

Syllabus Mapper

VOLUME I: APPLIED ANATOMY		
Syllabus for Applied Anatomy	**Chapters/Unit from the Book**	**Additional Content**
UNIT– I Introduction		
Introduction to anatomical terms relative to position- anterior, ventral, Posterior dorsal, superior, inferior, median, lateral, proximal, distal, superficial, deep, prone, supine, palmar and plantar	Chapter 2	
Anatomical planes (axial/transverse/ horizontal, sagittal/vertical	Chapter 2	
Movements (flexion, extension, abduction, adduction, medial rotation, lateral rotation, inversion, eversion, supination, pronation, plantar flexion, dorsal flexion and circumduction	Chapter 2	
Cell structure, Cell division	Chapter 3	
Tissue-definition, types, characteristics, classification, location	Chapter 3	
Membrane, glands- classification and structure	Chapter 4 and Chapter 5	
Identify major surface and bony landmarks in each body region, Organization of human body	Chapter 2	
Hyaline, fibro cartilage, elastic cartilage	Chapter 7	
Features of skeletal, smooth and cardiac muscle	Chapter 8	
Application and implication in nursing	The initial eight chapters are introductory in nature and do not have any direct applications in nursing. However the relavant applied anatomy has been added to each chapter.	
UNIT – II The Respiratory system		
Structure of the organs of respiration	Chapers 9 and 10	
Muscles of respiration	Chapter 10	
Application and implication in nursing	Incorporated into each chapter	
UNIT – III The Digestive system		
Structure of alimentary canal and accessory organs of digestion	Chapters 11, 12 and 13	
Application and implications in nursing	Incorporated into each chapter	
UNIT- IV The Circulatory and lymphatic system		
1. Circulatory System.		
Structure of blood components, blood vessels- Arterial and Venous system	Chapter 14 (The structure of blood components are described in the accompanying Physiology textbook)	
Position of heart relative to the associated structures	Chapter 15	
Chambers of heart, layers of heart	Chapter 16	
Heart valves, coronary arteries	Chapter 16	
Nerve and blood supply to heart	Chapter 15	

VOLUME I: APPLIED ANATOMY		
Syllabus for Applied Anatomy	**Chapters/Unit from the Book**	**Additional Content**
Lymphatic tissue	Chapter 17	
Veins used for IV injections	Chapter 14	
Application and implication in nursing	Incorporated into each chapter	
UNIT- V The Endocrine system		
Structure of Hypothalamus, Pineal Gland, Pituitary gland,Thyroid, Parathyroid, Thymus, Pancreas and Adrenal glands	Chapter 18	
UNIT- VI The Sensory organs		
Structure of skin, eye, ear, nose and tongue	Chapters 19 and 20	
Application and implications in nursing	Incorporated into each chapter	
UNIT- VII The Musculoskeletal system: The skeletal system		
Anatomical positions	Chapter 2	
Bones-Types, structure, growth and ossification	Chapter 21	
Axial and Appendicular skeleton	Chapters 22 and 23	
Joints- classification, major joints and structure	Chapters 24 and 25	
Application and implications in nursing	Incorporated into each chapter	
The Muscular System		
Types and structure of Muscles	Chapter 8	
Muscle groups-muscles of the head, neck, thorax, abdomen, pelvis, upper limb and lower limbs	Chapters 26 and 27	
Principal muscles- deltoid, biceps, triceps, respiratory, abdominal, pelvic floor, pelvic floor muscles, gluteal muscles and vastus lateralis	Chapters 26 and 27	
Major muscles involved in nursing procedures	Chapters 26 and 27	
UNIT- VIII The Renal System		
Structure of kidney, ureters, bladder, urethra	Chapters 28 and 29	
Application and implication in nursing	Incorporated into each chapter	
UNIT- IX The Reproductive System		
Structure of male reproductive organs	Chapter 31	
Structure of female reproductive organs	Chapter 30	
Structure of breast	Chapter 30	
UNIT- X The Nervous system		
Review Structure of neurons	Chapter 32	
CNS, ANS and PNS (Central, autonomic and peripheral)	Chapter 32	
Structure of brain, spinal cord, cranial nerves, spinal nerves, peripheral nerves, functional areas of cerebral cortex	Chapters 33, 34 and 35	
Ventricular system, formation, circulation, and drainage	Chapters 32, 34 and 35	
Application and implication in nursing	Incorporated into each chapter	

Competency Mapper

1
SECTION

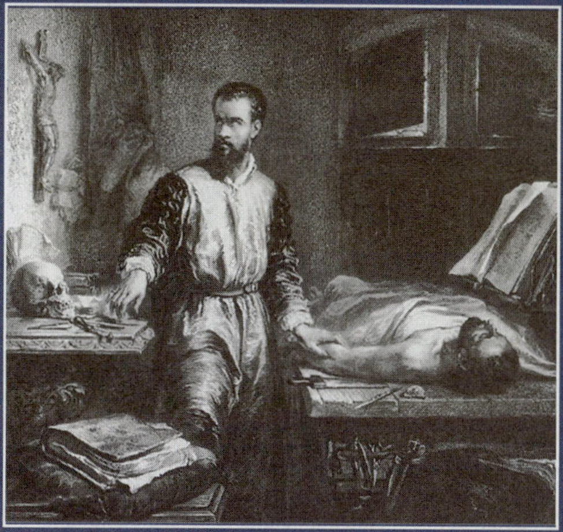

Introduction to Anatomical Terms and Organization of the Human Body

Section Outline

SECTION 1

Introduction to Anatomical Terms and Organization of the Human Body

CHAPTER 1

What Is Anatomy?

SPECIFIC LEARNING OBJECTIVES

At the end of this chapter, the student should be able to:

- Explain the importance of anatomy in health sciences.
- Describe in brief the history of anatomy.
- Name the major subdivisions of anatomy.
- Describe the scope of each these subdivisions.

GLOSSARY OF TERMS

- **Anatomy:** a study of the structural organization of the human body at different levels
- **Gross anatomy:** a study of the structures of the human body visible to the naked eye
- **Histology:** a study of the microscopic structure of the human body
- **Embryology:** a study of the developing human from the time of conception till birth
- **Surface anatomy:** a study of the surface projections of the various structures of the human body
- **Radiologic anatomy:** a study of bodily structures using radiographic techniques

INTRODUCTION

The structure and function of the human body have been a matter of great interest for millennia. Over the last few centuries, considerable progress has been made in our understanding of these aspects. This spurt in knowledge has partially resulted from the wide array of techniques now available to study the human body. This chapter will provide an insight about the place of anatomy in health sciences as well as the important historical events that enabled advances in the field. The broad subdivisions and scope of each of these fields of anatomy will also be briefly explained.

ROLE OF ANATOMY IN HEALTH SCIENCES

The knowledge of anatomy is important to perform a simple procedure like the palpation of a pulse or a complicated surgery. In the departments of pathology and radiology, it is essential that the normal structure of the organs being studied is known in order to make accurate diagnoses of disease conditions. It is in this context that one of the subjects of study in the first year of any health science course includes human anatomy. Wherever possible, the clinical relevance of the anatomical facts will be emphasized in each chapter of this book.

A BRIEF HISTORY OF HUMAN ANATOMY

When human beings were hunter-gatherers, they would have observed the various body parts of the kills that they made. Subsequently, the ancient **Egyptian civilizations** were known to have mastered the art of mummification for religious purposes (Fig. 1.1). This enabled them to preserve bodies almost indefinitely. Prior to the mummification process, various organs were removed and preserved in jars. Special chemicals and elaborate processes were used for preservation.

In India, **Sushrutha** had a detailed enough knowledge of anatomy to perform plastic surgeries of the face (Fig. 1.2). The **Greek** and **Roman** civilizations contributed greatly to the knowledge of human anatomy. **Hippocrates** and **Herophilus** were two Greek physicians who made some of the earliest systematic studies of human anatomy. **Galen**, who was of Greek origin, was a prominent physician in the Roman Empire. His teachings on many medical subjects including anatomy were considered as the most authoritative sources of information from the 2nd century AD till the 14th century AD.

Mondino d'Luzzi, **Leonardo da Vinci** and **Vesalius** (Fig. 1.3) were pioneers in the field of gross anatomy. Much of the present-day knowledge of gross anatomy is derived from the

FIG. 1.1 An Egyptian mummy.

FIG. 1.2 Sushrutha performing a surgery of the ear.

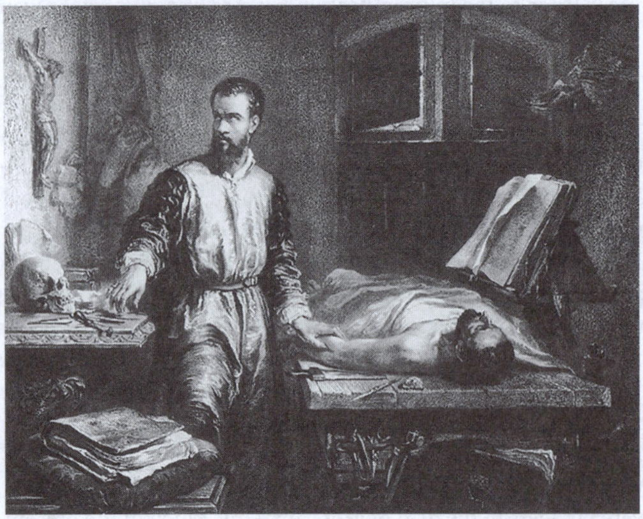

FIG. 1.3 Andreas Vesalius performing a dissection.

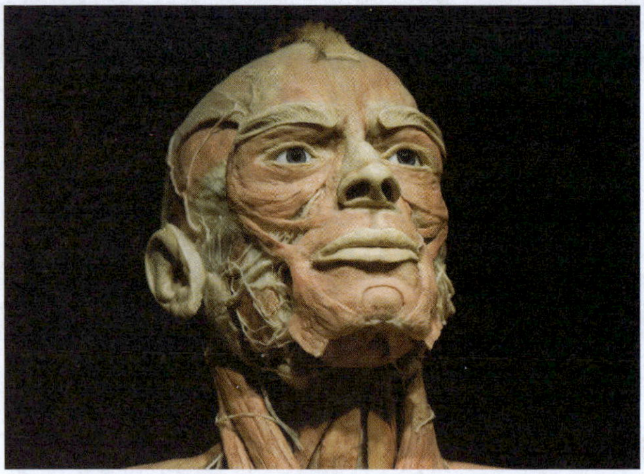

FIG. 1.4 A plastinated specimen.

observations, dissections and detailed diagrams of these great anatomists from 14th to 16th centuries AD. In the 17th century, **William Harvey** discovered the circulation of blood. Around this time, microscopic anatomy was given an impetus with the invention of the first light microscopes. **Robert Hooke** was the first person to observe cells under the light microscope. This eventually led to the formulation of the cell theory by **Rudolf Virchow**, **Schleiden** and **Schwann** in the 19th century.

William and **John Hunter** were brothers from England who contributed greatly to the advancement of anatomical knowledge in the 18th century. The famous Hunterian Museum in Glasgow displays the large number of anatomical specimens that were collected principally by John Hunter. William Hunter contributed to developing modern embalming methods for the preservation of human bodies. These methods were further developed in the 19th century in America by **Thomas Holmes**, who is considered the father of embalming.

The 20th and 21st centuries have seen a revolution in visualizing human anatomy through various radiological methods such as roentgenography, computer tomography (CT), ultrasound, endoscopy and magnetic resonance imaging (MRI). Additionally, it is possible to visualize submicroscopic structures through great advances in microscopic techniques such as electron microscopy, confocal microscopy and fluorescent microscopy to name a few. Plastination is a novel technique for the lifelike preservation of human remains invented by a German scientist **Gunther von Hagens** (Fig. 1.4). The greatest advantage of this technique of body preservation is that the structures retain their flexibility and can be preserved almost indefinitely.

SUBDIVISIONS OF ANATOMY AND THEIR SCOPE

Gross anatomy refers to structures of the human body that can be studied with the naked eye. There are two main approaches to studying gross anatomy, systematic anatomy and regional anatomy. In the systematic approach, the body is organized by systems, for example digestive, nervous and endocrine, for the purpose of studying it. This is the approach followed in this book. In the regional approach, structures are studied based on the region of the body that they belong to, for example upper and lower extremities, thorax, abdomen, pelvis, head and neck and neuroanatomy. While a basic knowledge of gross anatomy is essential for all health care professionals, a more detailed knowledge would be required for surgeons.

Microscopic anatomy or **histology** is the study of the microscopic structure of organs and tissues of the body. This forms the basis for histopathology, which is the study of diseased tissues and plays a key role in the diagnosis of many diseases especially tumours.

Developmental anatomy or **embryology** looks at the development of the zygote from the time of its formation till its development into a full-term foetus. Many congenital anomalies can be explained and more effectively treated or prevented with knowledge of their developmental basis.

Surface anatomy deals with the study of the surface projections of various internal structures. This knowledge is particularly important for access to internal structures from the outside, for example draining of excessive fluid from the pleural cavity.

Radiologic anatomy is the visualization of bodily structures using radiographic procedures like roentgenographs, CT scans, MRI and ultrasound. These procedures are extremely useful in making a sound diagnosis of many conditions such as a stroke caused by bleeding into the brain.

SUMMARY

- Anatomy is a study of the structure of the human body.
- A working knowledge of anatomy is essential for the management of patient problems.
- Anatomy has an ancient history, but major advances in anatomical knowledge have occurred after the 16th century AD.
- Our knowledge of living anatomy has grown immensely with advances in radiological methods.
- The subdivisions of anatomy include gross anatomy, histology, embryology, surface anatomy and radiologic anatomy.

CHAPTER 2

Anatomical Terminology

SPECIFIC LEARNING OBJECTIVES

At the end of this chapter, the student should be able to:

- Define the anatomical position of the body.
- Describe the planes of the body.
- Use the common accepted terms of reference to correctly describe structures of the human body and their movements.
- Describe the major surface and bony landmarks of the body.

GLOSSARY OF TERMS

- **Anatomical position:** the position of the body which is used as a reference position for describing various structures
- **Planes of the body:** the body viewed from different aspects like sagittal, coronal and transverse
- **Terms of reference:** anatomical terms used to describe the position of various structures in relation to one another

INTRODUCTION

There are many technical terms that are used to describe the relative positions of the various structures of the body. This is required to ensure clarity and uniformity when health professionals communicate with one another. This chapter will describe the most common terms of reference used in anatomy.

ANATOMICAL POSITION (Fig. 2.1)

The anatomical position is defined as the position in which an individual is standing erect, with the head facing forwards and the eyes looking straight ahead at the horizon, the upper limbs by the side of the body with the palms facing forwards and the lower limbs together with the feet directed forwards. All anatomical structures are described in relation to the anatomical position regardless of the actual position of the body.

PLANES OF THE BODY (Fig. 2.1)

Three following planes of the body have been described:

- **Sagittal plane:** divides the body into left and right halves
- **Coronal (frontal) plane:** divides the body into front and back parts
- **Transverse plane:** divides the body into upper and lower parts

SECTIONS OF THE BODY

The structures of the body have characteristic appearances when they are sectioned along particular planes. Three types of sections have been described as follows:

- **Longitudinal section:** section along the length of a structure
- **Transverse section (cross-section or axial section):** section across the length of a structure
- **Oblique section:** section that passes obliquely through a structure

TERMS OF RELATIONSHIP (Fig. 2.1)

The following terms are used to describe the relative positions of body structures:

- **Superior and inferior:** towards the head and away from the head
- **Medial and lateral:** towards the midline and away from the midline
- **Anterior and posterior:** towards the front of the body and back of the body
- **Cranial and caudal:** similar to superior and inferior, sometimes used for the trunk
- **Proximal and distal:** similar to superior and inferior, sometimes used for the limbs

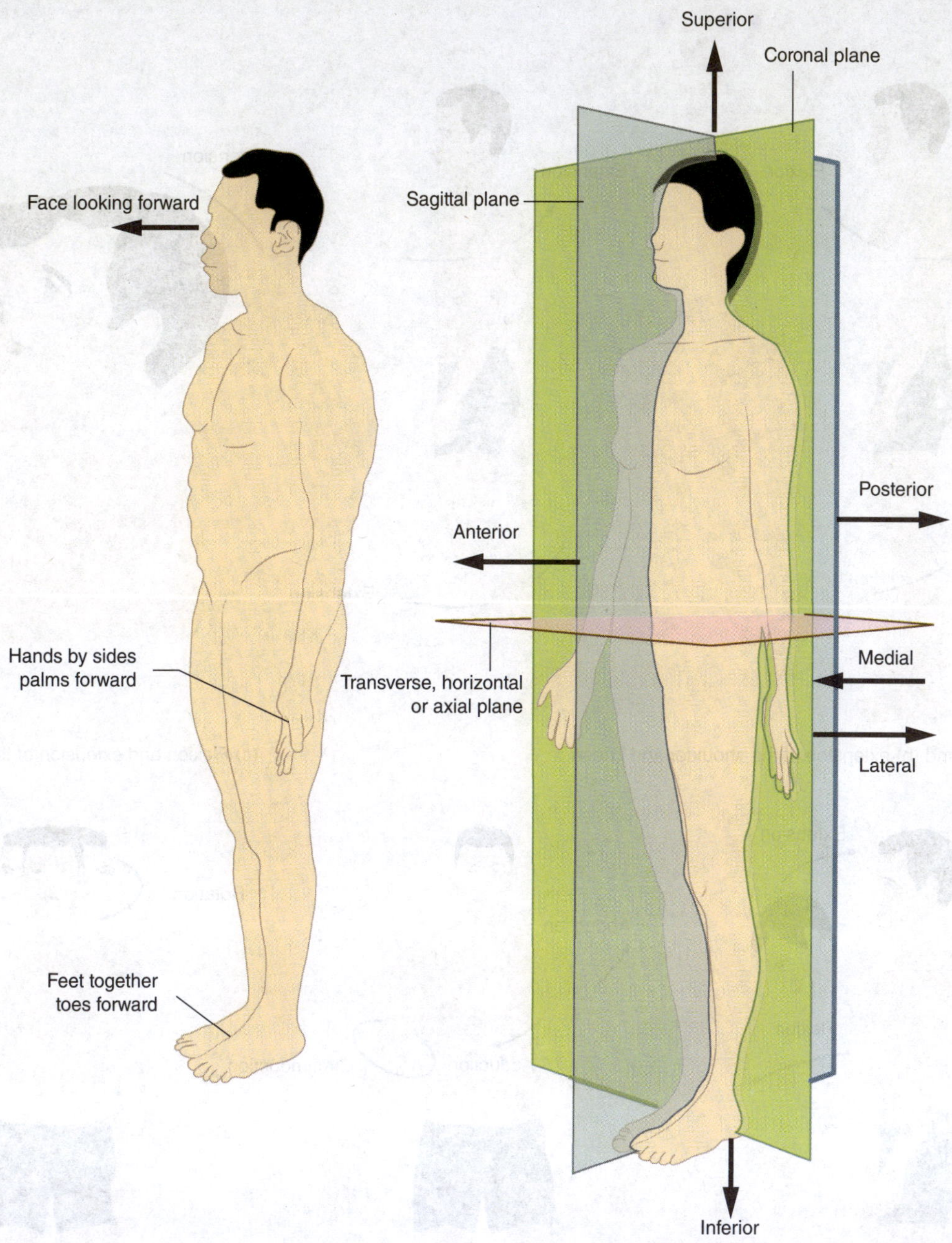

FIG. 2.1 The anatomical position, planes and terms of reference.

- **Ventral and dorsal:** similar to anterior and posterior, sometimes used for the trunk
- **Palmar and dorsal:** similar to anterior and posterior, used for the hand
- **Dorsal and plantar:** similar to anterior and posterior, used for the foot
- **Superficial and deep:** towards and away from the surface of the body, terms used to describe the depth of structures

MOVEMENTS OF THE BODY (Figs 2.2 and 2.3)

The following are the terms that are used to describe the movements of various body parts relative to one another:

- **Flexion:** bending or decreasing the angle between bones
- **Extension:** straightening or increasing the angle between bones
- **Abduction:** moving away from the midline in the coronal plane
- **Adduction:** moving towards the midline in the coronal plane
- **Medial (internal) rotation:** brings the anterior surface of a limb closer to the midline
- **Lateral (external) rotation:** takes the anterior surface of a limb away from the midline
- **Circumduction:** mixture of flexion, extension, abduction and adduction
- **Pronation:** movement of the forearm and hand such that the palm faces anteriorly

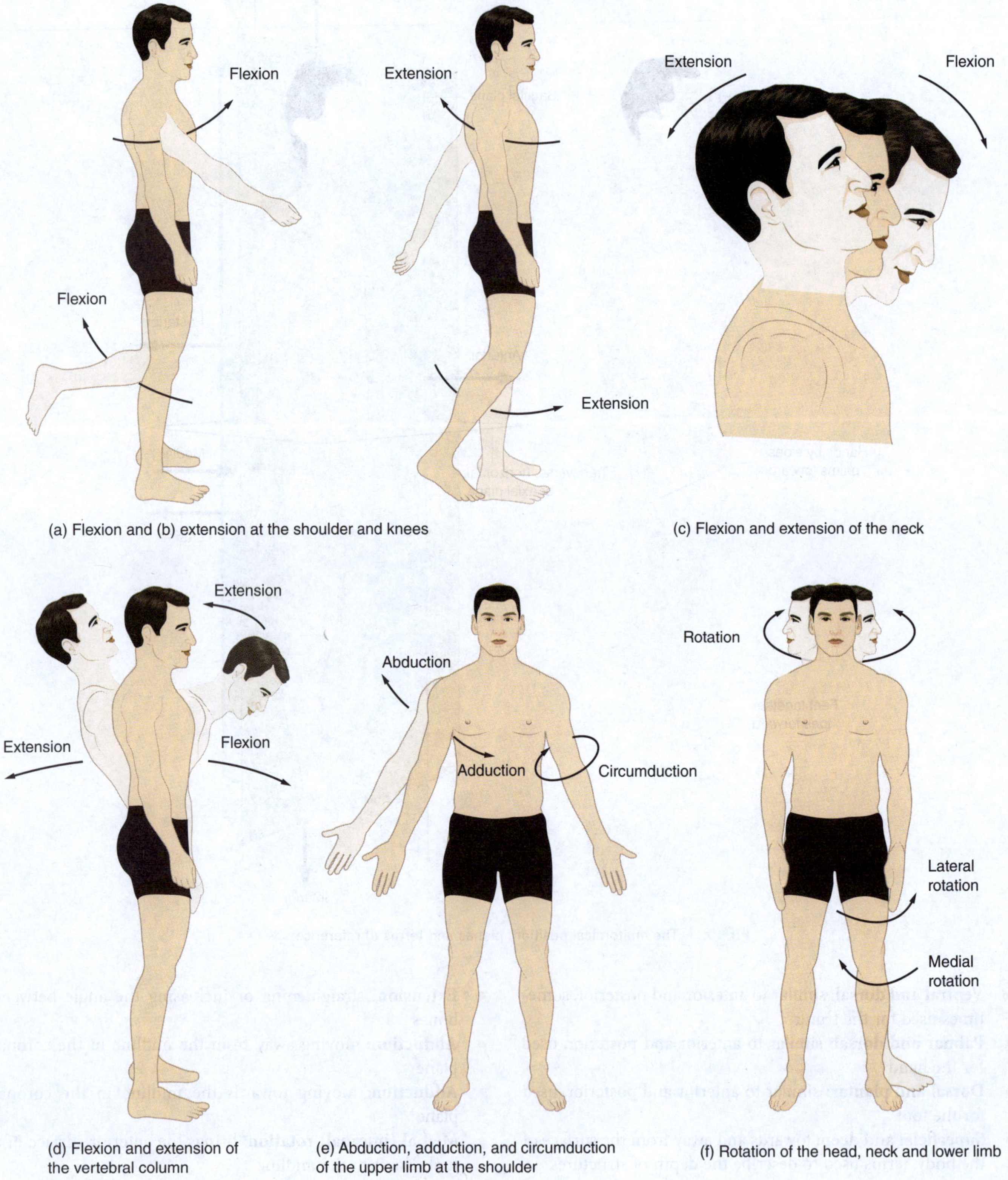

FIG. 2.2 Movements of the body.

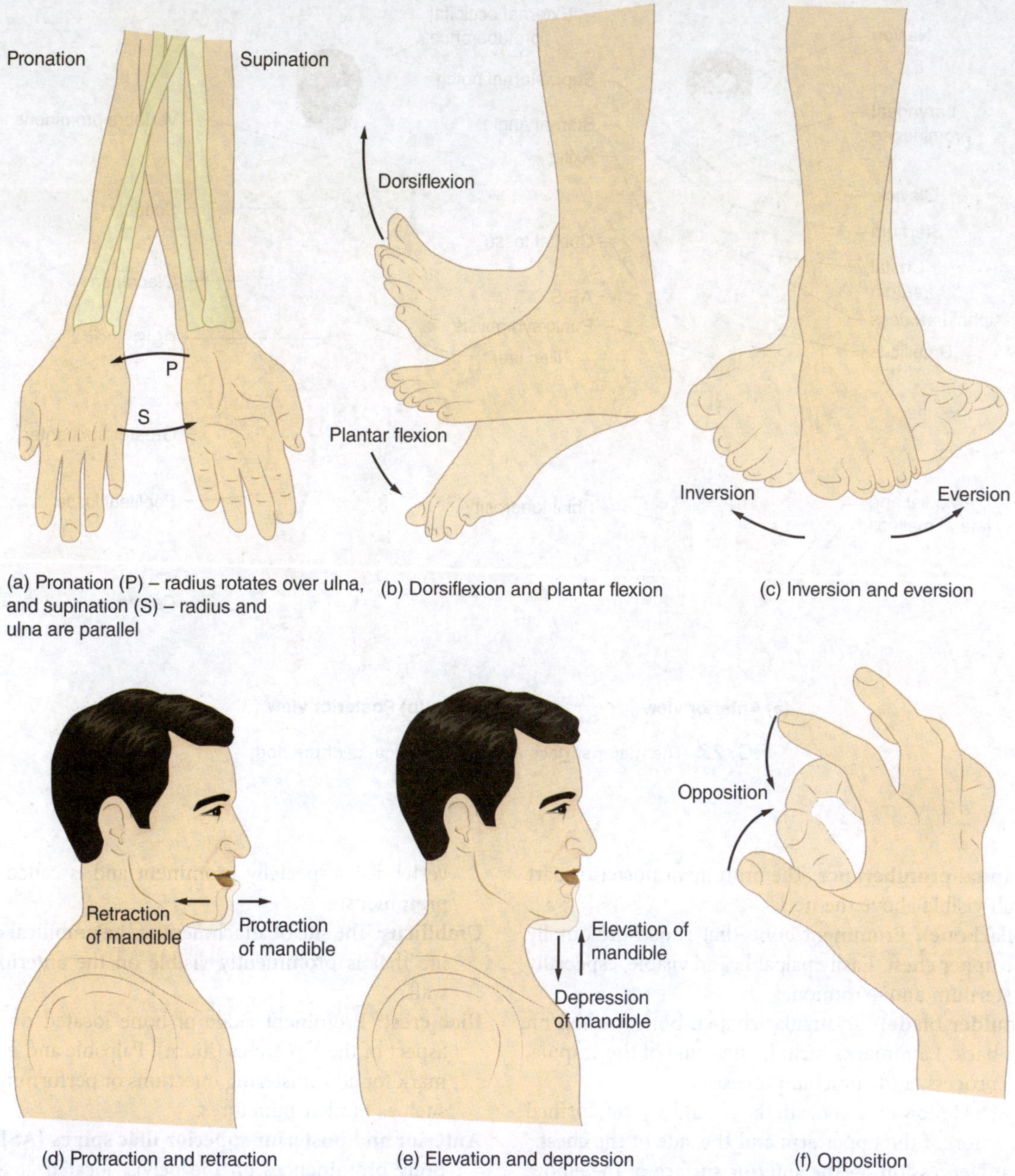

FIG. 2.3 Movements of the jaw and extremities.

- **Supination:** movement of the forearm and hand such that the palm faces posteriorly
- **Opposition:** movement such that the tip of the thumb touches the tips of the other fingers
- **Reposition:** reverse movement of opposition such that the thumb is brought back after touching the tips of the other fingers
- **Dorsiflexion:** upward movement of the foot
- **Plantar flexion:** downward movement of the foot
- **Inversion:** movement of the foot such that the medial border is raised
- **Eversion:** movement of the foot such that the lateral border is raised
- **Protraction:** movement of a body part anteriorly
- **Retraction:** reverse movement of protraction such that the body part moves posteriorly
- **Elevation:** upward movement of a body part
- **Depression:** downward movement of a body part

MAJOR SURFACE AND BONY LANDMARKS OF THE BODY (Fig 2.4)

Surface and bony landmarks are important anatomical reference points used to identify specific structures on the human body. They serve as guides for various medical procedures, physical examinations, and anatomical descriptions. Here are some major surface and bony landmarks of the human body:

Nasion: The midpoint between the eyes where the frontal and nasal bones meet.

Laryngeal prominence (Adam's apple): The forward projection of the thyroid cartilage of the larynx visible on the front of the neck.

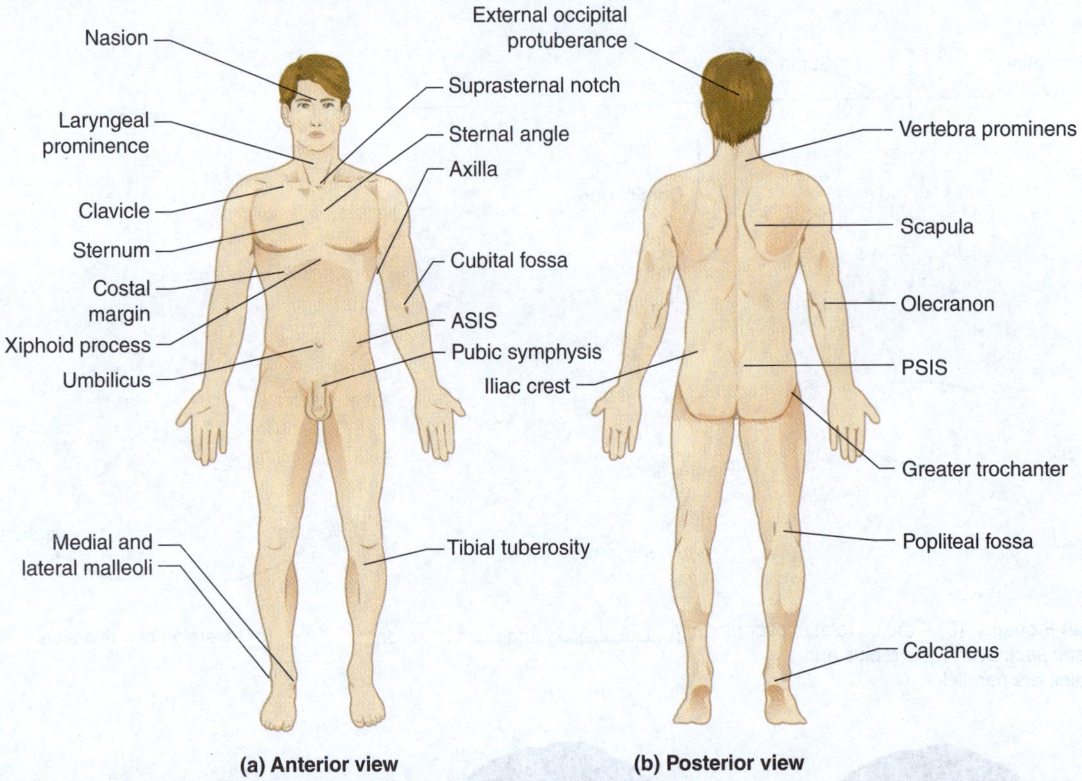

FIG. 2.4 The major surface and bony landmarks of the body.

External occipital protuberance: The prominent posterior part of the skull visible above the neck.

Clavicle (collarbone): Prominent bone that runs horizontally across the upper chest. Easily palpable and visible, especially near the sternum and acromion.

Scapula (shoulder blade): Triangular-shaped bone located on the upper back. Landmarks include the spine of the scapula, acromion process, and coracoid process.

Axilla (armpit): Hollow area beneath the shoulder joint, formed by the junction of the upper arm and the side of the chest.

Cubital fossa: Depression on the anterior surface of the elbow, commonly used for venipuncture.

Olecranon: The point of the elbow, part of the ulna.

Sternum (breastbone): Long, flat bone located in the center of the chest. Consists of three parts: the manubrium, body, and xiphoid process.

Suprasternal notch (jugular notch): Depression at the base of the neck, between the clavicles, above the sternum.

Sternal angle (angle of Louis): Junction between the manubrium and body of the sternum, at the level of the second rib.

Xiphoid process: Small, cartilaginous extension at the inferior end of the sternum.

Costal margin: The lower palpable margin of the rib cage that passes inferolaterally from the xiphoid process.

Spinous processes of vertebrae: These can be palpated in the midline posteriorly. The spinous process of the 7th cervical vertebra is especially prominent and is called the vertebra prominens.

Umbilicus: The site of attachment of the umbilical cord in foetal life that is prominently visible on the anterior abdominal wall.

Iliac crest: Prominent ridge of bone located on the superior aspect of the hip bones (ilium). Palpable and used as a landmark for administering injections or performing procedures such as lumbar punctures.

Anterior and posterior superior iliac spines (ASIS and PSIS): Bony prominences on the pelvis, located at the front and back of the iliac crests, respectively. The ASIS is commonly used as a reference point for measuring limb length and diagnosing pelvic fractures.

Pubic symphysis: Cartilaginous joint that connects the pubic bones anteriorly. Located in the midline of the pelvis, palpable as a slight ridge.

Greater trochanter: Bony prominence on the proximal end of the femur. Easily palpable on the lateral aspect of the hip and used as a reference point for assessing hip joint pathology.

Patella (kneecap): Sesamoid bone located within the quadriceps tendon. Palpable in the anterior knee and serves as a protective covering for the knee joint.

Tibial tuberosity: Bony prominence located on the anterior aspect of the proximal tibia. Attachment site for the patellar ligament and quadriceps muscles.

Popliteal fossa: Depression behind the knee joint which becomes prominent when the leg is flexed at the knee joint.

Medial and lateral malleolus: Bony prominences on the distal ends of the tibia and fibula, respectively. Easily palpable on the medial and lateral aspects of the ankle joint.

Calcaneus (heel bone): Large bone at the back of the foot, palpable beneath the ankle joint.

SUMMARY

- The three planes of the body are the sagittal, coronal and transverse planes.
- The terms of relationship of the body are important because they are the terms used by health care professionals to communicate about the human body.
- Movements of the human body relative to one another also have specific anatomical terminology.
- There are certain surface and bony landmarks that serve as useful reference points for health care professionals to examine the body and perform procedures.

CHAPTER 3

Structural Organization of the Human Body

SPECIFIC LEARNING OBJECTIVES

At the end of this chapter, the student should be able to:

- Describe the structural organization of the human body from cells to organ systems.
- Draw a neat, labelled diagram of the ultrastructure of an animal cell.
- Correlate the structure and function of the cell organelles.
- Compare and contrast mitosis and meiosis.

GLOSSARY OF TERMS

- **Cell:** the structural and functional unit of the body
- **Tissues:** groups of cells that are structurally and functionally similar
- **Organs:** a collection of tissues that have a specific function
- **Organ systems:** a collection of organs that work together and control major body functions
- **Cell organelles:** cellular components that are responsible for regulating cellular functions

INTRODUCTION

The human body is a collection of millions of cells. These cells are organized in a specific manner to work together and perform the functions of the body. This chapter will focus on the basic structure of cells and their organization in the human body into larger units. This knowledge is helpful for health science professionals as bodily disorders can usually be traced back to defective cellular functions in specific organ systems.

STRUCTURAL ORGANIZATION OF THE HUMAN BODY (Fig. 3.1)

The structural and functional unit of the human body is the **cell**. Cells aggregate to form **tissues**. The four basic types of tissues are epithelial, connective, muscular and nervous tissues (Fig. 3.2). Epithelial tissue lines the external and internal body surfaces. Connective tissue forms the supporting framework of the body. Muscular tissue consists of molecular motors that facilitate movement. Nervous tissue forms a vast communication network that helps to regulate the functioning of the body and its response to external stimuli. The different types of tissues come together to form **organs** like the brain, liver and lungs. A collection of organs form **organ systems** which perform specific body functions (Fig. 3.3). For example, the stomach, liver and pancreas are all separate organs within the digestive system. An **organism** consists of several organ systems working together in harmony.

THE CELL THEORY

Robert Hooke was the first person to observe cells under the microscope in 1665. In 1883, Mathias Schleiden and Theodor Schwann proposed that all plants and animals were composed of cells which were the basic building blocks of life. In 1855, Rudolf Virchow stated that new cells arise from the division of pre-existing cells and that chemical reactions needed for life occur inside the cell.

All this work led to the formation of the **cell theory**. The cell theory states that:

- All organisms are composed of one or more cells.
- Cells are the basic unit of structure and function in organisms.
- All cells arise from other cells.

CLASSIFICATION OF CELLS

Cells may be either prokaryotic or eukaryotic (Figs 3.4 and 3.5). Bacterial cells are prokaryotic and are less specialized than eukaryotic cells. **Eukaryotic cells** can further be divided into plant and animal cells. The description that follows will be

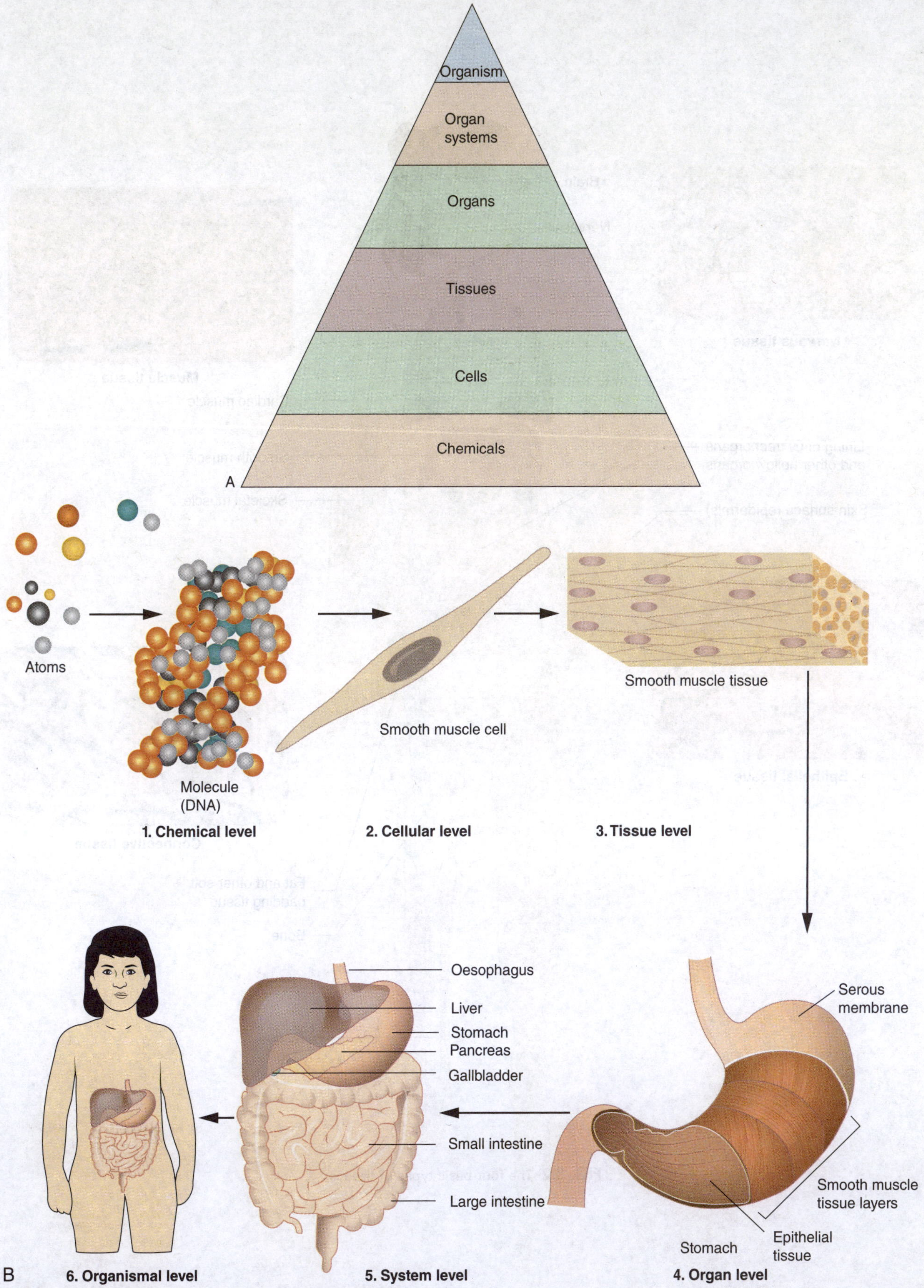

FIG. 3.1 (A) Schematic representation of the structural organization of the human body. (B) Structural organization of the human body.

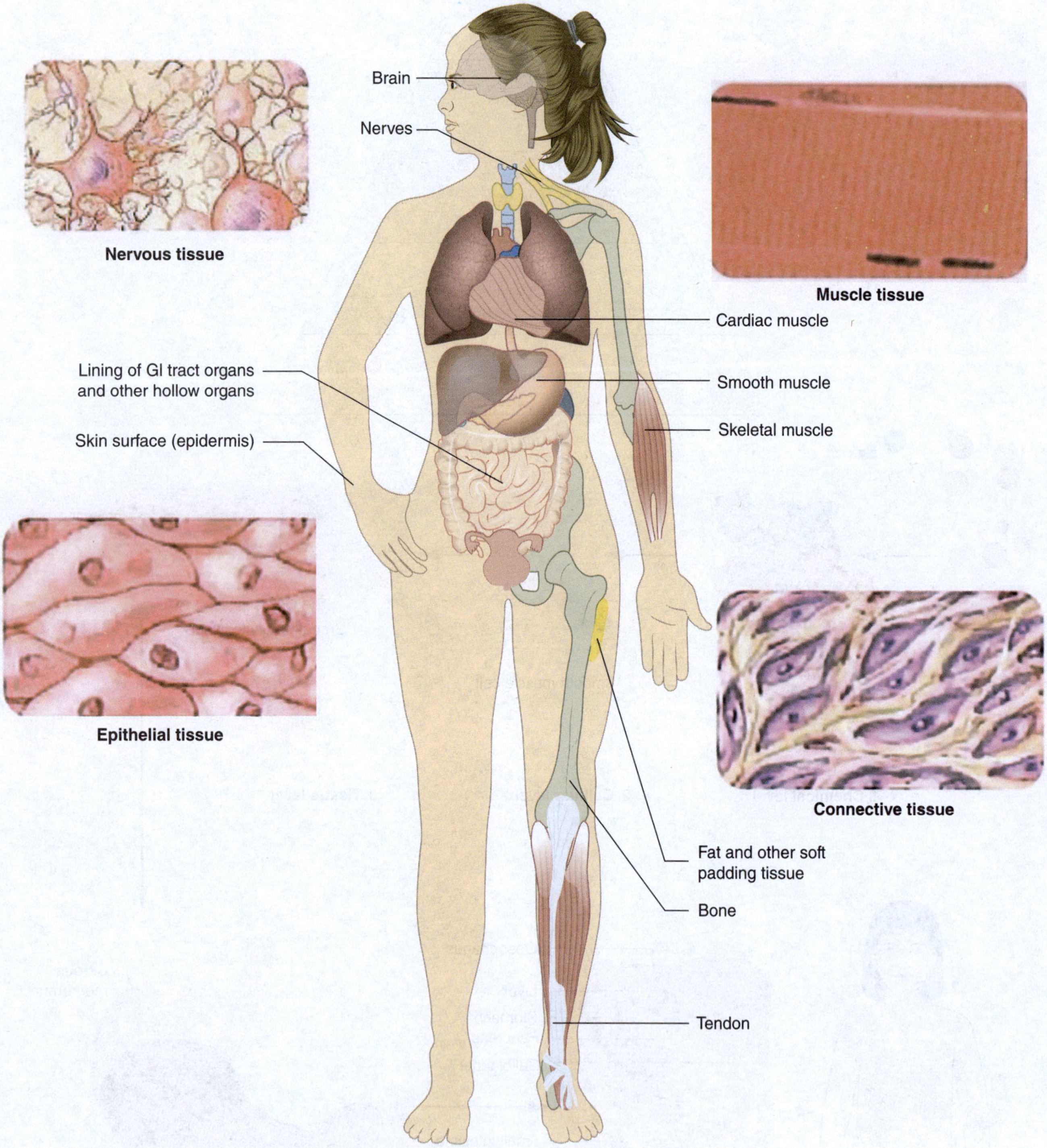

FIG. 3.2 The four basic types of tissues.

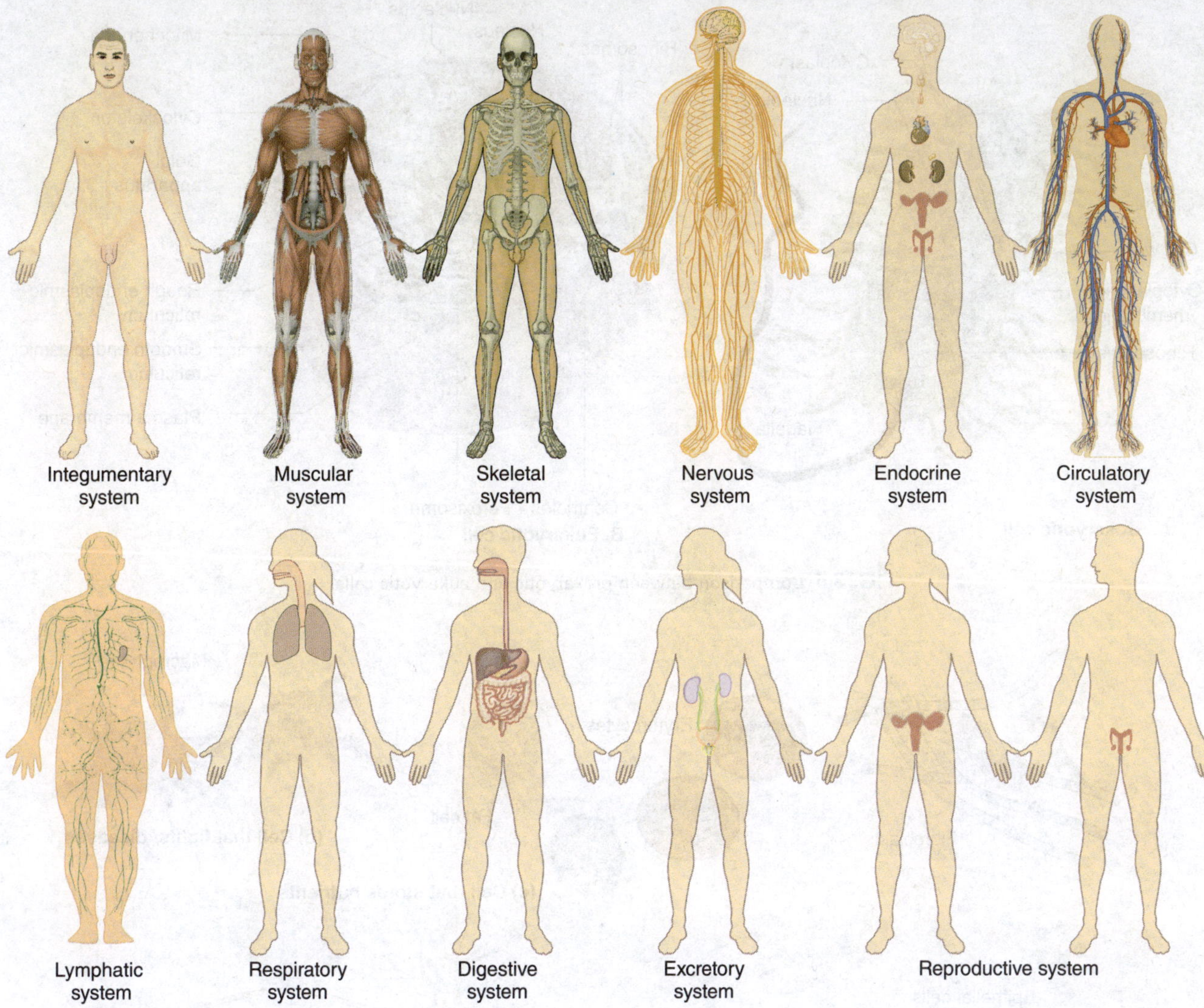

FIG. 3.3 The organ systems of the body.

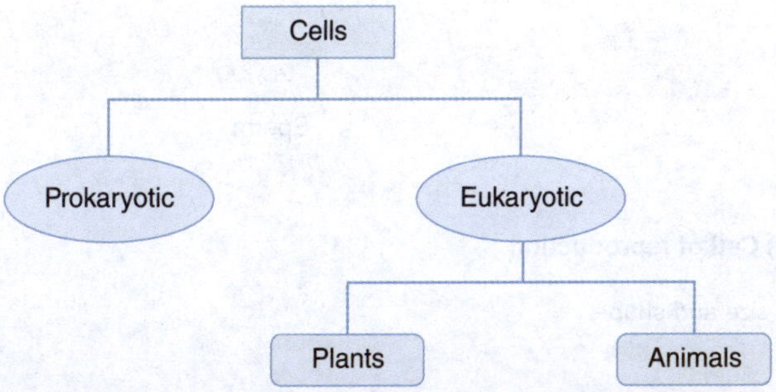

FIG. 3.4 The classification of cells.

restricted to **animal cells**. Although cell structure is diverse (Fig. 3.6), they all share common characteristics.

ULTRASTRUCTURE OF AN ANIMAL CELL (Fig. 3.7)

Cells have a **nucleus** which contains DNA. They are surrounded by a cell membrane within which is a jelly-like substance called **cytoplasm**. Contained within the cytoplasm is the nucleus, other organelles and cell inclusions. Organelles control functions within the cell. The important **cell organelles** include ribosomes, endoplasmic reticulum, Golgi apparatus, mitochondria, lysosomes, filaments and microtubules, centrosomes and peroxisomes. **Cell inclusions** include secretory granules, nutritive substances, pigments, crystals, vacuoles and foreign material.

The **cell membrane** consists of a lipid bilayer in which membrane proteins are embedded. A similar membrane also surrounds most cell organelles within the cytoplasm. The **nucleus** is surrounded by a porous nuclear membrane and contains chromatin. Chromatin consists of DNA and histone proteins forming the genetic machinery of the cell. The **nucleolus** is located within the nucleus and is responsible for ribosome synthesis and assembly. **Ribosomes** may be located free within the cytoplasm or bound to the endoplasmic reticulum. They contain RNA and are responsible for protein synthesis within the cell. The **endoplasmic reticulum** is a series of membrane-bound stacks within the

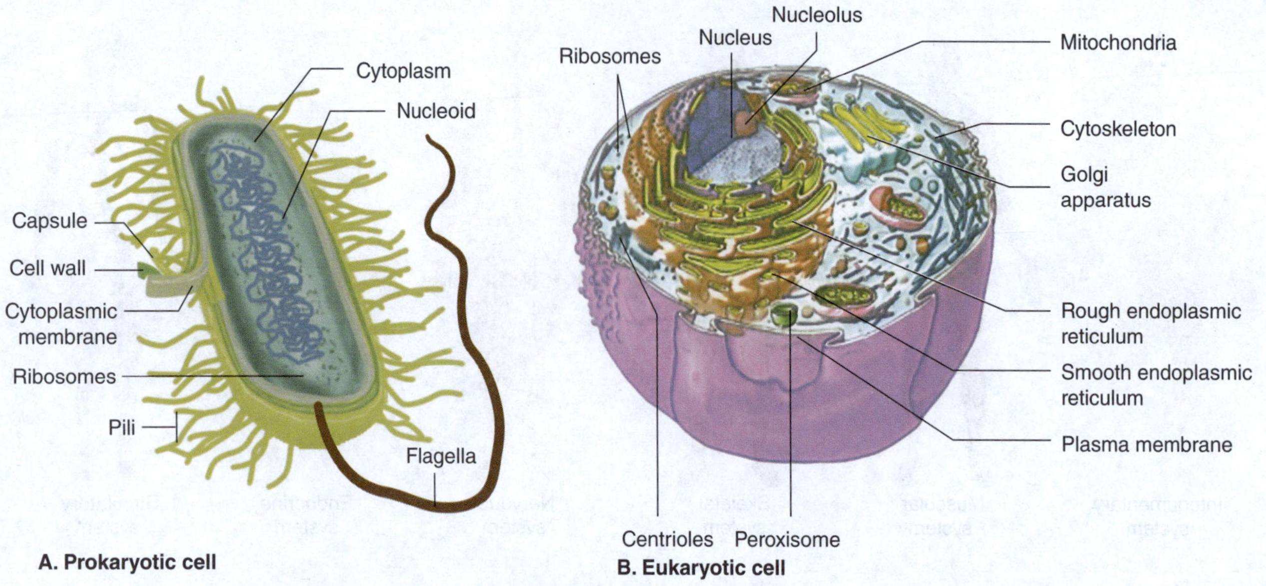

FIG. 3.5 Comparison between prokaryotic and eukaryotic cells.

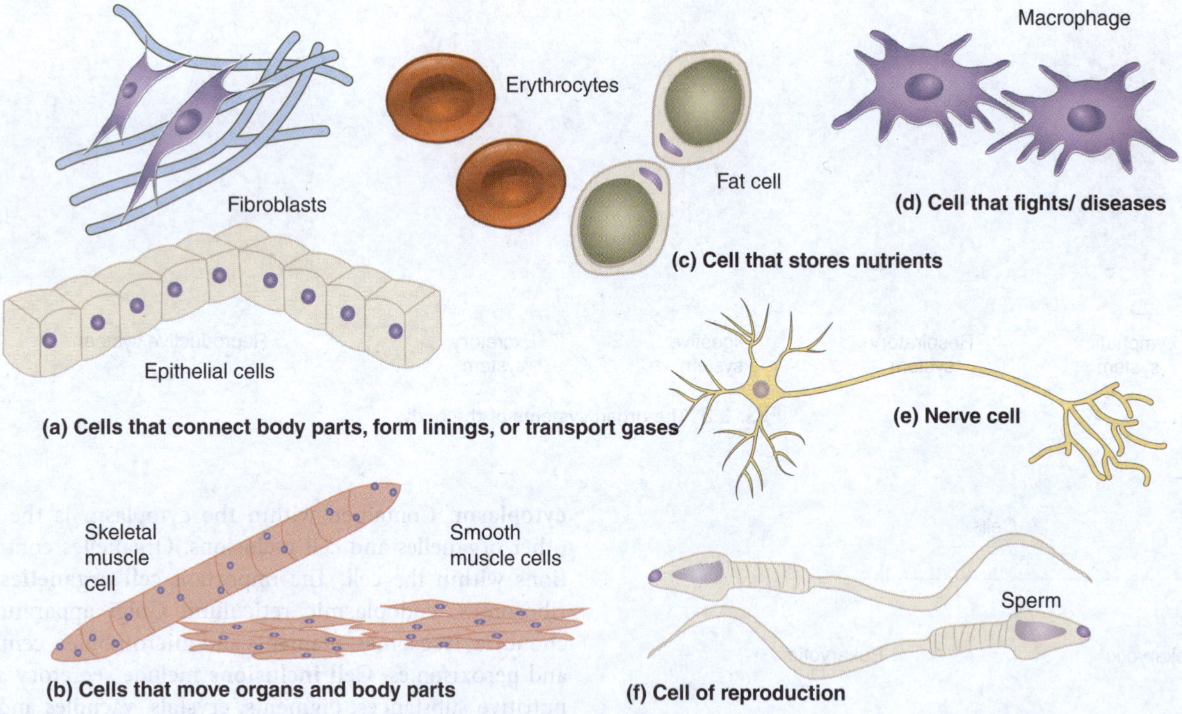

FIG. 3.6 Diversity in cell size and shape.

cytoplasm. It may be either smooth or rough. **Smooth endoplasmic reticulum** is responsible for lipid synthesis and is abundant in cells that produce lipids. **Rough endoplasmic reticulum** (RER) contains ribosomes within its walls and is responsible for protein synthesis and transport within the cell.

The **Golgi apparatus** contains cisternae from which vesicles bud off. It is a cell organelle that modifies the protein manufactured in the RER before its secretion from the cell. The **mitochondria** are small ovoid structures covered by a bilaminar membrane whose inner layer contains folds called cristae. They contain enzymes which catalyse the production of energy for the functioning of the cell. Mitochondria are also unique in that they are the only organelles other than the nucleus that contain DNA. This DNA is transmitted maternally to the offspring. **Lysosomes** are membrane-bound vesicles containing hydrolytic enzymes that are required to break down damaged organelles and nutritive materials engulfed by cells.

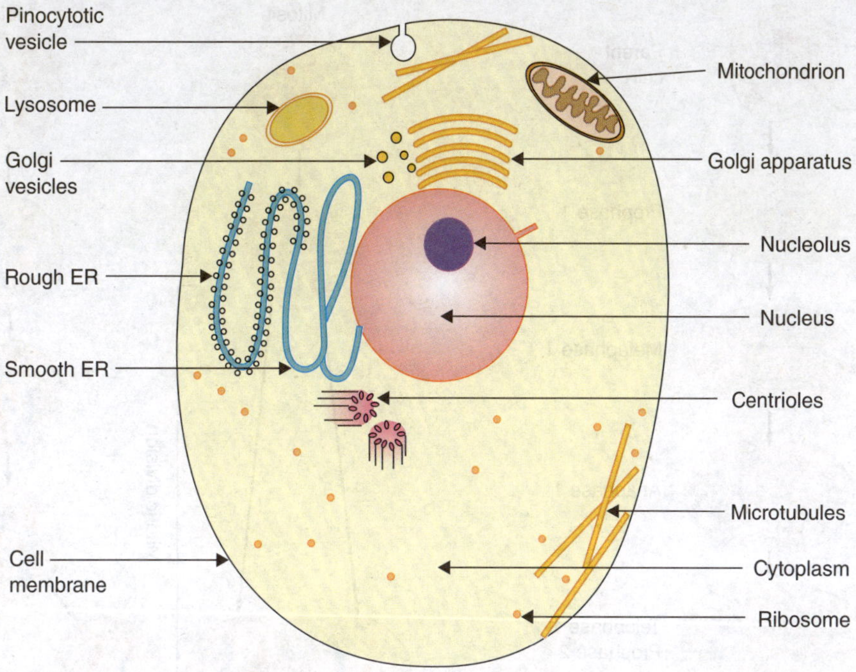

FIG. 3.7 Ultrastructure of an animal cell.

Peroxisomes are small organelles enclosed by plasma membrane that contain oxidative enzymes which are important for detoxification especially in the liver and kidneys. They are also involved in fatty acid metabolism. **Centrosomes** are located close to the nucleus and consist of a pair of centrioles placed at right angles to each other. Each centriole consists of nine triplets of microtubules arranged in a cylindrical manner. The centrosomes are the centre of production of microtubules within a cell. They are also required for cell division. Every cell contains **microfilaments** and **microtubules** which are required to maintain its structural integrity and to provide molecular motors for movement within it. **Cell inclusions** include nonliving components of a cell that are not membrane bound. The most common inclusions include glycogen and lipids which are used as the major raw materials for cellular metabolism. Other inclusions are crystals and pigments such as haemoglobin and melanin.

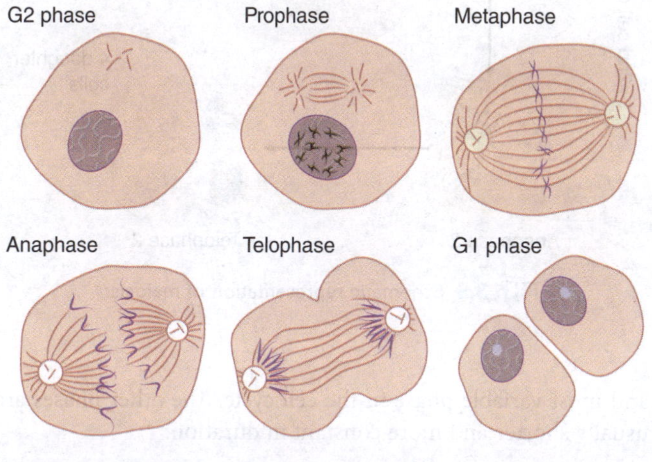

FIG. 3.8 Schematic representation of mitosis.

CELL DIVISION

After fertilization, the zygote divides repeatedly to form the cells of the body. The process of cell division and cell death has to take place in a well-regulated manner to maintain the proper functioning of an individual. ***Mitosis*** and ***meiosis*** are the two types of cell division. Mitosis is the most common method of cell division and occurs in all somatic cells and immature germ cells. It is also called homotypical or equating division. It usually takes about 1–2.5 hours to complete. The four phases of mitosis include prophase, metaphase, anaphase and telophase (Fig. 3.8). Meiosis, however, yields haploid daughter cells from a diploid parent cell. It occurs only in sex cells present in the testes and ovaries by a process called gametogenesis. It is also called heterotypical division. It consists of two consecutive divisions and the whole process can take years instead of hours (Fig. 3.9). Fig. 3.10 shows the comparison between mitosis and meiosis.

THE CELL CYCLE (Fig. 3.11)

The **cell cycle** consists of the processes that occur between and during cell divisions. The phase between cell divisions is called interphase. The interphase is further divided into G1, S and G2 phases. The G1 phase is usually much longer than the other phases of the cell cycle. During this phase, cells differentiate and perform their specific functions. This is then followed by an S phase where DNA replication occurs in preparation for cell division. During the G2 phase, which is relatively short, the cells prepare for mitotic division. The G1 phase is usually the longest

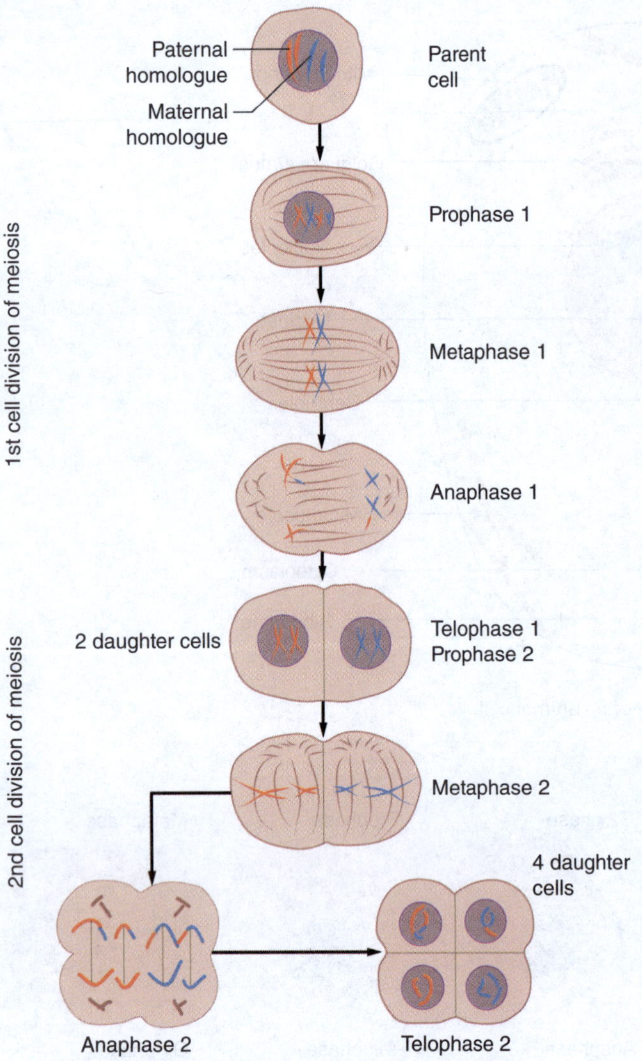

FIG. 3.9 Schematic representation of meiosis.

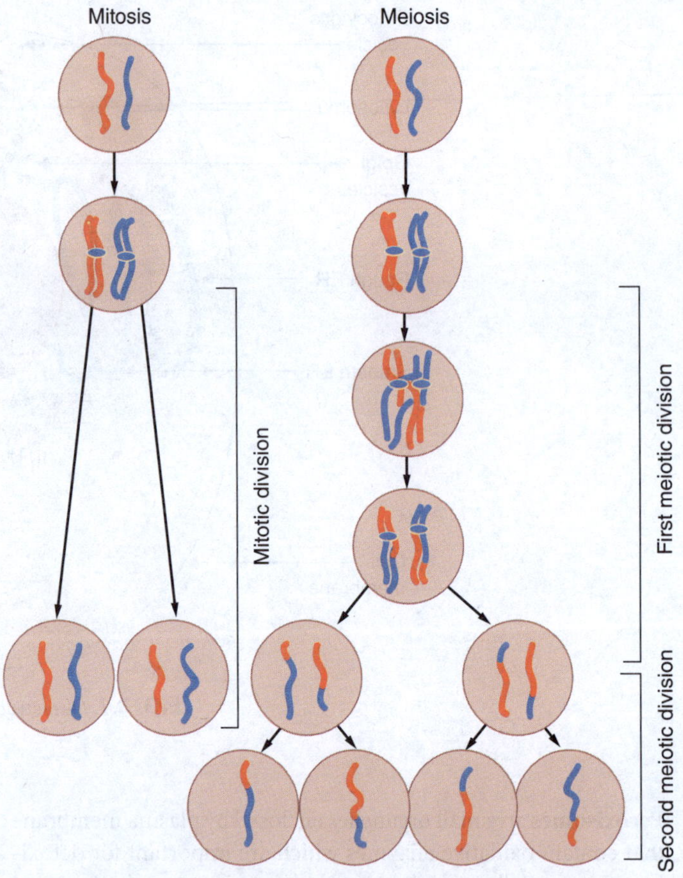

FIG. 3.10 Comparison between mitosis and meiosis.

and most variable phase in the cell cycle. The other phases are usually shorter and more constant in duration.

Rapidly dividing cells like cells in the skin have a quick turnover and quickly move through all the phases of the cell cycle. Facultative dividers such as hepatocytes enter a protracted G0 phase after mitosis and enter back into the cell cycle only when there is a need such as after liver injury. However, terminally differentiated cells such as neurons exit from the cell cycle and lose the ability to divide.

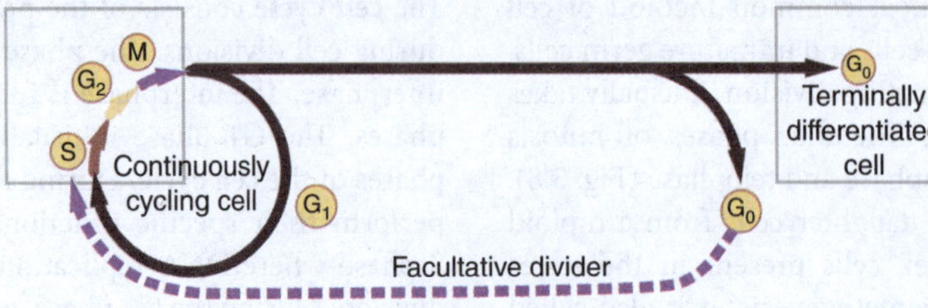

FIG. 3.11 The cell cycle.

APPLIED ANATOMY

- Pathologies affecting different organ systems cause specific symptoms and signs that enable clinicians to identify the most probable site of the abnormality. For example, conditions that affect the respiratory system often cause breathing difficulties (dyspnoea) and cough.
- The normal organization of tissues in organs is disrupted in diseases. This study of tissue abnormalities is called pathology.
- Specific cells may be affected by specific disease processes. For example, in malaria, the red blood cells show pathological changes.
- Stem cell research has shown the ability of certain embryonic cells to develop into specific tissue types under special circumstances. This approach holds promise in developing therapies for diseases such as Parkinson disease in which specific cells in the brain are damaged.

SUMMARY

- The structural and functional unit of the body is the cell.
- Cells are organized into tissues, which may be of four types, namely epithelial, connective, muscle and nervous.
- Tissues are organized into organs, which in turn are organized into organ systems.
- Cells of the human body are eukaryotic animal cells.
- Cells have a plasma membrane surrounding a nucleus and cytoplasm.
- The cytoplasm contains cell organelles such as the ribosomes, smooth and rough endoplasmic reticulum, Golgi apparatus, mitochondria, centrosomes, peroxisomes, lysosomes, filaments and microtubules, all of which help to maintain cellular structure and function.
- The cytoplasm also contains cell inclusions such as glycogen, fat, crystals and pigments.
- Mitosis and meiosis are the two types of cell division that occur in the body.
- The cell cycle regulates the rate of cell production in various tissues of the body.

Epithelial Tissue

SPECIFIC LEARNING OBJECTIVES

At the end of this chapter, the student should be able to:

- Describe the characteristics of epithelial tissue.
- Correlate the structure and function of epithelial tissue.
- Classify epithelial tissue with suitable examples.
- Describe the mechanisms by which epithelial cells adhere to one another.

GLOSSARY OF TERMS

- **Epithelial tissue:** one of the four basic types of tissues that consist of cells that line body surfaces
- **Basement membrane:** connective tissue layer on which the epithelial cells rest
- **Microvilli:** cell surface projections that help to increase the surface area for absorption
- **Stereocilia:** long microvilli that resemble cilia but are nonmotile
- **Cilia:** whip-like, motile cell surface modifications
- **Junctional complexes:** mechanism by which adherence of epithelial cells to one another is regulated

INTRODUCTION

Epithelial tissue is one of the four basic types of tissues in the body. Epithelia form boundaries between environments, both internal and external. The structure of the epithelial layer is dependent on the function that it must perform. Epithelia are made of **sheets** of **tightly connected cells** with an underlying **basement membrane** that attaches the epithelium to the connective tissue beneath. Attachment to a basement membrane is essential for epithelial development and function. Epithelial cells exhibit **polarity**, which means that different surfaces of the cell exhibit different properties. Epithelial tissue is **avascular** but often **richly innervated**. Epithelial cells have a **regenerative capacity** which is dependent on their location and function.

FUNCTIONS OF EPITHELIAL TISSUE

The functions of epithelia are highly variable depending on their location. In areas of the body exposed to the environment or noxious stimuli, the epithelium is thick with the main function of **protection**, for example skin. In the intestine, the main function of the lining epithelium is **absorption**. The epithelia lining the tubules of the kidney are specialized for **filtration** and **ion transport**. Glandular epithelia are specialized to **secrete**, such as in the salivary glands. Epithelia are thin where **diffusion** occurs, like the alveoli of the lungs. In certain areas of the body, like the serous lining of body cavities, epithelia provide smooth, **slippery surfaces** to reduce friction during movement. Elsewhere, like in the skin, there are specialized sensory **receptors** within the epithelium.

ARRANGEMENT OF EPITHELIAL TISSUE

Epithelial tissues are arranged in the form of either **membranes** or **glands**. Epithelial membranes include **cutaneous membranes**, for example epidermis of the skin; **mucous membranes**, for example lining of the gastrointestinal tract; and **serous membranes**, for example pleura. The arrangement of glandular epithelia varies depending on the type of gland. In **exocrine glands**, they are usually arranged around a lumen, into which the secretions are poured and subsequently drained by a duct. In **endocrine glands**, where the secretions are poured into the blood, epithelial cells are usually arranged in clusters or cords surrounded by numerous blood vessels.

CLASSIFICATION OF EPITHELIAL TISSUE (Fig. 4.1; Table 4.1)

Epithelia are classified based on the number of **layers** and **shape** of the cells. An epithelium with a single layer is called simple, whereas an epithelium with two or more layers is called stratified. Pseudostratified epithelia have an appearance of a stratified

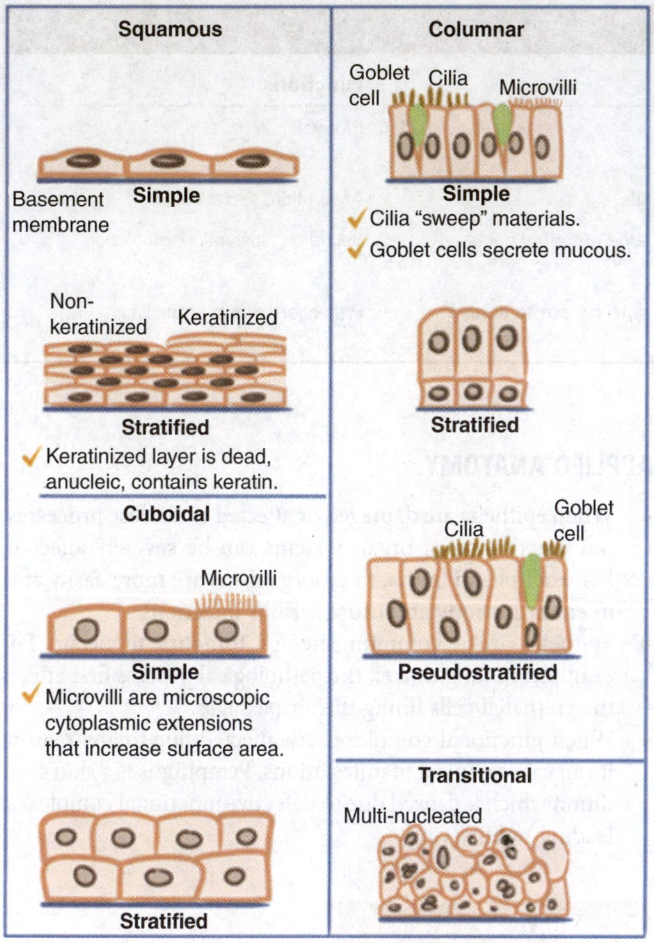

FIG. 4.1 Classification of epithelia.

epithelium but are in reality a single layer. Cells may be flattened, cuboidal or columnar. Stratified epithelium is named according to the shape of cells that are closest to the free surface. **Cell surface modifications** such as cilia, microvilli and stereocilia are also specified when describing epithelia. Microvilli are finger-like extensions of the plasma membrane of the apical portion of epithelial cells and increase the surface area available for absorption, for example small intestine. Stereocilia are long microvilli found on absorptive or secretory cells, for example epididymis, and are nonmotile unlike cilia. They are also found on special sensory cells in the ear (cochlea) where their bending is a stimulus for sound or position sensation. Cilia are whip-like, motile extensions of the cell that have the important functions of moving mucus over epithelial surfaces and aiding the movement of ova along the fallopian tube. Flagella are extra-long cilia that are seen in spermatozoa, which help in their rapid movement.

EPITHELIAL CELL JUNCTIONS (Fig. 4.2)

Epithelial cells are connected to neighbouring cells via **junctional complexes**. The strength of these connections varies depending on the function. For example, in areas of the body where protection is the main function as in the skin, neighbouring cells are tightly adherent to one another. In other areas where large molecules need to pass through the epithelium as in blood vessels of endocrine glands, they are less adherent to one another. Junctional complexes include tight junctions, zonula adherens and desmosomes. They restrict entry of substances between cells and help to maintain cell polarity. Gap junctions are spot-like junctions that are seen in many tissues of the body. They allow small molecules to pass to neighbouring cells.

Table 4.1 Classification of Epithelia

Type	Shape of Surface Cells	Sample Locations	Functions
Simple			
Squamous	Flattened	*Lining:* pulmonary alveoli, loop of Henle, parietal layer of Bowman capsule, inner and middle ears, blood and lymphatic vessels, pleural and peritoneal cavities	Limiting membrane, fluid transport, gaseous exchange, lubrication, reducing friction (thus aiding movement of viscera), lining membrane
Cuboidal	Cuboidal	Ducts of many glands, covering of ovary, kidney tubules	Secretion, absorption, protection
Columnar	Columnar	*Lining:* oviducts, ductuli efferentes of testis, uterus, small bronchi, much of digestive tract, gallbladder, large ducts of some glands	Transportation, absorption, secretion, protection
Pseudostratified	All cells rest on basal lamina but not all reach epithelial surface; surface cells are columnar	*Lining:* most of trachea, primary bronchi, epididymis and ductus deferens, auditory tube, part of tympanic cavity, nasal cavity, lacrimal sac, male urethra, large excretory ducts	Secretion, absorption, lubrication, protection, transportation
Stratified			
Squamous, nonkeratinized	Flattened (with nuclei)	***Lining:*** mouth, epiglottis, oesophagus, vocal folds, vagina	Protection

Continued

Table 4.1 Classification of Epithelia—Cont'd

Type	Shape of Surface Cells	Sample Locations	Functions
Squamous, keratinized	Flattened (without nuclei)	Epidermis of skin	Protection
Cuboidal	Cuboidal	*Lining:* ducts of sweat glands	Absorption, secretion
Columnar	Columnar	Conjunctiva of eye, some large excretory ducts, portions of male urethra	Secretion, absorption, protection
Transitional	Dome-shaped (relaxed), flattened (distended)	***Lining:*** urinary tract from renal calyces to urethra	Protection, allows stretching

Adapted from *Junqueira's Basic Histology*, 12th ed.

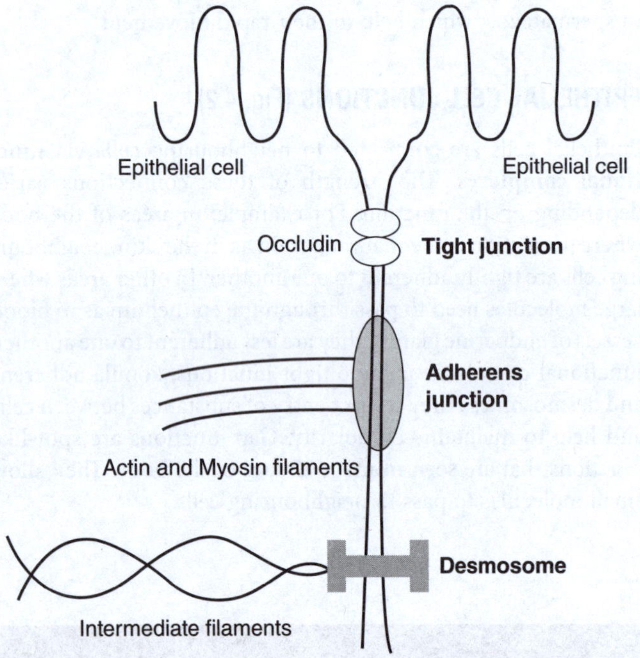

FIG. 4.2 Junctional complexes between epithelial cells.

APPLIED ANATOMY

- When epithelia are damaged or affected by disease processes, the functioning of organ systems can be severely affected. For example, in burns, microorganisms are more easily able to enter the body and cause serious infections.
- Epithelia are a common site for tumours to occur. For example, in lung cancer, the pathological process first affects the epithelial cells lining the air passages.
- When junctional complexes are affected due to any reason, it can cause clinical manifestations. Pemphigus is a skin condition which is caused due to defective junctional complexes, leading to blistering.

SUMMARY

- Epithelial tissue is one of the four basic types of tissues.
- Epithelial cells line body surfaces, both internal and external.
- Epithelia have various functions depending on their location.
- They can be organized either as membranes or in the form of glands.
- Epithelia are classified based on the number of layers, shape of cells and presence of cell surface modifications.
- Epithelial cells adhere to one another through junctional complexes.

CHAPTER 5

Exocrine Glands

SPECIFIC LEARNING OBJECTIVES

At the end of this chapter, the student should be able to:

- Define glands.
- Classify glands based on their structure and function.
- Describe the general features of exocrine glands.

GLOSSARY OF TERMS

- **Gland:** epithelial cells specialized to synthesize and secrete a specific product
- **Endocrine glands:** ductless glands pouring their secretions directly into the blood
- **Exocrine glands:** glands with ducts that carry the secretions onto the surface
- **Capsule:** connective tissue covering of a gland
- **Septa:** inward prolongations of the capsule into the substance of the gland
- **Parenchyma:** the secretory portion of a gland
- **Stroma:** the supporting connective tissue of a gland
- **Lobule:** a unit of a glandular tissue delimited by septa
- **Myoepithelial cells:** contractile cells associated with glands and ducts that help to expel glandular secretions

INTRODUCTION

Glands are composed of epithelial cells specialized to synthesize and secrete a specific product. The glandular cells develop from the covering epithelium. Glands can be divided into two major categories, namely **endocrine** and **exocrine** (Fig. 5.1). **Endocrine glands**, otherwise known as ductless glands, pour their secretions into the blood. **Exocrine glands** in contrast have a well-defined duct system that carries the glandular secretions. In this chapter, the general features of exocrine glands will be described.

GENERAL FEATURES OF EXOCRINE GLANDS (Fig. 5.2)

All large exocrine glands have certain common features. The secretory tissue of the glands is the **parenchyma**, while the supporting connective tissue is called the **stroma**. Both these are covered by a **capsule** made up of connective tissue. The capsule sends in prolongations into the substance of the gland called **septa**, dividing it into **lobules**. Within each lobule, there is more delicate connective tissue supporting the glandular elements. The **secretory cells** in the parenchyma can be organized in a variety of ways.

The key feature of all exocrine glands is the presence of **ducts**, which carry secretions to the surface. Ducts are relatively simple tubular structures with a conspicuous cuboidal to columnar epithelial lining. They are not just passive tubes, as some duct segments actively modify the secretory product passing through. The smaller ducts within lobules are called **intralobular ducts**, which drain into larger **interlobular ducts** located within the septa between lobules. These finally drain into the **main duct** which opens onto the surface. In many glands, the glandular elements and duct system are surrounded by **myoepithelial cells**. These cells are located between the glandular epithelium and the basal lamina. Myoepithelial cells, also called basket cells, are stellate or spindle-shaped cells which contain actin and myosin filaments and are contractile. Their contraction aids in the secretory process.

CLASSIFICATION OF EXOCRINE GLANDS (Figs 5.3 and 5.4)

Exocrine glands can be classified in several ways. Depending on their **mode of secretion**, they may be classified as **merocrine, apocrine** or **holocrine**. The secretory cells in **merocrine glands** discharge their secretions through secretory vesicles without any part of the cell being lost in the process. Typical examples of merocrine glands are the salivary glands. **Apocrine glands**, however, secrete their product covered by plasma membrane of the apical portion of the cell. The mammary gland is an example of an apocrine gland. The secretions of

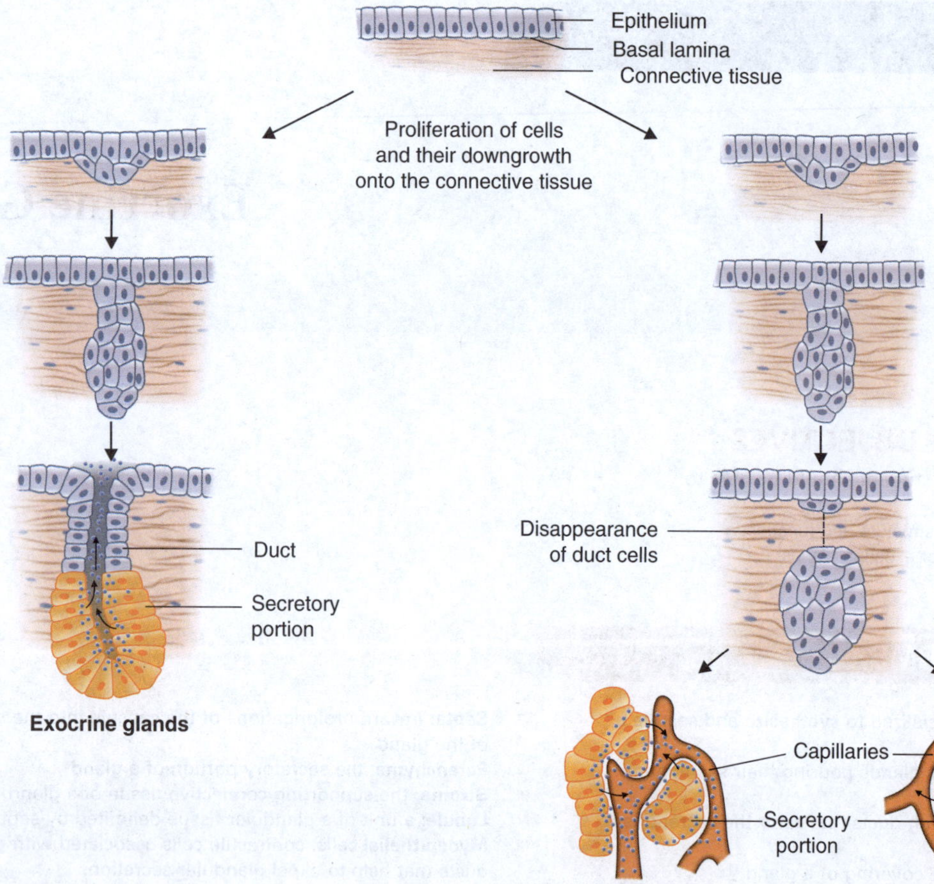

FIG. 5.1 Development of exocrine and endocrine glands.

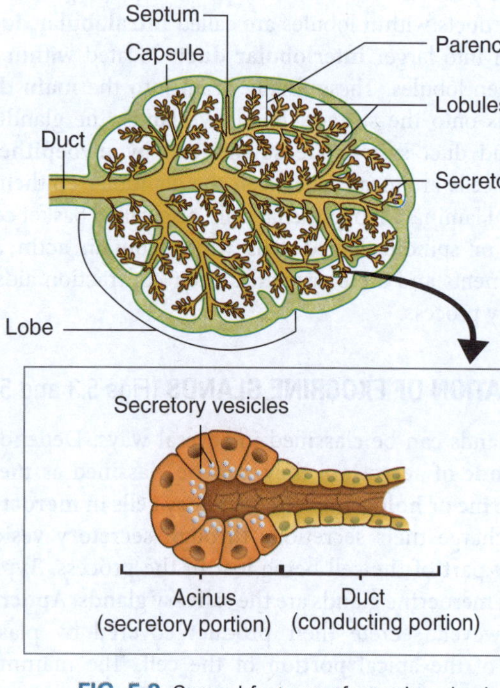

FIG. 5.2 General features of exocrine glands.

holocrine glands occur by disintegration of the secretory cells themselves, like in sebaceous glands.

Depending on the **type of secretion**, exocrine glands may be classified as **mucous**, **serous** and **mixed.** The secretions of **serous glands** are watery, containing mainly poorly glycosylated or nonglycosylated proteins. Examples include the parotid gland and exocrine part of the pancreas. **Mucous glands** secrete mucus which contains extensively glycosylated proteins. The secretions are viscous and slimy. Examples include Brunner's glands of the duodenum and oesophageal glands. **Mixed glands** secrete a mixture of serous and mucous secretions, for example the submandibular salivary gland. Glands may be **unicellular**, like goblet cells, or **multicellular**, like most other glands.

Another classification of exocrine glands is based on their **structure**. In this classification, the **shape** of the **secretory component** of the gland and the **branching pattern** of the **duct** are used to classify exocrine glands. Based on the **shape** of the secretory component, glands may be classified as **tubular**, **acinar** and **alveolar**. If the **duct system** is branched, it is called a **compound gland**, else it is a simple gland. Examples of the various types of glands are given in Fig. 5.3.

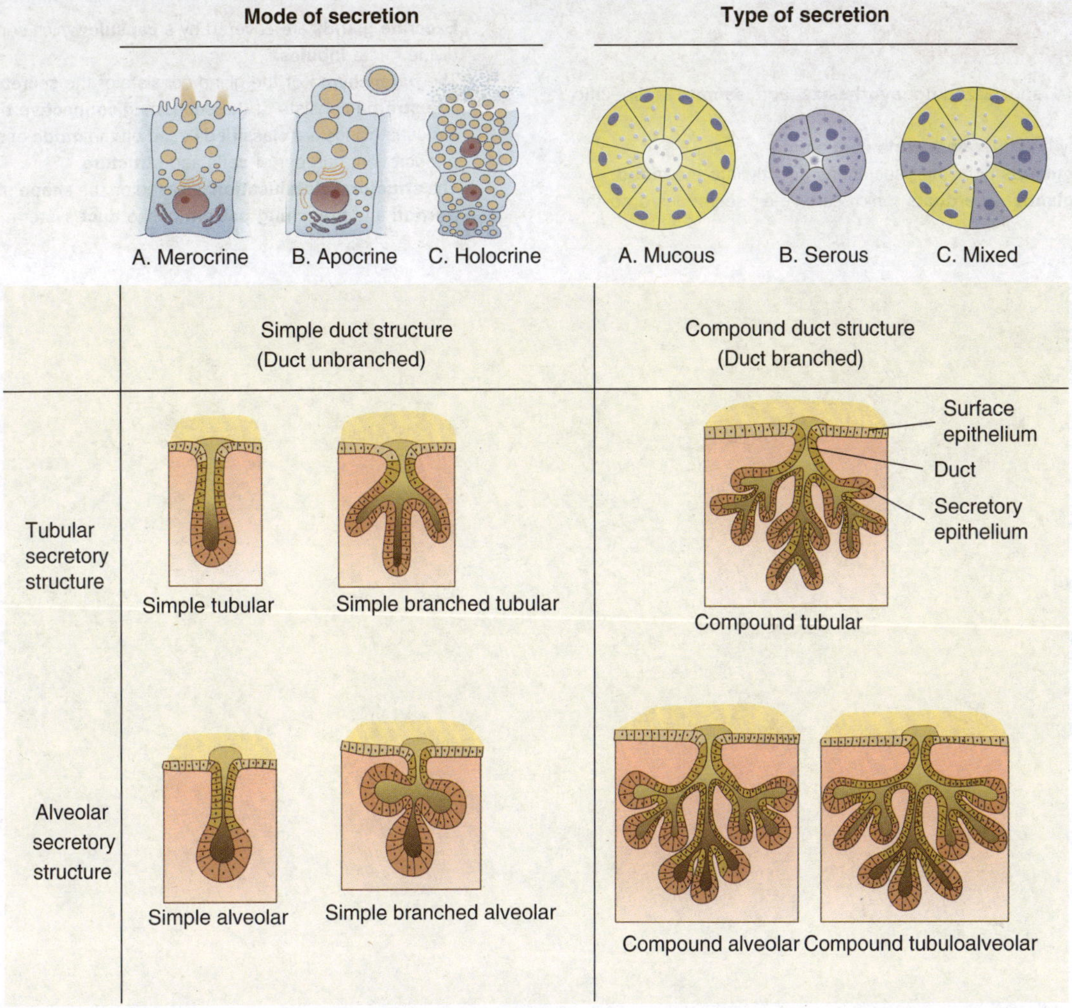

FIG. 5.3 Classification of exocrine glands.

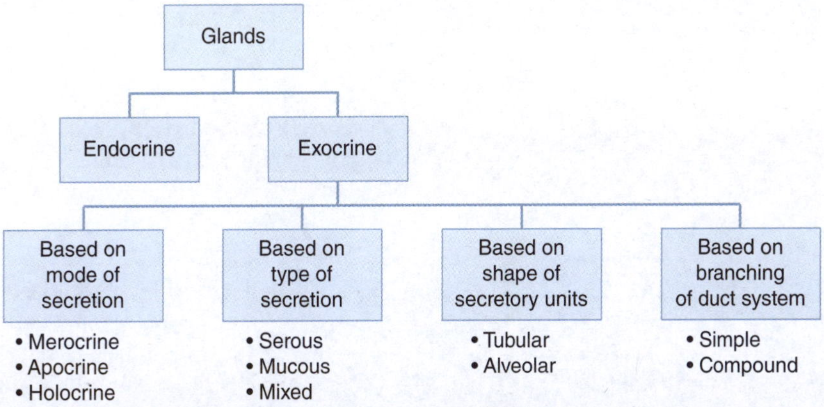

FIG. 5.4 Classification of glands.

APPLIED ANATOMY

- Certain diseases specifically affect glands. For example, in **mumps**, a viral infection, the salivary glands are commonly enlarged and painful.
- **Cystic fibrosis** is an autosomal recessive disorder in which secretions of glands such as the pancreas, glands within the lung and sweat glands are altered leading to frequent infections.
- **Sjogren syndrome** is an autoimmune disease in which an immune response is mounted to components of exocrine glands, specifically the lacrimal and salivary glands leading to dryness of the eyes and mouth.

SUMMARY

- **Glands** are specialized to **synthesize** and **secrete** a specific product.
- Glands may be either **endocrine** or **exocrine**.
- **Endocrine glands** pour their secretions directly into the **blood**.
- **Exocrine glands** have **ducts** which carry their secretions onto the surface.
- **Exocrine glands** are covered by a **capsule** which sends in **septa** to divide it into **lobules**.
- The **parenchyma** of the gland consists of the **secretory** portions.
- The **stroma** consists of the supporting **connective tissue**.
- Exocrine glands are **classified** based on the **mode** of secretion, **type** of secretion, number of **cells** and **structure**.
- The **structural classification** is based on the **shape** of the **secretory portion** and **branching pattern** of the **duct** system.

CHAPTER 6

Connective Tissue

SPECIFIC LEARNING OBJECTIVES

At the end of this chapter, the student should be able to:

- Describe the general features of connective tissue.
- Classify connective tissue based on its characteristics.

GLOSSARY OF TERMS

- **Connective tissue:** a type of tissue in which cells are widely separated by a matrix which is highly variable in its structure
- **Matrix:** the intervening material between the cells
- **Fibres:** elongated proteins which are part of the matrix and may be collagen, elastic or reticular in nature
- **Ground substance:** part of the matrix seen between the fibres, which is amorphous and composed of glycoproteins
- **Embryonic connective tissue:** type of connective tissue seen in the developing foetus
- **Connective tissue proper:** type of connective tissue that is seen in most parts of the body, serving the role of a dynamic filler material between other tissue components
- **Specialized connective tissue:** connective tissue with special properties and functions such as cartilage, bone and blood

INTRODUCTION

Connective tissue is the most abundant tissue type in the body. There is a great degree of variability in the structure and function of the different types of connective tissue. The main feature of connective tissue is the relatively wide separation of the cellular constituents. The **functions** of connective tissue are numerous, including protection of vital organs, providing scaffolding for the body, binding together other tissues, separating different body compartments, storing energy reserves and transporting materials. This chapter will focus on the **general features** of connective tissue and its **classification.**

GENERAL FEATURES (Fig. 6.1)

Connective tissue has a relatively sparse population of **cells** surrounded by a **matrix.** The matrix is the extracellular material of connective tissue. It contains fibres, fluid and dissolved molecules. The type of matrix determines the function of a specific type of connective tissue. For example, the matrix is watery in blood and dense in bone. The nonfibre component of the matrix is called the **ground substance.** The **fibres** in connective tissue consist of proteins and are of three types, collagen, elastic and reticular. The amount of blood supply of connective tissue is variable. Bone has a rich blood supply, whereas cartilage is avascular. The rapidity of healing after an injury is greater in more vascular tissues.

Collagen fibres are the most numerous and run in long, wavy bundles. They are found in the skin, capsules of organs, cartilage, bone, blood vessels, tendons and ligaments. They provide the tensile strength required in these areas. **Elastic fibres** are found in the skin, certain types of cartilage, large arteries and a few ligaments. They have the property of retaining their original length even after considerable stretching. **Reticular fibres** are thin and delicate and found within organs and glands, where they provide the necessary support. The ground substance contains **proteoglycans** which are a combination of proteins and polysaccharides. Specific proteoglycans are present in different tissues, contributing to their properties.

The cellular component of connective tissue is variable. In nonspecialized connective tissue, the predominant cell seen is the **fibroblast,** which produces and maintains all the components of the matrix. Other cells often seen include white blood cell derivatives such as **mast cells, macrophages, plasma cells, neutrophils, eosinophils** and **lymphocytes.** All these cells serve an immune function. The cellular component of specialized connective tissue will be explained in subsequent chapters.

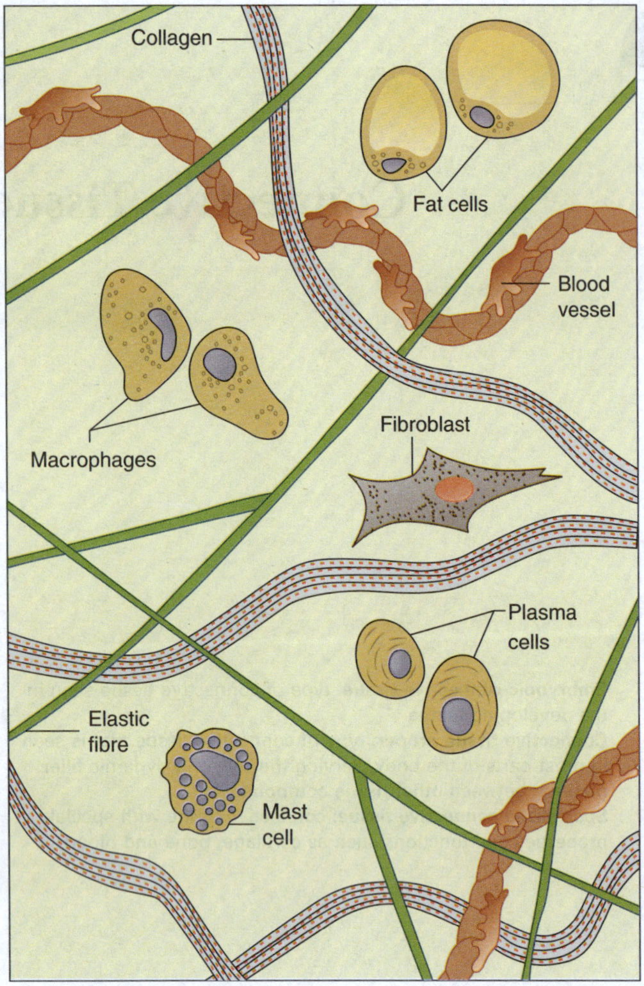

FIG. 6.1 General features of connective tissue.

CLASSIFICATION (Figs 6.2 and 6.3)

The classification of connective tissue is dependent on the characteristics of the matrix. Connective tissue can be divided into three broad categories: **embryonic**, **proper** and **specialized** (Fig. 6.3). As the name suggests, **embryonic connective tissue** is found in all developing organs in the foetus. It consists of cells embedded in a loose, amorphous matrix with thin fibres. Mucoid connective tissue has a gel-like matrix and is found in the umbilical cord.

Connective tissue proper is further classified into **loose, dense, adipose** and **reticular**. *Loose connective tissue* has more ground substance, with fewer fibres and cells. It is found in the subcutaneous tissues of the body. *Dense connective tissue* has more fibres, with less ground substance. When these fibres are arranged irregularly, it is called dense irregular connective tissue, whereas if regularly arranged, it is dense regular connective tissue. Dense irregular connective tissue is found in the dermis of the skin, where it is subject to forces in several directions. Dense regular connective tissue is seen in locations where the major forces are in a specific direction, for example tendons and ligaments. *Reticular connective tissue* is seen within organs, like the kidneys and liver, where it forms the delicate supporting framework for the tissues within it. *Adipose tissue* contains cells called adipocytes, which are filled with fat and serve as energy stores. It is seen in subcutaneous tissue and around viscera. **Specialized connective tissue** will be discussed in separate chapters. The constituents of blood and their functions will be dealt with in detail in the physiology section of this book.

APPLIED ANATOMY

- **Oedema** is a term used to indicate swelling of tissues due to excessive accumulation of fluid, usually within the loose connective tissues of the body. It is usually caused by disease processes that increase the permeability of blood vessels, leading to extravasation of fluid into the surrounding connective tissues.
- Certain **inflammatory diseases** such as rheumatoid arthritis and systemic lupus erythematosus specifically affect connective tissue and are known as connective tissue disorders. The symptoms produced in these conditions are the result of autoantibodies produced by the body against its own connective tissue.
- Certain **genetic disorders** are caused by defective genes controlling for components of connective tissue. This can lead to several clinical manifestations like laxity of the skin, heart valve defects and joint hypermobility. Examples include Ehlers–Danlos syndrome and Marfan syndrome.
- In **obesity**, excessive fat is stored in adipocytes and is especially visible in the subcutaneous tissues around the lower abdomen.
- **Lipomas** are common benign tumours of adipocytes that are often seen as soft 'lumps' on the skin.

SUMMARY

- Connective tissue is the most widespread among the four basic types of tissue.
- It is characterized by a wide separation of the cellular elements by a matrix.
- The matrix consists of fibres and ground substance.
- Fibres may be collagen, elastic or reticular.
- The ground substance consists of tissue-specific glycoproteins.
- Connective tissue is classified based on the type of matrix present.
- The three broad categories of connective tissue are embryonic, proper and specialized.
- The main cell in connective tissue proper is the fibroblast, which produces the components of the matrix.
- Other cells like macrophages, mast cells, eosinophils, neutrophils and lymphocytes that may be seen in connective tissue belong to the immune system.

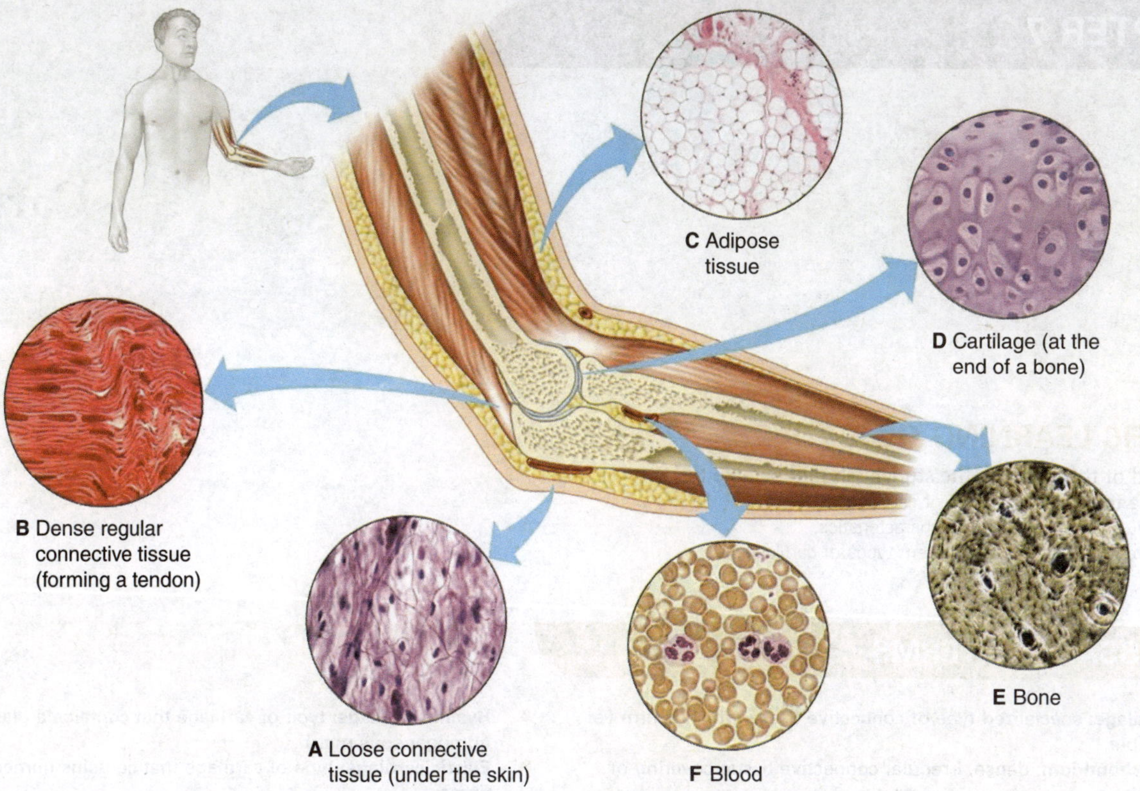

FIG. 6.2 Types of connective tissue.

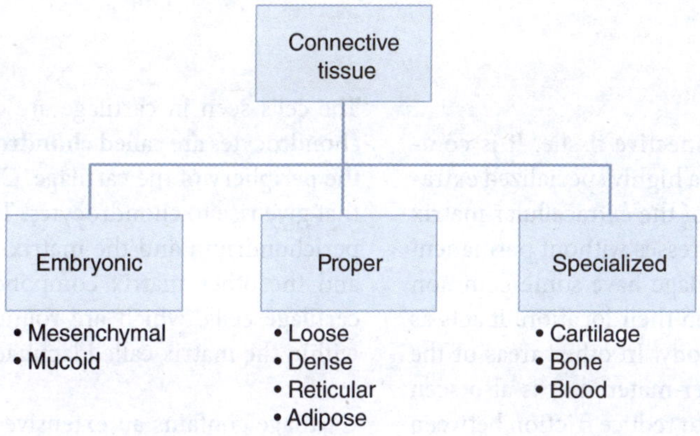

FIG. 6.3 Classification of connective tissue. (Adapted from *Colour Textbook of Histology*, Gartner and Hiatt, 3rd edition.)

CHAPTER 7

Cartilage

SPECIFIC LEARNING OBJECTIVES

At the end of this chapter, the student should be able to:

- Describe the general features of cartilage.
- Classify cartilage based on its characteristics.
- Compare and contrast the different types of cartilage.

GLOSSARY OF TERMS

- **Cartilage:** specialized type of connective tissue which is firm yet flexible
- **Perichondrium:** dense, irregular connective tissue covering of cartilage
- **Chondrocytes:** connective tissue cells seen within cartilage
- **Chondroblasts:** immature chondrocytes
- **Lacunae:** spaces within the matrix that contain chondrocytes
- **Hyaline cartilage:** type of cartilage that contains a glassy, homogeneous matrix
- **Elastic cartilage:** type of cartilage that contains numerous elastic fibres
- **Fibrous cartilage:** type of cartilage that contains numerous collagen bundles

INTRODUCTION

Cartilage is a specialized form of connective tissue. It is composed of cells called chondrocytes and a highly specialized extracellular matrix. The firm consistency of the extracellular matrix allows the tissue to bear mechanical stresses without permanent distortion. Although all types of cartilage have some common features, their function is dependent on their location. It acts as a support for the soft tissues of the body. In other areas of the body, it acts as a shock-absorbing filler material. It is also seen in locations where there is a necessity to reduce friction between adjoining moving surfaces. Finally, it is essential for the growth and development of the bones in the body. This chapter will focus on the **general features** of cartilage, its **classification** and **microstructure**.

GENERAL FEATURES

Cartilage is unusual, in that it is avascular. Nutrients reach the cartilage by diffusion via blood vessels in the adjacent perichondrium. In the absence of perichondrium, synovial fluid nourishes it. Cartilage does not have any nerve supply and lymphatic drainage. Most cartilage is covered by a layer of dense, irregular connective tissue containing collagen fibres and fibroblasts called the **perichondrium**. The perichondrium has an outer fibrous and an inner cellular layer and contains blood vessels, nerves and lymphatics.

The cells seen in cartilage are called **chondrocytes**. Immature chondrocytes are called **chondroblasts** and are usually seen near the periphery of the cartilage. Chondroblasts are small, flat cells that give rise to chondrocytes. They line the border between the perichondrium and the matrix. Chondroblasts secrete collagen and the other matrix components. Chondrocytes are mature cartilage cells, which are rounded in shape and lie in spaces within the matrix called lacunae.

Cartilage contains an extensive extracellular matrix with fibres and ground substance. Both collagen and elastic fibres may be seen depending on the type of cartilage. The ground substance contains glycosaminoglycans like chondroitin sulphate, keratin sulphate and hyaluronic acid. Proteoglycans are glycosaminoglycans conjugated with a core protein. These macromolecules, fibres and water bind together and give the characteristic firm yet flexible property to cartilage.

Cartilage can grow in two ways, interstitial and appositional. Interstitial growth occurs due to mitotic division of chondrocytes and simultaneous synthesis of matrix around them. This type of growth expands the cartilage matrix from within. It is seen in epiphyseal plates and articular cartilage. Appositional growth occurs on the surface and leads to an increase in girth. Perichondrial cells differentiate into chondroblasts, which then synthesize the matrix. Growth hormone, thyroid hormone and

TABLE 7.1 Main Features of the Three Types of Cartilage

Type of Cartilage	Microscopic Features (Fig. 7.1)	Location (Fig. 7.2)
1. Hyaline cartilage	• Perichondrium present • Chondrocytes present within lacunae in aggregations called cell nests • Glassy, homogeneous basophilic matrix	• Embryonic skeleton • Epiphyseal plates • Joint surfaces • Nose • Larynx • Trachea • Bronchi • Costal cartilage
2. Elastic cartilage	• Perichondrium present • Chondrocytes present within lacunae either singly or in small groups • Matrix with numerous elastic fibres	• External ear • Eustachian tubes • Epiglottis of larynx
3. Fibrous cartilage	• Perichondrium absent • Chondrocytes present within lacunae in rows • Matrix with numerous collagen fibre bundles	• Intervertebral discs • Pubic symphysis • Menisci of knee joint • Discs within joints

testosterone accelerate the synthesis of glycosaminoglycans, whereas cortisol and oestradiol inhibit their synthesis.

CLASSIFICATION AND SPECIFIC FEATURES

Cartilage is classified into **hyaline**, **elastic** and **fibrous** types, based on the nature of the matrix. The features of the three types of cartilage are summarized in Table 7.1. Hyaline cartilage is seen in regions of the body where bone growth occurs, friction needs to be reduced or support must be provided. Elastic cartilage has the property of being deformable but returning to its original shape once the deforming force is removed. Fibrous cartilage is considered transitional between dense connective tissue and hyaline cartilage and merges into the neighbouring tissues. It provides strength, elasticity and resistance to repeated pressure and friction.

APPLIED ANATOMY

- **Osteoarthritis** is a common clinical condition in elderly patients in which the hyaline cartilage lining joint surfaces degenerates due to wear and tear leading to joint pains, deformities and limitation of movement. It most often affects the knee joint.
- Intervertebral **disc prolapse** is caused due to damage to the intervertebral discs. This can lead to the compression of spinal nerves emerging from the spinal cord.
- **Achondroplasia** is a common cause for dwarfism. It is a genetic disorder which results in poor bone growth because of abnormalities in the epiphyseal growth plates.

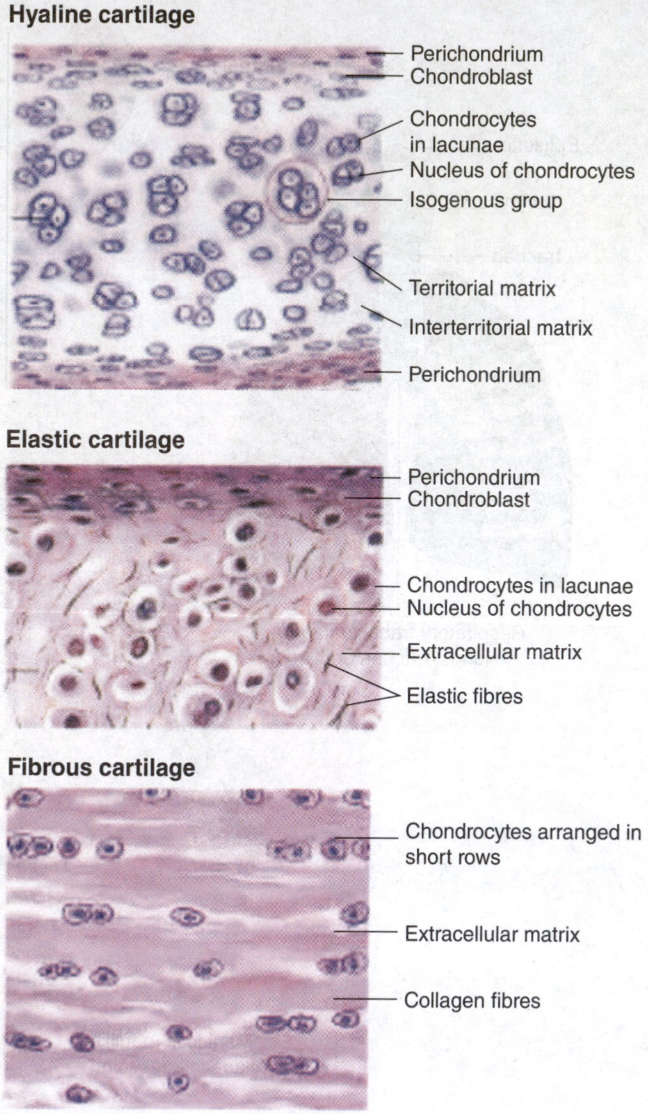

FIG. 7.1 Microscopic features of cartilage.

- **Gigantism** is a clinical condition in which excessive growth occurs due to higher levels of growth hormone. This is due to the action of growth hormone on epiphyseal cartilages.

SUMMARY

- Cartilage is a specialized form of connective tissue that is firm yet flexible.
- The cells in cartilage are called chondrocytes.
- Chondrocytes are seen within spaces in the matrix called lacunae.
- The matrix in cartilage contains proteoglycans and different fibres, depending on the type of cartilage.
- The three types of cartilage are hyaline, elastic and fibrous.
- Hyaline cartilage has a glassy, homogeneous appearance.
- Elastic cartilage contains numerous elastic fibres in the matrix.
- Fibrous cartilage contains numerous bundles of collagen fibres in the matrix.

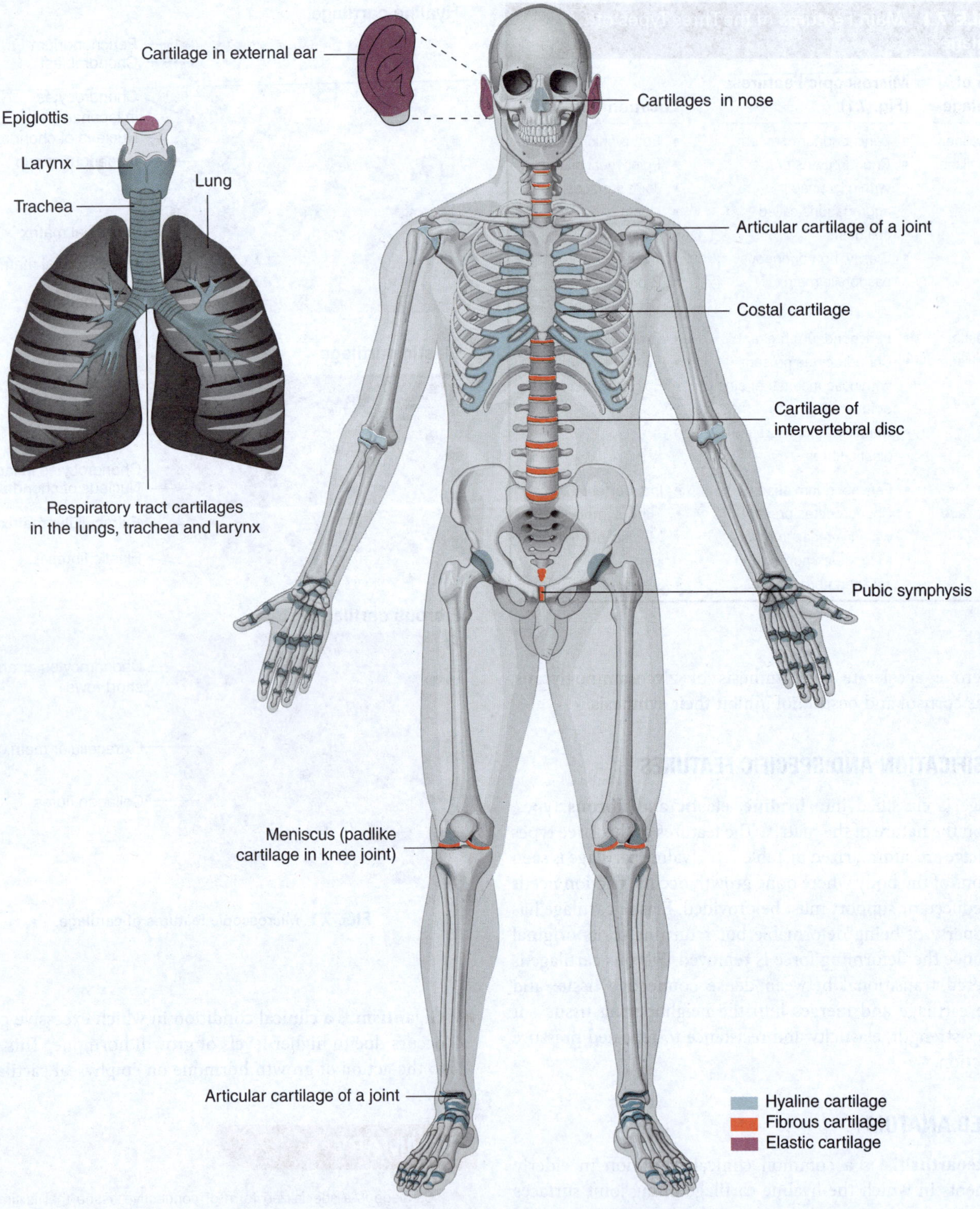

FIG. 7.2 Sites in the body where the three types of cartilage are found.

CHAPTER 8

Muscle Tissue – General Introduction, Types and Microscopic Structure

SPECIFIC LEARNING OBJECTIVES

At the end of this chapter, the student should be able to:

- Classify muscles based on their structure and function.
- Compare and contrast the light microscopic features of skeletal, cardiac and smooth muscles.
- Describe the general gross anatomical features of skeletal muscles.

GLOSSARY OF TERMS

- **Muscle:** one of the four basic types of tissues of the body which are specialized to contract
- **Sarcolemma:** plasma membrane of muscle cells
- **Sarcoplasm:** cytoplasm of muscle cells
- **Sarcoplasmic reticulum:** smooth endoplasmic reticulum of muscle cells
- **Skeletal muscle:** voluntary, striated muscle supplied by the somatic nervous system
- **Cardiac muscle:** involuntary, striated muscle supplied by the autonomic nervous system
- **Smooth muscle:** involuntary, nonstriated muscle supplied by the autonomic nervous system
- **Fascicle:** collection of muscle fibres within a muscle
- **Epimysium:** connective tissue covering of the entire muscle
- **Perimysium:** connective tissue covering of fascicles
- **Endomysium:** connective tissue covering of individual muscle fibres
- **Cross-striations:** alternate dark (A band) and light (I band) bands seen in skeletal and cardiac muscles under the microscope
- **T tubule:** inward extension of the plasma membrane into the cytoplasm of muscle cells
- **Terminal cisternae:** expansions of the sarcoplasmic reticulum adjacent to the T tubule
- **Triad:** one central T tubule flanked by two terminal cisternae
- **Sarcomere:** the contractile unit of a muscle that extends between two Z lines
- **Intercalated disc:** specialized cell junctions between cardiac muscle fibres
- **Tendon:** connective tissue attaching muscles to bones
- **Origin:** the proximal, relatively fixed end of a muscle
- **Insertion:** the distal, relatively mobile end of a muscle
- **Neuromuscular junction:** the junction between the nerve terminals of a motor neuron and muscle fibres
- **Motor unit:** all skeletal muscle fibres supplied a single motor neuron
- **Red fibres:** skeletal muscle fibres with a high content of myoglobin
- **White fibres:** skeletal muscle fibres with a low content of myoglobin
- **Parallel arrangement:** skeletal muscle fibres arranged in a parallel manner
- **Pennate arrangement:** oblique arrangement of skeletal muscle fibres
- **Spiral arrangement:** twisted arrangement of skeletal muscle fibres
- **Cruciate arrangement:** crossed arrangement of skeletal muscle fibres

INTRODUCTION

The main characteristic of muscle is its contractility, which is its ability to shorten with force. This ability of muscle enables it to perform its various functions which include body movements, maintenance of posture, constriction of organs and vessels, initiating and maintaining the heartbeat, respiration, production of body heat and communication. Specific terms are used when describing muscle tissue. The plasma membrane of muscle cells is called sarcolemma enclosing the cytoplasm called sarcoplasm. The smooth endoplasmic reticulum is called sarcoplasmic reticulum. Muscle cells have a basal lamina and reticular fibre network around them.

CLASSIFICATION OF MUSCLES (Figs 8.1 and 8.2)

Muscles are classified into three types, namely **skeletal**, **cardiac** and **smooth**. **Skeletal muscles** show prominent cross-striations under the microscope. They are attached to bones and exhibit quick and forceful contractions which are usually voluntary. Involuntary contractions of skeletal muscles may occur as part of reflexes. They are innervated by the somatic nervous system.

Cardiac muscle is found only in the heart. The muscle fibres show cross-striations that are not as prominent as those seen in skeletal muscle. Contractions of cardiac muscle are involuntary and controlled by the autonomic nervous system.

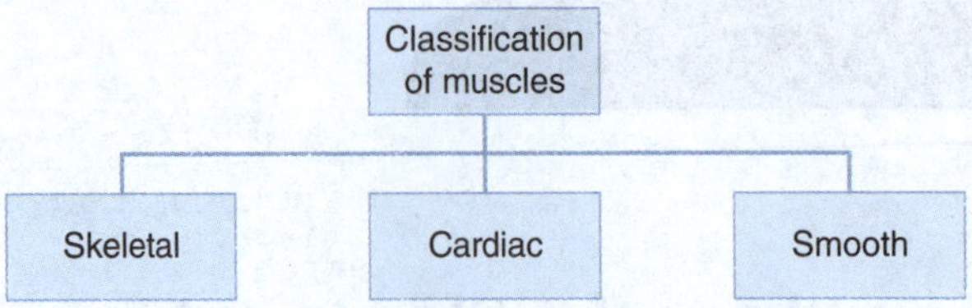

FIG. 8.1 Classification of muscles.

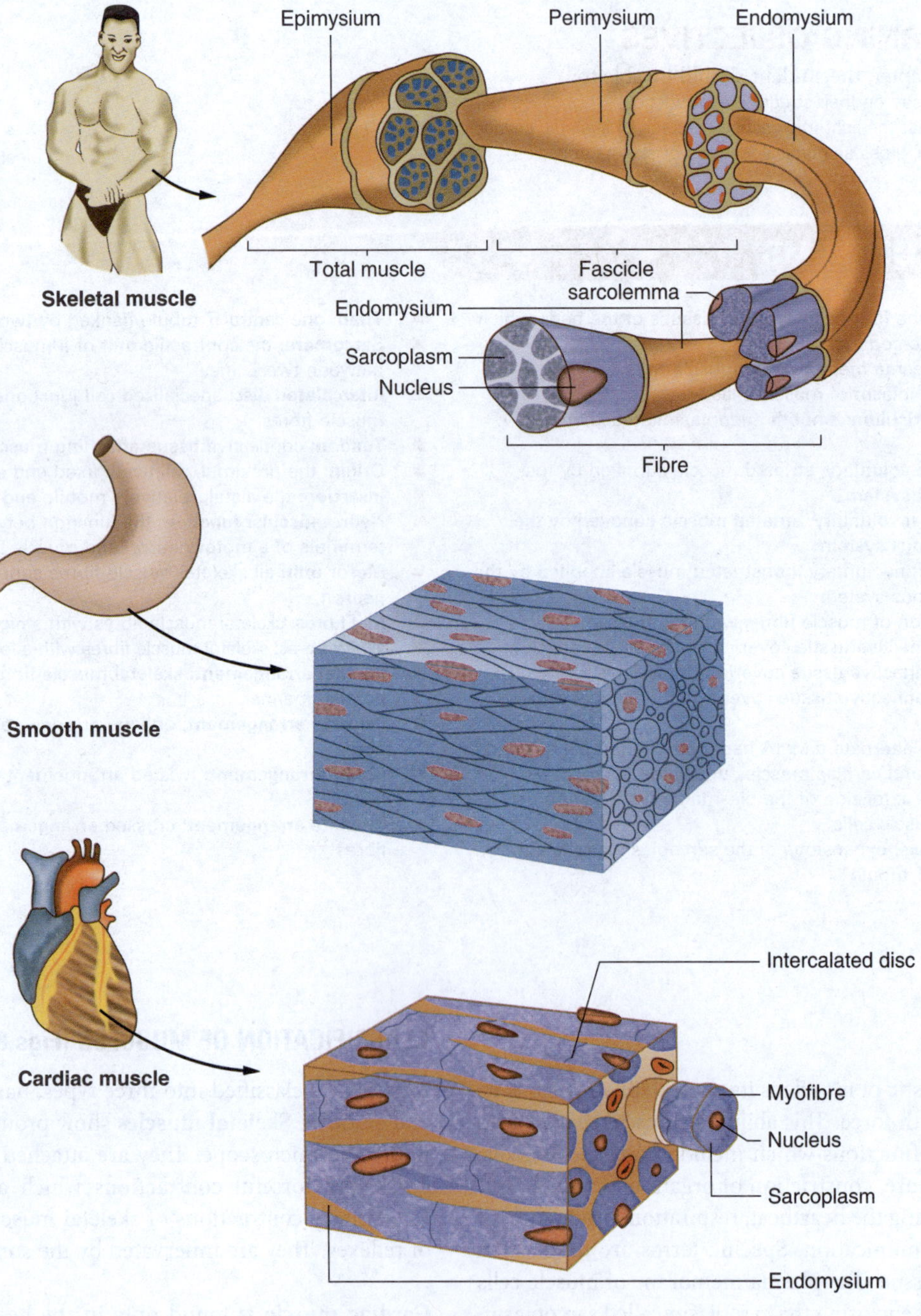

FIG. 8.2 Types of muscles.

TABLE 8.1 Differences in the Microscopic Features of the Types of Muscles

S. No.	Microscopic Features	Skeletal Muscle	Cardiac Muscle	Smooth Muscle
1.	Shape of fibres	Cylindrical	Elongated	Spindle shaped
2.	Cross-striations	Prominent	Present	Absent
3.	Number of nuclei	Multinucleated	Single	Single
4.	Position of nuclei	Peripheral	Central	Central
5.	Intercalated discs	Absent	Present	Absent

Smooth muscles are located in the walls of hollow organs, blood vessels, eyes, glands and skin. They are nonstriated, involuntary and more variable in form and function than either cardiac or skeletal muscle. Smooth muscle fibres are innervated by the autonomic nervous system. Other stimuli including mechanical and hormonal can also cause contraction of smooth muscle. The contraction of smooth muscle is slower and longer lasting compared to that of skeletal muscle. Smooth muscle can shorten and stretch to a greater extent than other muscle types. The fibres are often arranged as bundles or sheets.

MICROSCOPIC FEATURES OF MUSCLES (TABLE 8.1)

Skeletal Muscle

Skeletal muscles are surrounded by a dense, irregular fibrous connective tissue sheath called the **epimysium**. Extensions from the epimysium pass inward to surround the fasciculi and form the **perimysium**. Individual muscle fibres within the fasciculi are covered by a more delicate connective tissue sheath called the **endomysium** (Fig. 8.3). When viewed under the light microscope, skeletal muscle fibres appear long and cylindrical. They exhibit prominent **cross-striations**. The cytoplasm is eosinophilic and each fibre has several nuclei (multinucleated) which are peripherally placed. The individual fibres are unbranched. Supporting cells called satellite cells are situated in close relation to the muscle fibres (Fig. 8.4).

Under the electron microscope, more minute details become visible (Fig. 8.5). The sarcolemma dips into the cytoplasm at periodic intervals to form T tubules. The sarcoplasmic reticulum is expanded in close relation to the T tubules to form terminal cisternae. Two T tubules in association with a terminal cisterna form a **triad**. This arrangement facilitates the release of calcium stored in the terminal cisternae during muscle contraction, the stimulus for which is transmitted via the T tubules. The cross-striations are produced due to the regular arrangement of myofibrils, which in turn are formed by myofilaments. The two important myofilaments are actin and myosin, which are thin and thick filaments, respectively. In addition, there are regulatory proteins like troponin and tropomyosin and structural proteins like titin, myomesin and dystrophin.

The regular arrangement of the myofibrils produces dark (A band) and light (I band) bands, which appear as cross-striations. A dark line called the Z line runs across the centre of each I band. Similarly, a light H zone with an M line runs across the centre of each A band. A **sarcomere** extends between two adjacent Z lines (Fig. 8.5). It is the contractile unit of the skeletal muscle fibres. The mechanism of contraction will be dealt with in detail in Chapter 88 of the physiology section of this book.

Cardiac Muscle (Fig. 8.6)

Cardiac muscle has similar connective tissue coverings as skeletal muscle, but they are less prominent. They have faint **cross-striations**. Individual fibres are long, with an eosinophilic cytoplasm. Each fibre has a single, ovoid, euchromatic nucleus, which is centrally placed. The fibres appear to branch and anastomose with one another. **Intercalated discs** which connect adjacent cardiac muscle fibres are a characteristic feature of

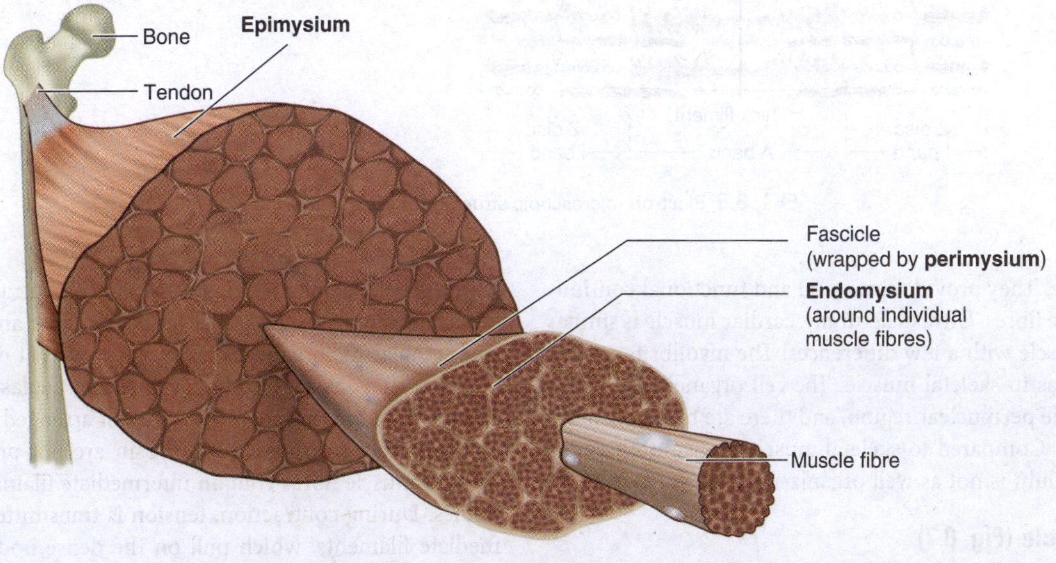

FIG. 8.3 Levels of organization in a skeletal muscle.

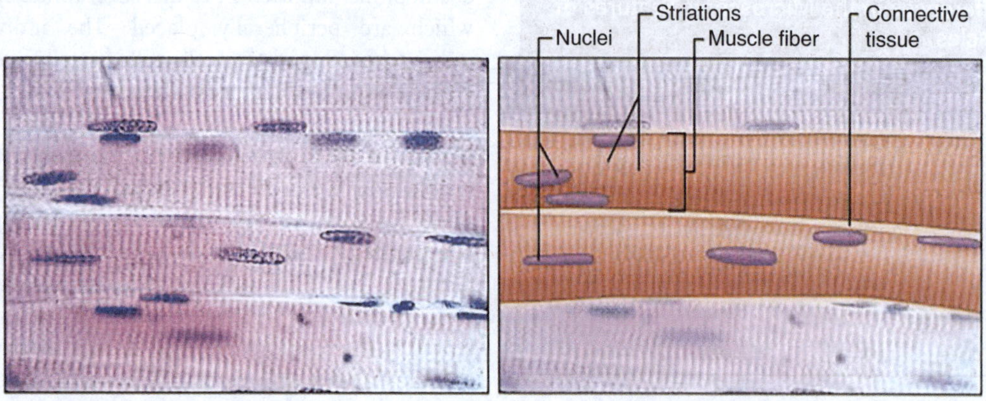

FIG. 8.4 Microscopic structure of skeletal muscle.

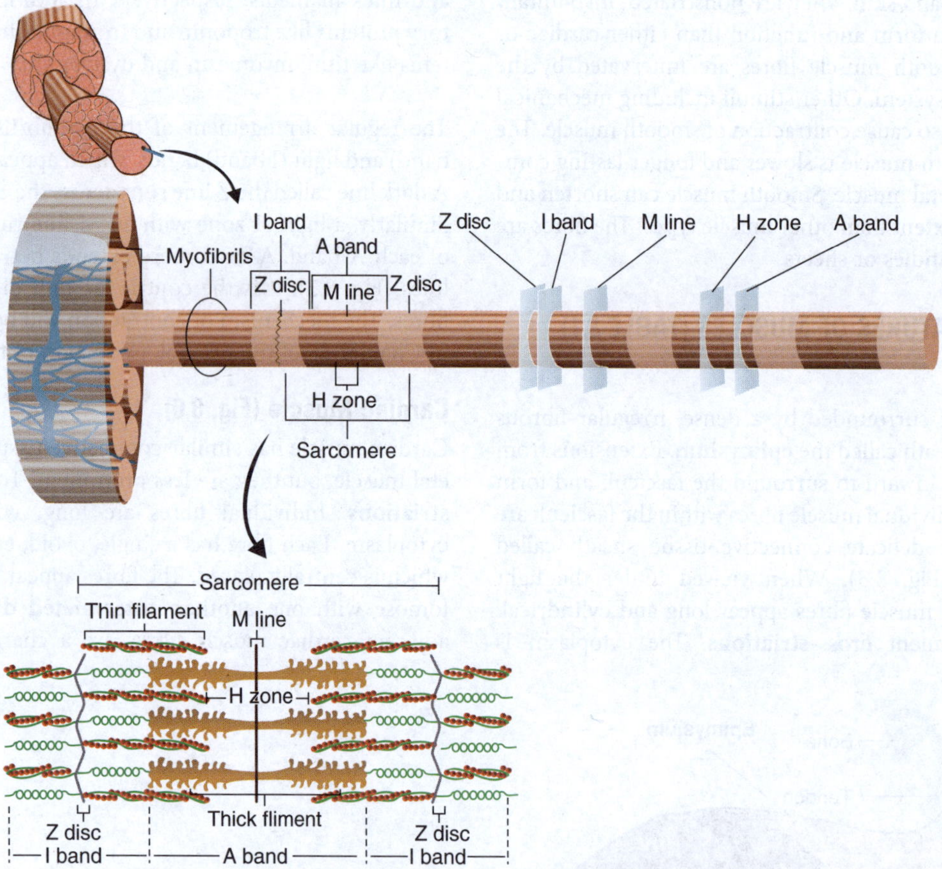

FIG. 8.5 Electron microscopic structure of skeletal muscle.

cardiac muscle. They provide structural and functional continuity between the fibres. Ultrastructurally, cardiac muscle is similar to skeletal muscle with a few differences. The myofibrils are not as distinctive as in skeletal muscle. The cell organelles are concentrated in the perinuclear region, and there are relatively more mitochondria. Compared to skeletal muscle, the smooth endoplasmic reticulum is not as well organized.

Smooth Muscle (Fig. 8.7)

Smooth muscle is **nonstriated** and made up of spindle-shaped cells of variable length. Each fibre has an eosinophilic cytoplasm with a single, elongated nucleus which is centrally placed. The fibres are arranged in parallel fasciculi. There are no T tubules and cytoplasmic organelles are concentrated at each end of the nucleus. They have a poorly developed sarcoplasmic reticulum. The actin and myosin filaments are not arranged in orderly sarcomeres. Troponin and tropomyosin are not present. Instead, smooth muscle fibres contain intermediate filaments and dense bodies. During contraction, tension is transmitted to the intermediate filaments, which pull on the dense bodies. Gap junctions (nexuses) are present between adjacent muscle fibres enabling functional continuity between the muscle fibres.

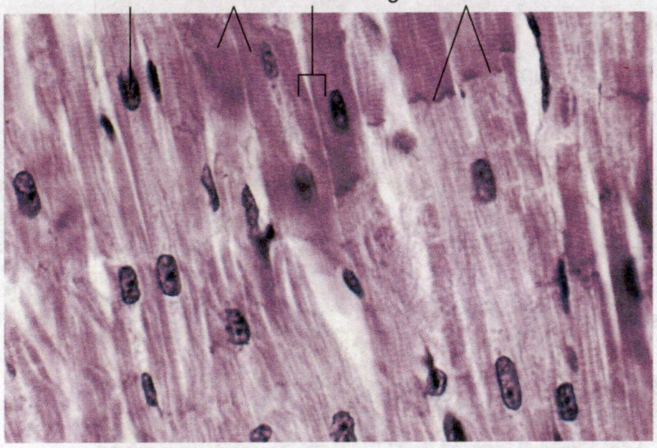

FIG. 8.6 Microscopic structure of cardiac muscle.

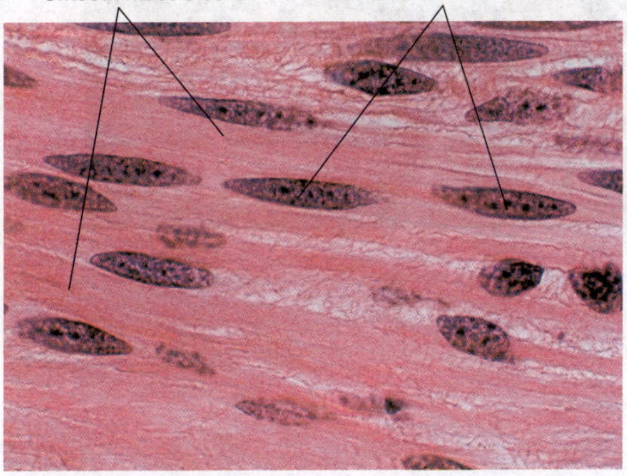

FIG. 8.7 Microscopic structure of smooth muscle.

GENERAL FEATURES OF SKELETAL MUSCLES

Skeletal muscles are attached to bones through **tendons**. The proximal attachment is usually fixed and termed the **origin**, whereas the distal attachment is more mobile and called the **insertion**. In its passage from origin to insertion, a muscle crosses a joint at which it causes a movement. Skeletal muscles are supplied by somatic nerves. The nerves come near the muscle fibres at **neuromuscular junctions**, where the nerve impulses stimulate the muscles to contract (Fig. 8.8). A **motor unit** consists of all muscle fibres that are supplied by a single motor neuron through its axon terminals.

NOMENCLATURE USED TO NAME SKELETAL MUSCLES

Muscles are named based on several characteristics including shape, size, number of bellies or heads, position, depth, attachments, actions and direction of fibres.

Shape

- Deltoid – triangular
- Quadratus – square
- Rhomboid – diamond-shaped
- Teres – round
- Gracilis – slender
- Rectus – straight
- Lumbrical – worm-like

Size

- Major – large
- Minor – small
- Longus – long
- Brevis – short
- Latissimus – broadest
- Longissimus – longest

Number of Heads or Bellies

- Biceps – two heads
- Triceps – three heads
- Quadriceps – four heads
- Digastric – two bellies

Position

- Anterior – in front
- Posterior – behind
- Interosseous – between bones
- Supraspinatus – above the spine of the scapula
- Infraspinatus – below the spine of the scapula
- Dorsi – of the back
- Abdominis – of the abdomen
- Pectoralis – of the chest
- Brachii – of the arm
- Femoris – of the thigh
- Oris – of the mouth

Depth

- Superficialis – superficial
- Profundus – deep
- Externus – towards the surface
- Internus – away from the surface

Attachment

- Sternocleidomastoid – from the sternum and clavicle to the mastoid process
- Coracobrachialis – from the coracoid process to the arm

Action

- Extensor
- Flexor
- Abductor
- Adductor
- Levator – elevator
- Depressor
- Supinator
- Pronator
- Constrictor
- Dilator

Direction of Fibres

- Rectus abdominis
- Oblique abdominis
- Transversus abdominis

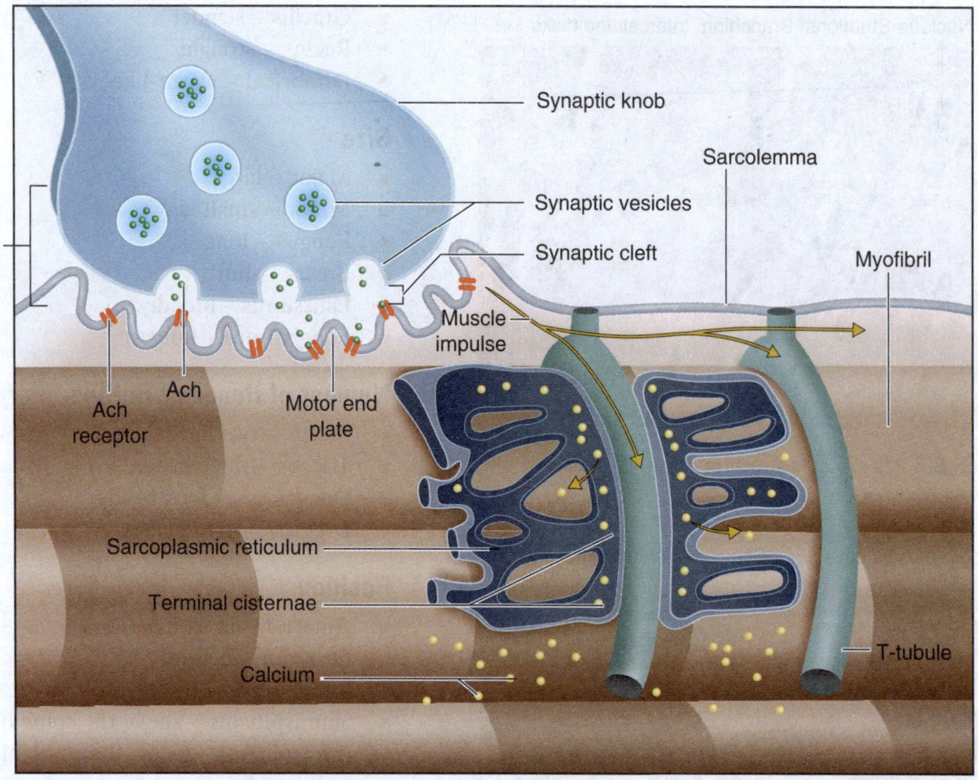

FIG. 8.8 A neuromuscular junction.

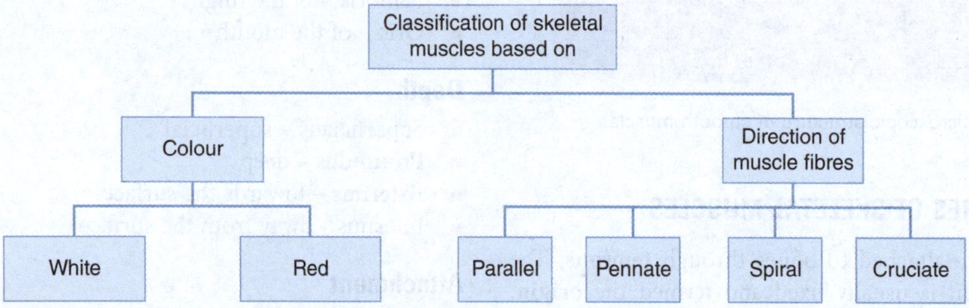

FIG. 8.9 Classification of skeletal muscle.

CLASSIFICATION OF SKELETAL MUSCLES

Skeletal muscles can be classified according to their **colour** and **direction of muscle fibres** (Figs 8.9 and 8.10). The colour of skeletal muscle depends on the density and amount of myoglobin in the sarcoplasm of the muscle cell. In **red fibres**, the myoglobin is abundant, whereas it is scarcer in **white fibres**. Red fibres contract more slowly, are fatigue resistant and have a richer blood supply. The diameter of individual muscle fibres is greater in white muscle. Red fibres are found in deep muscles, deeper aspects of superficial muscles and antigravity muscles of the trunk. White fibres are found in the superficial muscles and extraocular muscles.

In muscles with a **parallel** arrangement, the muscle fibres are parallel to the line of pull. The range of movement is more, since the muscle fibres are long. However, the total force of contraction is relatively low, since the number of fibres in a given volume is less. Examples include the rectus abdominis, quadratus lumborum and biceps brachii. In **pennate** muscles, on the other hand, the muscle fibres are oblique to the line of pull. Due to this, there is a diminished range of movement. However, there is an increased force of contraction due to the greater number of muscle fibres that can be packed into a given volume. The arrangement of fibres in a pennate muscle can be unipennate, bipennate, multipennate or circumpennate. Examples of such

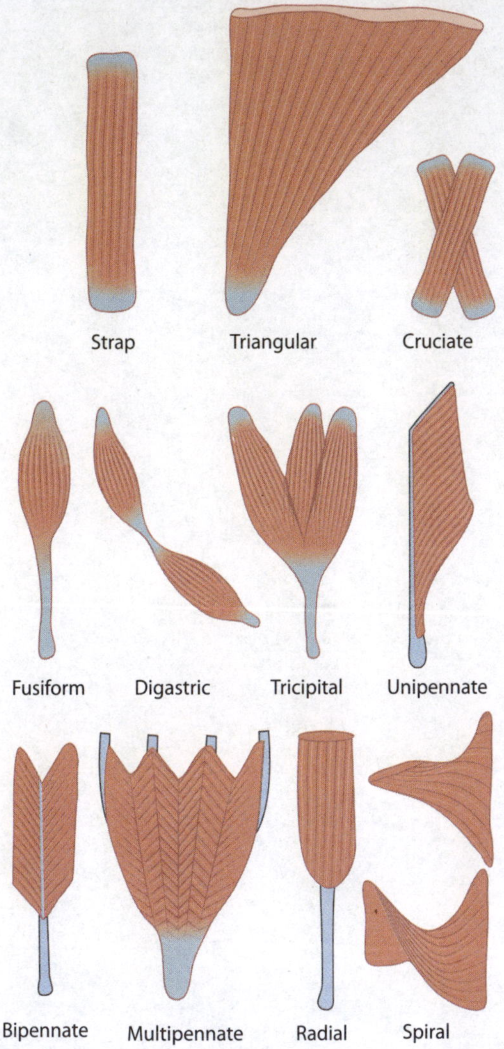

FIG. 8.10 Different types of arrangements of skeletal muscle fibres.

muscles include the flexor pollicis longus, interossei of the hand and foot, acromial fibres of the deltoid and tibialis anterior, respectively. Some muscles such as the pectoralis major have a twisting of fibres close to their insertion and are called **spiral** muscles. Other muscles have superficial fibres and deep fibres that cross each other like the letter X. These are called **cruciate** muscles, an example of which is the sternocleidomastoid muscle.

APPLIED ANATOMY

- The loss of motor power of a muscle is called **paralysis.** It can be caused due to damage to the nerve supplying it or disease of the muscle itself, termed **myopathy.**
- Muscles can go into states of prolonged contraction called **spasms.** Localized spasms are seen in 'muscle pulls', whereas generalized spasms are seen in conditions such as epilepsy and tetanus.
- The tone of a muscle can be either decreased or increased. A decreased tone is called **hypotonia**, whereas an increased tone is called **hypertonia**. Hypotonia is seen when the nerve supply to a muscle is affected and in cerebellar disorders. Hypertonia is classically seen in Parkinson disease.
- Wasting of a muscle is called **atrophy** and typically occurs due to disuse or denervation. Enlargement of a muscle is called **hypertrophy** as is seen among body builders.
- **Regeneration** of different types of muscles varies considerably. Cardiac muscles have no power of regeneration and are therefore replaced by scar tissue after a myocardial infarction. Skeletal muscle fibres have a limited power of regeneration, one of the functions of the satellite cells surrounding them. Smooth muscles cells have a considerable ability to regenerate.

SUMMARY

- Muscle is a basic type of tissue that is specialized to contract.
- The three types of muscles are skeletal, cardiac and smooth.
- Skeletal muscles are voluntary, striated and supplied by the somatic nervous system.
- The connective tissue covering of the entire muscle, fascicles and individual fibres is called epimysium, perimysium and endomysium, respectively.
- Cardiac muscle is involuntary, striated and supplied by the autonomic nervous system.
- Smooth muscle is involuntary, nonstriated and supplied by the autonomic nervous system.
- Microscopically, skeletal muscle fibres appear long and cylindrical, with prominent cross-striations and multiple, peripherally placed nuclei.
- Cardiac muscle fibres appear elongated, with less prominent cross-striations, intercalated discs and a single, centrally placed nucleus.
- Smooth muscle fibres are spindle-shaped and nonstriated, with a single, centrally placed nucleus.
- Skeletal muscles are attached to bones through tendons and have an origin and insertion.
- Skeletal muscles are supplied by motor neurons at neuromuscular junctions.
- Skeletal muscles can be classified based on their colour and arrangement of fibres.
- Red fibres are rich in myoglobin, whereas white fibres are poor in myoglobin.
- The fibres in skeletal muscles may be arranged in a parallel manner, obliquely, spirally or in a cruciate manner.

2 SECTION

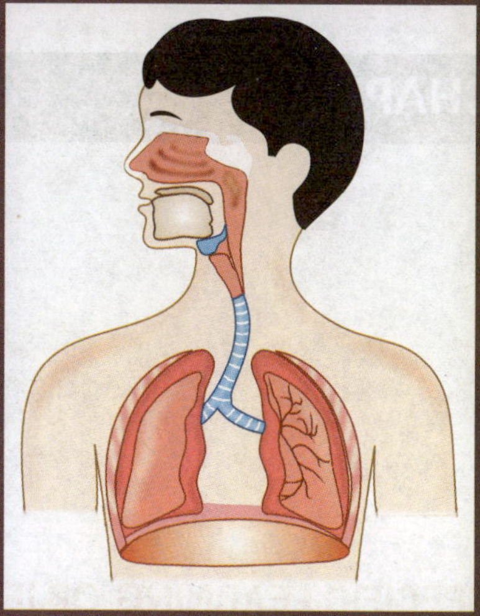

The Respiratory System

Section Outline

CHAPTER 9

The Upper Respiratory System and Larynx

SPECIFIC LEARNING OBJECTIVES

At the end of this chapter, the student should be able to:

- Name the structures that constitute the respiratory system.
- Describe the functions of each part.
- Describe the gross anatomy of the nasal cavity.
- Describe the location and openings of the paranasal air sinuses.
- Describe the parts and structure of the pharynx.
- Describe the gross anatomy of the larynx.

GLOSSARY OF TERMS

- **External nose:** bony and cartilaginous framework of the nose that is visible externally
- **Nasal cavity:** part of the nose extending from the nostrils to the choanae
- **Choanae:** posterior apertures of the nasal cavity
- **Nasal septum:** partition between the nasal cavities
- **Conchae:** bony projections from the lateral wall of the nose
- **Turbinates:** conchae covered by the mucous membrane
- **Meatuses:** spaces under the turbinates which receive the openings of the paranasal air sinuses
- **Paranasal air sinuses:** air-filled spaces in the skull opening into the nasal cavity
- **Pharynx:** muscular tube extending from the base of the skull to the oesophagus
- **Nasopharynx:** part of the pharynx posterior to the nasal cavity
- **Oropharynx:** part of the pharynx posterior to the oral cavity
- **Laryngopharynx:** part of the pharynx posterior to the larynx
- **Piriform fossa:** space in the laryngopharynx on either side of the larynx
- **Larynx:** the 'voice box' responsible for speech production and made up of cartilages, membranes and muscles
- **Vestibule:** interior of the larynx superior to the false cords
- **Ventricle or glottis:** interior of the larynx between the true and false cords
- **Infraglottic part:** interior of the larynx below the true vocal cords
- **Extrinsic muscles:** have attachments outside the larynx
- **Intrinsic muscles:** have attachments entirely within the larynx

INTRODUCTION (Fig. 9.1)

The primary function of respiration is to ensure oxygen supply to the body and removal of carbon dioxide that is produced. Respiration can be divided into **external respiration** and **internal respiration**. External respiration involves the process of gases being exchanged between the lungs and blood. Internal respiration refers to the exchange of gases between blood and tissues. The **parts** of the respiratory system include the nose and nasal cavity, pharynx, larynx, trachea, bronchial tree, lungs and accessory structures like the oral cavity, thoracic cage and diaphragm. The **upper respiratory system** consists of all the structures up to the larynx, the remaining structures constituting the **lower respiratory system**. The **conducting zone** extends from the nose to the terminal bronchioles, while the **respiratory zone**, where gaseous exchange occurs, extends from the respiratory bronchioles to the alveoli. The **functions** of the upper respiratory system include conditioning of the inhaled air, providing defence against pathogens and olfaction. The lower respiratory system is responsible for the production of speech and other respiratory sounds, gas exchange and maintenance of homeostasis.

THE NOSE

The nose can be divided into the **external nose** and **nasal cavity**. The external nose is visible from the outside and consists of a framework of hyaline **cartilages**, **bones** and **dense connective tissue** covered by the skin (Fig. 9.2). Rudimentary muscles are also present beneath the skin and are responsible for the slight movements of the external nose, especially the ala. The main **parts** of the external nose are the root, bridge, dorsum, tip, septum, nostrils or external nares and the ala. The presence of cartilage in the external nose ensures that the nasal cavity remains open at all times yet, allowing for some flexibility.

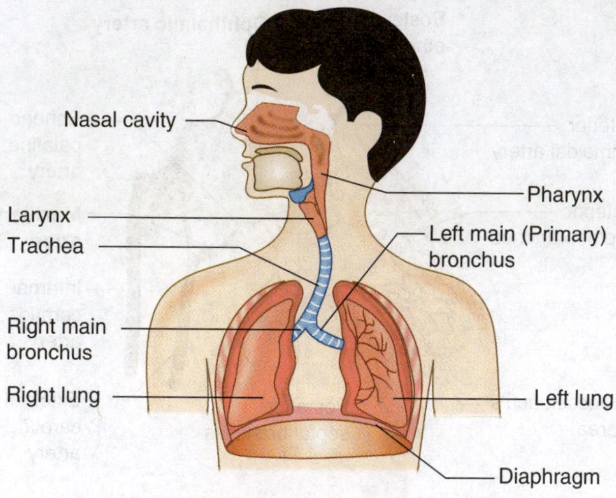

FIG. 9.1 The parts of the respiratory system.

The **nasal cavity** extends from the anterior to the posterior nares called the **nostrils** and **choanae**, respectively. It is divided by a **nasal septum** into two halves. Each half has three regions, namely the **vestibule, respiratory region** and **olfactory region** (Fig. 9.3). The vestibule, respiratory region and olfactory region are lined by the skin, respiratory epithelium and olfactory epithelium, respectively. The openings of the nasal cavity are the anterior and posterior nares. The nasal cavity contains a **roof, medial wall, lateral wall** and **floor** (Fig. 9.4). The roof is formed by the ethmoid and sphenoid bones. Small foramina are present in the cribriform plate of the ethmoid bone which forms the roof. These foramina allow for the passage of rootlets of the olfactory nerve. The floor is formed by the hard palate consisting of the maxilla and palatine bones. This boundary separates the nasal cavity and oral cavity.

The nasal septum forms the medial wall and separates the two halves of the nasal cavity (Fig. 9.5). The nasal septum is partly **cartilaginous** and partly **bony**. The major bony components are the perpendicular plate of the **ethmoid** and **vomer**. The rest of the septum is formed mainly by the **septal cartilage**. Three **conchae**, the superior, middle and inferior, project from the lateral wall of the nasal cavity. The superior and middle conchae are part of the ethmoid bone, while the inferior concha is a separate bone. **Turbinates** are formed when mucosa covers the conchae (Fig. 9.4). The spaces under the turbinates are called **meatuses**. Meatuses receive the openings of the paranasal air sinuses and nasolacrimal duct. The presence of turbinates constricts the passageways, creating air turbulence, which helps to warm and moisten the incoming air and trap dust particles.

The mucosa of the respiratory region is lined by **pseudostratified ciliated columnar epithelium** resting on a lamina propria. The epithelium contains ciliated columnar, goblet and basal cells. **Seromucous glands** and **sinusoids** are seen in the lamina propria. The mucus produced by goblet cells helps to trap dust particles, which are transported towards the oropharynx by ciliary movement for removal by coughing. The glands and sinusoids help to moisten and warm the inhaled air, respectively.

The **arterial supply** of the nose is via branches from the maxillary, facial and ophthalmic arteries (Fig. 9.6). The largest artery supplying the nose is the sphenopalatine artery which is a branch of the maxillary artery. The **veins** drain into the internal jugular vein and pterygoid plexus of veins. Branches from ophthalmic and maxillary divisions of the trigeminal nerve provide sensory **nerve supply** to the nose (Fig. 9.7). Olfactory sensations are carried by the olfactory nerve rootlets present in the olfactory epithelium lining the upper one-third of the nasal cavity. **Lymphatic drainage** of the nose is into the submandibular and retropharyngeal lymph nodes.

THE PARANASAL AIR SINUSES (Fig. 9.8)

These are **four pairs** of air-containing spaces within the skull that drain into the nasal cavity. They are named according to the

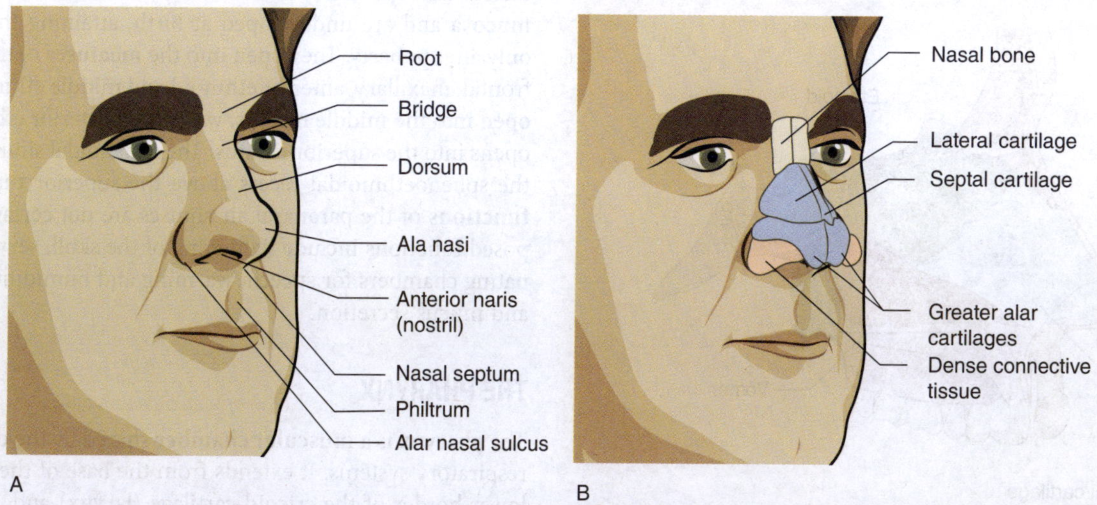

FIG. 9.2 The parts and structure of the external nose.

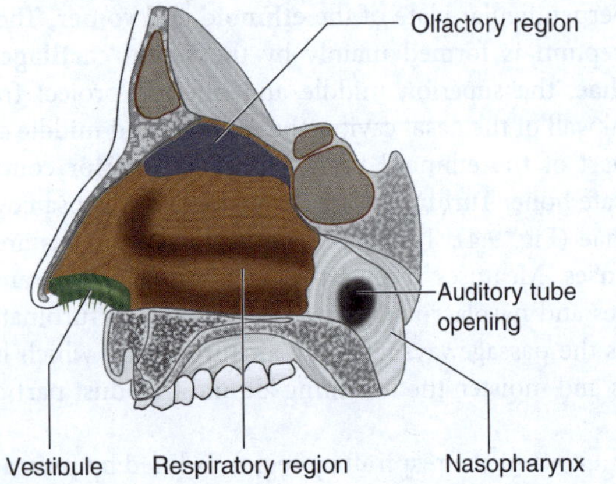

FIG. 9.3 The regions of the nasal cavity (sagittal section).

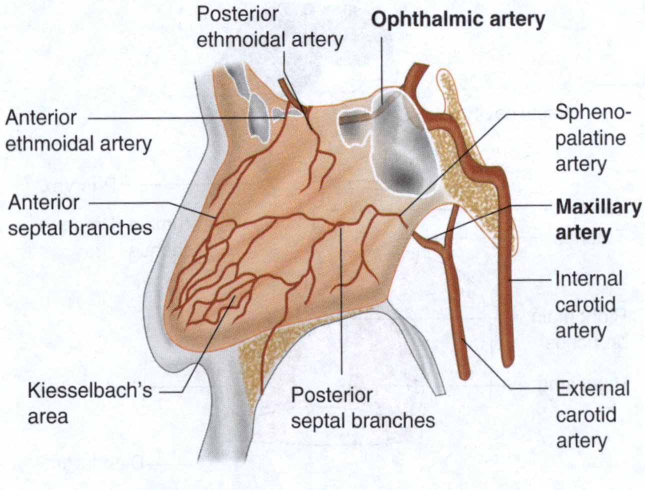

FIG. 9.6 The arterial supply of the nose.

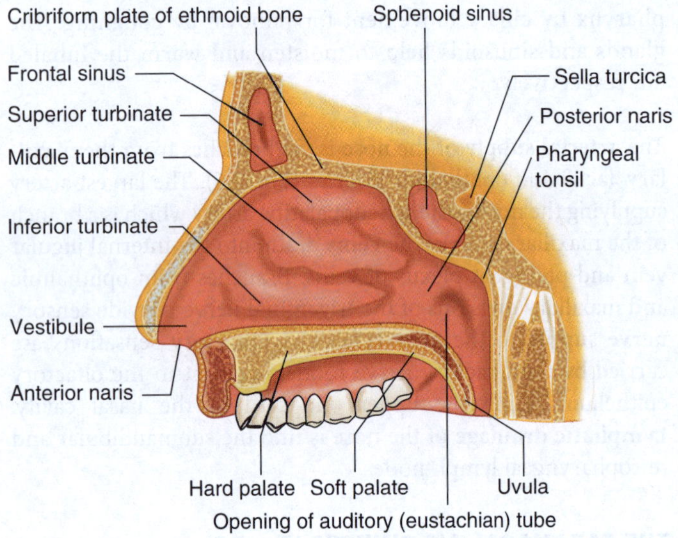

FIG. 9.4 The nasal cavity.

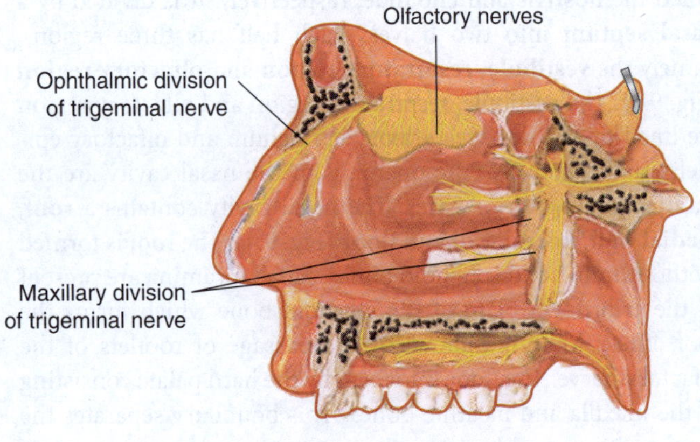

FIG. 9.7 The nerve supply of the nose.

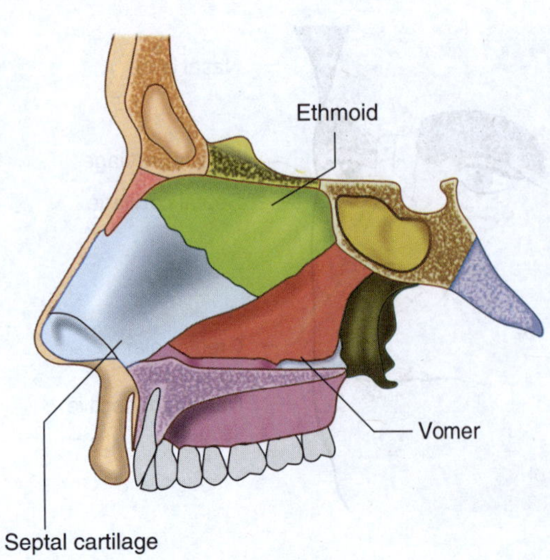

FIG. 9.5 The major components of the nasal septum.

bones in which they lie. The four pairs of paranasal air sinuses are the **maxillary, frontal, ethmoid (anterior, middle and posterior)** and **sphenoid** sinuses. They are lined with **respiratory mucosa** and are undeveloped at birth, attaining their full size only after puberty. They open into the **meatuses** of the nose. The frontal, maxillary, anterior ethmoid and middle ethmoid sinuses open into the middle meatus, while the posterior ethmoid sinus opens into the superior meatus. The sphenoidal sinus opens into the sphenoethmoidal recess above the superior turbinate. The **functions** of the paranasal air sinuses are not certain. The proposed functions include lightening of the skull, serving as resonating chambers for speech, warming and humidification of air and mucus secretion.

THE PHARYNX

The pharynx is a **muscular chamber** shared by the digestive and respiratory systems. It extends from the base of the skull to the lower border of the cricoid cartilage (larynx) and continues as the oesophagus. Its walls contain **skeletal muscle** arranged as

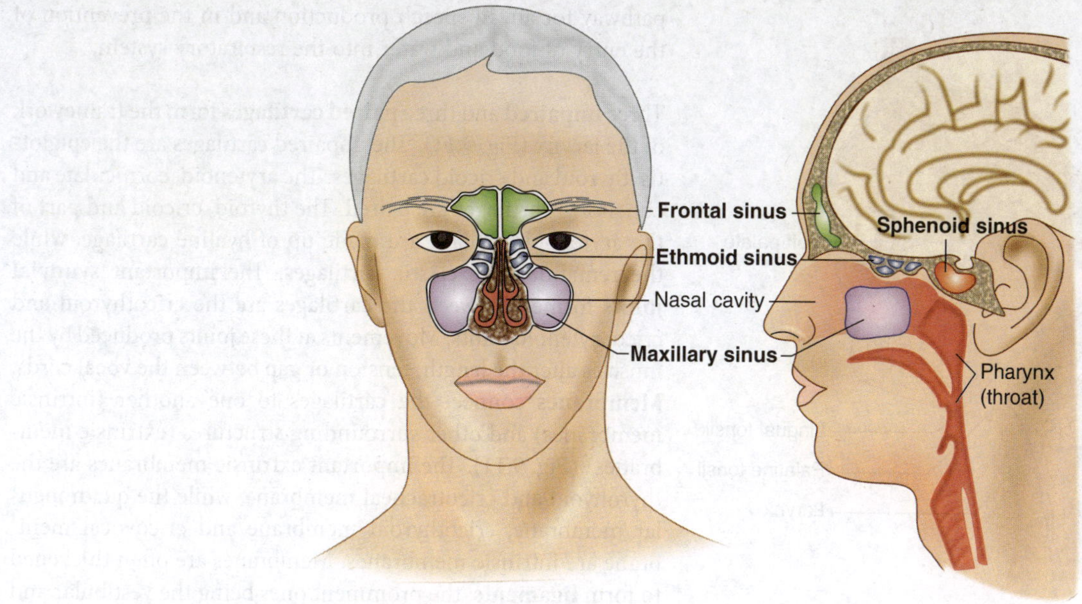

FIG. 9.8 The paranasal air sinuses.

inner longitudinal and outer circular (constrictor muscles) layers. It is subdivided from superior to inferior into **nasopharynx, oropharynx** and **laryngopharynx** lying posterior to the nasal cavity, oral cavity and larynx, respectively (Fig. 9.9). The **functions** of the pharynx are the regulation of the passage of air, water and food, immune protection through Waldeyer's ring and acting as a resonating chamber after sound production by the larynx. The features of the different parts of the pharynx are summarized in Table 9.1. The pharynx is supplied by the **pharyngeal plexus** of nerves which contain motor, sensory and sympathetic components.

THE LARYNX

The larynx or **voice box** is located between the root of the tongue and the upper end of the trachea. It consists of a framework of **cartilages** articulating at **joints**. The cartilages are connected by **membranes** and lined by the mucous membrane. The cartilages are moved by small **skeletal muscles**. The larynx **functions** as a

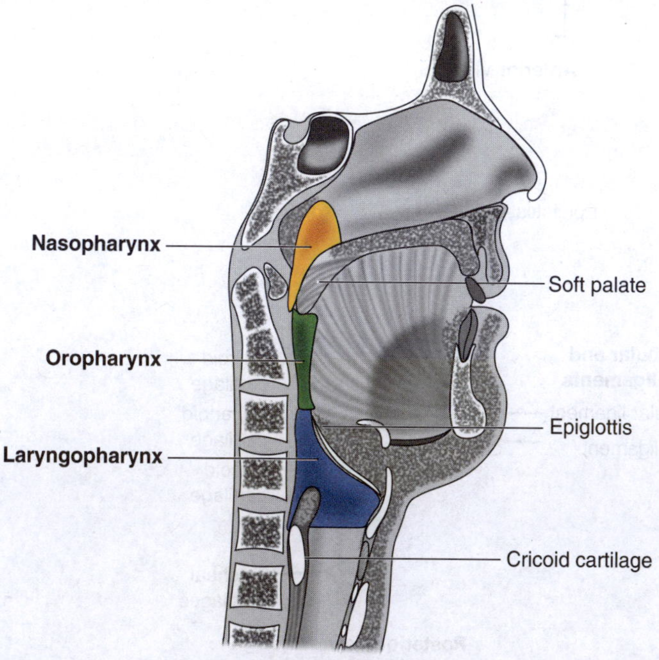

FIG. 9.9 The parts of the pharynx.

TABLE 9.1 The Features of the Different Parts of the Pharynx (Fig. 9.10)

	Nasopharynx	Oropharynx	Laryngopharynx
Location	Behind nasal cavity	Behind oral cavity	Behind larynx
Extent	Base of skull to soft palate	Soft palate to tip of epiglottis	Tip of epiglottis to lower border of cricoid cartilage
Passage for	Only air	Food and air	Food and air
Lining	Pseudostratified ciliated columnar epithelium	Stratified squamous nonkeratinized epithelium	Stratified squamous nonkeratinized epithelium
Important features	Contains the pharyngeal tonsil and opening of the auditory tube	Contains the palatine tonsil	Contains the piriform fossa which is a space on either side of the larynx

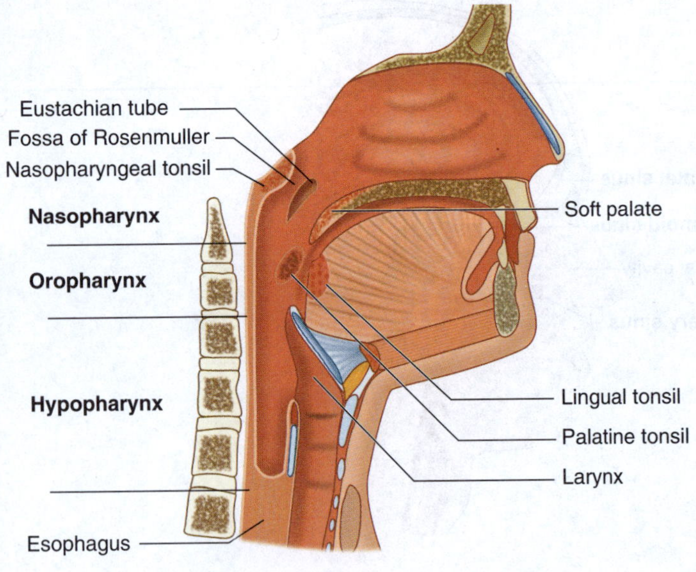

FIG. 9.10 The interior of the pharynx.

pathway for air, in speech production and in the prevention of the entry of food and water into the respiratory system.

Three **unpaired** and three **paired cartilages** form the framework of the larynx (Fig. 9.11). The unpaired cartilages are the epiglottis, thyroid and cricoid cartilages. The arytenoid, corniculate and cuneiform cartilages are paired. The thyroid, cricoid and part of the arytenoid cartilage are made up of hyaline cartilage, while the remaining are elastic cartilages. The important **synovial joints** formed between the cartilages are the cricothyroid and cricoarytenoid joints. Movements at these joints produced by the muscles alter the length, tension or gap between the vocal cords. **Membranes** connect the cartilages to one another (intrinsic membranes) and other surrounding structures (extrinsic membranes) (Fig. 9.11). The important extrinsic membranes are the thyrohyoid and cricotracheal membrane, while the quadrangular membrane, cricothyroid membrane and cricovocal membrane are intrinsic membranes. Membranes are often thickened to form **ligaments**, the prominent ones being the vestibular and vocal ligaments.

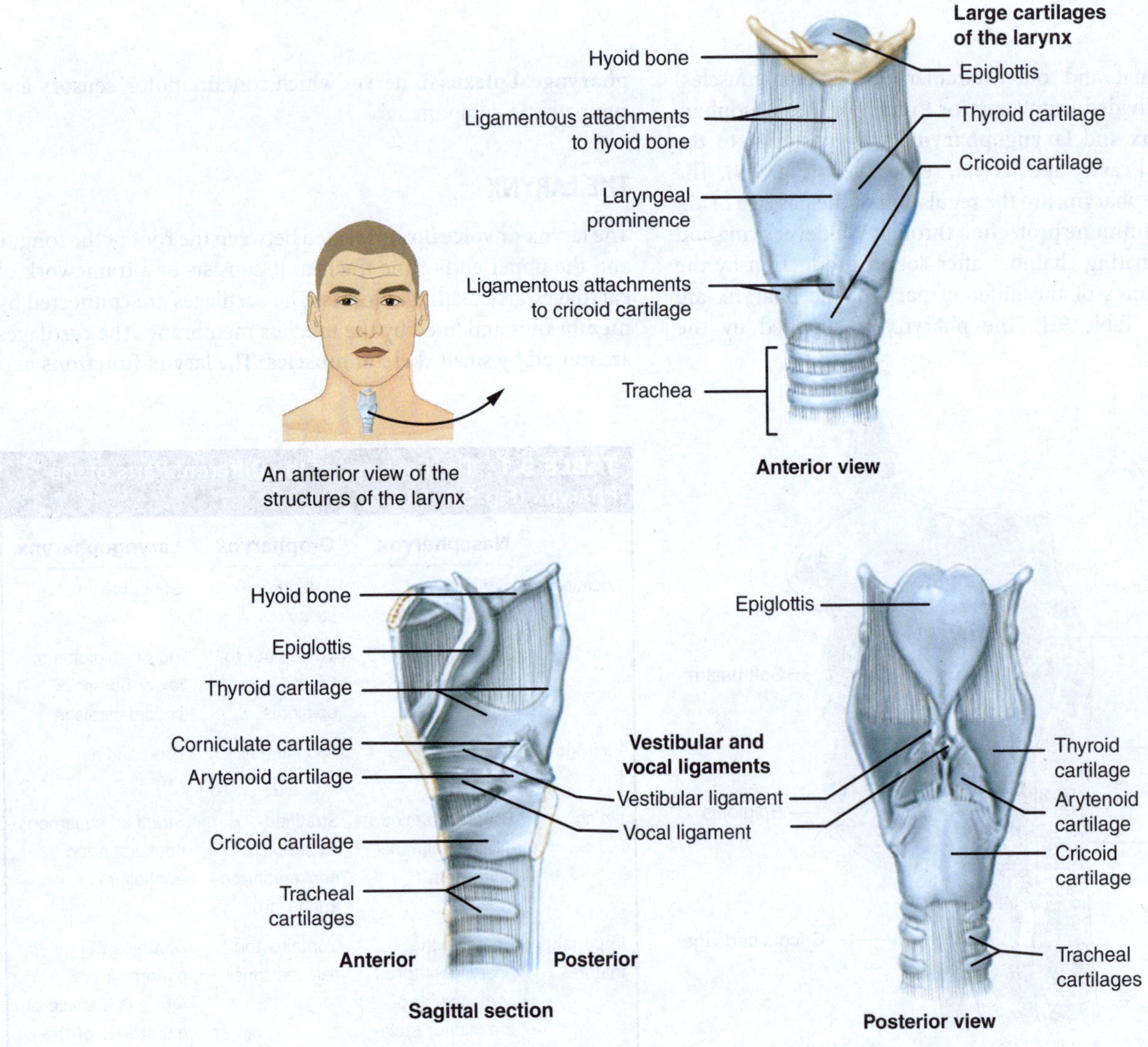

FIG. 9.11 The cartilages, membranes and ligaments of the larynx.

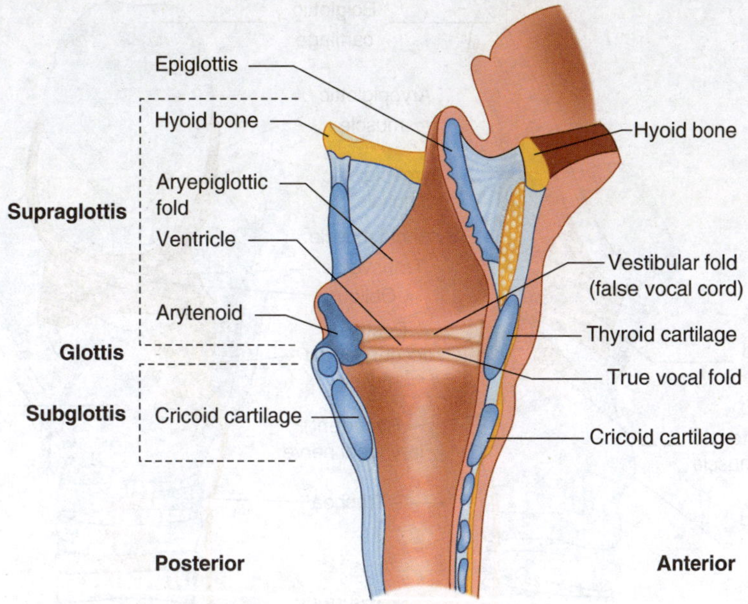

FIG. 9.12 The interior of the larynx (sagittal section).

The **interior** of the larynx is divided into three parts by vocal (true vocal cords) and vestibular (false vocal cords) folds which are formed when ligaments of the same name are covered by mucous membrane (Fig. 9.12). The **voice** is produced by vibration of the true vocal cords when bursts of air pass across them. The three parts are the **vestibule**, **ventricle (glottis)** and **infraglottic part**. **Respiratory epithelium** lines the inside of the larynx except for the vocal cords, part of epiglottis and upper border of the quadrangular membrane. These portions are lined by **stratified squamous nonkeratinized epithelium**.

The **muscles** of the larynx are categorized into **intrinsic** and **extrinsic** muscles. Intrinsic muscles are entirely contained within the larynx, whereas extrinsic muscles have attachments to structures outside the larynx. Extrinsic muscles include some of the strap muscles and the inferior constrictor. Intrinsic muscles can be classified according to their actions on the inlet and glottis (Figs 9.13 and 9.14). Functionally, the most important muscle is the **posterior cricoarytenoid** which is the only abductor of the vocal cords, thus serving to keep the airway open. All intrinsic muscles are supplied by the **recurrent laryngeal nerve** except the cricothyroid which is supplied by the **external laryngeal nerve**. The sensory nerve supply above the vocal folds is by the **internal laryngeal nerve** and below the vocal folds by the recurrent laryngeal nerve. **Blood supply** to the larynx is by the superior and inferior laryngeal vessels.

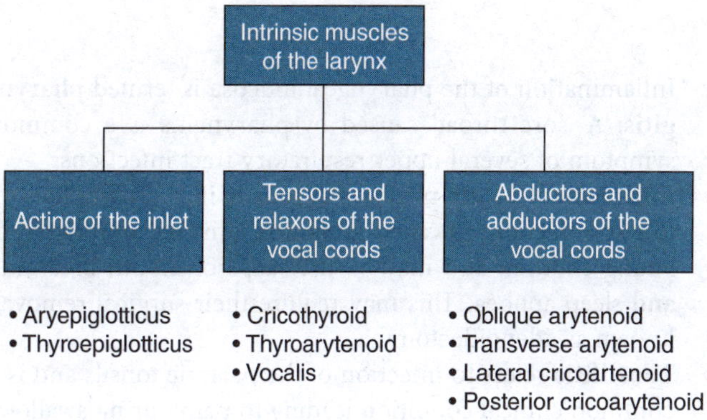

FIG. 9.13 The actions of the intrinsic muscles of the larynx.

APPLIED ANATOMY

- Inflammation of the nasal mucosa is called **rhinitis** and commonly occurs due to viral infections and allergies.
- The most **fractured bone** in the skull is the **nasal bone**, often due to trauma.
- **Deviation of the nasal septum** is not uncommon. When the deviation is extreme, it may cause blockage of the nasal passages and meatuses of the paranasal sinuses and subsequent infections.
- Bleeding from the nose is called **epistaxis.** This usually occurs from an area called Little's area in the anteroinferior portion of the nasal septum from an arterial plexus called Kiesselbach's plexus. It is more common in children from trauma due to nose picking.
- Infection of the paranasal air sinuses is called **sinusitis**, causing pain and tenderness over the sinuses.
- **Polyps** can originate from the mucosa of the paranasal sinuses due to chronic infections or allergies and cause nasal blockage.
- **Functional endoscopic sinus surgery** uses nasal endoscopes to perform surgical procedures for infections and growths in the paranasal sinuses.

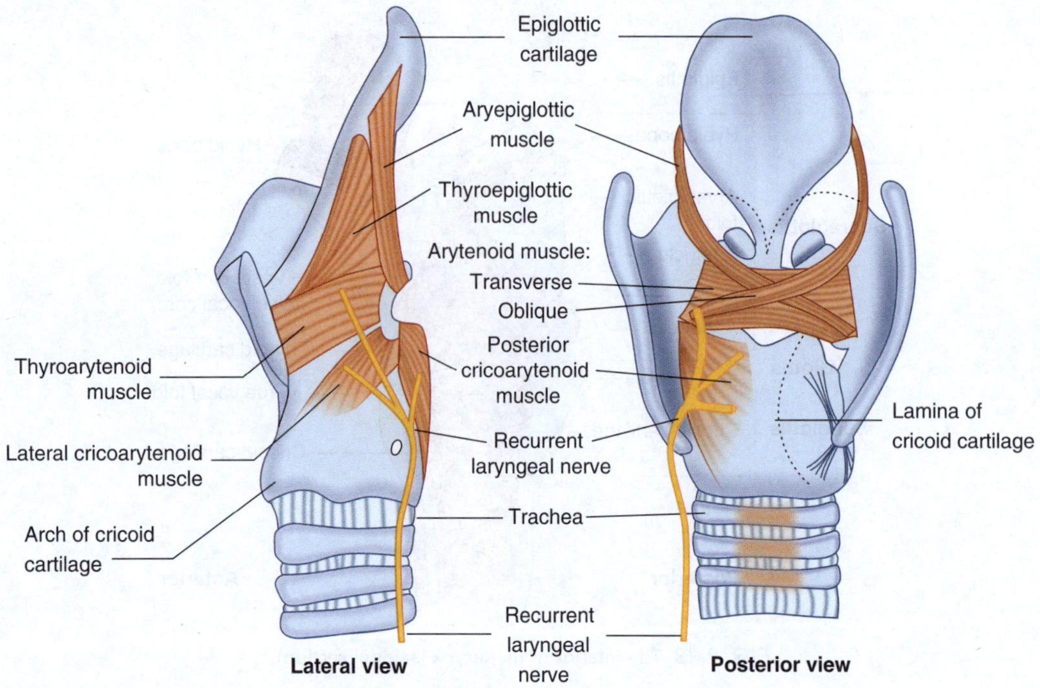

FIG. 9.14 The intrinsic muscles of the larynx.

- Inflammation of the pharyngeal mucosa is termed **pharyngitis**. A 'sore throat' caused by pharyngitis is a common symptom of several upper respiratory tract infections.
- Enlargement of the pharyngeal tonsils in the nasopharynx due to infections is called **adenoids**. This occurs mainly in young children and may be the cause of mouth breathing and sleep apnoea. This may require their surgical removal, known as adenoidectomy.
- **Tonsillitis** refers to infection of the palatine tonsils and is a common clinical condition leading to pain during swallowing and painful cervical lymphadenopathy. When infections become chronic, surgical removal of the tonsils known as tonsillectomy may be required.
- The interior of the larynx may be viewed as a reflection from a mirror or directly through a laryngoscope, and these procedures are known as indirect and direct **laryngoscopy**, respectively.
- Inflammation of the larynx is termed **laryngitis.** This causes hoarseness of voice due to swelling of the vocal cords due to the inflammation.
- **Laryngeal oedema** is a potentially life-threatening medical emergency that is usually caused by an allergic reaction.
- The nerves supplying the larynx are liable to get damaged during thyroidectomy causing hoarseness of the voice.
- **Tumours** of the vocal cord can be caused by excessive smoking.

APPLICATIONS IN NURSING

- Bleeding from the nose (**epistaxis**) is a common complaint in patients and can often be controlled by squeezing the external nose just above the nostrils with the head tilted forwards.
- **Upper respiratory infections** can cause excessive secretions and blockage of the nasal cavities. Steam inhalation is a simple and effective method to relieve this blockage.
- Nasal, oropharyngeal and nasopharyngeal **swabs** are used to diagnose respiratory infections produced by organisms like coronavirus.
- Nurses in intensive care units need to care for patients who are attached to ventilators. In these patients, secretions collected in the pharynx need to be drained out by **suctioning.**

SUMMARY

- The parts of the nose include the external nose and nasal cavity.
- The external nose is made up of hyaline cartilages and the nasal bones.
- The parts of the external nose include the root, bridge, dorsum, tip, septum, alae and nostrils.
- The nasal cavity extends from the nostrils to the choanae.
- Each half of the nasal cavity is lined mainly by respiratory epithelium except the vestibule and the upper third which are lined by skin and olfactory epithelium, respectively.
- It has four walls, namely medial (septum), lateral, roof and floor.
- The medial wall is known as the nasal septum and is mainly composed of the septal cartilage, perpendicular plate of the ethmoid and vomer.

- The lateral wall has three shelf-like projections (superior, middle and inferior) known as conchae, which when covered by the mucous membrane are called turbinates.
- Meatuses are spaces beneath the conchae and are named according to the concha under which they are located.
- The roof has the cribriform plate of the ethmoid through which the rootlets of the olfactory nerve pass.
- The floor is formed by the hard palate which separates it from the oral cavity.
- The main arteries supplying the nose are the maxillary, facial and ophthalmic arteries.
- Sensory nerve supply to the nose is by branches of the ophthalmic and maxillary divisions of the trigeminal nerve.
- Paranasal air sinuses are spaces within the skull lined by the mucous membrane that open into the nasal cavity.
- The four pairs of paranasal sinuses are the maxillary, frontal, ethmoidal and sphenoidal air sinuses.
- The maxillary, frontal, anterior and middle ethmoidal sinuses open into the middle meatus, whereas the posterior ethmoidal and sphenoidal sinuses open into the superior meatus and sphenoethmoidal recess, respectively.
- The pharynx is a muscular tube that extends from the base of the skull to the lower border of the cricoid cartilage.
- Both longitudinal (inner) and circular (constrictors, outer) skeletal muscles form part of the wall of the pharynx.
- The parts of the pharynx are the nasopharynx, oropharynx and laryngopharynx, situated posterior to the nasal cavity, oral cavity and larynx, respectively.
- While the nasopharynx is lined by respiratory epithelium, the other two are lined by stratified squamous nonkeratinized epithelium.
- The nasopharynx contains the opening of the auditory tube and the pharyngeal tonsils.
- The palatine tonsils are situated in the oropharynx.
- The laryngopharynx contains a space on either side of the larynx called the piriform fossa.
- Both sensory and motor supply to the pharynx is via the pharyngeal plexus of nerves.
- The larynx is composed of cartilages, membranes and muscles.
- The three unpaired cartilages are the epiglottis, thyroid and cricoid cartilages, whereas the paired cartilages are the arytenoid, corniculate and cuneiform cartilages.
- Extrinsic membranes connect the larynx to the surrounding structures, whereas intrinsic membranes connect the laryngeal cartilages.
- Two thickenings of the intrinsic membranes covered by the mucous membrane form the true and false vocal cords.
- The cavity of the larynx is divided into the vestibule, ventricle and infraglottic part by the true and false cords.
- Except for the true cords, portions of the epiglottis and inlet of the larynx which are lined by stratified squamous nonkeratinized epithelium, the rest of the larynx is lined by respiratory epithelium.
- The muscles of the larynx act on the inlet and the vocal cord to alter their length and tension.
- The posterior cricoarytenoid muscle is the most important muscle in the larynx as it is the only muscle that abducts the vocal cords.
- The recurrent laryngeal nerve is the most important nerve that supplies the larynx.

CHAPTER 10

The Lower Respiratory System

SPECIFIC LEARNING OBJECTIVES

At the end of this chapter, the student should be able to:

- Describe the gross and microscopic anatomy of the trachea.
- Describe the subdivisions, boundaries, contents and applied importance of the mediastinum.
- Describe the gross and microscopic anatomy and applied importance of the lungs.
- Describe the subdivisions and microscopic anatomy of the bronchial tree.
- Describe the anatomical features of the pleura.
- Describe the muscles of respiration.

GLOSSARY OF TERMS

- **Trachea:** the windpipe, which extends from the larynx to the primary bronchi
- **Carina:** the ridge formed by the last tracheal ring
- **Mediastinum:** space between the two pleural cavities containing important structures including the heart
- **Hilum:** region on the medial surface of the lung where structures either enter or leave the lung
- **Bronchi:** air-conducting tubes formed as divisions from the trachea containing cartilage and smooth muscles in their walls
- **Bronchopulmonary segment:** volume of lung tissue supplied by a segmental or tertiary bronchus
- **Bronchioles:** smaller subdivisions in the bronchial tree which have only smooth muscle, but no cartilage in their wall
- **Alveolus:** final subdivision of the bronchial tree lined by simple squamous epithelium
- **Pleura:** double-layered covering of the lungs enclosing a pleural cavity
- **Pleural recess:** unusually wide area of the pleural cavity meant to accommodate the lung during deep inspiration

INTRODUCTION

The **lower respiratory tract** consists of the larynx, trachea and lungs with the bronchial tree. The anatomy of the upper respiratory tract and larynx was described in the last chapter. The **trachea** is a tube-like structure that divides into the primary **bronchi** which enter the **lungs** and undergo multiple divisions till they form millions of **alveoli**. The structure of the trachea is such that it is constantly open to allow for passage of air during respiration. Entry and removal of air from the alveoli is facilitated by the bronchial tree. **Gaseous exchange** occurs between the deoxygenated blood that is carried to the lungs via the pulmonary arteries and air in the alveoli. These functions are aided by accessory respiratory structures like the intercostal muscles and thoracoabdominal diaphragm. The **pleura** covers the lungs. The negative pressure in the pleural cavity is important for lung expansion during inspiration.

THE TRACHEA (Fig. 10.1)

The trachea extends from the lower border of the cricoid cartilage into the thoracic cavity, where it branches into right and left primary bronchi at the level of the sternal angle. Therefore, it has a **cervical part** in the neck and a **thoracic part** in the thoracic cavity. It has 15–20 C-shaped **hyaline cartilaginous rings** which keep the trachea open at all times. The 'C' opens posteriorly to allow the oesophagus to expand while swallowing. The **carina** is a ridge produced by the last tracheal ring and is an important landmark during bronchoscopy. The important posterior relations of the trachea are the oesophagus and recurrent laryngeal nerve. Anterior to the trachea are the isthmus of the thyroid gland superiorly and arch of the aorta inferiorly. Lateral relations include the lobes of the thyroid gland and the carotid sheath with its contents. The **blood supply** of the trachea is via inferior thyroid and bronchial arteries and the inferior thyroid veins.

Microscopically the trachea is seen to have **four layers** (Fig. 10.1). From inside out, they are the **mucosa, submucosa, fibromusculocartilaginous layer** and **adventitia**. The mucosa consists of **respiratory epithelium** lying on a lamina propria. The submucosa contains loose connective tissue, seromucous glands, blood vessels and nerves. External to the submucosa are seen **C-shaped hyaline cartilages** which are connected

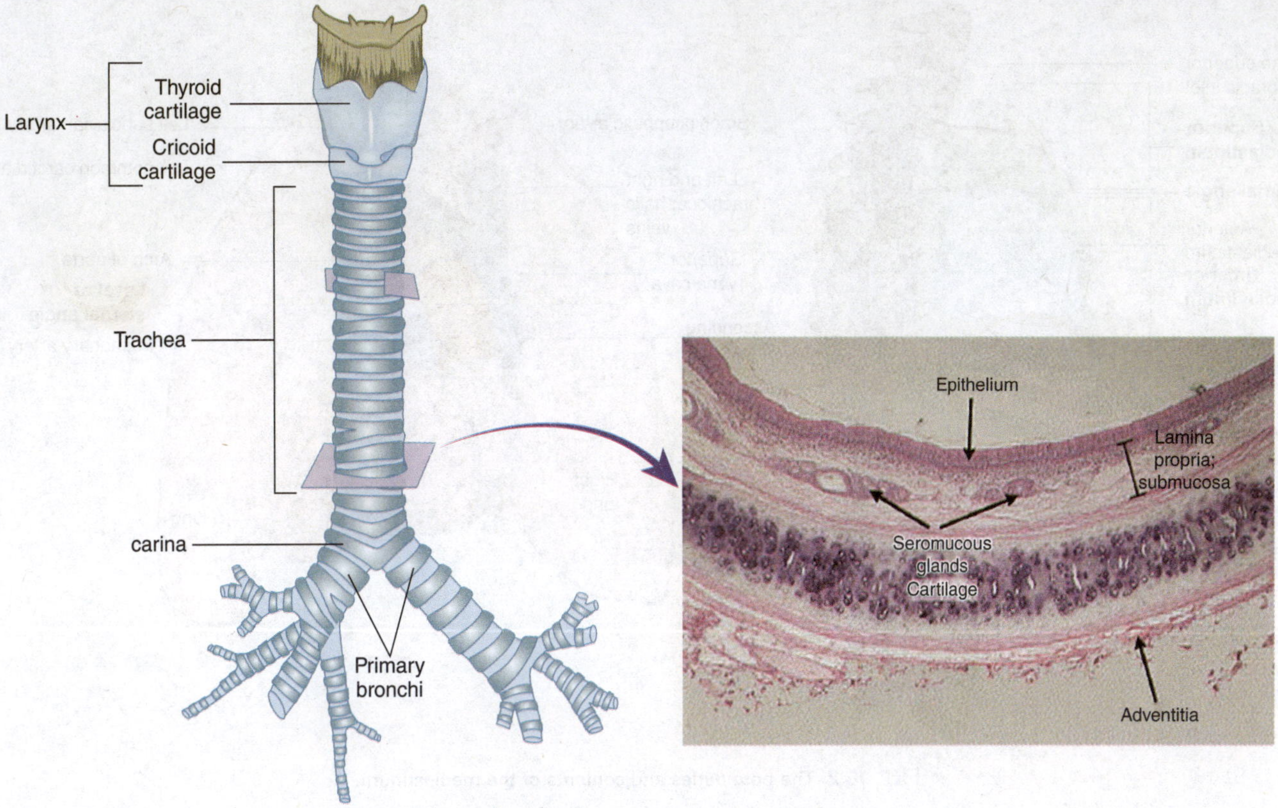

FIG. 10.1 Gross and microscopic anatomy of the trachea.

posteriorly by the trachealis muscle. The intervals between the cartilages are filled by connective tissue. Irregular fibrous connective tissue containing blood vessels, nerves and lymphatics is seen in the adventitia. The respiratory epithelium in the trachea has similar **functions** to other parts of the respiratory system, namely warming and humidification of the inspired air and trapping and clearing particulate matter from it. The trachealis muscle helps to regulate the diameter of the lumen of the trachea and contracts when there is a requirement for forceful expulsion of air as in coughing.

THE MEDIASTINUM (Fig. 10.2)

Most of the thoracic cavity is occupied by the lungs. The mediastinum is a **space** between the **two pleural cavities** which contains several important structures. It provides a passage for structures that either enter or leave the thoracic cavity. The mediastinum is bounded **laterally** by the pleura covering the mediastinal surfaces of the lung, **anteriorly** by the sternum and **posteriorly** by the bodies of the 12 thoracic vertebrae. **Superiorly** it extends up to the thoracic inlet and **inferiorly** it is bounded by the thoracoabdominal diaphragm. It is divided into **superior** and **inferior parts** by an imaginary horizontal plane that passes anteriorly through the sternal angle and posteriorly through the disc between the fourth and fifth thoracic vertebrae. The inferior mediastinum is further divided by the heart and pericardium into an **anterior, middle** and **posterior mediastinum**. The subdivisions, boundaries and contents of the mediastinum are shown in Table 10.1.

THE EXTRAPULMONARY BRONCHI

The **right** and **left primary bronchi** are formed by branching of the trachea. The right primary bronchus is wider, shorter, more in line with the trachea and divides earlier than the left primary bronchus. They are accompanied by the pulmonary arteries and veins as well as the bronchial vessels. They enter the lung at the **hilum**. The arch of the aorta arches over the left primary bronchus. They are similar to the trachea in structure but have complete cartilaginous rings.

THE LUNGS (Fig. 10.3)

The lungs are **paired, cone-shaped organs** in the **thoracic cavity**. They extend from the diaphragm below to the root of the neck above and are separated by the mediastinum. The pleural membrane surrounds the lungs. The lungs are divided into **lobes** by **fissures**. The right lung has two fissures, oblique and transverse, dividing it into three lobes. A single oblique fissure divides the left lung into upper and lower lobes.

Each lung has a superior, narrow **apex**, a wide **base** that rests on the diaphragm, a **costal surface** that is related to the ribs and a **medial surface**. The medial surface is further divided into a

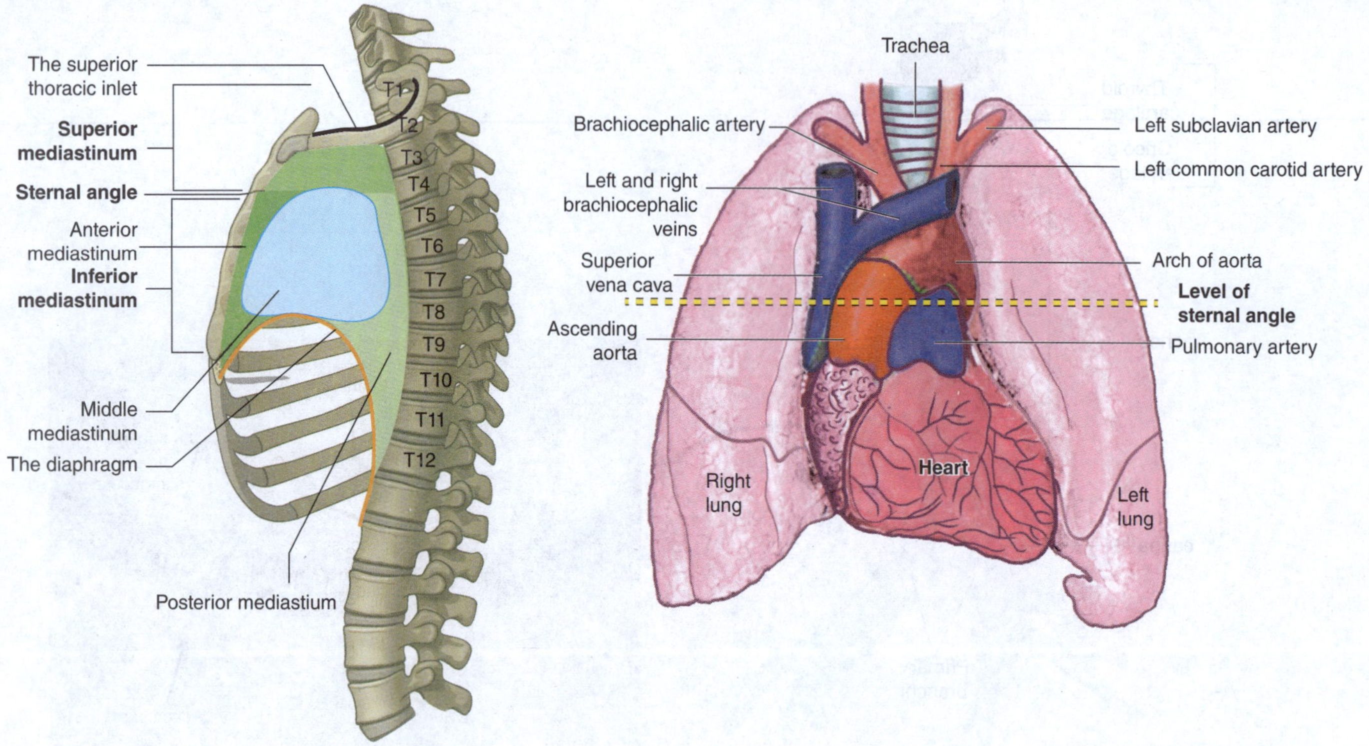

FIG. 10.2 The boundaries and contents of the mediastinum.

TABLE 10.1 The Subdivisions, Boundaries and Contents of the Mediastinum (Fig. 10.2)

		Boundaries	Important Contents
	Superior mediastinum	• Superior – inlet of thorax • Inferior – imaginary plane passing through sternal angle • Anterior – manubrium of sternum • Posterior – T1 to T4 vertebrae	• Veins – right and left brachiocephalic and superior vena cava • Arteries – arch of aorta and its branches • Nerves – phrenic and vagus • Trachea • Oesophagus • Thoracic duct
Inferior mediastinum	Anterior mediastinum	• Superior – imaginary plane passing through sternal angle • Inferior – diaphragm • Anterior – body of sternum • Posterior – pericardium	• Thymus
	Middle mediastinum	• Superior – imaginary plane passing through sternal angle • Inferior – diaphragm • Anterior – pericardium • Posterior – pericardium	• Pericardium, heart and adjacent parts of great vessels
	Posterior mediastinum	• Superior – imaginary plane passing through sternal angle • Inferior – diaphragm • Anterior – pericardium • Posterior – T5 to T12 vertebrae	• Descending thoracic aorta • Oesophagus • Azygos vein • Thoracic duct • Vagus nerves

mediastinal surface related to the mediastinal structures and a **vertebral surface** related to the bodies of the vertebrae. The mediastinal surface of the right lung is mainly related to venous structures like the superior and inferior vena cava, arch of the azygos vein, right atrium and trachea. On the left side are arterial structures, namely the arch of the aorta and its last two branches, the descending thoracic aorta, left ventricle and oesophagus. The surfaces are separated by **borders**. The **anterior border** is sharp and separates the mediastinal and costal surfaces. The costal surface is separated from the vertebral surface by the rounded

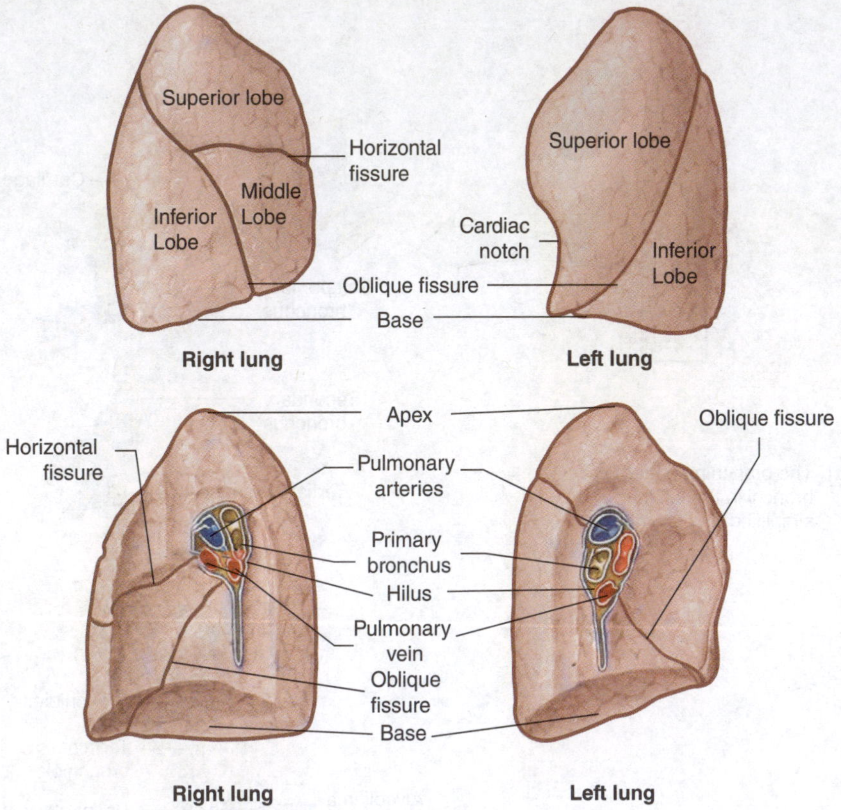

FIG. 10.3 The gross anatomy of the lungs.

posterior border. The sharp **inferior border** separates the base from the costal surface. The differences between the right and left lungs are summarized in Table 10.2.

The **roots** connect the lungs to the heart and trachea. The **hilum** is a triangular depression where the structures which form the root of the lung enter or leave it. These include the pulmonary artery, the superior and inferior pulmonary veins, and the primary bronchus with bronchial vessels surrounding it. Other structures found at the hilum include the pulmonary plexuses of nerves, lymphatic vessels, bronchial lymph nodes and areolar tissue. All these structures are enclosed by a reflection of the pleura. On either side, the phrenic and vagus nerves pass anterior and posterior to the hilum, respectively.

TABLE 10.2 The Differences Between the Right and Left Lungs (Fig. 10.3)

	Right Lung	Left Lung
Size and dimensions	• Broader • Shorter (because of the presence of the liver on the right side) • Heavier	• Narrower • Longer • Lighter
Anterior border	• Anterior border is straight	• Anterior border has cardiac notch (to accommodate the heart) which delineates the lingua
Fissures	• Oblique • Transverse	• Only oblique
Lobes	• Superior • Middle • Inferior	• Superior • Inferior

THE BRONCHIAL TREE (Fig. 10.4)

The anatomy of the extrapulmonary bronchi has been described earlier. **Lobar bronchi** or secondary bronchi arise from the primary bronchi and supply each of the lobes. Thus, there are three lobar bronchi on the right and two on the left. These in turn divide into tertiary or **segmental bronchi**. The segmental bronchi undergo numerous divisions till they become minute tubular structures called bronchioles which lack cartilage in their wall. The bronchioles too undergo divisions to eventually form alveolar ducts, alveolar sacs and alveoli.

A **bronchopulmonary segment** is a volume of lung tissue supplied by a single tertiary bronchus and separated from adjacent segments by connective tissue. It is pyramidal in shape, with its base towards the surface and apex facing centrally. It contains branches of the bronchial and pulmonary arteries which accompany the segmental bronchus. However, the veins run intersegmentally. There are 10 bronchopulmonary segments on each side. The bronchopulmonary segments on each side differ because of the absence of a middle lobe in the left lung.

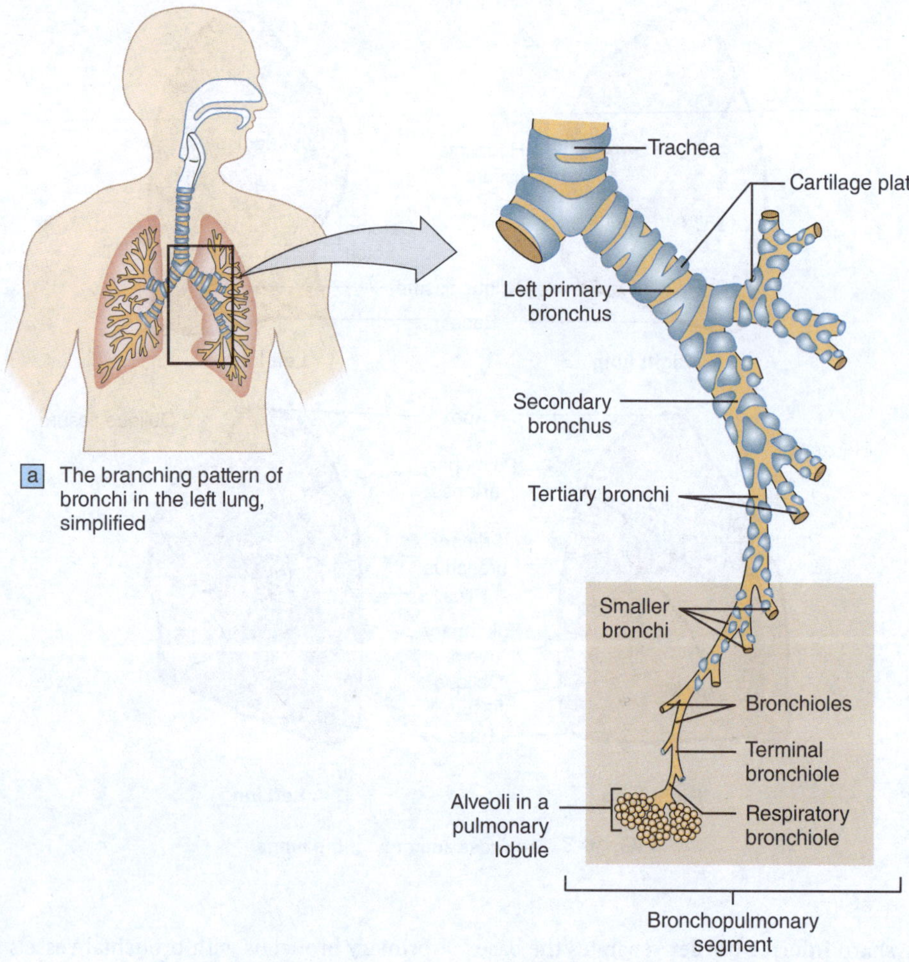

FIG. 10.4 The various subdivisions of the bronchial tree.

Bronchi have a similar structure to the trachea but have cartilaginous plates instead of rings and a well-developed smooth muscle layer inner to the cartilage. The walls of smaller bronchi contain progressively less cartilage and more smooth muscle. **Bronchioles** do not have cartilage in their walls, but a well-developed smooth muscle layer that helps to regulate their diameter. They have fewer glands and goblet cells and their lining epithelium becomes shorter.

Respiratory bronchioles have alveoli arising from their walls and form the first part of the bronchial tree where gaseous exchange takes place. **Alveoli** are lined by simple squamous epithelium which contains two types of cells, type I cells which enable gaseous exchange and type II cells which produce surfactant. Alveolar macrophages are present in the alveolar walls and serve an immune function. Alveoli are surrounded by an extensive capillary network to enable gaseous exchange to take place. Gaseous exchange takes place across the respiratory membrane. The respiratory membrane consists of alveolar lining cells, endothelial cells and basement membranes of both the cells. Fig. 10.5 shows the main features of the microscopic anatomy of the lung.

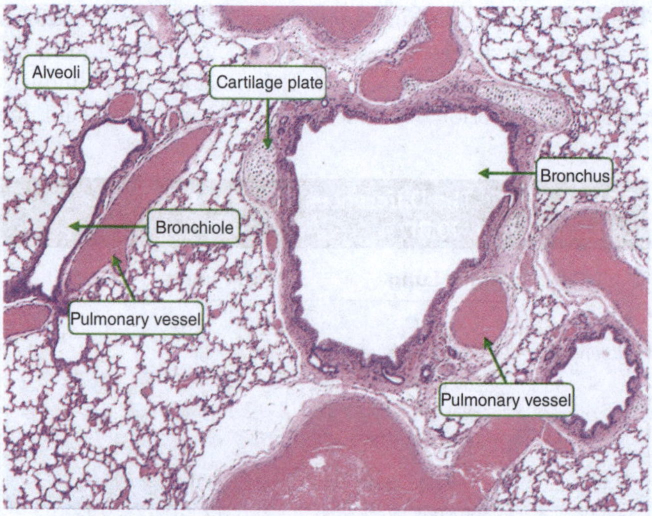

FIG. 10.5 The microscopic anatomy of the lung.

The conducting parts of the bronchial tree are supplied by the **bronchial vessels**. The **pulmonary arteries** carry deoxygenated blood from the heart to the lungs where gaseous exchange takes place in the alveolar capillaries. Once the blood is oxygenated in the lungs, it is carried to the left atrium by the **pulmonary veins**. The **nerve supply** to the lungs is by the pulmonary plexus which contains both sympathetic and parasympathetic (vagus) fibres.

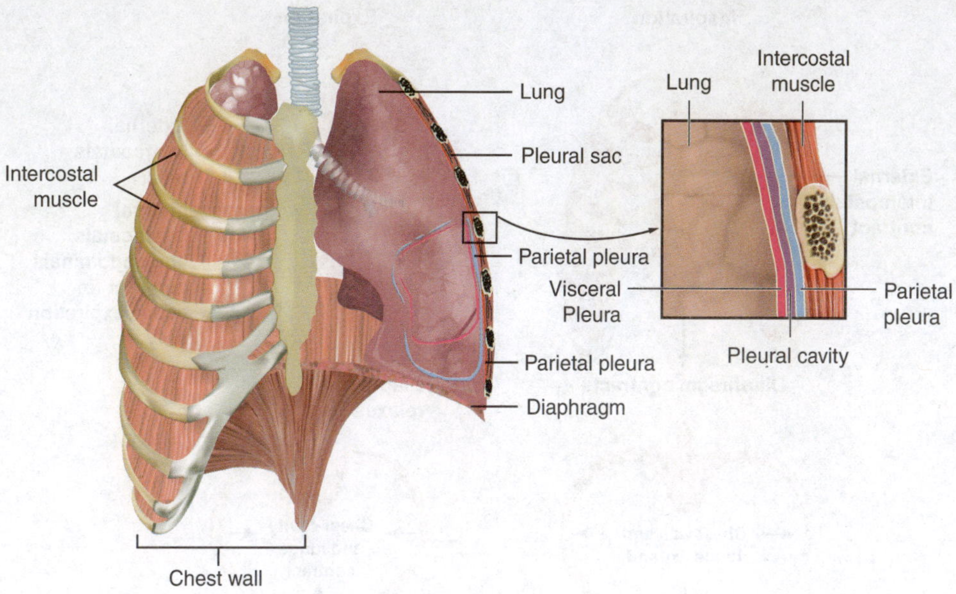

FIG. 10.6 The gross anatomy of the pleural cavity.

The **lymphatic drainage** of the lungs is into the bronchopulmonary and tracheobronchial lymph nodes and eventually into the right lymphatic and thoracic duct.

THE PLEURA (Fig. 10.6)

The pleura consists of serous membranes which line a narrow cavity called the **pleural cavity**. Two layers of pleura are present, namely the **visceral pleura** which lines the lungs and **parietal pleura** that lines the thoracic cavity. The pleural cavity contains **pleural fluid** which assists in respiration and reduces friction. Some parts of the pleural cavity are roomier as there is a greater separation between the two layers of pleura. These parts of the pleural cavity are called **recesses** and help to accommodate lung expansion, especially in deep inspiration. These two recesses are the costodiaphragmatic and costomediastinal recesses. The parietal pleura is **pain sensitive** and is supplied by somatic nerves, whereas the visceral pleura is **pain insensitive** and supplied by autonomic nerves.

MUSCLES OF RESPIRATION (Fig. 10.7)

The muscles of respiration include the **thoraco-abdominal diaphragm**, the **intercostal muscles**, **accessory muscles**, and muscles of the **anterior abdominal wall**. These muscles work together to create changes in thoracic volume that facilitate airflow in and out of the lungs during the respiratory cycle. The diaphragm plays the most significant role during normal, quiet breathing, while the other muscles contribute more during deep breathing.

The dome-shaped **diaphragm** which separates the thoracic and abdominal cavities is the primary muscle of respiration. It contracts and flattens during inhalation, increasing thoracic volume and decreasing pressure to draw air into the lungs.

The **intercostal muscles** are located between the ribs and assist in respiration. The external intercostal muscles elevate the ribs during inhalation, expanding the chest cavity, while the internal intercostal muscles depress the ribs during forced exhalation, reducing the volume of the chest cavity.

The **accessory muscles** include the sternocleidomastoid and scalenes, which elevate the upper ribs and sternum, increasing chest volume during deep inhalation. The **muscles** of the **anterior abdominal wall** including the rectus abdominis, external oblique, internal oblique, and transversus abdominis compress the abdominal contents, pushing the diaphragm up and aiding in forced exhalation.

APPLIED ANATOMY

- **Tracheostomy** is a procedure in which an opening is made in the cervical part of the trachea in patients with proximal airway blockage.
- **Tracheitis** is an inflammation of the trachea usually secondary to rhinitis or pharyngitis.
- The trachea can be **palpated** suprasternally and is usually placed centrally or a little to the right. In certain conditions of the lung, like pleural effusion or collapse of the lung, it can be shifted from its usual position. Mediastinal tumours can also cause a tracheal shift.
- Inflammation of structures in the mediastinum is called **mediastinitis**. As spaces in the neck are in direct continuity with the mediastinum, infections can spread from the neck to the mediastinum.
- **Mediastinal tumours** can occur and commonly arise from the thymus or lymph nodes in the mediastinum.
- Inhaled **foreign bodies** are lodged more commonly in the right bronchus and lung because the right bronchus is wider,

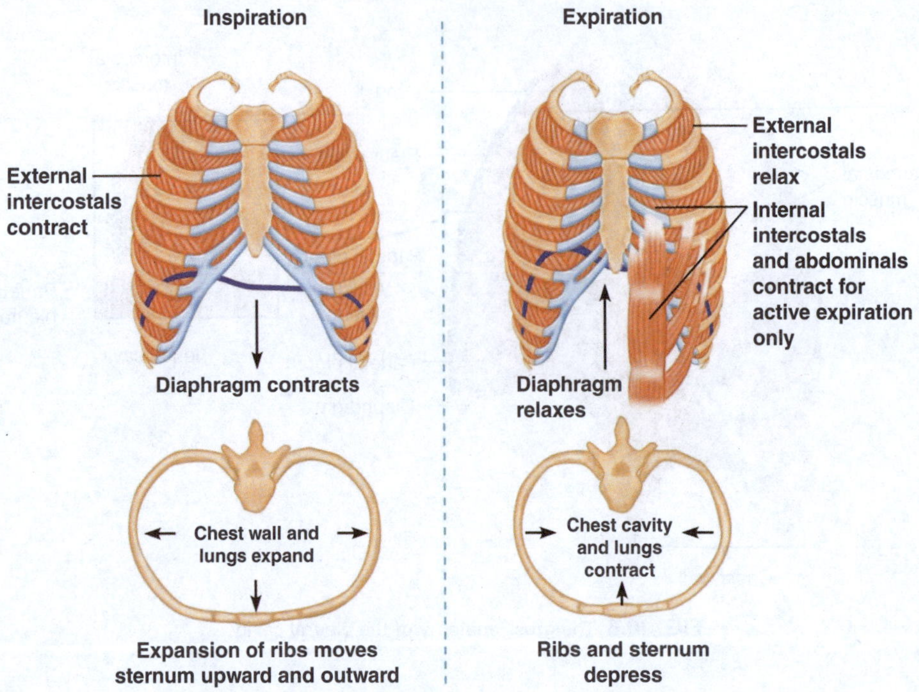

FIG. 10.7 The muscles of respiration and their actions.

shorter and more in line with the trachea as compared to the left bronchus.

- **Carcinomas** of the lung arising from the bronchi are called bronchogenic carcinomas and are usually of the squamous cell variety. Cigarette smoking has a strong association with bronchogenic carcinomas.
- Many **infections** are contained within bronchopulmonary segments as they cannot break the connective tissue barrier between adjacent segments. Tuberculosis and cancers, however, can spread through the connective tissue barrier.
- **Segmental resection** of individual bronchopulmonary segments is possible.
- Direct visualization of the bronchi via an endoscopic tube is called **bronchoscopy**.
- Inflammation of the bronchi is called **bronchitis** and causes the usual symptoms of a lower respiratory tract infection such as coughing, breathlessness and wheezing.
- Inflammation of lung tissue usually due to infections primarily affecting the alveoli is called **pneumonia**. The alveoli become filled with inflammatory fluid causing cough and breathlessness.
- **Pulmonary tuberculosis** is a chronic infection of the lung tissue by *Mycobacterium tuberculosis*. This can lead to destruction of portions of lung tissue, cavity formation and pleural effusion.
- **Bronchial asthma** is a condition of hyper-reactivity of the bronchial tree to stimuli such as pollen and dust. The smooth muscle of the bronchi and bronchioles contract (bronchospasm) and there is increased secretion from seromucous glands of the airway. This causes narrowing of the airways, breathlessness and wheezing.
- **Emphysema** is a condition in which alveolar destruction occurs usually due to excessive cigarette smoking. This leads to the formation of large air-filled spaces in the lung which are incapable of gaseous exchange.
- **Chronic obstructive pulmonary disease** encompasses several lung conditions in which irreversible damage occurs to lung tissue over a period causing severe breathlessness and is often accompanied by heart failure.
- Blood clots in the venous system or right atrium can get dislodged and obstruct the small vessels in the lung causing impaired gaseous exchange and acute breathlessness. This potentially fatal condition is called **pulmonary embolism**.
- **Respiratory distress syndrome** is an acute condition usually seen in premature infants due to collapse of alveoli because of inadequate surfactant levels.
- Inflammation of pleura is called **pleurisy** and is usually associated with pneumonias. It causes a pricking type of pain due to inflammation of the parietal pleura.
- Accumulation of fluid in the pleural cavity is known as **pleural effusion**. In India, a common cause of pleural effusion is tuberculosis.
- **Pneumothorax** occurs due to accumulation of air in the pleural cavity. This can cause collapse of the lungs as the negative pressure in the pleural cavity is lost.
- The procedure for the drainage of pleural fluid from the pleural cavity through an intercostal space is known as **pleural tap**. This is usually done through the centre of an intercostal space to avoid damage to neurovascular structures.

APPLICATIONS IN NURSING

- **Metered-dose inhalers** are commonly advised for patients with respiratory conditions like bronchial asthma. The drugs used in the inhalers act locally to produce bronchodilation and relieve the symptoms of the patient. The nurse will often have to educate the patient on the correct procedure for using these devices.
- **Oxygen therapy** is required for patients with hypoxia. The two common modes of delivery of oxygen are via face masks and nasal cannulas. The proper placement of nasal cannulas and face masks is critical for adequate oxygenation and is usually the responsibility of nurses.
- **Incentive spirometry** is a method to ensure that the respiratory mechanisms are maintained after thoracic and abdominal surgeries, reducing the possibility of collapse of the lungs. The patient is asked to breathe slowly and deeply through the spirometer.
- Nursing personnel will be involved in **tracheostomy care**, which includes properly securing the tube, inflating the cuff to an appropriate pressure, maintaining patency by suctioning and providing oral hygiene.
- A **chest tube** is often inserted to remove fluid, blood or air from the pleural cavity. Once the tube is in position, care of the tube will be the responsibility of the nurses. Kinking of the tube and infections are two possibilities that need to be guarded against.

SUMMARY

- The trachea extends from the lower border of the cricoid cartilage to the level of the sternal angle, where it branches into two primary bronchi.
- It has a cervical and a thoracic part.
- The isthmus of the thyroid gland and oesophagus are important anterior and posterior relations of the trachea.
- The wall of the trachea has C-shaped cartilaginous rings which help to keep it always patent.
- The last tracheal ring causes a ridge called the carina which is an important bronchoscopic landmark.
- The ends of the 'C' are joined by the trachealis muscle which regulates the diameter of the trachea and allows expansion of the oesophagus during deglutition.
- Microscopically, the trachea consists of the mucosa, submucosa, fibromusculocartilaginous layer and adventitia from within outwards.
- The mucosa is lined by respiratory epithelium and the submucosa contains seromucous glands.
- The space between the two pleural cavities, limited superiorly by the thoracic inlet and inferiorly by the diaphragm, is called the mediastinum.
- The mediastinum is divided by an imaginary horizontal plane passing through the sternal angle into a superior and an inferior mediastinum.
- The inferior mediastinum is further divided by the heart and pericardium into an anterior, middle and posterior mediastinum.
- The important contents of the mediastinum are the heart and pericardium, the great vessels and their branches and tributaries, the trachea, the oesophagus, the vagus and phrenic nerves, the thoracic duct and the thymus.
- The primary bronchi arise from the trachea, the right one being shorter, wider and more in line with the trachea.
- The lungs extend from the root of the neck to the diaphragm.
- The right lung has oblique and transverse fissures separating three lobes, namely superior, middle and inferior.
- A single oblique fissure separates the left lung into upper and lower lobes.
- The lungs have a superior apex and an inferior base that rests on the diaphragm.
- The borders of the lung are the sharp anterior and inferior borders and the blunt posterior border.
- The surfaces of the lung are the costal, the medial (divided into mediastinal and vertebral) and the inferior surface or base.
- The costal surface is related to the ribs, while the mediastinal surface is related to the mediastinal structures, mainly venous structures on the right including the right atrium and the arterial structures on the left including the left ventricle.
- The hilum of the lungs contains the primary bronchi and accompanying vessels and nerves.
- The right and left lungs differ in a few ways primarily because the heart is located more to the left, necessitating anatomical changes to accommodate it.
- The bronchial tree consists of many divisions of the trachea sequentially forming bronchi, bronchioles, alveolar ducts, alveolar sacs and alveoli.
- The primary bronchi divide into lobar or secondary bronchi which in turn divide into tertiary or segmental bronchi. Subsequently there are a number of divisions till bronchioles are formed.
- Segmental or tertiary bronchi supply bronchopulmonary segments which are independent lung units delineated by connective tissue and containing bronchial vessels and branches of the pulmonary artery.
- Bronchi are similar in structure to the trachea except for cartilage plates instead of rings and a complete layer of smooth muscles inner to the cartilage.
- Bronchioles are much smaller than bronchi and do not have cartilage in their walls.
- Alveoli are lined by simple squamous epithelium consisting of type I and type II alveolar cells.
- Gaseous exchange takes place through the respiratory membrane which consists of the alveolar cells and endothelium along with their basement membranes.
- The bronchi are supplied by bronchial vessels. Branches of the pulmonary artery and tributaries of the pulmonary vein also enter or exit the substance of the lung from the hilum.
- Branches from the pulmonary plexus supply the lung with sympathetic and parasympathetic (vagus) fibres.
- The lymph from the lungs drains into the bronchopulmonary nodes and subsequently into the tracheobronchial nodes.
- The outer parietal and inner visceral pleura cover the lungs enclosing a pleural cavity containing pleural fluid.
- The pleural cavity is expanded in certain areas known as recesses. The two recesses are the costomediastinal and costodiaphragmatic recesses.
- The parietal pleura is supplied by somatic nerves and is pain sensitive, while the visceral pleura is supplied by visceral nerves and is pain insensitive.
- The muscles of respiration include the thoraco-abdominal diaphragm, the intercostal muscles, accessory muscles, and muscles of the anterior abdominal wall.
- These muscles work together to create changes in thoracic volume that facilitate airflow in and out of the lungs during the respiratory cycle.

3
SECTION

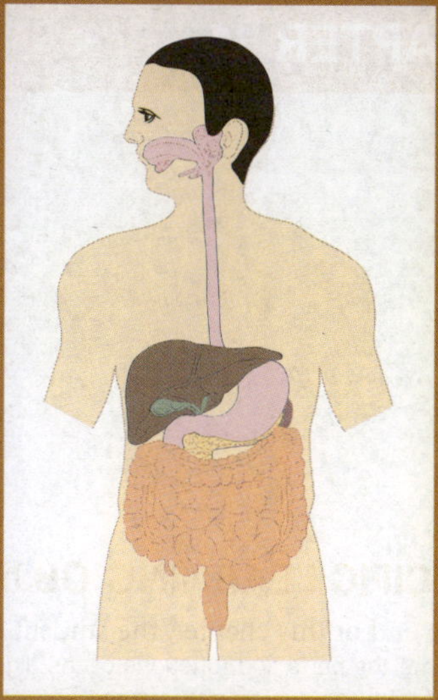

The Digestive System

Section Outline

CHAPTER 11

The Upper Alimentary Canal

SPECIFIC LEARNING OBJECTIVES

At the end of this chapter, the student should be able to:

- Name the parts and functions of the digestive system.
- Describe the anatomical features of the oral cavity including the teeth.
- Describe the gross anatomy of the hard and soft palate.
- Describe the gross and microscopic anatomy of the tongue.
- Describe the gross and microscopic features of the major salivary glands.
- Describe the gross anatomy of the pharynx.
- Describe the gross and microscopic anatomy of the oesophagus.

GLOSSARY OF TERMS

- **Vestibule:** part of the oral cavity between the teeth and gums on one side and the cheek and lips on the other side
- **Pulp space:** space within the tooth that contains blood vessels and nerves along with loose connective tissue
- **Dentine:** bone-like material forming the major part of the tooth
- **Enamel:** hard covering of the dentine in the crown of the tooth
- **Cementum:** covering of the dentine in the root of the tooth
- **Periodontal membrane:** tough connective tissue that connects the cementum with the bone of the tooth socket
- **Pharyngeal plexus:** plexus of nerves that provides both motor and sensory supply to the soft palate and pharynx
- **Sulcus terminalis:** V-shaped sulcus that separates the anterior two-thirds and posterior one-third of the tongue
- **Papillae:** minute elevations on the dorsum of the tongue that usually contain taste buds
- **Frenulum:** fold of the mucous membrane that connects the tongue to the floor of the mouth
- **Pharyngobasilar fascia:** thickened submucosa of the pharynx
- **Buccopharyngeal fascia:** thickened adventitia of the pharynx
- **Nasopharynx:** part of the pharynx posterior to the nasal cavity
- **Oropharynx:** part of the pharynx posterior to the oral cavity
- **Laryngopharynx:** part of the pharynx posterior to the larynx

INTRODUCTION

The digestive system is responsible for breaking down ingested food into their simplest constituents, so that they can be absorbed for metabolic activities. It is formed by the alimentary canal and its associated digestive glands. The alimentary canal extends from the oral cavity to the anus. It consists of the oral cavity, pharynx, oesophagus, stomach, small intestine, large intestine, rectum and anal canal. The associated digestive glands are the salivary glands, the liver with the extrahepatic biliary apparatus and the pancreas (Figs 11.1 and 11.2). The part of the alimentary canal from the stomach distally is known as the gastrointestinal tract. The alimentary canal transports its contents in a proximodistal direction by peristalsis. The lining of the small and large intestines is specialized for absorption. In the walls of the canal are located different types of glands that aid in the process of digestion. Several sphincters are located along the length of the canal to regulate the passage of its contents. The secretions of the digestive glands that open into the alimentary canal contain enzymes that help to digest the contents in the canal.

THE ORAL CAVITY (Fig. 11.3)

The oral cavity is divided into two parts, an **oral cavity proper** and the **vestibule**. The vestibule is the space between the gums and teeth internally and lips and cheeks externally. The **roof** of the oral cavity proper is formed by the palate, while the **floor** is formed by the tongue. There are two sets of **teeth** located in each jaw. These are the **temporary** or **milk teeth**, which are 20 in number, 10 in each jaw. Half of each jaw contains two incisors, one canine and two molars. There are 32 **permanent teeth**, 16 in each jaw. Two incisors, one canine, two premolars and three molars are seen in one-half of each jaw. The incisors are used for cutting, canines for tearing and molars for grinding food. Each tooth has a **crown**, **neck** and **root**. The crown is the portion that

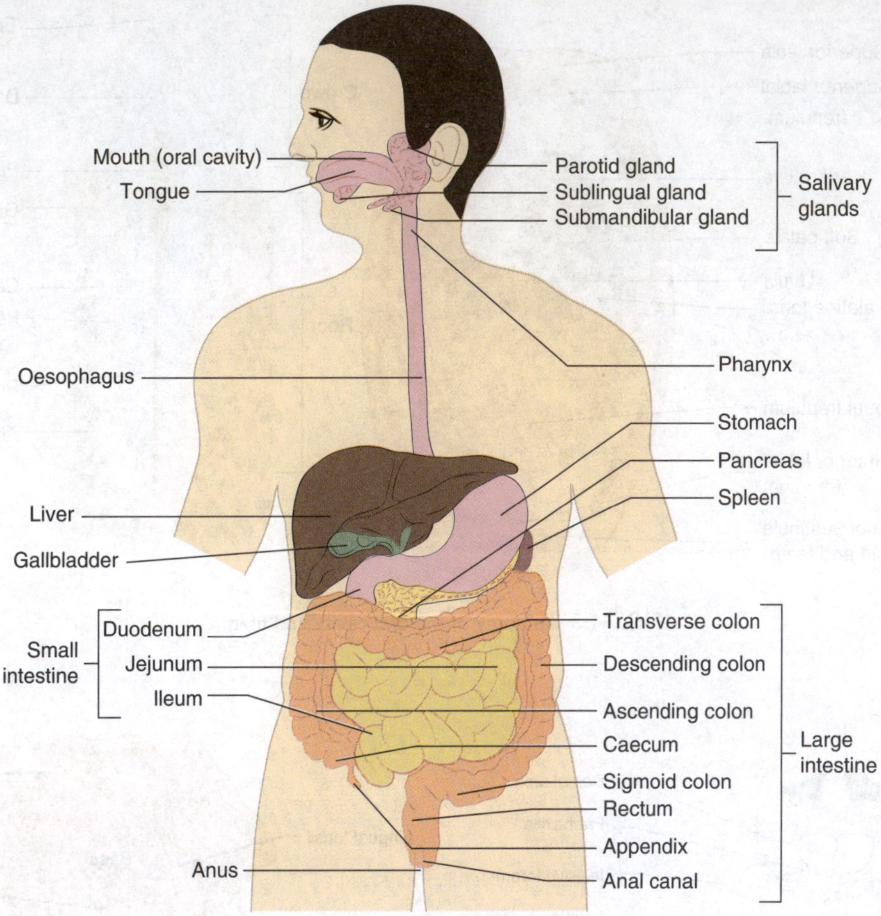

FIG. 11.1 The parts of the digestive system.

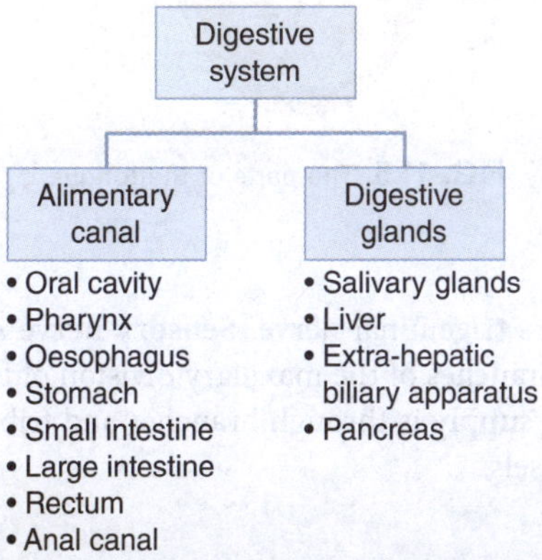

FIG. 11.2 The parts of the digestive system.

is visible externally, while the root lies within the alveolar socket of the bone. The constricted portion between the crown and the root is called the neck. Microscopically each tooth contains a **pulp space** covered by a bone-like material called **dentine**. The dentine in the crown is covered by an extremely hard material called **enamel**. Covering the dentine of the root is the **cementum**, which is tightly bound to the bone of the alveolar socket through the **periodontal membrane**. The pulp cavity continues inferiorly as the **root canal**, which ends at an **apical foramen**. The blood vessels and nerves supplying the tooth are located within the pulp cavity after traversing the apical foramen and root canal. The branches and tributaries of the maxillary vessels provide **blood supply** to the teeth. **Nerve supply** to the teeth is via branches of the maxillary (upper jaw) and mandibular (lower jaw) divisions of the trigeminal nerve.

THE PALATE (Fig. 11.4)

The palate is formed by an anterior **hard** and a posterior **soft** palate. The **hard palate** is an arched structure formed by the **maxilla** anteriorly and **palatine bone** posteriorly. **Mucous membrane** covers the hard palate. It consists of stratified squamous nonkeratinized epithelium resting on a lamina propria of dense connective tissue, which in turn is firmly attached to the underlying bone. The **soft palate** is a posterior extension of the hard palate and consists of a core of **skeletal muscle** covered on either side by the mucous membrane. It functions to close off the nasopharynx during the process of deglutition to prevent nasal

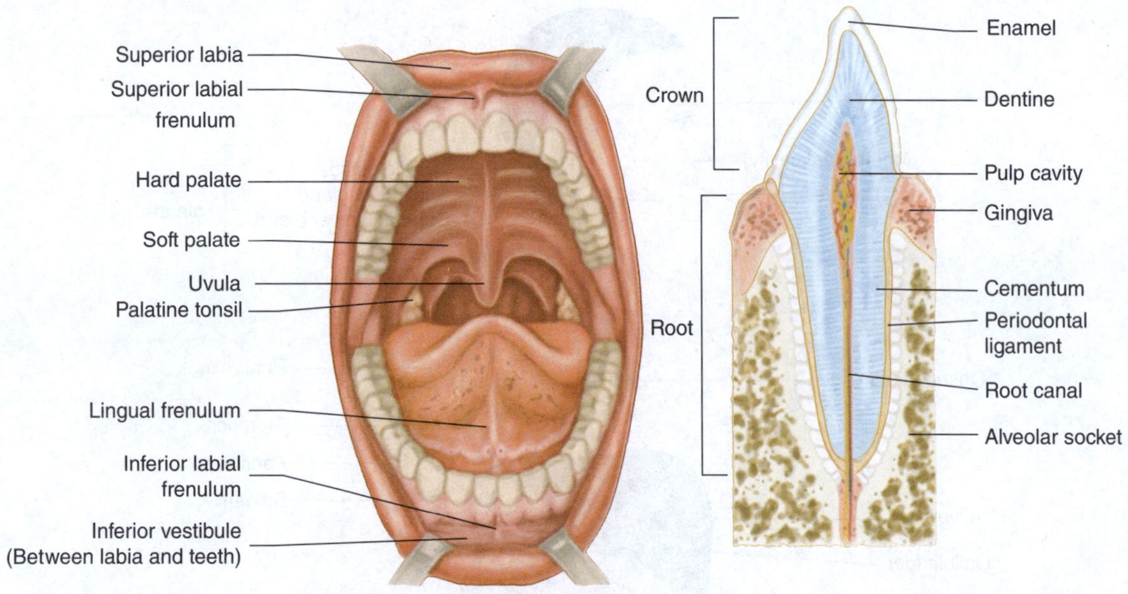

FIG. 11.3 Anatomy of the oral cavity and teeth.

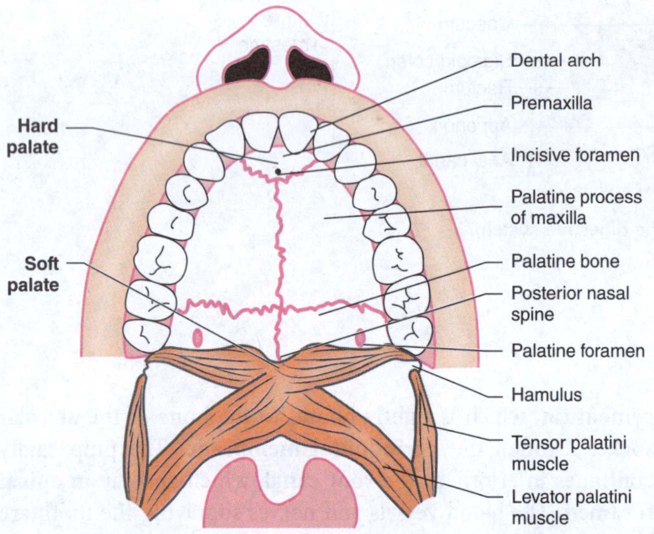

FIG. 11.4 Anatomy of the palate as viewed from below.

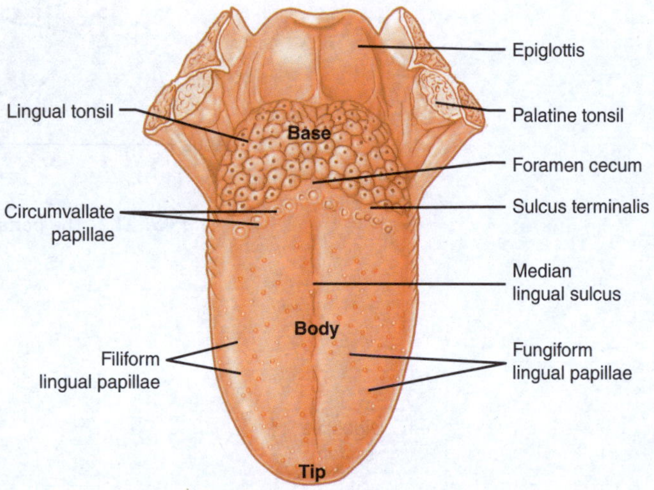

FIG. 11.5 The parts of the tongue.

regurgitation. The soft palate is mobile due to the skeletal muscle contained within it. The **tensor palati** muscle forms the palatine aponeurosis which provides a stable base for the other muscles to act. Elevation of the soft palate occurs by contraction of the **levator palati**. The **palatopharyngeus** and **palatoglossus** pull the pharynx and base of the tongue upwards, respectively, during the process of deglutition. The **musculus uvulae** help to move the uvula. **Stratified squamous nonkeratinized epithelium** covers the anterior and lower part of the posterior surface of the soft palate. The remaining portion of the posterior surface is lined by **respiratory epithelium**. The muscles of the soft palate are supplied by the **pharyngeal plexus**, except for the tensor palati which is supplied by a branch from the mandibular division of the trigeminal nerve. **Sensory nerve supply** to the palate is via branches of the maxillary division of the trigeminal nerve. **Blood supply** is through branches and tributaries of the maxillary vessels.

THE TONGUE

The tongue is a **muscular organ** covered on either side by epithelium. The tongue has a **tip**, **body** and **base** (Fig. 11.5). The body is formed by the anterior two-thirds of the tongue and is separated from the base by a V-shaped **sulcus terminalis**. Attached to the mandible and hyoid bones is the **root** of the tongue. Two **surfaces**, dorsal and ventral, are seen on the tongue, which are separated by a lateral **border**. The dorsal surface is rough because of the presence of elevations called **papillae**. In

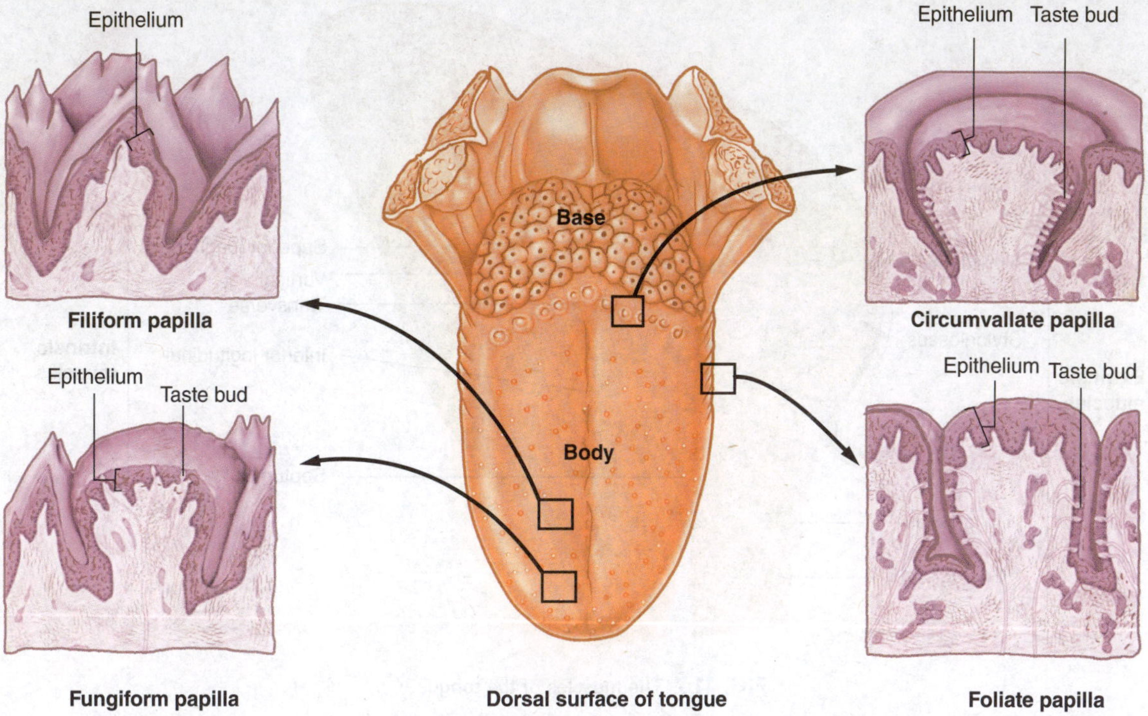

FIG. 11.6 The different types of papillae.

contrast, the ventral surface is smooth and is connected to the floor of the mouth by a fold called the **frenulum**. The base of the tongue is rough due to the presence of lymphatic tissue known as the **lingual tonsils**.

Four types of **papillae**, filiform, fungiform, circumvallate and foliate, can be seen on the dorsal surface (Fig. 11.6). When viewed with the naked eye, **filiform papillae** appear as small white elevations on the tongue. Microscopically they are conical structures, capped with keratin, do not contain taste buds and serve a purely mechanical function. **Fungiform papillae** are mushroom-shaped and concentrated near the tip of the tongue. They have **taste buds** on their dorsal aspects. **Circumvallate papillae** are seen in a row parallel to and anterior to the sulcus terminalis. They are the largest of the papillae and can be easily seen macroscopically. They are cylindrical and surrounded by a trough all around. Taste buds are seen on the sides of the papillae as well as along the walls of the trough. Serous glands called Von Ebner's glands open into the bottom of the trough. **Foliate papillae** are seen along the posterior margins of the tongue and contain taste buds. However, they are not prominent in humans. The various taste sensations are best appreciated in different areas of the tongue.

The **muscles** of the tongue can be divided into **intrinsic** and **extrinsic** (Fig. 11.7). **Intrinsic muscles** are seen entirely within the tongue without any attachment to other structures. They modify the shape of the tongue during mastication and speech. The muscles are oriented transversely, longitudinally and vertically to perform their functions. **Extrinsic muscles**, on the other hand, have attachments to skeletal structures outside the tongue such as the mandible, hyoid bone, palate and styloid process. They are thus named genioglossus, hyoglossus, palatoglossus and styloglossus. These muscles can alter both the shape and the size of the tongue. All muscles of the tongue are supplied by the **hypoglossal nerve** except for the palatoglossus which is supplied by the pharyngeal plexus.

The **arterial supply** to the tongue is via the lingual artery which is a branch of the external carotid artery. **Venous drainage** from the tongue is via veins that eventually drain into the internal jugular vein. As mentioned previously, the **motor nerve supply** is mainly through the hypoglossal nerve (Figs 11.8 and 11.9). The **sensory nerve supply** of the tongue can be divided into **general sensory** and **special sensory** components. General sensations from the anterior two-thirds of the tongue are carried by the **lingual nerve**, whereas the sensation of taste is carried by a branch of the **facial nerve**. Sensations from the posterior one-third of the tongue, both general and special, are carried by the **glossopharyngeal nerve**. The posterior-most part of the tongue is supplied by branches of the **vagus nerve**. **Lymph** from the tongue eventually drains into the deep cervical group of lymph nodes. Most of the lymphatic drainage of the tongue is bilateral, except for the margins.

THE SALIVARY GLANDS (Fig. 11.10)

The salivary glands produce saliva, which is then transported into the oral cavity via ducts. The saliva helps to maintain the oral pH, assists with food intake, lubricates the food bolus, contains amylase for carbohydrate digestion, helps in mouth cleansing and oral hygiene, limits oral pathogen growth and reduces

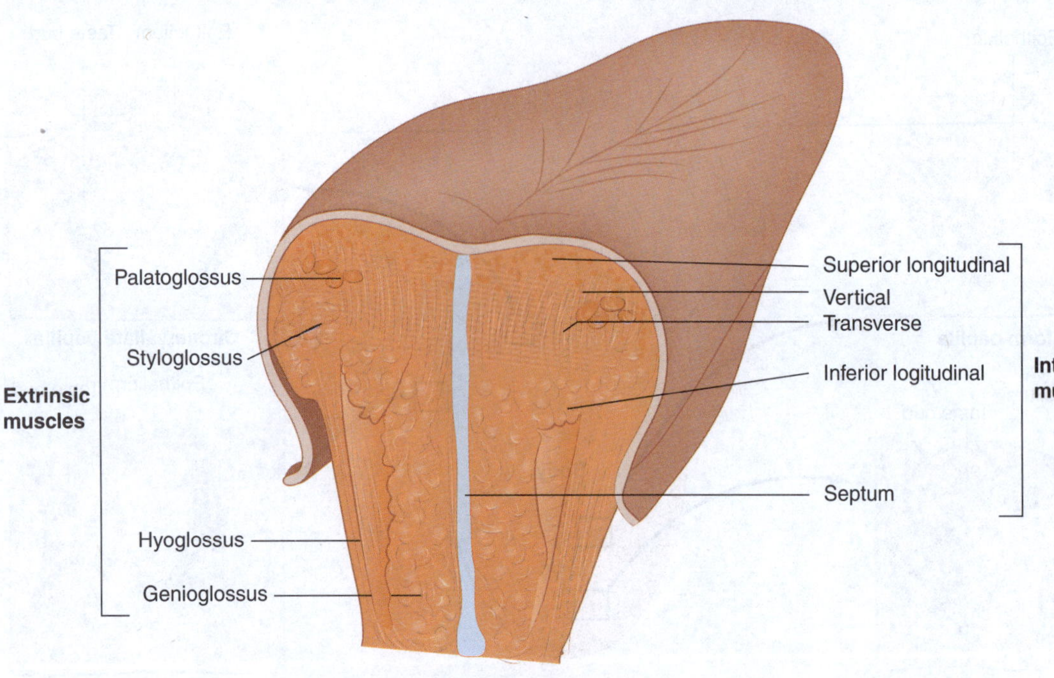

FIG. 11.7 The muscles of the tongue.

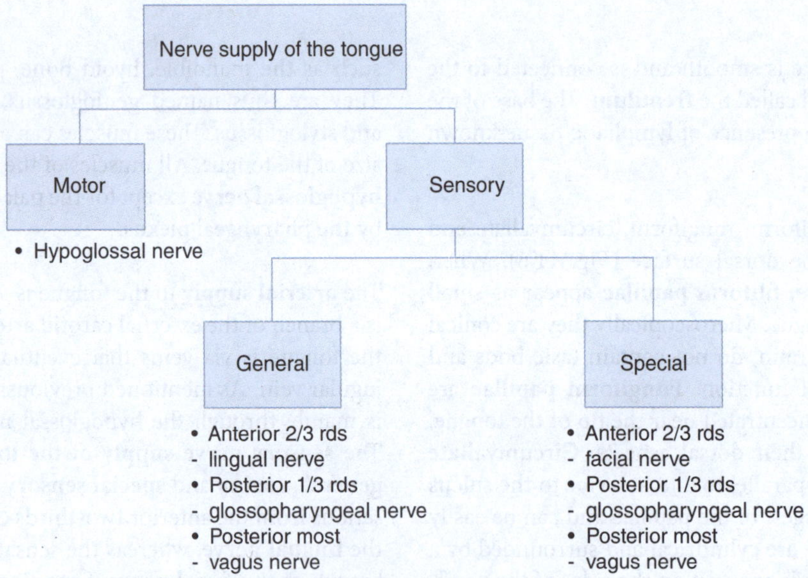

FIG. 11.8 The nerve supply of the tongue.

oral odour (halitosis). Salivary glands can be divided into **minor** and **major glands**. Minor salivary glands are scattered throughout the oral cavity. The major salivary glands are located on each side of the face. They are the **parotid gland, submandibular gland** and **sublingual gland**.

The **parotid gland** is the largest of the salivary glands (Fig. 11.11). It is an irregular, lobulated and yellowish organ. The gland occupies an area posterior to the mandibular ramus, anterior and inferior to the ear. Vertically, the gland extends from the zygomatic arch to the angle of the mandible. It appears as an inverted, flat, **three-sided pyramid** with an outer **false capsule** and inner **true capsule**. The true capsule is a condensation of fibrous stroma, whereas the false capsule or parotid sheath is formed by splitting of the investing layer of deep cervical fascia. The **apex** of the pyramid is directed downward, while the **base** or superior surface faces upward. The gland has three other **surfaces**, superficial, anteromedial and posteromedial. Separating the surfaces are three **borders**, anterior, posterior and medial. The base is closely related to the external acoustic meatus, while the apex lies posteroinferior to the angle of the mandible. The anteromedial surface is moulded to the ramus of the mandible and is separated

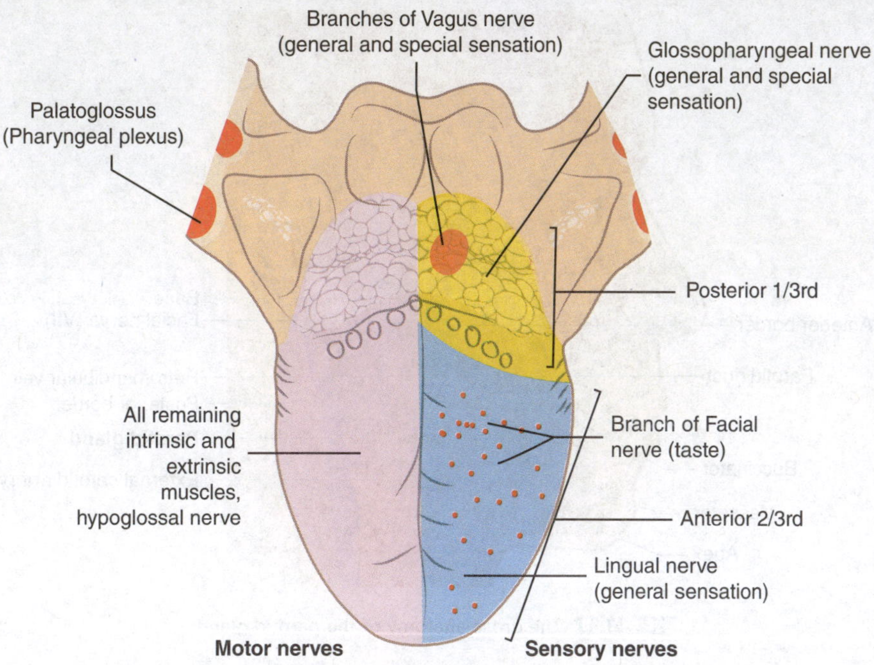

FIG. 11.9 The nerve supply of the tongue.

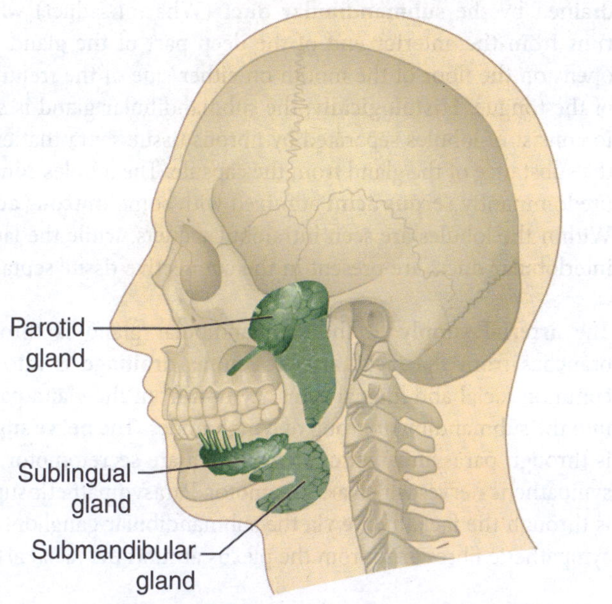

FIG. 11.10 The three major salivary glands.

from the posteromedial surface by the medial border. Related to the posteromedial surface is the mastoid process and muscles attached to it. The superficial surface is related to the skin and is separated from the other two surfaces by the anterior and posterior borders.

Three major structures course through the substance of the parotid gland. From superficial to deep, they are the **facial nerve, retromandibular vein** and **external carotid artery** (Fig. 11.11). The branches and tributaries of these structures emerge from the margins of the parotid gland. The **duct** of the parotid gland (Stensen's duct) emerges from the anterior border of the parotid gland. It is formed within the parotid gland by the union of two vertical ducts. The duct courses anteriorly over the masseter muscle before passing medially through the structures forming the cheek to open into the vestibule of the mouth opposite the upper second molar tooth on either side. **Histologically**, the parotid gland is seen to consist of lobules of **serous acini**, separated by fibrous tissue septa that enter the substance of the gland from the capsule (Fig. 11.12). Within the lobules are seen intralobular ducts, while the larger interlobular ducts are present in the connective tissue septa.

The **arterial supply** to the parotid gland is through branches from the external carotid artery. **Venous drainage** is into the external jugular vein. Lymph from the gland passes into the parotid group of lymph nodes which drain into the superficial and deep cervical group of lymph nodes. The **nerve supply** is through parasympathetic nerves which are secretomotor and sympathetic nerves which are vasomotor. Parasympathetic supply is through the glossopharyngeal nerve via the otic ganglion. The sympathetic fibres arise from the plexus around the external carotid artery.

The submandibular salivary gland is the second largest salivary gland that is seen in close relation to the posterior part of the base of the mandible (Fig. 11.13). **Deep cervical fascia** completely encloses the gland. It is roughly **J-shaped** and divided by the mylohyoid muscle into a larger **superficial part** and smaller **deep part**. The **superficial part** is seen within the digastric triangle and has inferior, lateral and medial surfaces. The inferior surface is superficial, while the lateral and medial surfaces are related to the inner surface of the base of the mandible and

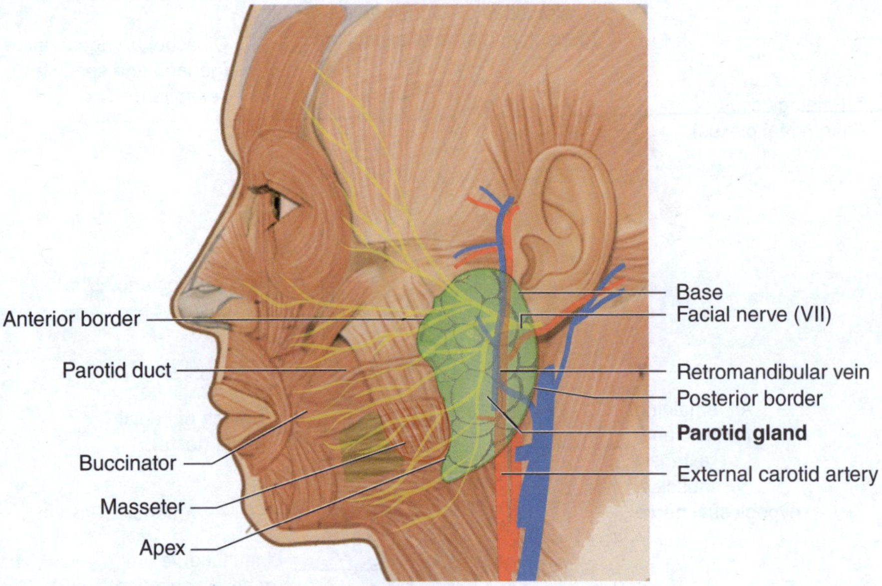

FIG. 11.11 The gross anatomy of the parotid gland.

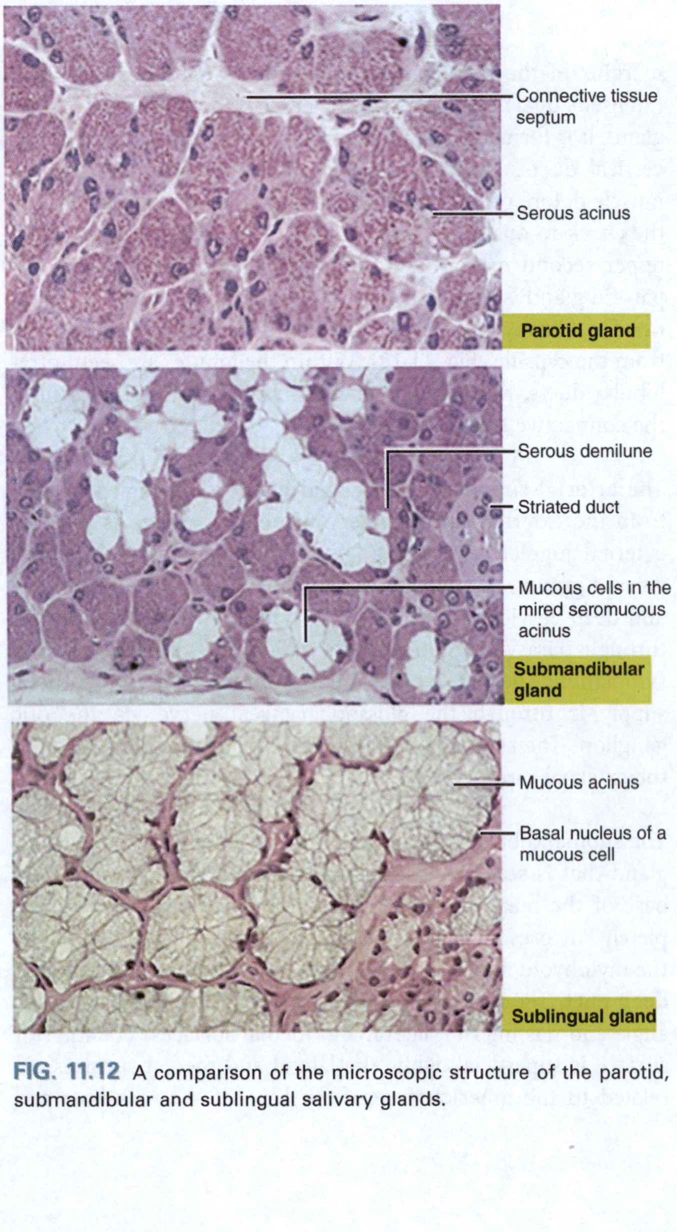

FIG. 11.12 A comparison of the microscopic structure of the parotid, submandibular and sublingual salivary glands.

mylohyoid muscle, respectively. The **deep portion** of the gland lies deep to the mylohyoid muscle. Secretions from the gland are drained by the **submandibular duct** (Wharton's duct) which runs from the anterior end of the deep part of the gland and opens on the floor of the mouth on either side of the frenulum of the tongue. **Histologically**, the submandibular gland is seen to consist of lobules separated by fibrous tissue septa that enter the substance of the gland from the capsule. The lobules contain predominantly **serous acini** admixed with some **mucous acini**. Within the lobules are seen intralobular ducts, while the larger interlobular ducts are present in the connective tissue septa.

The **arterial supply** to the submandibular gland is through branches from the facial artery. **Venous drainage** is into the common facial and lingual veins. **Lymph** from the gland passes into the submandibular group of lymph nodes. The **nerve supply** is through parasympathetic nerves which are secretomotor and sympathetic nerves which are vasomotor. Parasympathetic supply is through the facial nerve via the submandibular ganglion. The sympathetic fibres arise from the plexus around the facial artery.

The **sublingual salivary glands** lie beneath the mucosa of the floor of the mouth (Fig. 11.13). About 15 **ducts** emerge from the gland and open directly into the floor of the mouth. **Histologically**, the sublingual gland is seen to consist of lobules of predominantly **mucous acini**. Within the lobules are seen a few intralobular ducts, while the larger interlobular ducts are present in the connective tissue septa. The **arterial supply** is through branches from the lingual artery. **Venous drainage** is into the lingual veins. **Lymph** from the gland passes into the submandibular group of lymph nodes. The **nerve supply** is through parasympathetic nerves which are secretomotor and sympathetic nerves which are vasomotor. Parasympathetic supply is through the facial nerve via the submandibular ganglion. The sympathetic fibres arise from the plexus around the lingual artery.

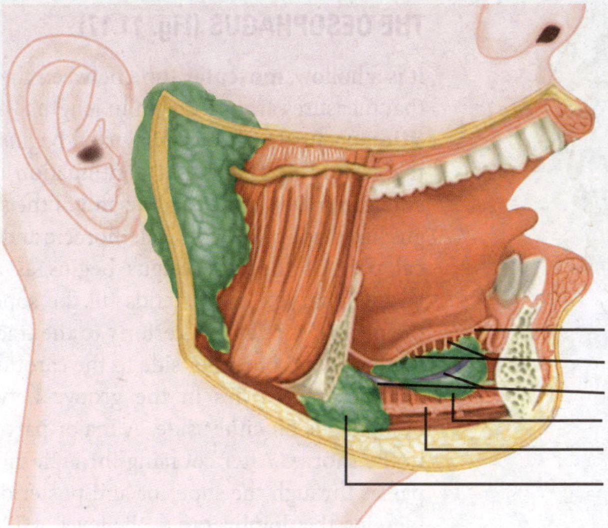

FIG. 11.13 The gross anatomy of the submandibular and sublingual salivary glands.

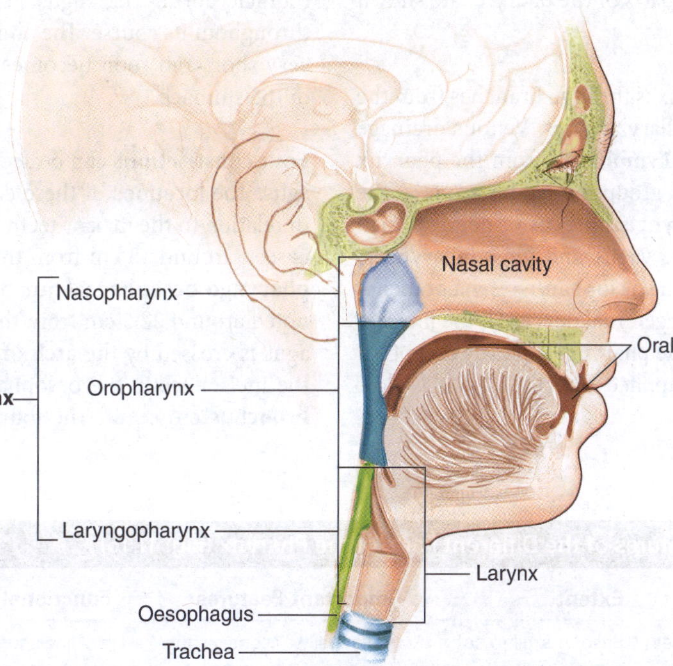

FIG. 11.14 The parts of the pharynx.

THE PHARYNX (Fig. 11.14)

The pharynx is a **musculo-membranous tube**, lined internally by the mucous membrane that extends from the **base of the skull** to the **sixth cervical vertebra** beyond which it continues as the oesophagus. Its interior is divided into **three parts**, the **nasopharynx, oropharynx** and **laryngopharynx (hypopharynx)**. As their names indicate, the three parts are located behind the nasal cavity, oral cavity and larynx. The wall of the pharynx has four layers from inside to outside, namely the mucosa, submucosa, muscular coat and areolar coat. The submucosa and areolar layers are thickened to form the **pharyngobasilar fascia** and **buccopharyngeal fascia**, respectively. **Inner longitudinal** and **outer circular** skeletal **muscle** layers are seen in the muscular coat (Fig. 11.15). The inner longitudinal muscles are the stylopharyngeus, palatopharyngeus and salpingopharyngeus. The outer circular muscles consist of the superior, middle and inferior constrictors. The longitudinal muscles converge from the styloid process, palate and auditory tube to the larynx. During **deglutition**, the larynx is pulled up by the longitudinal muscles. The constrictors are attached to the base of the skull,

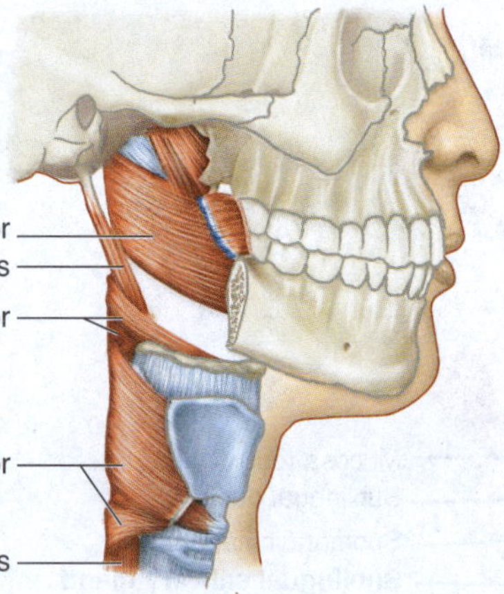

FIG. 11.15 The muscles of the pharynx.

mandible, hyoid bone and larynx from where they pass posteriorly to get inserted into a midline raphe which extends from the base of the skull to the lower limit of the larynx. These muscles contract sequentially to move the bolus of food into the oesophagus. The features of the different parts of the pharynx are shown in Table 11.1.

The **arterial supply** to the pharynx is through branches from the external carotid, facial and maxillary arteries. Venous drainage is into the corresponding veins. **Lymphatics** from the pharynx drain into the retropharyngeal group of lymph nodes. The pharynx is supplied by the **pharyngeal plexus** of nerves which is formed by branches from the vagus and glossopharyngeal nerves. Sensory nerve supply of the nasopharynx is via branches of the maxillary division of the trigeminal nerve. All the muscles of the pharynx are supplied by the pharyngeal plexus except for the stylopharyngeus which is supplied directly from the glossopharyngeal nerve.

THE OESOPHAGUS (Fig. 11.17)

It is a hollow, **muscular tube** between the pharynx and stomach that measures around 25 cm in length. The final phase of **deglutition** occurs in the oesophagus. It begins at the lower border of the **cricoid cartilage** as a continuation of the laryngopharynx and terminates at the **cardiac end** of the **stomach**. The oesophagus has **three parts**, cervical, thoracic and abdominal. The **cervical part** of the oesophagus begins as a continuation of the laryngopharynx and extends till the superior mediastinum. In the neck, it is related anteriorly to the trachea, posteriorly to the vertebrae and on either side to the carotid sheath. The recurrent laryngeal nerve lies in the groove between the trachea and oesophagus on either side. A major part of the oesophagus lies in the **thorax**. After coursing through the neck, the oesophagus passes through the superior and posterior mediastinum, before piercing the **diaphragm** at the level of T10 vertebra. Within the mediastinum, the oesophagus is related on either side to the mediastinal surfaces of the lungs. The trachea continues to lie anterior to the oesophagus in the superior mediastinum. In the posterior mediastinum, it is closely related to the descending thoracic aorta. The vagus nerves accompany the oesophagus throughout its course. The **abdominal part** of the oesophagus is very short and soon becomes continuous with the cardiac end of the stomach.

Four constrictions can be seen along the course of the oesophagus. The locations of these constrictions are usually described in relation to the incisor teeth (Fig. 11.17). The first constriction is seen around 15 cm from the incisor teeth and represents the **pharyngo-oesophageal junction**. The second constriction is noted around 22.5 cm from the incisor teeth where the oesophagus is crossed by the **arch of the aorta**. Around 27.5 cm from the incisor teeth, the oesophagus is constricted where the **left bronchus** crosses it. The fourth constriction occurs where the

TABLE 11.1 The Salient Features of the Different Parts of the Pharynx (Fig. 11.16)

Part of Pharynx	Location	Extent	Important Features	Functional Aspects
Nasopharynx	Posterior to the nasal cavity	Base of skull to soft palate (C1 vertebra)	• Lateral wall contains the opening of the auditory tube • Posterior wall contains the pharyngeal tonsil	• Allows for passage of air from the nasal cavity • Is kept permanently open by the pharyngobasilar fascia • The opening of the auditory tube allows for equalization of pressure in the middle ear cavity • The pharyngeal tonsil forms part of Waldeyer's ring to protect the upper aerodigestive passages
Oropharynx	Posterior to the oral cavity	Soft palate to tip of epiglottis (C1 to C3 vertebra)	• Lateral wall contains the palatine tonsil • The oropharyngeal isthmus lies between the oral cavity and the oropharynx	• Allows for passage of both food and air • The palatine tonsil forms part of Waldeyer's ring • The muscles around the oropharyngeal isthmus regulate the passage of food from the oral cavity to the oropharynx
Laryngopharynx	Posterior to the larynx	Tip of epiglottis to lower border of cricoid cartilage (C3 to C6 vertebra)	• The piriform fossa is a space located laterally on either side in the laryngopharynx	• Mainly allows for passage of food and some air • Regulates the passage of food from the pharynx to the oesophagus

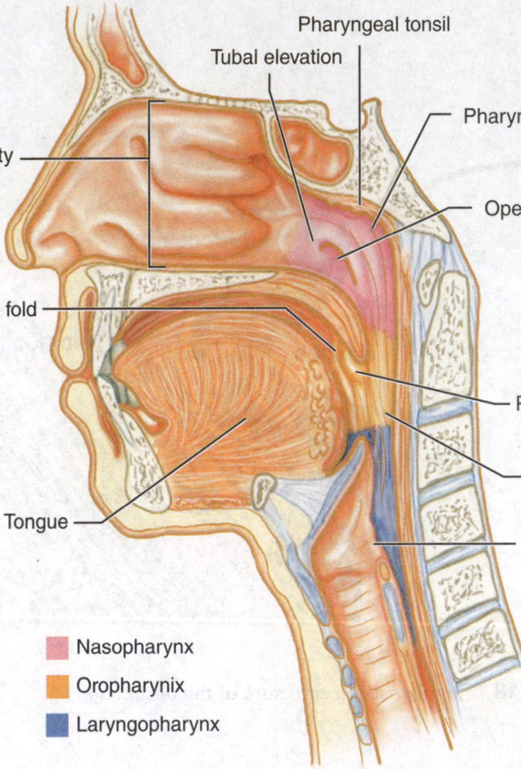

FIG. 11.16 The features of the different parts of the pharynx.

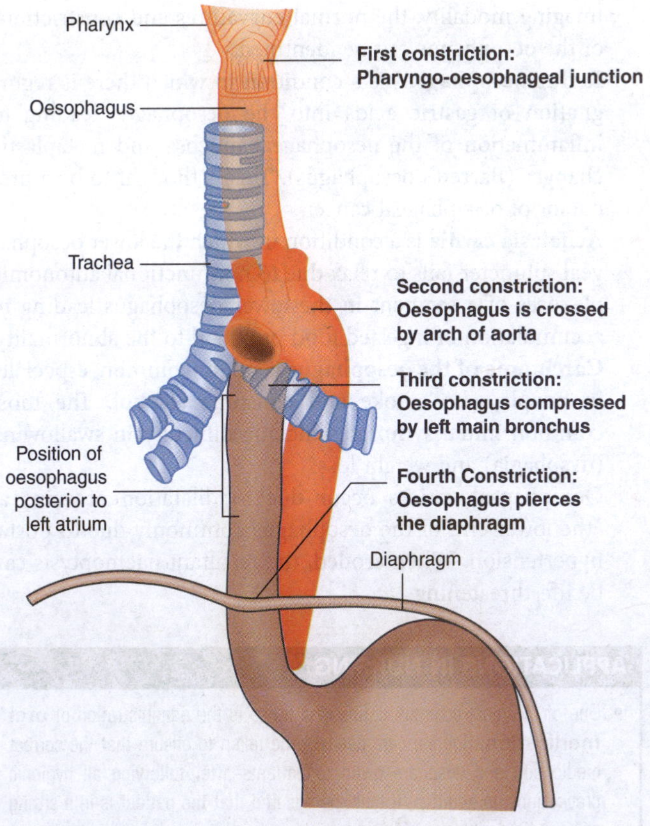

FIG. 11.17 The sites of constrictions of the oesophagus.

oesophagus pierces the **diaphragm**, 37.5 cm from the incisor teeth. Two **sphincters** at either end of the oesophagus, upper and lower, regulate the passage of food through the oesophagus.

Histologically, the oesophagus contains the same layers that are seen in the other parts of the gut, the mucosa, submucosa, muscularis externa and adventitia (Fig. 11.18). The **mucosa** is formed by stratified squamous nonkeratinized epithelium and a well-defined lamina propria and muscularis mucosae. Mucus-secreting oesophageal glands are seen in the submucosa. The **muscularis externa** is somewhat unusual in that it contains striated muscle in its upper one-third, a mix of striated muscle and smooth muscle in its middle third and smooth muscle in its lower third. The **adventitia** consists of a layer of loose connective tissue. Only the lowest part of the oesophagus possesses a serosa.

The **arterial supply** of the cervical, thoracic and abdominal parts of the oesophagus is through branches of the inferior thyroid artery, aorta and left gastric artery, respectively. **Venous drainage** of the corresponding parts is through the brachiocephalic, azygos and left gastric veins. **Lymphatic drainage** of the cervical, thoracic and abdominal parts is into the deep cervical, mediastinal and coeliac nodes, respectively. Parasympathetic fibres via the vagus nerve and sympathetic fibres from the upper segments of the thoracic spinal cord supply the oesophagus through an **oesophageal plexus** of nerves.

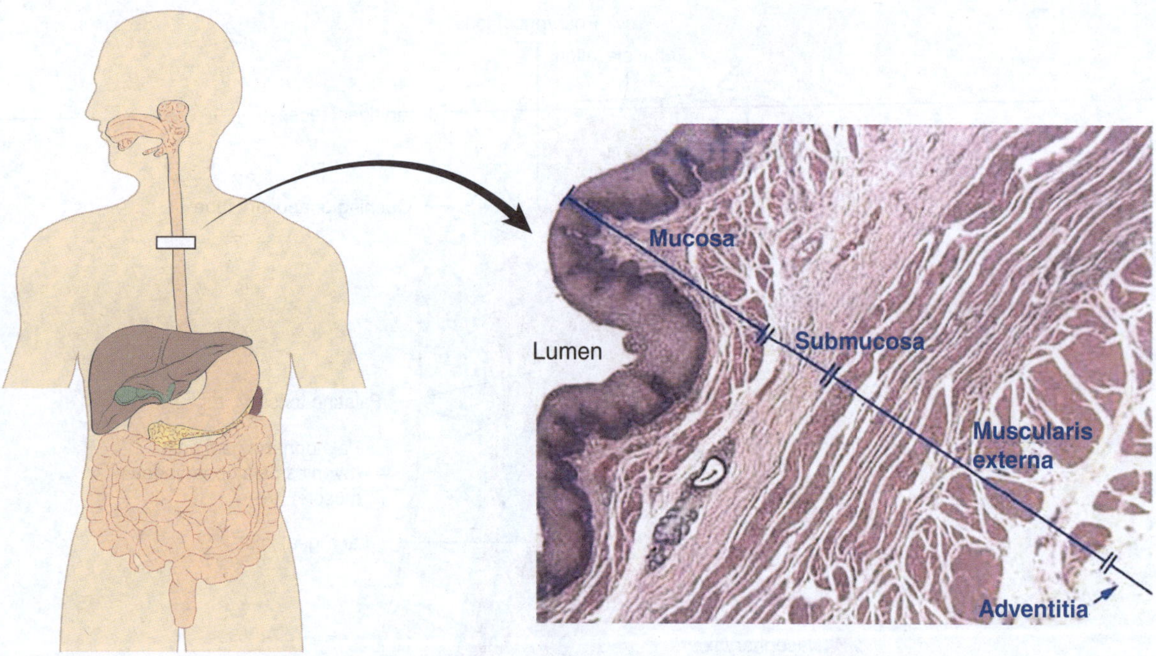

FIG. 11.18 The microscopic structure of the oesophagus.

APPLIED ANATOMY

- **Aphthous ulcers** are painful ulcers, usually of unknown cause, with a white base that are commonly seen in the oral mucosa.
- **Dental caries** is a common clinical condition in which there is a breakdown of the enamel and dentine of the teeth due to action of acids secreted by bacteria. This causes pain and sensitivity of the teeth due to stimulation of nerves in the pulp cavity.
- Several vitamin deficiencies can cause atrophy of the papillae of the tongue, leading to a 'bald tongue' that is painful and inflamed. This condition is called **glossitis.**
- Metastases of **carcinomas** of the tongue are often extensive due to the bilateral nature of its lymphatic drainage.
- **Hypoglossal nerve lesions** result in atrophy of muscles of the tongue leading to deviation of the protruded tongue.
- **Pleomorphic adenoma** is the most common tumour of the salivary glands that is usually seen in the parotid gland. As its name suggests, the tumour has a highly variable appearance on histopathological examination.
- Stone formation in the salivary glands or **sialolithiasis** is most common in the submandibular glands due to the thick, viscous nature of their secretions.
- **Cysts** or ranulas can form in relation to the sublingual glands either due to trauma or obstruction of the ducts.
- Inflammation of the pharynx is known as **pharyngitis** and is a common feature of upper respiratory tract infections. This is experienced by the patient as a sore throat.
- Infections of the palatine tonsils are known as **tonsillitis.** This condition causes fever and pain during swallowing. In patients with recurrent tonsillitis, the tonsils may have to be removed surgically, a procedure called tonsillectomy.
- Outpouchings of the pharyngeal mucosa called **pharyngeal diverticula** may arise in the laryngopharynx due to incoordination in the muscular contraction of the inferior constrictor muscle.
- The oesophagus can be visualized radiographically through a contrast radiograph called a **barium swallow**. Using this imaging modality, the normal curvatures and constrictions of the oesophagus can be identified.
- **Reflux oesophagitis** is a condition in which there is regurgitation of gastric acids into the oesophagus leading to inflammation of the oesophageal mucosa and metaplastic changes (Barrett's oesophagus). This is thought to be a precursor of oesophageal cancer.
- **Achalasia cardia** is a condition in which the lower oesophageal sphincter fails to relax due to nonfunctional autonomic plexuses of a segment in the lower oesophagus leading to accumulation of ingested food proximal to the abnormality.
- **Carcinoma of the oesophagus** is not uncommon, especially in people who smoke and consume alcohol. The most common initial symptoms include difficulty in swallowing (dysphagia) and weight loss.
- Oesophageal varices occur due to dilatation of veins at `the lower end of the oesophagus commonly due to portal hypertension. When eroded, the resultant haemoptysis can be life-threatening.

APPLICATIONS IN NURSING

- One of the most common duties of a nurse is the administration of **oral medication**. Routine care needs to be taken to ensure that the correct medication and dose are given to patients after following all hygienic precautions. In addition, it must be ensured that the patient is in a sitting position if possible or a side-lying position if sitting is not possible to prevent

APPLICATIONS IN NURSING—Cont'd

aspiration. Prior to administering the medication, it must be confirmed that the patient is able to swallow adequately.

- Nursing personnel may be required to perform **oral care** of unconscious or critically ill patients. These patients are prone to drying and ulceration of the oral mucosa. The presence of thickened secretions in the oral cavity could lead to aspiration and subsequent pneumonia. Oral care may include toothbrushing, mouth gargles and oral suctioning.

SUMMARY

- The digestive system is formed by the alimentary canal and its associated digestive glands.
- The alimentary canal extends from the oral cavity to the anus.
- It is constituted by the oral cavity, pharynx, oesophagus, stomach, small intestine, large intestine, rectum and anal canal.
- The associated digestive glands are the salivary glands, liver with the extrahepatic biliary apparatus and pancreas.
- The part of the alimentary canal from the stomach distally is known as the gastrointestinal tract.
- The oral cavity is divided into two parts, an oral cavity proper and vestibule.
- The vestibule is the space between the gums and teeth internally and lips and cheeks externally.
- There are temporary or milk teeth, which are 20 in number, 10 in each jaw in children.
- Half of each jaw contains two incisors, one canine and two molars.
- There are 32 permanent teeth, 16 in each jaw in adults.
- Two incisors, one canine, two premolars and three molars are seen in one-half of each jaw.
- Each tooth has a crown, neck and root.
- Microscopically, each tooth contains a pulp space covered by a bone-like material called dentine.
- The dentine in the crown is covered by an extremely hard material called enamel.
- Covering the dentine of the root is the cementum, which is tightly bound to the bone of the alveolar socket through the periodontal membrane.
- The pulp cavity continues inferiorly as the root canal, which ends at an apical foramen.
- The palate is formed by an anterior hard and posterior soft palate.
- The hard palate is an arched structure formed by the maxilla anteriorly and palatine bone posteriorly.
- The soft palate is a posterior extension of the hard palate and consists of a core of skeletal muscle covered on either side by mucous membrane.
- The skeletal muscles within the soft palate are the tensor palati, levator palati, palatopharyngeus, palatoglossus and musculus uvulae.
- The muscles of the soft palate are supplied by the pharyngeal plexus, except for the tensor palati which is supplied by a branch from the mandibular division of the trigeminal nerve.
- The tongue has a tip, body and base.
- The body is formed by the anterior two-thirds of the tongue and is separated from the base by a V-shaped sulcus terminalis.
- Two surfaces, dorsal and ventral, are seen on the tongue, separated by a lateral border.
- The dorsal surface is rough because of the presence of elevations called papillae.
- The ventral surface is smooth and is connected to the floor of the mouth by a fold called the frenulum.
- The base of the tongue is rough due to the presence of lymphatic tissue known as the lingual tonsils.
- Four types of papillae, filiform, fungiform, circumvallate and foliate, can be seen on the dorsal surface.
- Filiform papillae are conical structures, capped with keratin, do not contain taste buds and serve a purely mechanical function.
- Fungiform papillae are mushroom-shaped, have taste buds and are concentrated near the tip of the tongue.
- Circumvallate papillae contain taste buds and are seen in a row parallel to and anterior to the sulcus terminalis.
- The muscles of the tongue can be divided into intrinsic and extrinsic groups.
- Intrinsic muscles are oriented transversely, longitudinally and vertically within the tongue.
- The extrinsic muscles are the genioglossus, hyoglossus, styloglossus and palatoglossus.
- All muscles of the tongue are supplied by the hypoglossal nerve except for the palatoglossus which is supplied by the pharyngeal plexus.
- The arterial supply to the tongue is via the lingual artery which is a branch of the external carotid artery.
- General and special sensations from the tongue are carried by branches of the mandibular division of the trigeminal nerve, facial nerve, glossopharyngeal nerve and vagus nerve.
- Lymph from the tongue eventually drains into the deep cervical group of lymph nodes.
- The major salivary glands are the parotid, submandibular and sublingual glands.
- The parotid gland is the largest of the salivary glands found overlying the mandibular ramus, anterior and inferior to the external ear.
- It appears as an inverted, flat, three-sided pyramid with an outer false capsule and inner true capsule.
- The gland has three other surfaces, superficial, anteromedial and posteromedial.
- Separating the surfaces are three borders, anterior, posterior and medial.
- Three major structures, the facial nerve, retromandibular vein and external carotid artery, course through the substance of the parotid gland.
- The branches and tributaries of these structures emerge from the margins of the parotid gland.
- The duct of the parotid gland (Stensen's duct) emerges from the anterior border of the parotid gland.
- The duct opens into the vestibule of the mouth opposite the upper second molar tooth on either side.
- Histologically, the parotid gland is seen to consist of lobules of serous acini, separated by fibrous tissue.
- Parasympathetic nerve supply is through the glossopharyngeal nerve via the otic ganglion.
- The submandibular salivary gland is the second largest salivary gland that is seen in close relation to the posterior part of the base of the mandible.
- It is roughly J-shaped and divided by the mylohyoid muscle into a larger superficial part and a smaller deep part.
- Secretions from the gland are drained by the submandibular duct (Wharton's duct) which opens on the floor of the mouth on either side of the frenulum of the tongue.
- Histologically, the submandibular gland is seen to consist of lobules of both serous and mucous acini separated by fibrous tissue septa that enter the substance of the gland from the capsule.
- Parasympathetic nerve supply is through the facial nerve via the submandibular ganglion.
- The sublingual salivary glands lie beneath the mucosa of the floor of the mouth.
- About 15 ducts emerge from the gland and open directly into the floor of the mouth.
- Histologically, the sublingual gland is seen to consist of lobules of predominantly mucous acini.
- Parasympathetic nerve supply is through the facial nerve via the submandibular ganglion.
- The pharynx is a musculo-membranous tube lined internally by the mucous membrane.

- It extends from the base of the skull to the sixth cervical vertebra beyond which it continues as the oesophagus.
- It is divided into three parts, the nasopharynx, oropharynx and laryngopharynx.
- The nasopharynx lies behind the nasal cavity, extends from the base of the skull to the soft palate and contains the opening of the auditory tube and pharyngeal tonsil.
- The oropharynx lies behind the oral cavity, extends from the soft palate to the tip of the epiglottis and contains the palatine tonsils.
- The laryngopharynx lies behind the larynx, extends from the tip of the epiglottis to the lower border of the cricoid cartilage and contains the piriform fossa.
- The wall of the pharynx has four layers from inside to outside, namely the mucosa, submucosa, muscular coat and areolar coat.
- Inner longitudinal and outer circular skeletal muscle layers are seen in the muscular coat.
- The inner longitudinal muscles are the stylopharyngeus, palatopharyngeus and salpingopharyngeus.
- The outer circular muscles consist of the superior, middle and inferior constrictors.
- The pharynx is supplied by the pharyngeal plexus of nerves which is formed by branches from the vagus and glossopharyngeal nerves.
- All muscles of the pharynx are supplied by the pharyngeal plexus except for the stylopharyngeus which is supplied directly from the glossopharyngeal nerve.

- The oesophagus is a hollow, muscular tube between the pharynx and stomach that measures around 25 cm in length.
- It begins at the lower border of the cricoid cartilage as a continuation of the laryngopharynx and terminates at the cardiac end of the stomach.
- The oesophagus has three parts, cervical, thoracic and abdominal.
- After coursing through the neck, the oesophagus passes through the superior and posterior mediastinum, before piercing the diaphragm at the level of T10 vertebra.
- Four constrictions, around 15, 22.5, 27.5 and 37.5 cm, from the incisor teeth can be seen along the course of the oesophagus.
- These constrictions are seen at the levels of the pharyngo-oesophageal junction, crossing of the arch of the aorta, crossing of the left bronchus and where the oesophagus pierces the diaphragm.
- Two sphincters at either end of the oesophagus, upper and lower, regulate the passage of food through the oesophagus.
- Histologically, the oesophagus contains the same layers that are seen in the other parts of the gut, namely the mucosa, submucosa, muscularis externa and adventitia.
- The mucosa is lined by stratified squamous nonkeratinized epithelium.
- Mucus-secreting oesophageal glands are seen in the submucosa.
- The muscularis externa contains striated muscle in its upper one-third, a mix of striated muscle and smooth muscle in its middle third and smooth muscle in its lower third.

CHAPTER 12

The Lower Alimentary Canal

SPECIFIC LEARNING OBJECTIVES

At the end of this chapter, the student should be able to:

- Describe the extent of the abdominal cavity and its surface projections on to the anterior abdominal wall.
- Describe the layers of the peritoneum and their relationship with the abdominal cavity and their contained viscera.
- Describe the gross and microscopic anatomy of the stomach.
- Describe the gross and microscopic anatomy of the small intestine.
- Describe the gross and microscopic anatomy of the large intestine.

GLOSSARY OF TERMS

- **Linea alba:** midline tendinous intersection formed by merging of the aponeuroses of the three muscles of the anterior abdominal wall from either side
- **Lesser sac:** portion of the peritoneal cavity behind the stomach
- **Greater sac:** the entire peritoneal cavity excluding the lesser sac
- **Omentum:** peritoneal folds attached to the stomach
- **Stomach bed:** the posterior relations of the stomach
- **Rugae:** folds seen within the stomach when it is empty
- **Mesentery:** peritoneal folds that suspend the intestine
- **Plicae circularis:** crescentic folds seen on the interior of the small intestine
- **Villi:** minute mucosal projections from the surface of the small intestine
- **Microvilli:** microscopic projections from the columnar cells lining the villi
- **Crypts of Lieberkühn:** simple tubular intestinal glands seen in the lamina propria
- **Peyer's patches:** prominent lymphatic tissue seen in the mucosa and submucosa of the ileum
- **Brunner's glands:** mucous glands seen in the submucosa of the duodenum
- **Sacculations:** pouch-like dilatations of the large intestine
- **Taeniae coli:** three bands of longitudinal smooth muscle visible on the outside of the large intestine
- **Appendices epiploicae:** peritoneal pouches of fat seen along the outer surface of the large intestine
- **Pectinate line:** line separating the upper portion of the anal canal from the remaining portion

INTRODUCTION

This chapter will describe the part of the alimentary canal that is located within the abdominal and pelvic cavities, otherwise known as the gastrointestinal tract. The abdominal and pelvic cavities are lined by peritoneum, which sends in folds to enclose certain parts of the gastrointestinal tract. The peritoneal cavity and folds allow for movements of the stomach and intestines, serve an immune function, allow for the passage of blood vessels, lymphatics and nerves and act as storehouses of fat. Food enters the stomach from the oesophagus and undergoes thorough mixing and digestion by the action of gastric acids and pepsin. This chyme then enters the duodenum, where it is exposed to pancreatic enzymes and bile, for the next stage of digestion to take place.

The chyme then starts its long passage through the small intestine where the final stages of digestion take place through enzymes secreted by the intestinal glands. Absorption of the contents occurs, aided by the surface modifications of the small intestinal epithelium. The absorbed substances pass into the portal system of veins to reach the liver which is the site of metabolism. Fat is absorbed through lacteals as chyle, eventually reaching the venous system through the thoracic duct. The main function of the large intestine is to absorb water, leading to solidification of faecal matter. Absorption of ions and vitamins produced by the gut flora is another function of the large intestine. The rectum stores the faecal material until it is ready to be expelled through the anal canal. This passage of chyme from the stomach to the anal canal is regulated by a complex system of sphincters.

THE ABDOMINAL CAVITY AND ITS WALLS

The abdominal cavity extends from the **diaphragm** above to the **pelvis** below and contains the abdominal part of the oesophagus, stomach, small and large intestines, liver, gallbladder, pancreas, kidneys, ureters, urinary bladder, blood vessels, nerves and lymphatics (Fig. 12.1). While superiorly the abdominal cavity is separated from the thoracic cavity by the thoracoabdominal diaphragm, it is continuous inferiorly with the pelvic cavity beyond the pelvic inlet. The extent of the abdominal cavity is greater than is externally visible due to its superior extension under the costal margin and inferior extension into the iliac fossae. The anterior abdominal wall is divided into **nine regions** by the midclavicular lines on either side and the subcostal and transtubercular lines superiorly and inferiorly (Fig. 12.2). These regions are the right and left hypochondriac, epigastric, right and left lumbar, umbilical, right and left iliac and hypogastric regions. The surface projections of the various organs in the abdominal cavity onto the anterior abdominal wall are important when clinically evaluating abdominal disease conditions.

The flexible and mobile **anterior abdominal wall** consists of **three layers** of **muscle** lined on the inside by peritoneum and on the outside by skin (Fig. 12.3). From outside to inside, the muscles are the external oblique, internal oblique and transversus abdominis. The aponeuroses of the muscles on each side pass medially to enclose the **rectus abdominis** muscle and merge with those of the opposite side in the midline at the **linea alba**. The rigid **posterior abdominal wall** is formed by three muscles, psoas major, quadratus lumborum and iliacus, on which run branches of the lumbar plexus (Fig. 12.4).

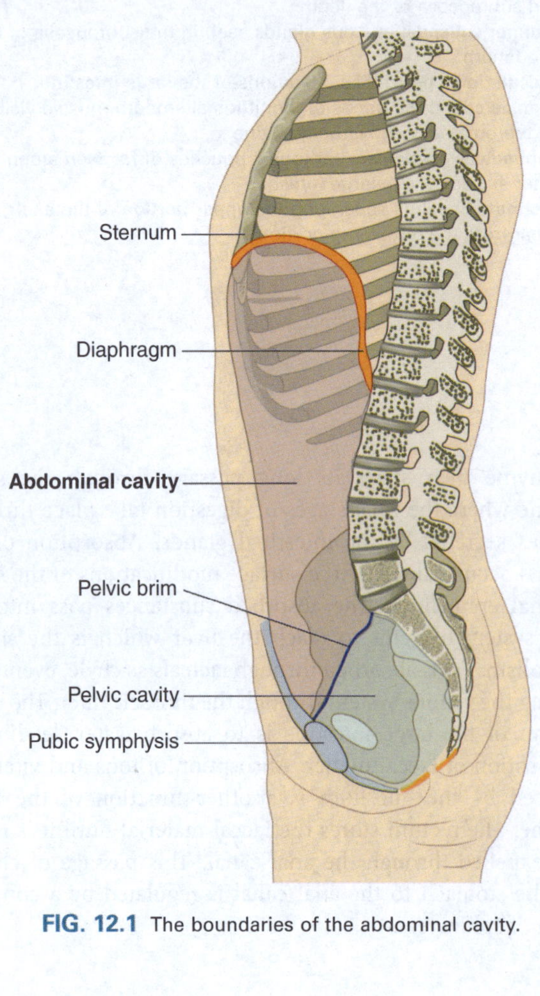

FIG. 12.1 The boundaries of the abdominal cavity.

THE PERITONEUM AND PERITONEAL CAVITY (Fig. 12.5)

The peritoneum is a thin **serous membrane** that lines the walls of the abdominal and pelvic cavities and covers the organs within these cavities. **Parietal peritoneum** lines the walls of the abdominal and pelvic cavities, whereas **visceral peritoneum** covers the organs. The **peritoneal cavity** is the potential space between the parietal and visceral layer of the peritoneum. In males, it is a closed sac, but in females, there is a communication with the exterior through the uterine tubes. The organs in the abdominal cavity may be divided into intraperitoneal and retroperitoneal. **Intraperitoneal organs** are surrounded by peritoneum, while retroperitoneal organs lie on the posterior abdominal wall and are covered by peritoneum only anteriorly. Examples of intraperitoneal organs include the stomach, superior part of duodenum, jejunum, ileum, caecum, vermiform appendix, transverse and sigmoid colon, spleen, liver, gallbladder, the upper part of the rectum and ovary. **Retroperitoneal organs** include the ascending and descending colon, kidneys, suprarenal glands, pancreas, descending and horizontal parts of the duodenum, middle and lower parts of the rectum and ureter. **Peritoneal folds** containing fat, blood vessels, nerves and lymphatics extend from the parietal to the visceral peritoneum covering the various organs. These folds will be discussed with the respective organs.

The peritoneal cavity can be divided into a **greater sac** and **lesser sac** (Fig. 12.6). The lesser sac is located behind the stomach and communicates with the greater sac through an opening called the epiploic foramen. The transverse colon and mesocolon divide the greater sac into supracolic and infracolic compartments. The supracolic compartment lies between the diaphragm and transverse colon and mesocolon. It is mainly occupied by the liver. The infracolic compartment is divided into right and left parts by the root of the mesentery. The left infracolic compartment is continuous with the pelvic cavity inferiorly. The infracolic compartment is bounded on three sides by the large intestine and contains numerous coils of the small intestine.

THE STOMACH (Fig. 12.7)

The stomach, also called the gaster, is a **muscular bag** that functions as both a reservoir and digestive organ. It is the widest, most **distensible** part of the alimentary canal. It is **located** within the upper and left part of the abdomen, occupying the epigastric, umbilical and left hypochondriac regions. The shape of the stomach depends on its degree of distension. An empty stomach is usually J-shaped, the stomach descending with distension. The stomach extends between the cardiac

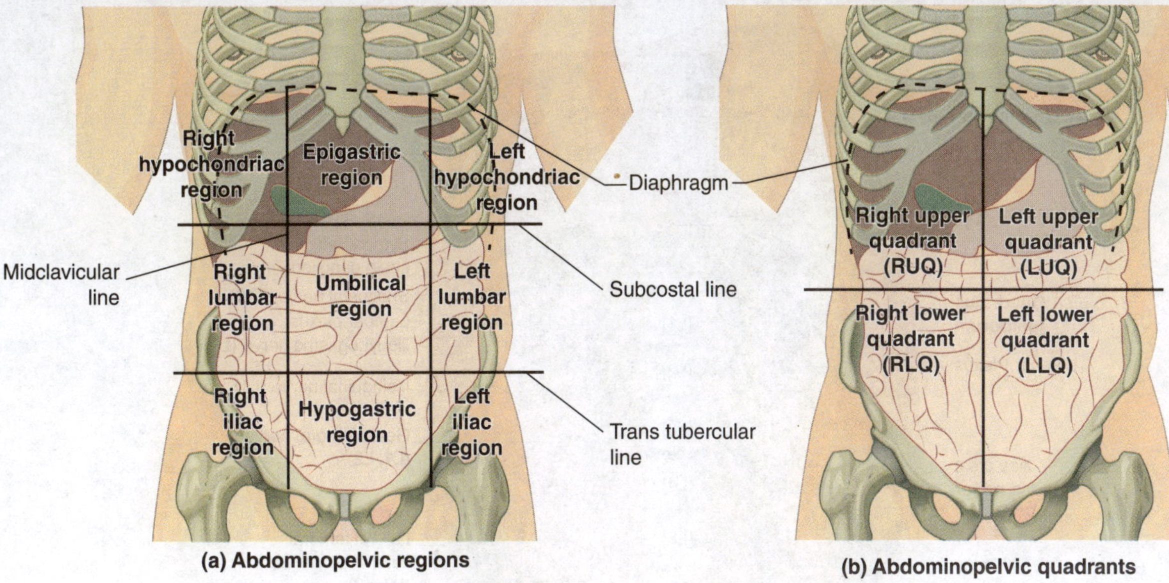

FIG. 12.2 Regions of the abdomen.

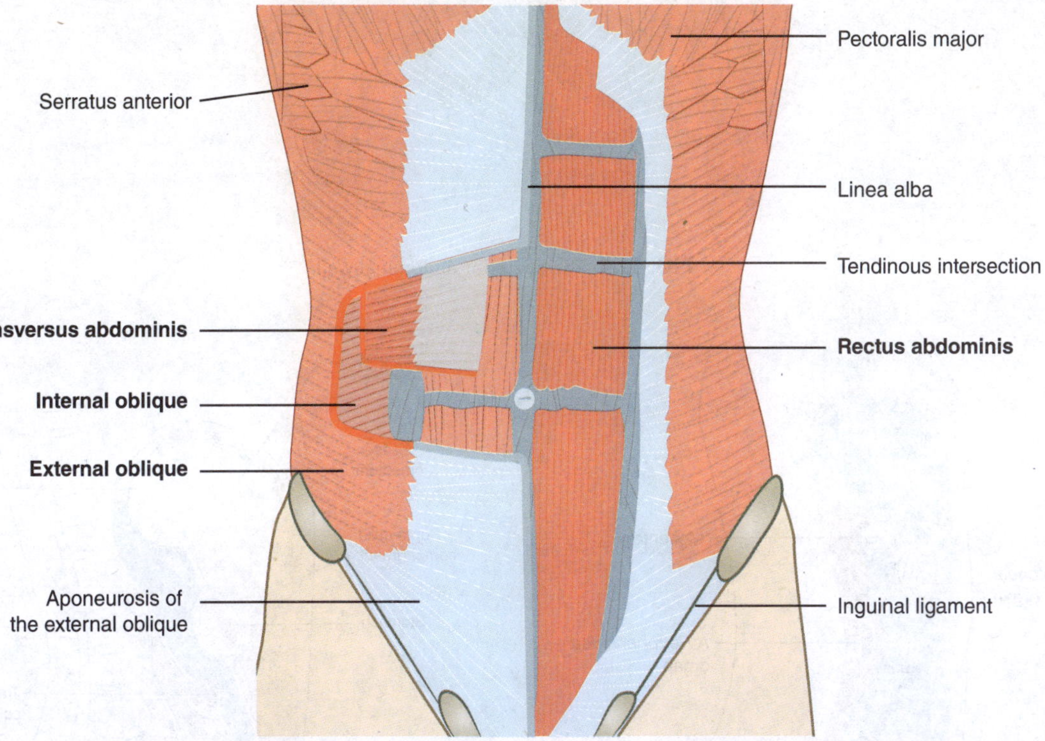

FIG. 12.3 Muscles of the anterior abdominal wall.

orifice superiorly and pyloric orifice inferiorly. It has a right concave border called the **lesser curvature** and a left convex border known as the **greater curvature**. These two borders separate an **anterior surface** and **posterior surface**. The lesser curvature contains an indentation distal to its middle called the incisura angularis. The junction between the greater curvature and the left border of the oesophagus is notched and called the cardiac notch.

Anatomically, the stomach is divided into a cardiac part, fundus, body or corpus and pylorus. The **cardia** is the region immediately surrounding the cardiac orifice. A horizontal plane through the cardia separates the superior dome-shaped **fundus** from the body. The junction between the body and pylorus is defined by a line passing from the incisura angularis to the greater curvature. The **pylorus** is further divided into the proximal dilated pyloric antrum and distal pyloric canal. There is a thickening of

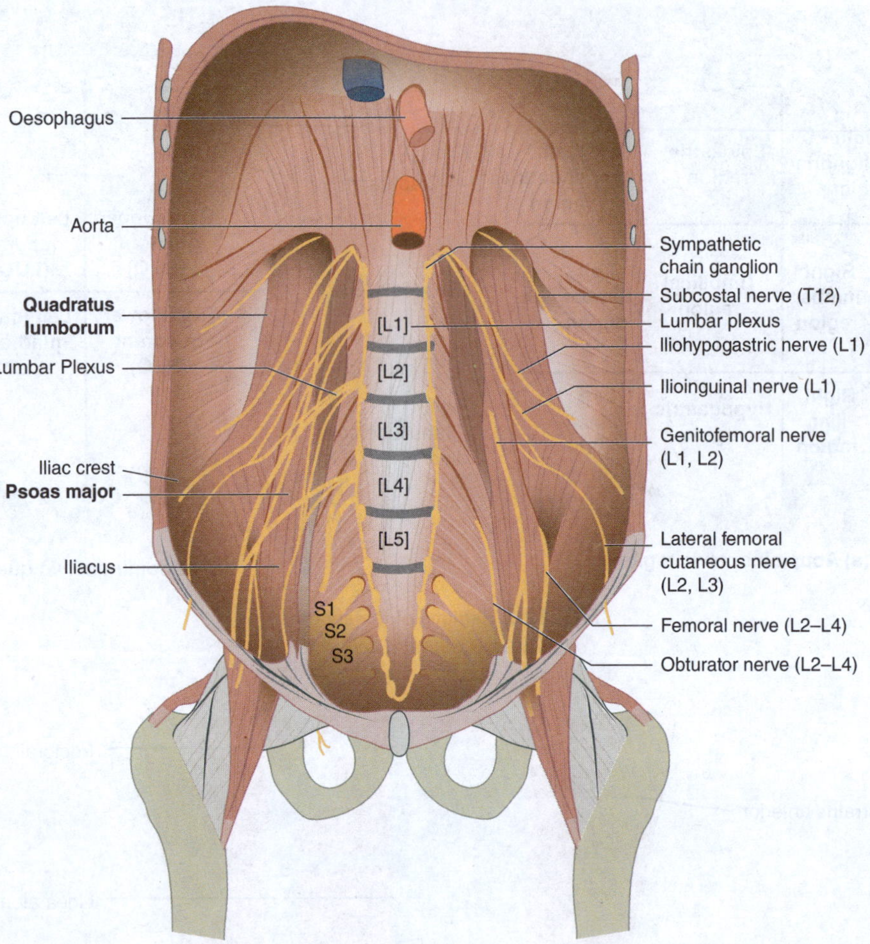

FIG. 12.4 The posterior abdominal wall.

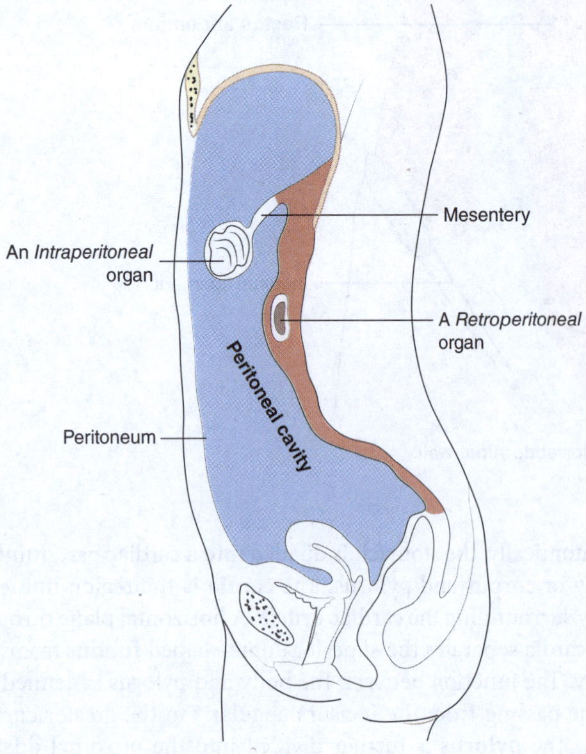

FIG. 12.5 The peritoneal cavity.

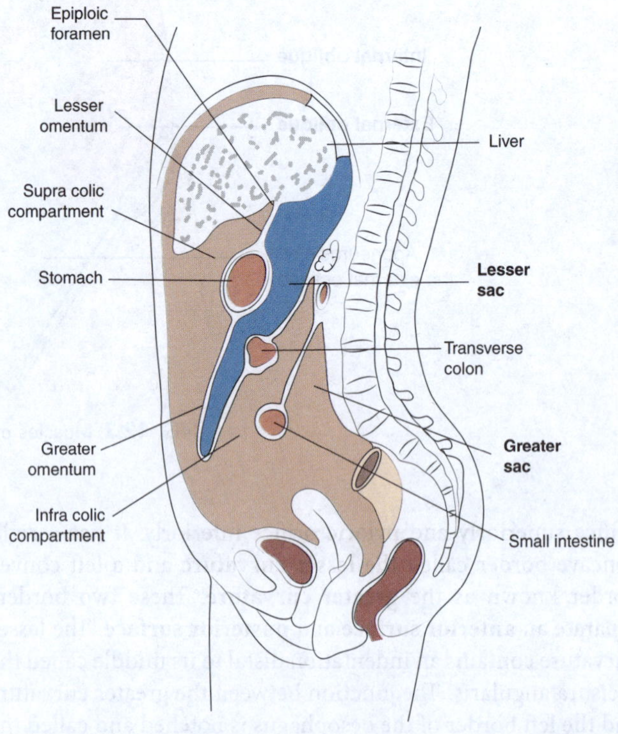

FIG. 12.6 The major subdivisions of the peritoneal cavity.

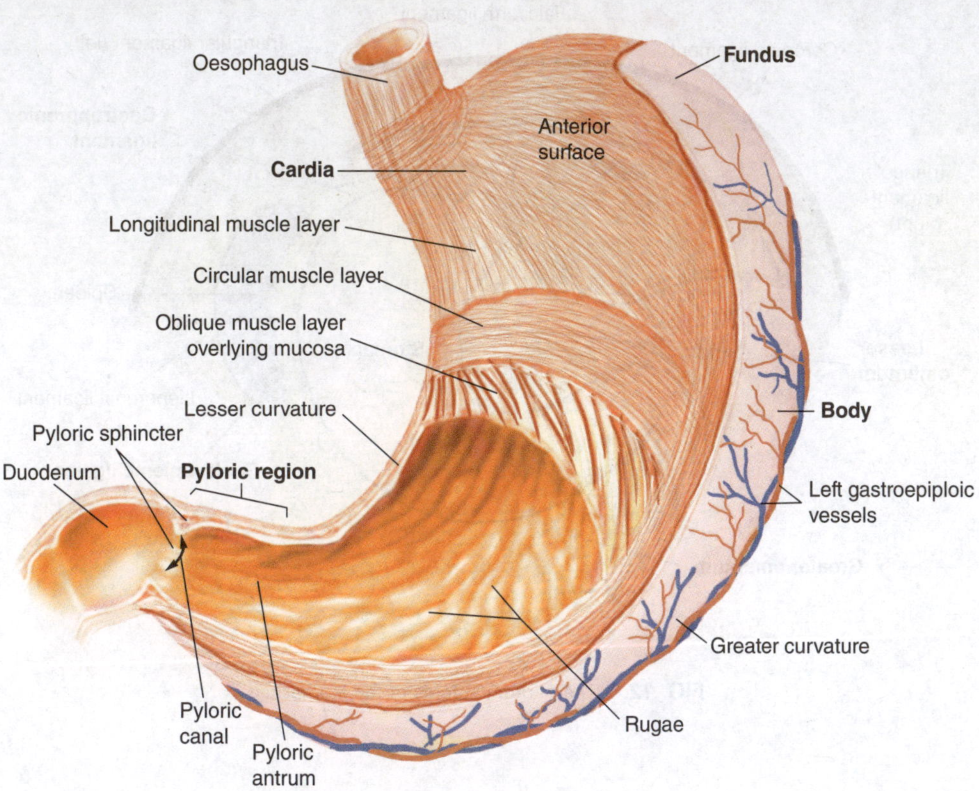

FIG. 12.7 The gross anatomy of the stomach (anterior view).

the circular smooth muscle in the distal part of the wall of the pylorus known as the pyloric sphincter which controls the passage of gastric contents into the duodenum. The stomach is covered by peritoneum and is related to some peritoneal folds. The **omentum** refers to a two-layered fold of peritoneum that extends from the stomach to the adjacent organs (Fig. 12.8). Attached to the lesser curvature and extending to the liver is the **lesser omentum** which contains the blood vessels that course along the lesser curvature of the stomach. The right free margin of the lesser omentum contains the common bile duct, hepatic artery and portal vein. The **greater omentum** is attached to a major part of the greater curvature and hangs like a fold inferiorly. The blood vessels running along the greater curvature of the stomach are located within the layers of the greater omentum. Connecting the spleen and stomach is the gastrosplenic ligament which is attached to the upper portion of the greater curvature. The blood vessels supplying the stomach from the splenic artery course through this ligament.

The **anterior surface** of the stomach is related to the liver, diaphragm and anterior abdominal wall. The posterior relations of the stomach form the **stomach bed** (Fig. 12.9). The stomach bed is formed by the diaphragm, left kidney, left suprarenal gland, pancreas, transverse mesocolon, splenic flexure of the colon and splenic artery. Separating the posterior surface of the stomach from the stomach bed is the lesser sac, which allows for easier movement and distension of the stomach. The interior of the empty stomach has several folds or ridges, called **rugae**, formed by the mucosa and submucosa. Most of these folds disappear on distension of the stomach. Minute pits are visible on the inner surface of the stomach known as **gastric pits**. **Gastric glands** release their secretions into these pits which act like ducts of the glands.

Histologically, regional differences are mainly restricted to the appearance of the gastric mucosa (Fig. 12.10). The gastric mucosa is thick and characterized by tightly packed **tubular glands** beneath a surface lined by **simple columnar epithelium**. Cells lining the surface are called surface mucous cells which produce a cloudy, viscous and alkaline mucus. There are numerous invaginations of the surface epithelium into the lamina propria called gastric pits or foveolae. These are also lined by surface mucous cells. Almost the entire mucosa is occupied by simple, tubular gastric glands, which open into the bottom of the gastric pits. In contrast to the surface epithelium, the cellular composition and function of the gastric glands are specialized in different parts of the stomach.

The cardiac region is a narrow area near the opening of the oesophagus. The glands are tubular and relatively short. They are composed almost entirely of mucus-secreting cells. Gastric pits in the cardiac region are shallow and their secretion protects the oesophagus against gastric reflux. The body of the stomach is occupied by the **principal glands**, corpus-fundic glands or fundic glands. These glands extend all the way to the muscularis mucosae and occupy almost the entire lamina propria. Each

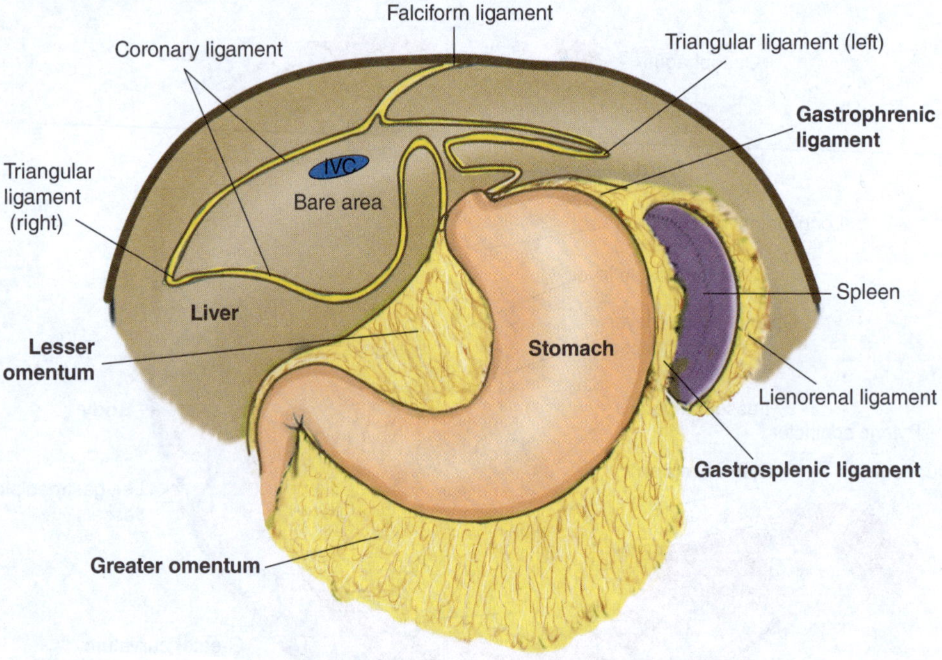

FIG. 12.8 The peritoneal folds of the stomach.

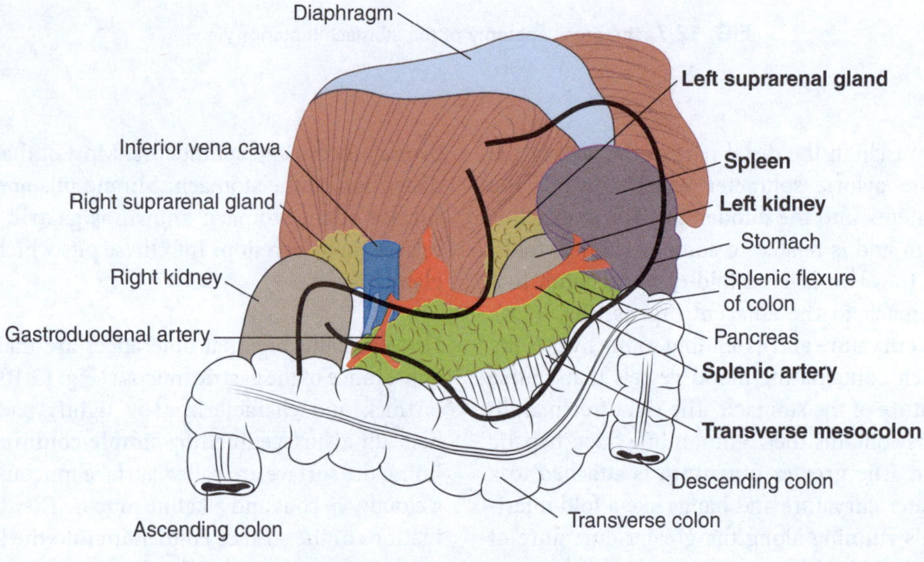

FIG. 12.9 The stomach bed.

gland has a long, narrow neck and a short, wider base. The glands contain mucous neck cells, parietal cells, chief cells, enteroendocrine cells and undifferentiated cells. Mucous neck cells are located in the neck region of the glands and secrete a soluble mucus under vagal stimulation. **Parietal or oxyntic cells** secrete hydrochloric acid and intrinsic factor and are found predominantly in the upper part of the gland, interspersed among the mucous neck cells. They are large, round cells with an intensely eosinophilic cytoplasm and central nucleus (fried egg appearance) that give the glands a beaded appearance. Pepsinogen-secreting **chief cells** are typical protein-secreting cells located mainly near the base of the glands. Enteroendocrine cells secrete gastrin and are seen near the base. Undifferentiated cells are found in the neck region and give rise to all the other cell types.

The pylorus contains **pyloric glands** which are short, coiled, branched tubular glands with a wide lumen. Glandular cells secrete mucus and are similar in appearance to the surface mucous cells. The gastric pits in this region are deep, going about halfway down to the muscularis mucosae. **Gastrin-producing cells** are more frequent than in the principal glands. The lamina propria is formed by a cell-rich loose connective tissue and the muscularis mucosae contains both circular and longitudinal

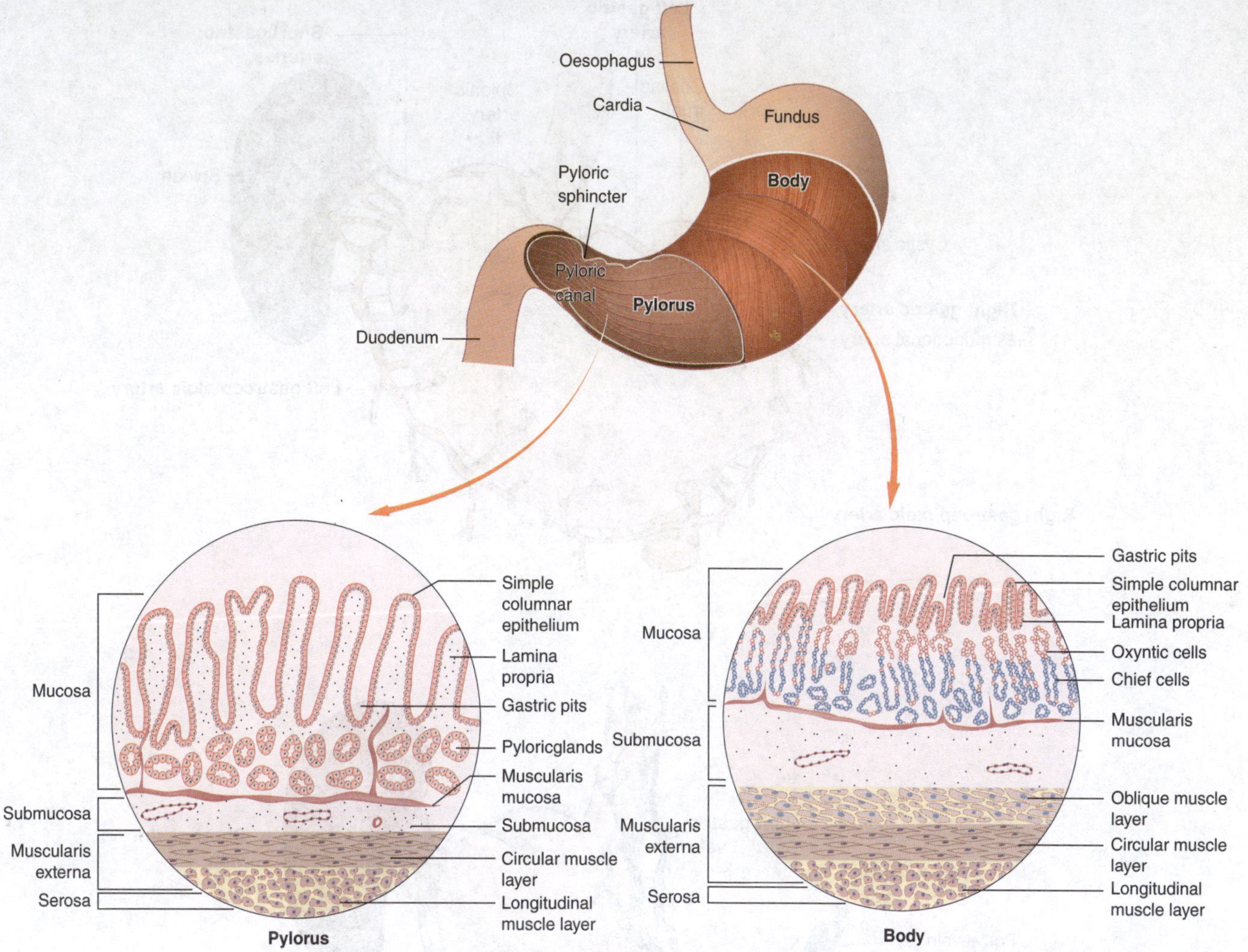

FIG. 12.10 The microscopic structure of the stomach.

layers of muscle cells. Blood vessels, lymph vessels and nerves are located in the submucosa which consists of moderately dense connective tissue. The muscularis externa consists of three indistinct layers, an inner oblique, middle circular and outer longitudinal layer. The circular muscle forms an annular mass at the **pyloric sphincter**. The serosa consists of connective tissue with large blood vessels, lymphatic vessels and nerves.

The **arterial supply** of the stomach is through branches of the coeliac trunk, namely the left gastric artery, right gastric artery, right gastroepiploic artery, left gastroepiploic artery and short gastric arteries (Fig. 12.11). **Venous drainage** is into the corresponding veins and eventually into the portal vein. The **lymphatic drainage** of the stomach is complex (Fig. 12.12). Lymph from the area adjacent to the greater curvature and fundus drains into lymph nodes on the left side of the stomach. The area along the lesser curvature drains into lymph nodes on the right side of the stomach. Lymph from the pyloric region drains in different directions into the adjacent lymph nodes. Eventually all the lymph drains into the coeliac group of lymph nodes, from where it reaches the cisterna chyli. The vagus supplies **parasympathetic nerve supply** to the stomach through the oesophageal plexus and gastric nerves. These nerves are motor and secretomotor in nature. **Sympathetic nerve supply** is from the spinal segments T6–T10 via the coeliac and hepatic plexuses. These nerves are vasomotor and motor to the pyloric sphincter and carry pain sensations from the stomach.

THE SMALL INTESTINE

It is a **6-m-long** tube that extends from the **pylorus** to the **ileocaecal junction**. The upper fixed part is the duodenum which is around 25 cm long. The lower mobile part is divided into the jejunum and ileum, which constitute the proximal two-fifths and distal three-fifths of its length, respectively. The **duodenum** is C-shaped and extends from the pylorus to the duodenojejunal flexure (Fig. 12.13). It is almost entirely **retroperitoneal** and has **four parts**. The first and third parts are horizontal, while the second part is vertical. The fourth part is the shortest one that extends upward and to the left to become continuous with the jejunum at the duodenojejunal flexure. The head of the pancreas is located within the concavity of the C of the duodenum. The

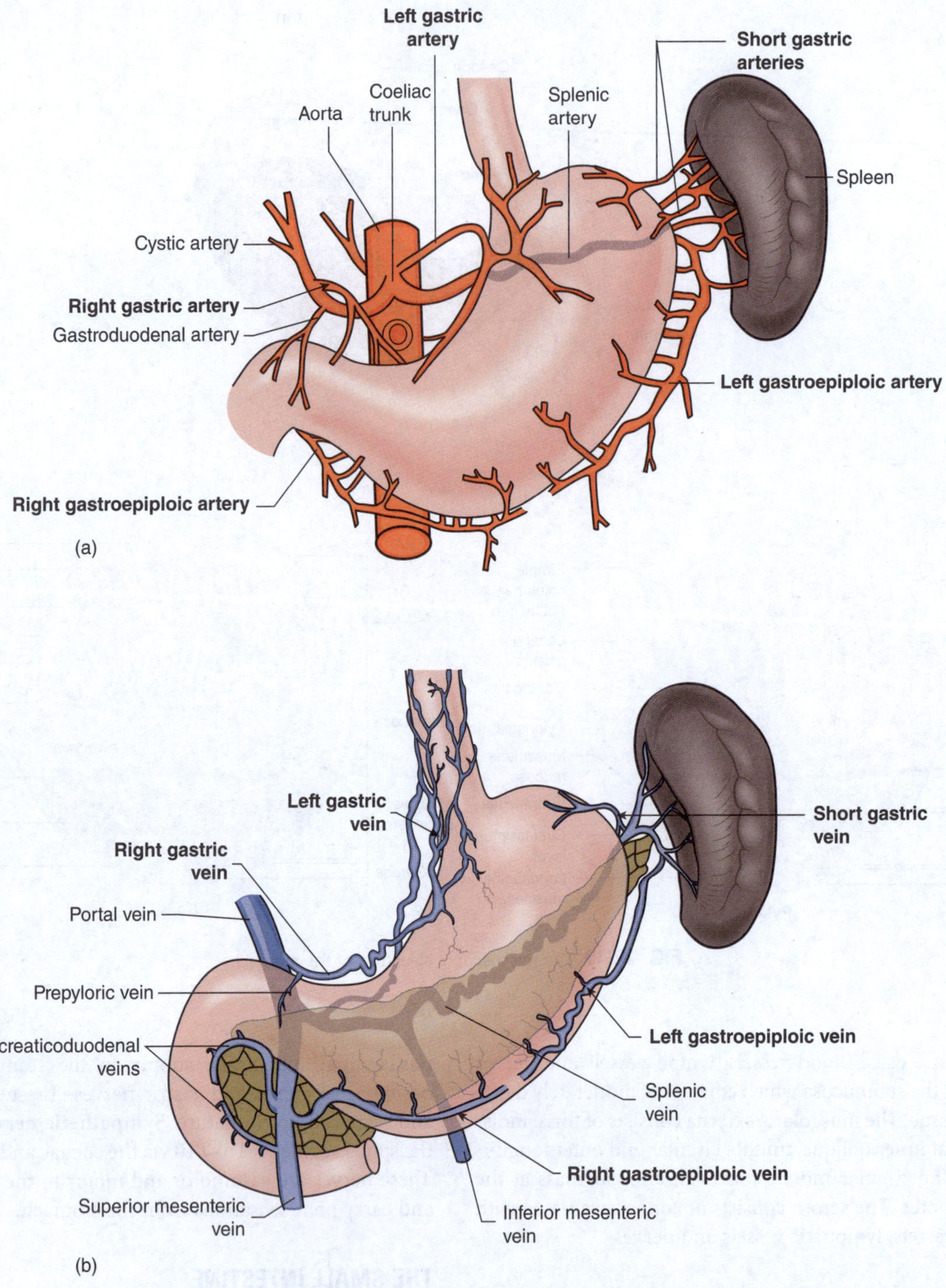

FIG. 12.11 The blood supply of the stomach.

second part of the duodenum contains an elevation called the **major duodenal papilla**. The main pancreatic duct and common bile duct join to form the ampulla of Vater which opens at the summit of the major duodenal papilla (Fig. 12.13).

The coils of the **jejunum** are mainly seen within the upper and left quadrant of the abdomen, while the **ileum** is located within the lower and right quadrant of the abdomen (Fig. 12.14). Both the jejunum and ileum are intraperitoneal structures, which are connected to the posterior abdominal wall through folds of the mesentery. At the ileocaecal junction is the **ileocaecal valve** that regulates the passage of contents from the small to the large intestine. The **anatomical differences** between the various parts of the small intestine are shown in Table 12.1. **The mesentery** suspends the small intestine from the posterior abdominal wall (Fig. 12.15). It is broad and fan-shaped and consists of two peritoneal layers. The **intestinal border** which is folded is the length of the jejunum and ileum, whereas the **root** of the mesentery is

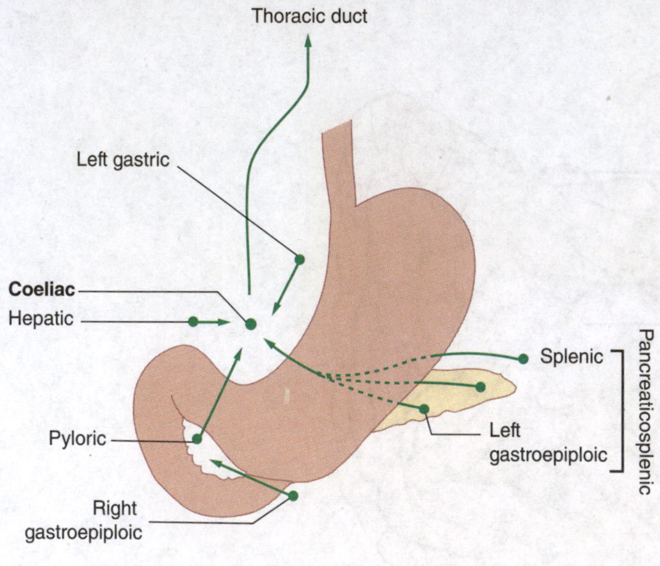

FIG. 12.12 The lymphatic drainage of the stomach.

around 15 cm long and directed obliquely from the left side of L2 vertebra to the front of the right sacroiliac joint. Between the two layers of the mesentery are seen blood and lymphatic vessels, lymph nodes, nerves and abundant fat. The interior of the small intestine has numerous macroscopically visible, crescent-shaped folds of mucosa and submucosa known as **plicae circulares**. Plicae circulares increase the surface area of the mucosa by a factor of around 3.

The three segments of the small intestine merge gradually and have the same basic **histological organization** as the rest of the alimentary canal. The mucosa of the small intestine has various structural features which considerably increase the luminal surface area for absorption (Fig. 12.16). These are the plicae circularis, villi and microvilli. **Plicae circularis** have been described earlier. The luminal surface of the small intestine is completely covered by several finger- or leaf-like projections called **villi**, each around 0.5–1.5 mm in length. Each villus contains a core of connective tissue covered by simple columnar epithelium. The core of each villus is richly supplied with capillaries and includes a single lacteal for transporting absorbed nutrients. Villi increase the surface area of the mucosa by a factor of around 10. Each absorptive cell or enterocyte of the lining epithelium possesses around 3000 **microvilli** (1 micron long and about 0.1 micron wide). Ultrastructurally, they are cylindrical protrusions of the cell membrane enclosing a core of actin filaments. Microvilli increase the surface area of the mucosa by a factor of around 20.

Between the intestinal villi are seen the openings of simple tubular intestinal glands, the **crypts of Lieberkühn** (Fig. 12.17). The crypts extend downwards towards the muscularis mucosae, and the **simple columnar epithelium** lining them is continuous with that covering the villi. Epithelial cells in the crypts correspond largely to those in the epithelium of the intestinal villi. One exception is Paneth cells which are located at the bottom of the crypts. Intestinal glands also contain mitotically active stem cells that replace intestinal epithelial cells that are constantly

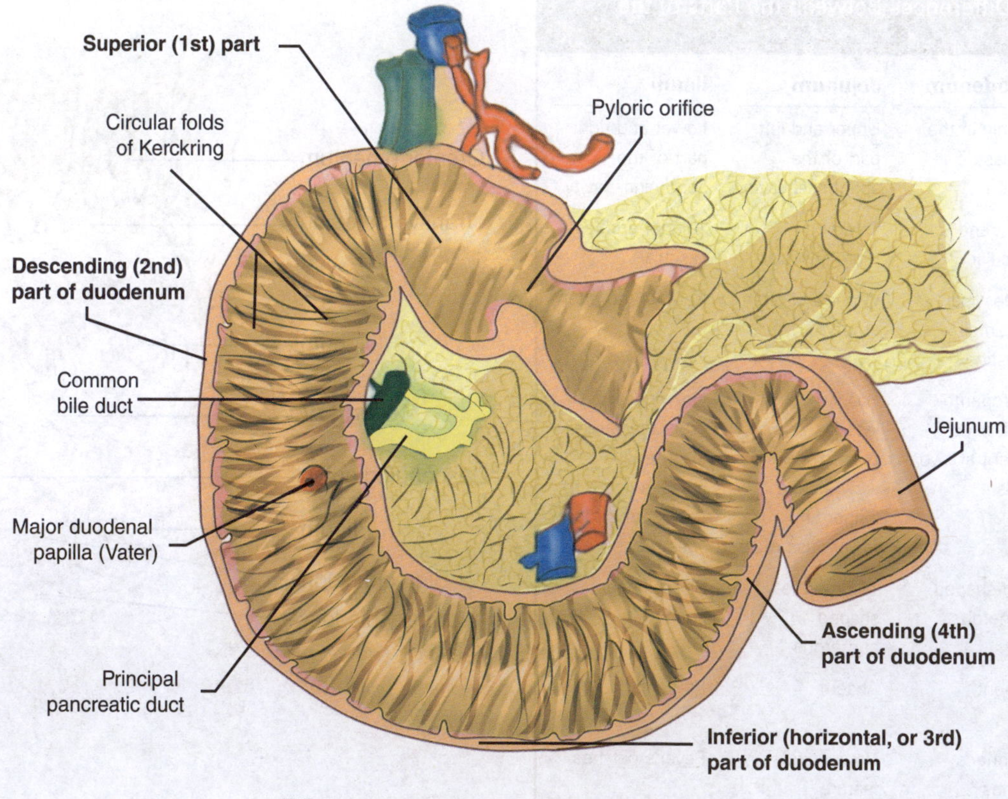

FIG. 12.13 The gross anatomy of the duodenum.

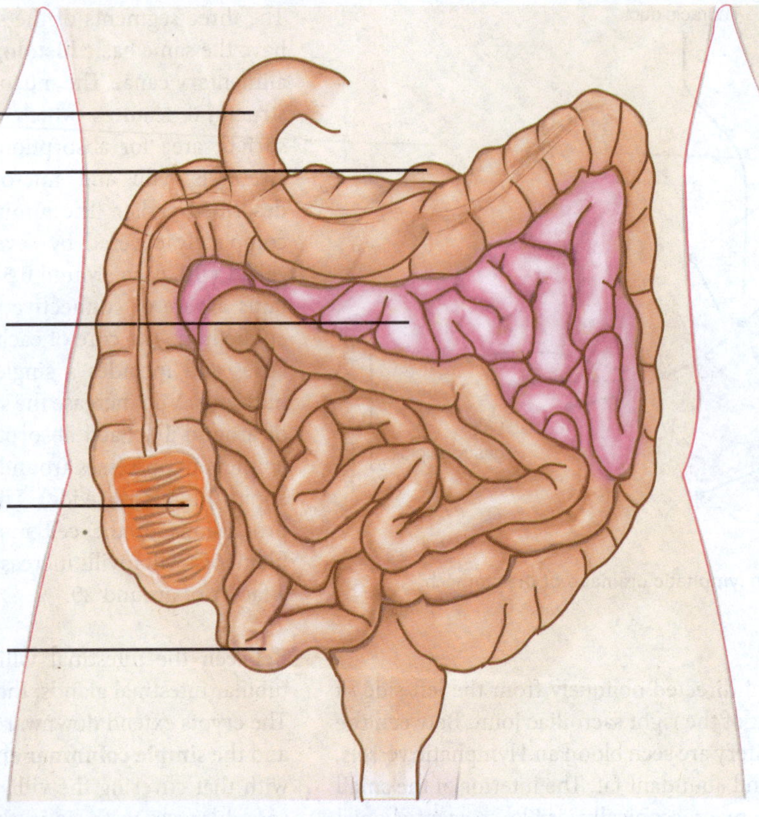

FIG. 12.14 The jejunum and ileum.

TABLE 12.1 Differences Between the Parts of the Small Intestine

	Duodenum	Jejunum	Ileum
Location	Mainly in the epigastric region	Upper and left part of the abdominal cavity	Lower and right part of the abdominal cavity
Walls	Thick and vascular	Thicker and more vascular	Thinner and less vascular
Lumen	Widest part of the small intestine	Wider and often empty	Narrow and often full
Mesentery	Retroperitoneal, fixed except at two ends	Has windows, less fat, one to two arterial arcades and longer and fewer vasa recta	No windows, more fat, three to six arterial arcades and shorter and more vasa recta
Villi	Leaf-shaped, numerous	Tall, tongue-shaped, numerous	Short, finger-shaped, few
Peyer's patches	Absent	Absent	Present
Submucosa	Brunner's glands	No specific feature	Peyer's patches

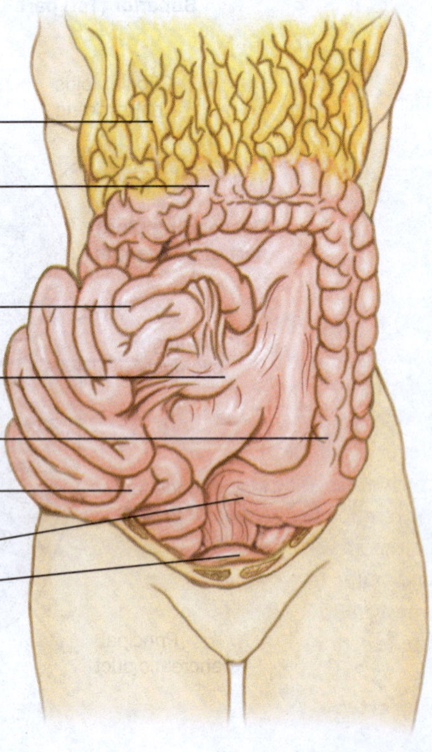

FIG. 12.15 The mesentery of the small intestine (anterior view).

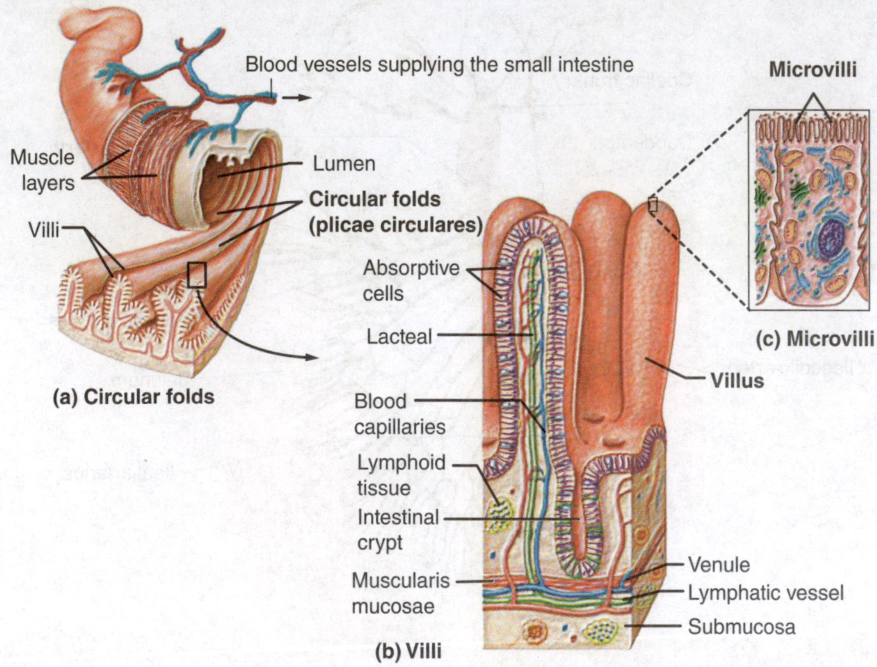

FIG. 12.16 The mechanisms to increase the absorptive surface area of the small intestine.

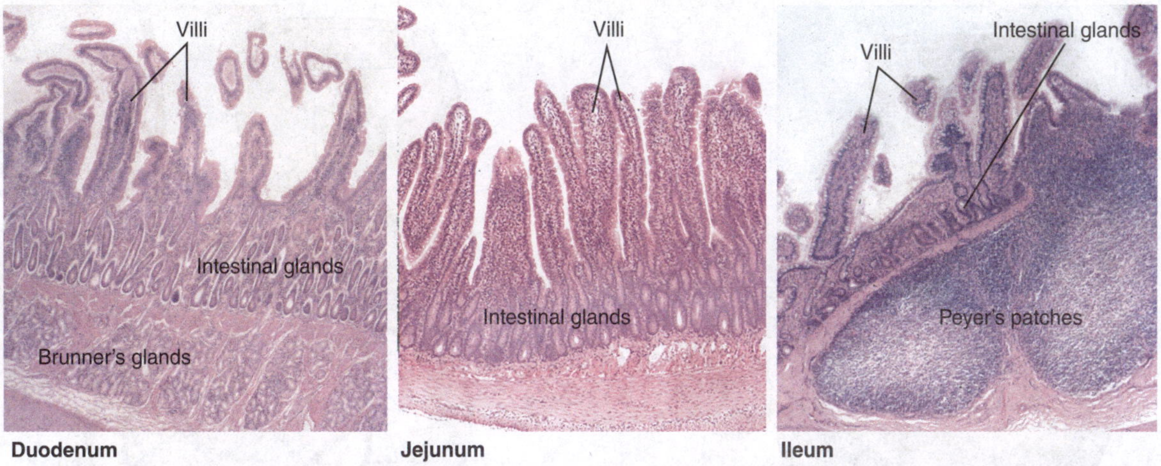

FIG. 12.17 The histology of the small intestine.

shed from the tip of the villus. The characteristic feature of the ileum is the presence of abundant mucosal lymphoid tissue, which forms conspicuous clusters of lymph nodules, called **Peyer's patches**. The submucosa of the small intestine is relatively unspecialized, except in the duodenum where it is packed with mucus-secreting **Brunner's glands**. The muscularis externa of the small intestine has the standard layers of inner circular and outer longitudinal smooth muscle. Over most of the small intestine, the outer layer is a serosa attached to the mesentery, the exception being the duodenum, which is retroperitoneal.

The **arterial supply** of the small intestine is through branches of the superior mesenteric artery that course through the mesentery to reach the intestine (Fig. 12.18). The proximal portion of the duodenum is supplied by branches from the coeliac trunk. Veins follow the arteries, their blood eventually reaching the portal vein. **Lymphatic drainage** is initially into lymph nodes located within the mesentery from where they pass into the preaortic group of lymph nodes and eventually into the cisterna chyli. The duodenum drains into the pancreaticoduodenal lymph nodes. The autonomic **nerve supply** of the small intestine is through the vagus for the parasympathetic component and spinal segments T9 and T10 for the sympathetic component.

THE LARGE INTESTINE

The parts of the large intestine are the caecum, appendix, colon with its ascending, transverse, descending and sigmoid

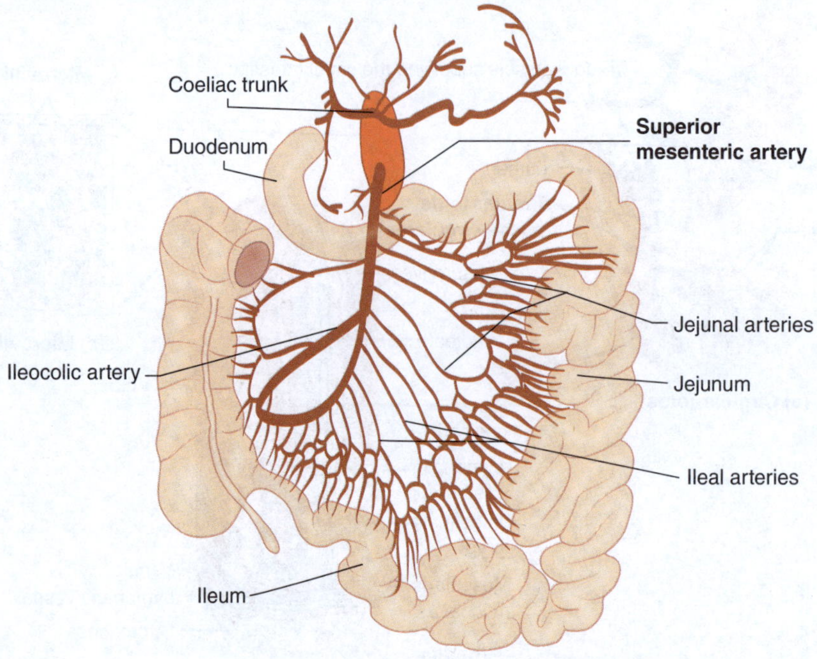

FIG. 12.18 The arterial supply of the small intestine.

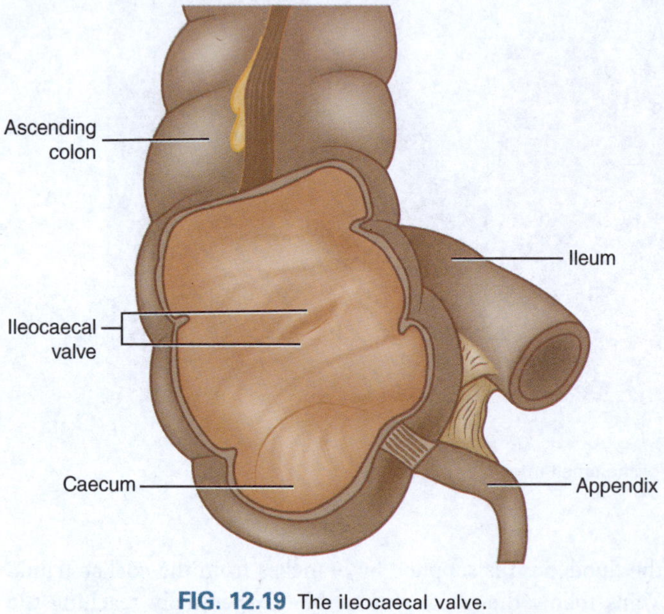

FIG. 12.19 The ileocaecal valve.

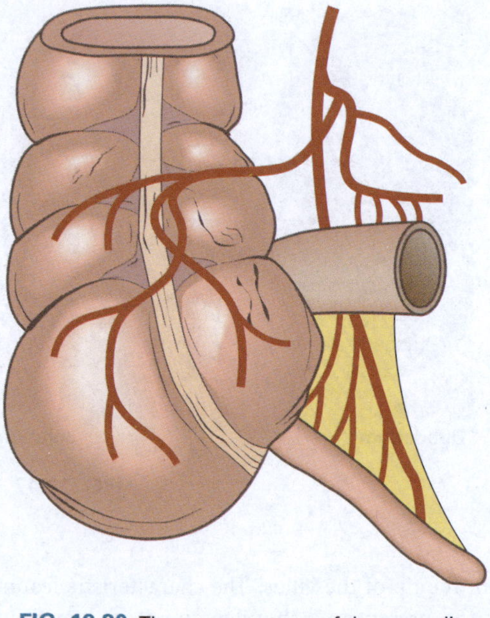

FIG. 12.20 The gross anatomy of the appendix.

components, rectum and anal canal. The **caecum** is a large blind sac that is situated in the right iliac fossa. It is broader (7.5 cm) than it is long (6 cm). The ileum opens into the caecum through the **ileocaecal valve** (Fig. 12.19). The valve has upper and lower lips with extensions on either side called frenula. The valve is closed actively by sympathetic stimulation and mechanically by distension of the caecum. It prevents reflux of food from the caecum to the small intestine and slows the passage of food from the small to the large intestine.

The **vermiform appendix** lies in the right iliac fossa (Fig. 12.20). It opens into the posteromedial wall of the caecum inferior to the ileocaecal junction. The appendix possesses a triangular mesentery called the **mesoappendix** that extends from the terminal part of the ileum to the appendix. The **position** of the appendix is defined by the location of its **tip**. While the **position** of the **base** of the appendix is fairly constant, around 2 cm below the ileocaecal junction, the position of the **tip** is highly variable (Fig. 12.21). The position is described with reference to a **clock-face** with the

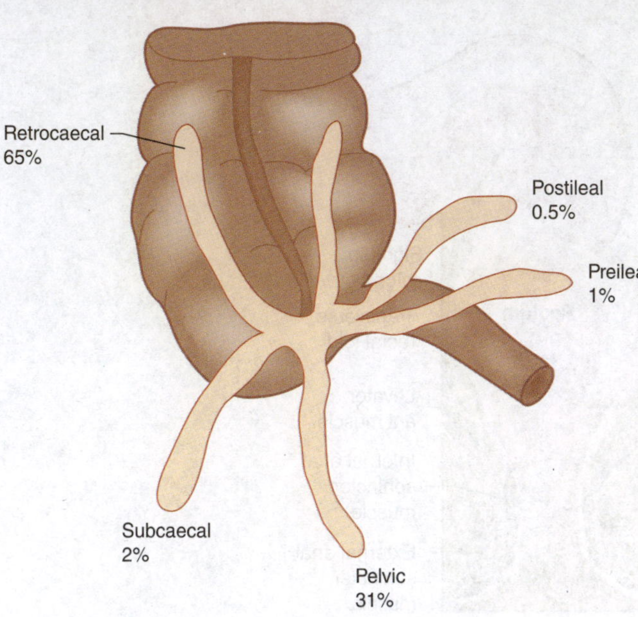

FIG. 12.21 The positions of the appendix.

12-o'clock position being defined as vertically behind the caecum. The **retrocaecal** (12-o'clock) and the **pelvic** (4-o'clock) positions are the most common. The **histological** features of the appendix are described along with the rest of the large intestine. **Blood supply** to the appendix is via the appendicular vessels which course through the free margin of the mesoappendix to reach the appendix. The appendicular artery arises from branches of the superior mesenteric artery, the vein draining into the superior mesenteric vein. **Lymphatic drainage** is eventually into the preaortic group of lymph nodes after passing through intermediate groups. Autonomic **nerve supply** is through the vagus for the parasympathetic component and spinal segments T10 and T11 for the sympathetic component.

The colon consists of the ascending, transverse, descending and sigmoid parts (Fig. 12.22). At the junctions between the transverse colon and the ascending and descending colon are the hepatic and splenic flexures of the colon. All parts of the colon have certain common anatomical features. These are the haustra or sacculations, taeniae coli and appendices epiploicae. **Sacculations** are periodic dilated segments of the colon that are separated by linear areas of constriction. **Taeniae coli** are three narrow bands of smooth muscle that are visible externally on the surface of the colon. They represent the outer longitudinal layer of the muscularis externa. Peritoneal pouches of fat known as **appendices epiploicae** are seen along the entire length of the colon.

The **ascending colon** passes superiorly along the posterior abdominal wall on the right side from the caecum till the visceral surface of the liver. It is **retroperitoneal** and covered only on its anterior surface by peritoneum. At the **hepatic flexure**, the ascending colon changes its direction and continues as the **transverse colon**. The transverse colon hangs between the hepatic flexure on the right and the **splenic flexure** on the left. The splenic flexure is situated at a higher level as compared to the hepatic flexure. The transverse colon possesses a mesentery called the **transverse mesocolon**. The **descending colon** passes inferiorly from the splenic flexure to the beginning of the sigmoid colon at the level of the left sacroiliac joint. Like the ascending colon, the descending colon is also **retroperitoneal**. The descending colon continues as the **sigmoid colon** which is

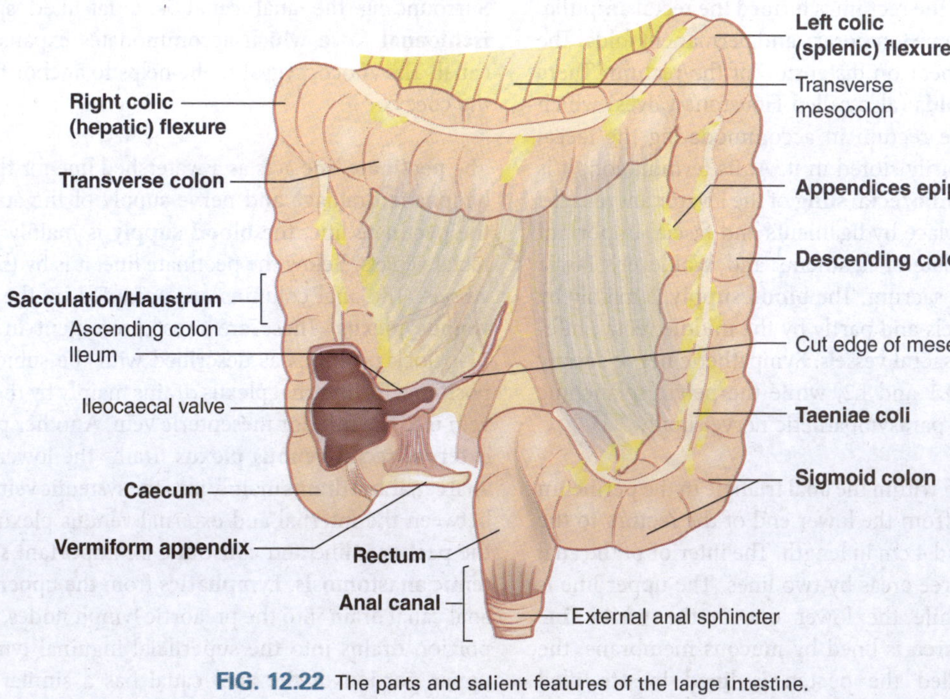

FIG. 12.22 The parts and salient features of the large intestine.

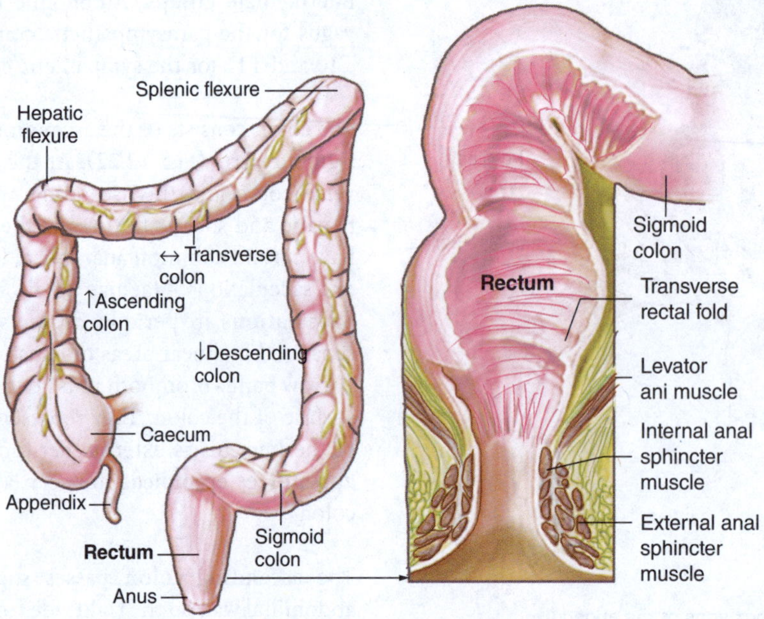

FIG. 12.23 The anatomy of the rectum.

situated in the **pelvic cavity**. The sigmoid colon continues as the rectum at the level of S3 vertebra near the midline. It possesses an inverted V-shaped mesentery called the **sigmoid mesocolon**.

The **rectum** is located in the **pelvic cavity** and extends from the sigmoid colon to the anal canal at the level of the tip of the coccyx (Fig. 12.23). It is around 12 cm in length and does not possess taeniae coli, appendices epiploicae or haustra. The rectum follows the **curvature** of the sacrum and coccyx. It also possesses three **lateral curvatures**, the upper and lower ones towards the right and the middle one towards the left. A dilatation of the lower part of the rectum is termed the rectal **ampulla**. The rectum possesses some temporary and permanent folds. The **temporary folds** disappear on distension of the rectum. There are three **permanent folds** (also called Houston's valves) which are thought to help the rectum in accommodating the faecal material that is temporarily stored in it. At its termination, it is pulled forward by the **puborectal sling** of the levator ani muscle. The rectum is held in place by ligaments and fascia, important among which are the lateral ligaments and Waldeyer's fascia which attaches it to the sacrum. The **blood supply** is mainly by the superior rectal vessels and partly by the middle rectal, inferior rectal and median sacral vessels. Sympathetic **nerve supply** is by spinal segments L1 and L2, while the pelvic splanchnic nerves (S2–S4) provide parasympathetic nerve supply.

The **anal canal** is located within the anal triangle in the perineum (Fig. 12.24). It extends from the lower end of the rectum to the anal orifice and is around 4 cm in length. The interior of the anal canal is divided into three areas by two lines. The upper line is the **pectinate line**, while the lower one is the **white line of Hilton**. The **upper area** is lined by mucous membrane, the **intermediate area** called the pecten is lined by stratified squamous nonkeratinized epithelium and the **lower area** is lined by true skin. The upper portion shows anal columns, anal valves, anal sinuses and anal glands. **Anal columns** are vertical folds of mucous membrane. These folds are connected to each other at the pectinate line by the **anal valves**. The spaces above each valve are called **anal sinuses**, which receive the openings of the **anal glands**. The muscle in the wall of the anal canal resembles a tube within a funnel. The funnel is formed by the levator ani muscle and **external anal sphincter**, both of which are skeletal muscles. The tube is formed by the **internal anal sphincter**, which is a continuation of the circular smooth muscle of the rectum. Surrounding the anal canal is a fat-filled space called the **ischioanal fossa** which accommodates expansion of the anal canal. The anococcygeal raphe helps to anchor the anal canal to the coccyx.

The **pectinate line** acts as a watershed line for the blood supply, lymphatic drainage and nerve supply of the anal canal. Above the pectinate line, the **blood supply** is mainly by the superior rectal vessels. Below the pectinate line, it is by the inferior rectal vessels. The anal columns are occupied by the **internal rectal venous plexus**. These are most prominent in the 3-, 7- and 11-o'clock positions as described with the subject in lithotomy position. The internal plexus drains mainly by the superior rectal vein into the inferior mesenteric vein. Another plexus called the **external rectal venous plexus** drains the lower portion of the anal canal and drains mainly into the systemic veins. Anastomoses between the internal and external venous plexus occur around the pectinate line and constitute an important site of **portosystemic anastomosis**. **Lymphatics** from the upper portions of the anal canal drain into the preaortic lymph nodes, while the lower portion drains into the superficial inguinal lymph nodes. The upper portion of the anal canal has a similar sensory **nerve**

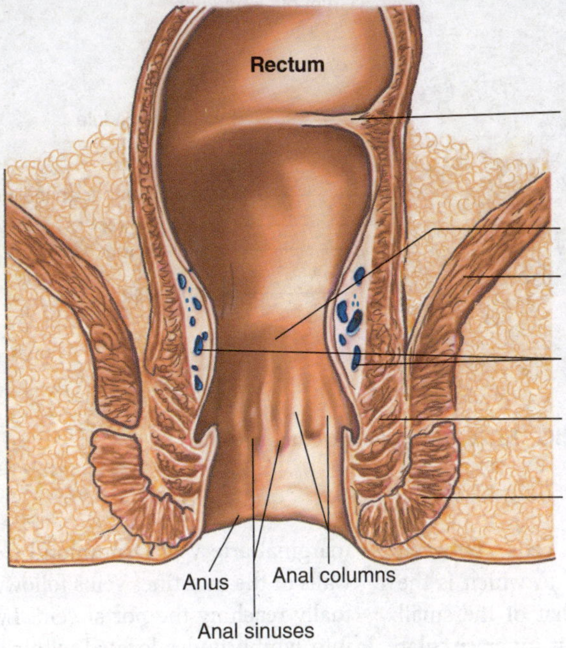

FIG. 12.24 The anatomy of the anal canal.

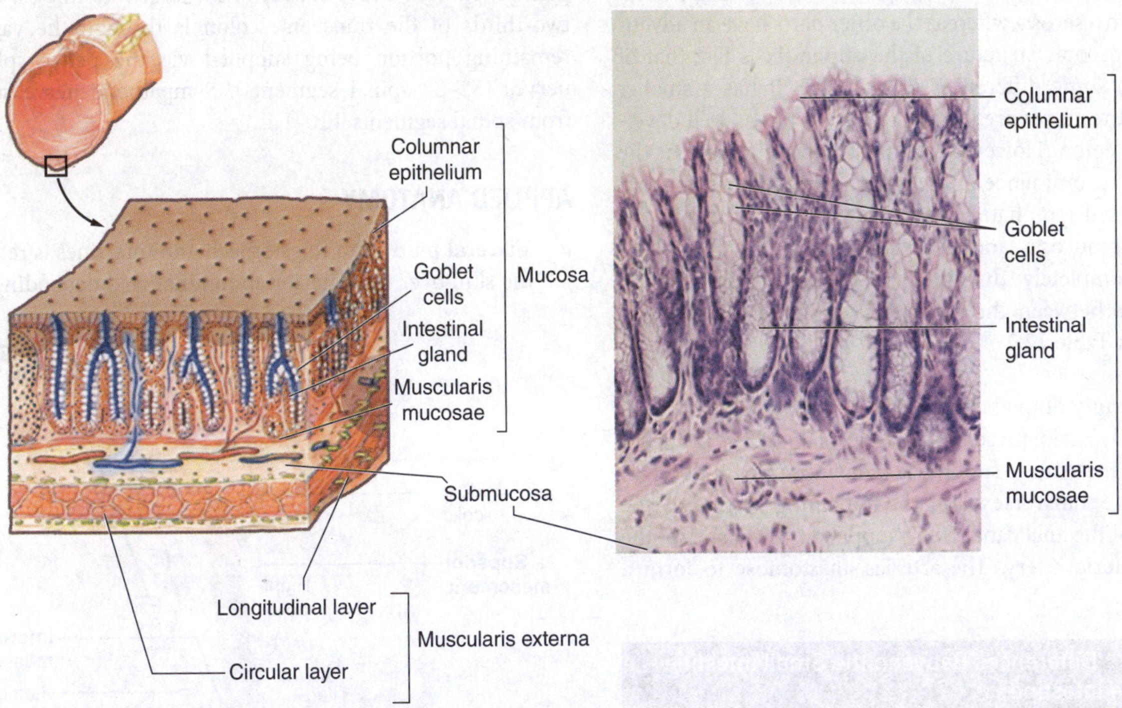

FIG. 12.25 The histology of the large intestine.

supply as the rectum, while the lower portion is supplied by the inferior rectal nerve.

Histologically, the large intestine shares the same layers that are present in the other parts of the gastrointestinal tract (Fig. 12.25). The caecum, appendix, colon and rectum all share a common mucosal description. The anal canal represents a transitional region, where the characteristics of the rectal mucosa change to those of the skin. The surface of the mucosa is relatively smooth as there are no plicae circulares or intestinal villi. The mucosa is raised into crescentic-shaped folds between the saccules. **Crypts of Lieberkühn** are present and are usually longer, more numerous and straighter than those of the small intestine. The lining epithelium of the luminal surface and crypts

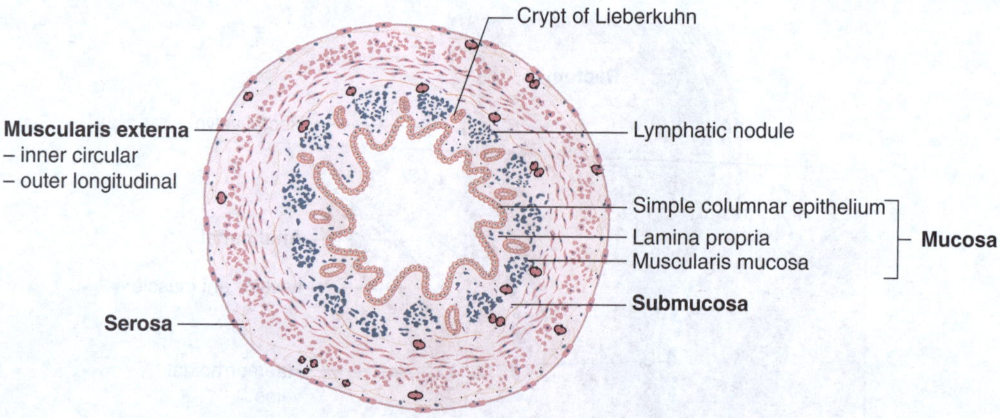

FIG. 12.26 The histology of the appendix.

is **simple columnar** with abundant **goblet cells**. Between the crypts is seen the lamina propria, external to which is the muscularis mucosae. The submucosa is like that of the small intestine. The muscularis externa consists of an inner circular and outer longitudinal layer. While the inner circular layer is typical, the outer longitudinal layer shows the presence of **taeniae coli**. The transverse colon, sigmoid colon and appendix are covered with a serosa, whereas the other parts have an adventitia. The microscopic structure of the **appendix** is like that of the colon with some differences (Fig. 12.26). It has a smaller diameter, and the crypts are farther apart and not as well developed as in the colon. However, the most notable feature of the appendix is the prominence of the **lymph nodules** arising from the gut-associated lymphatic tissue. They can be found in the mucosa or submucosa, and very frequently, the muscularis mucosae is completely disrupted. Taeniae coli are absent. The differences between the small and the large intestine are summarized in Table 12.2.

The **arterial supply** of the large intestine is through branches of the superior and inferior mesenteric arteries (Fig. 12.27). Branches of the superior mesenteric supply the large intestine till the right two-thirds of the transverse colon, the remaining portion till the pectinate line of the anal canal being supplied by branches of the inferior mesenteric artery. The arteries anastomose to form a marginal artery of Drummond from which branches reach the walls of the intestine. Veins follow the arteries, their blood eventually reaching the portal vein. **Lymphatic drainage** is initially into lymph nodes located within the respective mesenteries or along the blood vessels, from where they pass into the preaortic group of lymph nodes and eventually into the cisterna chyli. The parasympathetic **nerve supply** of the large intestine till the right two-thirds of the transverse colon is through the vagus, the remaining portion being supplied via the pelvic splanchnic nerves (S2–S4 spinal segments). Sympathetic nerve supply is from spinal segments T10–L2.

TABLE 12.2 Differences Between the Small Intestine and the Large Intestine

	Small Intestine	Large Intestine
Dimensions	Longer and narrower	Shorter and wider
Fixity	Greater part is mobile	Large part is fixed
Plicae circularis	Present	Absent
Villi	Present	Absent
Haustrations	Absent	Present
Appendices epiploicae	Absent	Present
Taeniae coli	Absent	Present

APPLIED ANATOMY

- **Visceral pain** from the stomach and intestines is referred to the skin over the anterior abdominal wall depending on the

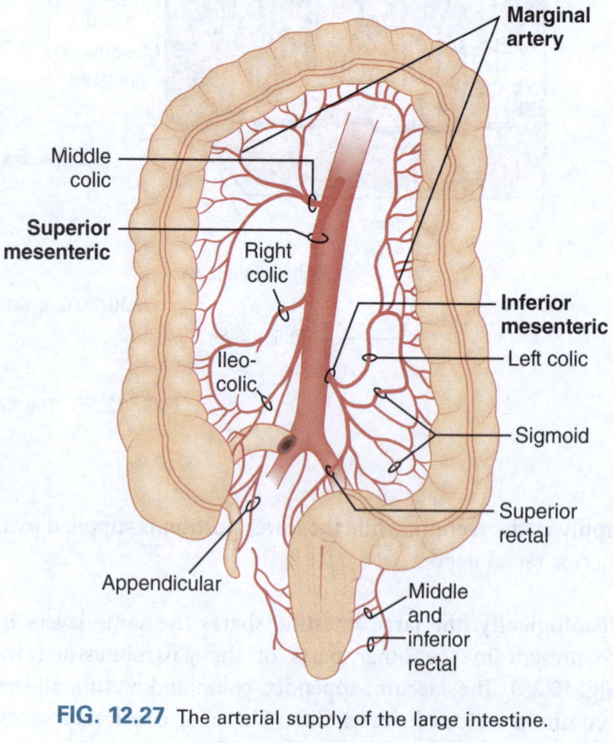

FIG. 12.27 The arterial supply of the large intestine.

spinal segments supplying them. Thus, pain from the stomach is felt in the epigastrium, that from the small intestine and appendix in the umbilical region and that from the large intestine in the hypogastrium and iliac regions.

- Entry into the abdominal cavity through incisions in the anterior abdominal wall is known as **laparotomy**.
- **Incisions** on the abdominal wall for surgeries may be made in the midline through the linea alba or through the muscles on either side. Midline incisions bleed less but take longer to heal, whereas the converse is true for incisions through muscles.
- Collection of fluid in the peritoneal cavity is known as **ascites.** This may be due to generalized conditions such as congestive heart failure and renal failure, or more localized conditions such as portal hypertension and abdominal cancers.
- Inflammation of the peritoneum, known as **peritonitis**, causes severe pain and board-like rigidity of the anterior abdominal wall.
- Drainage of the ascitic fluid from the peritoneal cavity through the anterior abdominal wall is called **paracentesis abdominis**.
- Introduction of endoscopic instruments into the peritoneal cavity through minute incisions in the anterior abdominal wall to perform surgeries is known as **laparoscopy**.
- Inflammation of the gastric mucosa is called **gastritis**. This can occur due to many reasons such as alcohol intake, drugs such as aspirin, smoking and excessively spicy food. Gastritis presents as burning pain felt in the epigastrium.
- **Gastric ulcers** can occur because of prolonged gastritis. There is a strong association between these ulcers and infection with *Helicobacter pylori*. Gastric ulcers typically cause epigastric pain which increases on eating. A serious complication of gastric ulcers is perforation, which can lead to peritonitis and haemorrhage.
- **Hiatus hernias** occur due to herniation of the cardiac end of the stomach into the thorax through the oesophageal opening of the diaphragm. This condition is more common in obese people and causes reflux of gastric contents into the oesophagus and resultant 'heartburn'.
- **Carcinomas of the stomach** are associated with smoking and infection with *H. pylori*. They can spread extensively due to the wide lymphatic drainage of the stomach. This may require the surgical removal of the stomach known as gastrectomy.
- The radiological visualization of the stomach can be done using barium sulphate as a contrast medium. This investigation is known as a **barium meal** and can be used for the diagnosis of gastric ulcers and carcinomas.
- Direct visualization of the interior of the stomach for pathologies can be performed using **gastric endoscopes**.
- **Duodenal ulcers** cause epigastric pain which increases when the patient is hungry. It is relieved by eating food, unlike gastric ulcers. The other features are like gastric ulcers.
- The **duodenal cap** refers to the radiological appearance of the proximal portion of the duodenum seen in a barium meal. The smooth outline of the cap is disrupted by duodenal ulcers.
- **Diarrhoea** is caused by the excessive production of fluid by the intestines or their inability to adequately absorb water and nutrients. This is commonly caused by bacterial and viral infections.
- The visualization of the small intestine using barium sulphate as a contrast medium is called a **barium follow through**. The small intestine has a characteristic feathery appearance due to the presence of plicae circularis. This appearance is more pronounced in the jejunum as compared to the ileum due to the better developed plicae in this region of the small intestine.
- **Meckel's diverticulum** is a remnant of the connection between the primitive gut and the yolk sac in the foetus. It is usually around 2 inches long and seen 2 feet proximal to the ileocaecal junction in 2% of the population. It can get inflamed and mimic acute appendicitis, requiring surgical removal.
- One of the most common causes of acute abdominal pain is inflammation of the appendix. This is thought to be caused by blockage and overstimulation of the abundant lymphoid tissue in its wall. The initial pain in **acute appendicitis** is felt in the umbilical region which then shifts to the right iliac fossa. Appendectomy refers to the surgical removal of the appendix.
- **Volvulus** refers to the twisting of the intestine on its mesentery, eventually causing obstruction to its blood supply and subsequent infarction. This commonly occurs in the sigmoid colon and caecum.
- **Hirschsprung's disease** occurs due to abnormalities of the enteric nervous system in a segment of the large intestine, usually the rectum. This causes constipation and requires surgical correction.
- **Carcinoma of the colon** is common, especially in Western countries due to the excessive intake of refined foods and red meat. This often requires the resection of a segment of the colon known as colectomy and the creation of a temporary or permanent opening of the colon to the exterior called a colostomy.
- The direct visualization of the colon through an endoscope inserted through the anal canal is known as colonoscopy.
- A **per-rectal examination** refers to the digital examination of the rectum and surrounding structures to make a clinical diagnosis. It is one of the most commonly performed clinical diagnostic procedures.
- **Proctoscopy** refers to the direct visualization of the rectum and anal canal using an instrument called a proctoscope.
- **Haemorrhoids** occur due to dilatation of the venous plexuses in the anal canal. If these plexuses are dilated above the pectinate line, they are referred to as internal haemorrhoids and are painless. Dilatation and subsequent thromboses of the venous plexuses below the pectinate line can be intensely painful and are known as external haemorrhoids.
- **Perianal abscesses** occur due to collections of pus in the spaces around the anal canal. They often arise from infection of the anal sinuses and require surgical drainage.
- **Anal fistulae** are abnormal communications between the anal canal and perianal skin usually arising as complications of anal abscesses.

- **Anal fissures** are linear ulcers in the interior of the anal canal caused by the passage of hard faecal material in constipated patients. They are extremely painful.

APPLICATIONS IN NURSING

- A **nasogastric or orogastric tube** (Ryle's tube) is inserted through the nasal or oral cavity into the stomach. This is done in patients who have functional gastrointestinal tracts but who are not able to meet their nutritional requirements. This may occur in patients with a risk of aspiration, certain clinical conditions that may interfere with ingestion or absorption of nutrients and reduced oral intake. The role of nurses includes the safe introduction of the tube into the stomach, administration of the appropriate nutrients via the tube and proper maintenance of the tube.
- For those patients in whom it is not possible to introduce a nasogastric tube, a tube known as a **gastrostomy tube** may have to be placed. This tube is introduced directly into the stomach through the anterior abdominal wall. Feeding patients via this tube and appropriate care of the tube are responsibilities of nursing personnel.
- In conditions like carcinoma of the colon, a segment of the intestine may need to be surgically resected. After the surgery, an opening called a **stoma** is often created in the anterior abdominal wall through which the contents of the intestine can be drained to the outside. A pouch of suitable size is placed over the stoma to collect the effluent from the stoma. This pouch needs to be appropriately maintained and periodically changed by a nurse.
- **Faecal impaction** refers to hard stools in the rectum which cannot be evacuated. This causes constipation, local discomfort, abdominal pain and diarrhoea (due to leaking around impacted stool). The impacted faeces may require to be digitally removed by a nurse. After adequate preparation of the patient, the gloved index and middle fingers are used to loosen the faecal mass. As this procedure can be uncomfortable and embarrassing for the patient, care needs to be taken to reassure the patient and ensure adequate privacy.
- **Rectal suppositories** contain medications that either act locally to produce faecal evacuation or are absorbed systemically through the rectal mucosa. They are indicated in patients with constipation or who are not able to tolerate oral medication for symptoms like pain and nausea. The nurse will sometimes be required to correctly insert and position the suppository in the rectum of the patient.
- **Enemas** are the instillation of solutions into the rectum and sigmoid colon to assist the process of complete evacuation of faecal matter in patients with constipation or as a preoperative procedure. Nurses will be required to administer enemas and need to ensure proper positioning of the patient in the left lateral (Sims') position. They will also need to monitor patients for any abdominal pain, bleeding from the rectum and changes in vital signs.

SUMMARY

- The abdominal cavity extends from the diaphragm above to the pelvis below and contains the abdominal part of the oesophagus, stomach, small and large intestines, liver, gallbladder, pancreas, kidneys, ureters, urinary bladder, blood vessels, nerves and lymphatics.
- The anterior abdominal wall is divided into nine regions by the midclavicular lines on either side and the subcostal and transtubercular lines superiorly and inferiorly.
- The flexible and mobile anterior abdominal wall consists of three layers of muscle lined on the inside by peritoneum and on the outside by skin.
- The rigid posterior abdominal wall is formed by three muscles, psoas major, quadratus lumborum and iliacus, on which run branches of the lumbar plexus.
- The peritoneum is a thin serous membrane that lines the walls of the abdominal and pelvic cavities and covers the organs within these cavities.
- Parietal peritoneum lines the walls of the abdominal and pelvic cavities, whereas the visceral peritoneum covers the organs.
- The peritoneal cavity is the potential space between the parietal and visceral layer of peritoneum.
- Intraperitoneal viscera are nearly surrounded by peritoneum, while retroperitoneal viscera lie on the posterior abdominal wall and are covered by peritoneum only anteriorly.
- Peritoneal folds containing fat, blood vessels, nerves and lymphatics extend from the parietal to the visceral peritoneum covering the various viscera.
- The peritoneal cavity can be divided into a greater sac and lesser sac.
- The lesser sac is located behind the stomach and communicates with the greater sac through an opening called the epiploic foramen.
- The transverse colon and mesocolon divide the greater sac into supracolic and infracolic compartments.
- The stomach is located within the upper and left part of the abdomen, occupying the epigastric, umbilical and left hypochondriac regions.
- An empty stomach is usually J-shaped, the stomach descending with distension.
- The stomach extends between the cardiac orifice superiorly and pyloric orifice inferiorly.
- It has a right concave border called the lesser curvature and a left convex border known as the greater curvature.
- These two borders separate an anterior surface and a posterior surface.
- The junction between the greater curvature and left border of the oesophagus is notched and is called the cardiac notch.
- Anatomically, the stomach is divided into a cardiac part, fundus, body or corpus and pylorus.
- The omentum refers to a two-layered fold of peritoneum that extends from the stomach to adjacent organs.
- Attached to the lesser curvature and extending to the liver is the lesser omentum which contains blood vessels that course along the lesser curvature of the stomach.
- The greater omentum is attached to a major part of the greater curvature and hangs like a fold inferiorly.
- The posterior relations of the stomach form the stomach bed.
- The stomach bed is formed by the diaphragm, left kidney, left suprarenal gland, pancreas, transverse mesocolon, splenic flexure of the colon and splenic artery.
- The interior of the empty stomach has several folds or ridges, called rugae, formed by the mucosa and submucosa.
- Minute pits are visible on the inner surface of the stomach known as gastric pits.
- The gastric mucosa is thick and characterized by closely packed tubular glands beneath a surface of simple columnar epithelium.
- The body of the stomach is occupied by the principal glands, corpus-fundic glands or fundic glands.
- These glands extend all the way to the muscularis mucosae and occupy almost the entire lamina propria.
- Parietal or oxyntic cells secrete hydrochloric acid and intrinsic factor and are found predominantly in the upper part of the glands.
- Pepsinogen-secreting chief cells are located mainly near the base of the glands and are typical protein-secreting cells.
- The pylorus contains pyloric glands which are short, coiled, branched tubular glands with a wide lumen.
- Gastrin-producing cells are more frequent than in the principal glands.
- The circular muscle forms an annular mass at the pyloric sphincter.
- The arterial supply of the stomach is through branches of the coeliac trunk.
- Venous drainage is into the corresponding veins and eventually into the portal vein.
- The lymphatic drainage of the stomach is complex, the lymph eventually draining into the coeliac group of lymph nodes.

- The small intestine is a 6-m-long tube that extends from the pylorus to the ileocaecal junction.
- The upper fixed part is the duodenum which is around 25 cm long.
- The lower mobile part is divided into the jejunum and ileum which constitute the proximal two-fifths and distal three-fifths of its length.
- The duodenum is C-shaped and extends from the pylorus to the duodenojejunal flexure.
- It is almost entirely retroperitoneal and has four parts.
- The head of the pancreas is located within the concavity of the C of the duodenum.
- The second part of the duodenum contains an elevation called the major duodenal papilla.
- The main pancreatic duct and common bile duct join to form the ampulla of Vater which opens at the summit of the major duodenal papilla.
- The coils of the jejunum are mainly seen within the upper and left quadrant of the abdomen, while the ileum is located within the lower and right quadrant of the abdomen.
- At the ileocaecal junction is the ileocaecal valve that regulates the passage of contents from the small to the large intestine.
- The mesentery suspends the small intestine from the posterior abdominal wall.
- Between the two layers of the mesentery are seen blood and lymphatic vessels, lymph nodes, nerves and abundant fat.
- The interior of the small intestine has numerous macroscopically visible, crescent-shaped folds of the mucosa and submucosa known as plicae circularis.
- The luminal surface of the small intestine is completely covered by several finger or leaf-like projections called villi, each around 0.5–1.5 mm in length. Each villus contains a core of connective tissue covered by simple columnar epithelium.
- Each absorptive cell or enterocyte of the lining epithelium possesses around 3000 microvilli.
- Between the intestinal villi are seen the openings of simple tubular intestinal glands, the crypts of Lieberkühn.
- The most conspicuous feature of the ileum is the presence of abundant mucosal lymphoid tissue, which forms clusters of lymph nodules, called Peyer's patches.
- The submucosa of the small intestine is relatively unspecialized, except in the duodenum where it is packed with mucus-secreting Brunner's glands.
- The arterial supply of the small intestine is through branches of the superior mesenteric artery.
- Veins follow the arteries, their blood eventually reaching the portal vein.
- Lymphatic drainage is initially into lymph nodes located within the mesentery from where they pass into the preaortic group of lymph nodes.
- The parts of the large intestine are the caecum, appendix, ascending, transverse, descending and sigmoid colon, rectum and anal canal.
- The caecum is a large blind sac that is situated in the right iliac fossa.
- The ileum opens into the caecum through the ileocaecal valve.
- The vermiform appendix lies in the right iliac fossa.
- It opens into the posteromedial wall of the caecum inferior to the ileocaecal junction.
- The appendix possesses a triangular mesentery called the mesoappendix that extends from the terminal part of the ileum to the appendix.
- The position of the appendix is defined by the location of its tip.
- The retrocaecal (12-o'clock) and the pelvic (4-o'clock) positions are the most common.
- Blood supply to the appendix is via the appendicular vessels which course through the mesoappendix.
- Autonomic nerve supply is through the vagus for the parasympathetic component and the spinal segments T10 and T11 for the sympathetic component.
- The colon consists of the ascending, transverse, descending and sigmoid parts.
- At the junctions between the transverse colon and the ascending and descending colon are the hepatic and splenic flexures of the colon.
- The common anatomical features of the large intestine are sacculations, taeniae coli and appendices epiploicae.
- The ascending colon passes superiorly along the posterior abdominal wall on the right side from the caecum till the visceral surface of the liver.
- At the hepatic flexure, the ascending colon changes its direction and continues as the transverse colon.
- The transverse colon hangs between the hepatic flexure on the right and the splenic flexure on the left.
- The transverse colon possesses a mesentery called the transverse mesocolon.
- The descending colon passes inferiorly from the splenic flexure to the beginning of the sigmoid colon at the level of the left sacroiliac joint.
- The descending colon continues as the sigmoid colon which is in the pelvic cavity.
- The sigmoid colon passes towards the right and continues as the rectum at the level of S3 vertebra near the midline.
- It possesses an inverted V-shaped mesentery called the sigmoid mesocolon.
- The rectum is located in the pelvic cavity and extends from the sigmoid colon to the anal canal.
- The rectum follows the curvature of the sacrum and coccyx.
- The rectum possesses some temporary and permanent folds.
- At its termination, it is pulled forward by the puborectal sling of the levator ani.
- The blood supply is mainly by the superior rectal vessels and partly by the middle and inferior rectal and median sacral vessels.
- The anal canal is located within the anal triangle in the perineum.
- It extends from the lower end of the rectum to the anal orifice.
- The interior of the anal canal is divided into three areas by two lines.
- The upper line is the pectinate line, while the lower one is the white line of Hilton.
- The upper area is lined by mucous membrane, the intermediate area called the pecten is lined by stratified squamous nonkeratinized epithelium and the lower area is lined by true skin.
- The upper portion shows anal columns, anal valves, anal sinuses and anal glands.
- The muscle in the wall of the anal canal resembles a tube within a funnel.
- The funnel is formed by the levator ani muscle and external anal sphincter, while the tube is formed by the internal anal sphincter.
- Surrounding the anal canal is a fat-filled space called the ischioanal fossa.
- The pectinate line acts as a watershed line for the blood supply, lymphatic drainage and nerve supply of the anal canal.
- Histologically, the caecum, appendix, colon and rectum all share a common mucosal description.
- Crypts of Lieberkühn are present and are usually longer, more numerous and straighter than those of the small intestine.
- The lining epithelium of the luminal surface and crypts is simple columnar with abundant goblet cells.
- While the inner circular layer is typical, the outer longitudinal layer shows the presence of taeniae coli.
- The most notable feature of the appendix is the prominence of the lymph nodules arising from the gut-associated lymphatic tissue.
- The arterial supply of the large intestine is through branches of both the superior and the inferior mesenteric arteries.
- Branches of the superior mesenteric supply the large intestine till the right two-thirds of the transverse colon, the remaining portion till the pectinate line of the anal canal being supplied by branches of the inferior mesenteric artery.
- The parasympathetic nerve supply of the large intestine till the right two-thirds of the transverse colon is through the vagus, the remaining portion being supplied via the pelvic splanchnic nerves (S2–S4 spinal segments).

CHAPTER 13

The Digestive Glands

SPECIFIC LEARNING OBJECTIVES

At the end of this chapter, the student should be able to:

- Describe the gross and microscopic anatomy of the liver.
- Describe the gross and microscopic anatomy of the extrahepatic biliary apparatus.
- Describe the gross and microscopic anatomy of the pancreas.

GLOSSARY OF TERMS

- **Falciform ligament:** peritoneal ligament connecting the liver and anterior abdominal wall
- **Ligamentum teres:** remnant of the left umbilical vein
- **Ligamentum venosum:** remnant of the ductus venosus
- **Porta hepatis:** area on the visceral surface of the liver meant for entry and exit of structures
- **Glisson's capsule:** connective tissue capsule of the liver
- **Kupffer cells:** macrophages of the liver
- **Uncinate process:** hook-like extension of the lower part of the head of the pancreas
- **Islets of Langerhans:** endocrine part of the pancreas

INTRODUCTION

The liver is the largest gland in the body (about 2% of the body weight in an adult). It is essentially an exocrine gland, secreting bile into the intestine. Additionally, it is an endocrine gland and a blood filter. It has many functions not typically associated with glands. The functions of the liver include formation and secretion of bile, protein and lipid synthesis, metabolic functions, storage of metabolites, detoxification and inactivation of noxious substances, phagocytic function, thermal energy production and haemopoiesis in foetal life. The pancreas has two independent roles, namely exocrine secretion of enzymes into the small intestine and endocrine secretion of several hormones into the blood. The extrahepatic biliary apparatus stores, modifies, concentrates and transports bile to the second part of the duodenum. Bile emulsifies fats that enter the duodenum, thereby increasing the surface area for lipases to break them down.

THE LIVER

The liver is located mainly in the **right upper quadrant** of the abdominal cavity just inferior to the diaphragm. However, a portion of the liver extends to the left of the midline. It thus occupies the right hypochondriac and epigastric regions of the abdominal cavity (Fig. 13.1). The liver is divided into anatomical **right** and **left lobes** by the attachment of the **falciform ligament**. Two additional lobes, the **caudate** and **quadrate lobes**, can be distinguished on the right lobe (Fig. 13.2). The liver has a diaphragmatic surface and visceral surface separated by a sharp **inferior border**. The **diaphragmatic surface** is related to the diaphragm, which separates it from the lower ribs and base of the right lung. Unlike the diaphragmatic surface, which is relatively smooth, the **visceral surface** is marked by a number of impressions (Fig. 13.3). Two fissures are seen to separate the right and left lobes. These are the **fissure** for the **ligamentum teres** inferiorly and the **fissure** for the **ligamentum venosum** superiorly. Two prominent impressions are seen to the right of the fissures. These are the **fossa** for the **gallbladder** inferiorly and the **groove** for the **inferior vena cava** superiorly. The plane that passes through these impressions is called the cystocaval plane and divides the liver into physiological right and left lobes. The **porta hepatis** or hilum of the liver is a transversely placed region of the liver that is situated centrally between the fissures. The hepatic artery, portal vein, right and left hepatic ducts, lymphatics and nerves pass through the hilum as they enter or leave the liver.

The **quadrate lobe** is defined by the fossa for the gallbladder to the right, the fissure for the ligamentum teres to the left, the hilum superiorly and the inferior border inferiorly (Fig. 13.3). The **caudate lobe** is bounded by the groove for the inferior vena cava on the right, the fissure for the ligamentum venosum on the left and the hilum inferiorly. **Related** to the **visceral surface**

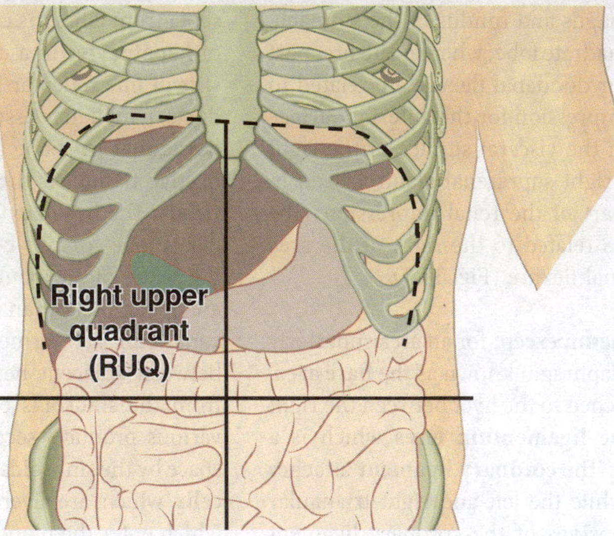

FIG. 13.1 The location of the liver.

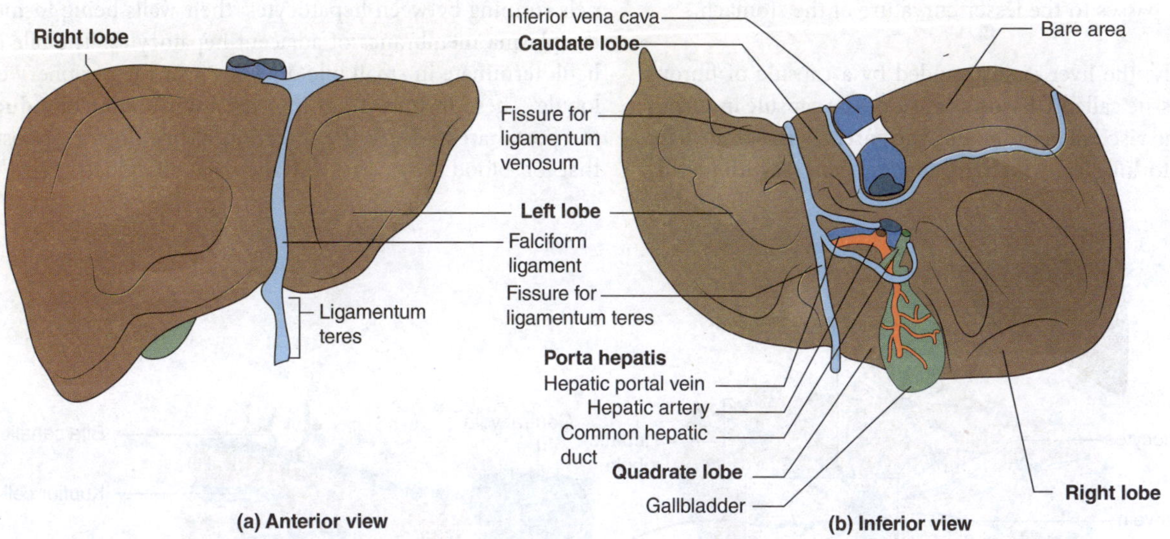

FIG. 13.2 The lobes of the liver.

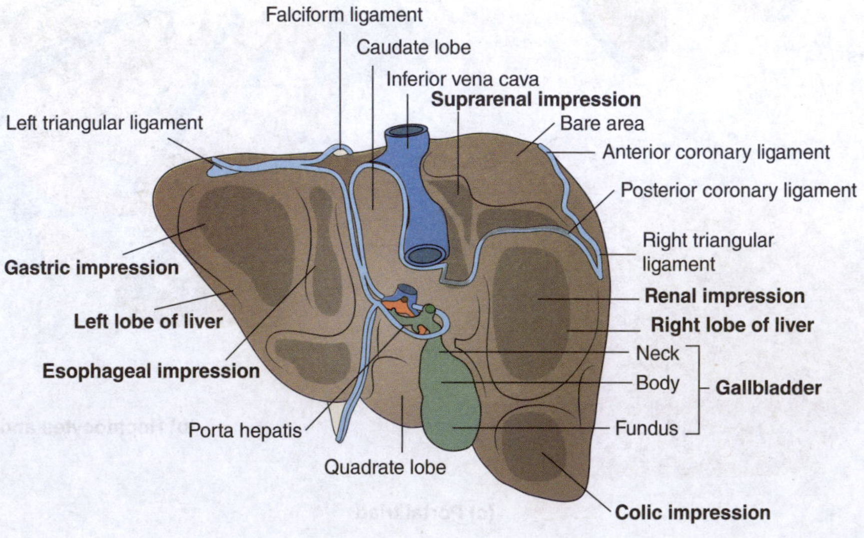

FIG. 13.3 The visceral surface of the liver.

of the left lobe are the oesophagus and fundus of the stomach. The pylorus is related to the quadrate lobe, whereas the first part of the duodenum and superior duodenal flexure are related to the right lobe. A prominent impression for the anterior surface of the right kidney is seen on the visceral surface of the right lobe. The impression for the right suprarenal gland is seen in close relation to the upper part of the renal impression. The hepatic flexure of the colon is related to the right of the area related to the superior duodenal flexure (Fig. 13.3).

The liver is covered by **peritoneum** except for an area superiorly that is directly related to the diaphragm known as the **bare area**. The **falciform ligament** is attached to the liver between the right and left lobes. It contains the **ligamentum teres** which is a remnant of the umbilical vein. The **coronary ligament** attaches the liver to the diaphragm, while the left and right triangular ligaments are the lateral extensions of the coronary ligament (Fig. 13.3). The **lesser omentum** has an L-shaped attachment to the fissure for the ligamentum venosum and porta hepatis. It subsequently passes to the lesser curvature of the stomach.

Histologically, the liver is surrounded by a capsule of fibrous connective tissue called **Glisson's capsule**. The capsule in turn is covered by the visceral peritoneum. The parenchyma of the liver is divided into **lobules**, which are incompletely partitioned by septa from Glisson's capsule (Fig. 13.4). Lobules consist of plates of **hepatocytes** in a connective tissue stroma. The stroma consists of fine reticular fibres within which run blood vessels, bile ducts, lymphatic vessels and nerves. Hepatic lobules are roughly **hexagonal** in shape and delimited by sparse interlobular connective tissue. At the angles of the hexagon are found **portal triads**. The hepatocytes are arranged in stacks of anastomosing plates, one- or two-cell thick, radiating from a **central vein** at the centre of the lobule towards the periphery. The plates of cells are separated by an anastomosing system of **sinusoids**. **Bile canaliculi** are formed by the separation of cell membranes between adjacent hepatocytes. The hepatocytes are separated from the sinusoids by the perisinusoidal space of Disse. The various products secreted by the liver are absorbed from this space by the sinusoids. Associated with the sinusoids are **Kupffer cells** which are liver macrophages that phagocytose bacteria which enter the blood.

Bile is secreted into **bile canaliculi**. Canaliculi consist of channels running between hepatocytes, their walls being formed by the plasma membranes of adjacent hepatocytes. The bile canaliculi terminate in small bile ductules near the periphery of the lobule. These in turn drain into the **interlobular bile ducts** at the portal areas. Thus, the direction of bile flow is opposite to that of blood flow. The intrahepatic bile ducts (Fig. 13.5)

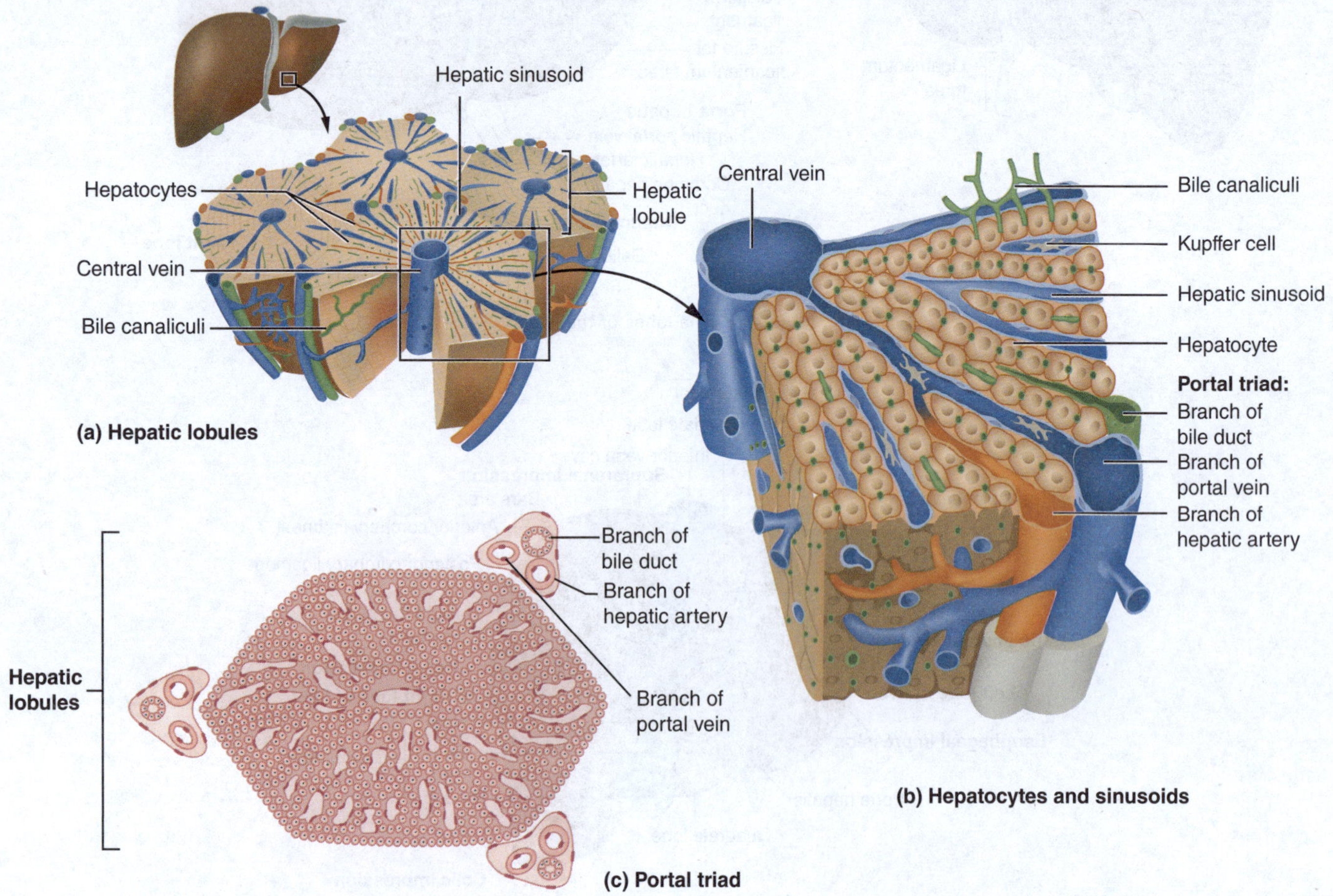

FIG. 13.4 The histology of the liver.

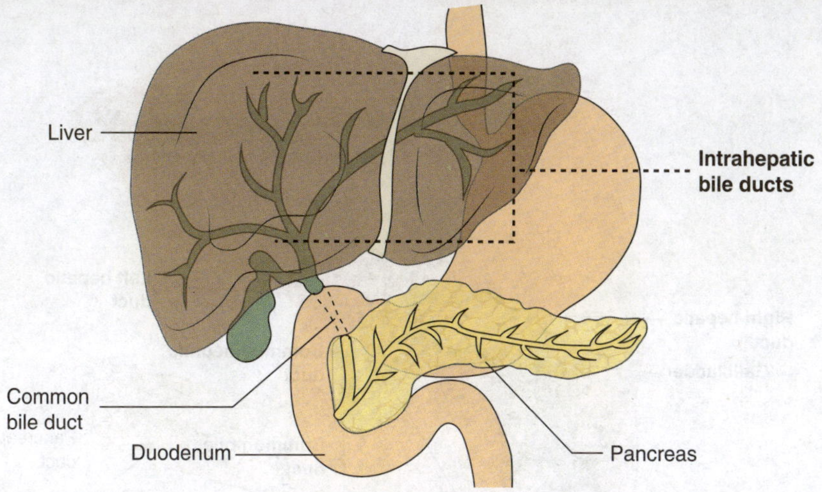

FIG. 13.5 The intrahepatic bile ducts.

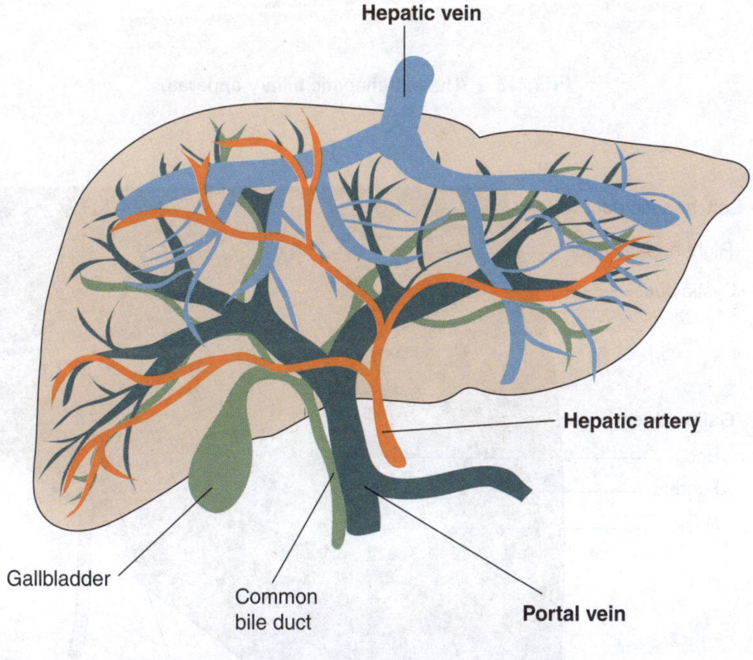

FIG. 13.6 The blood supply of the liver.

eventually join to form the right and left **hepatic ducts** which exit at the porta hepatis.

The liver has a dual **blood supply** (Fig. 13.6). Oxygenated blood reaches the liver via the **hepatic artery** (20% of blood), whereas blood from the abdominal viscera is carried to the liver by the **portal vein** (80% of blood). Both the portal vein and hepatic artery enter at the hilum and then branch repeatedly and run in parallel along the corners between adjacent lobules. Blood from both the portal vein and the hepatic artery mixes in the hepatic sinusoids. Blood drains out of the lobule through the central vein from periphery to centre. Blood collected in the central veins goes to the sublobular veins, then to collecting veins and **hepatic veins**, finally draining into the inferior vena cava. **Lymph** from the liver moves in the same direction as bile, reaching the hepatic lymph nodes near the porta hepatis. From here, the lymph eventually reaches the coeliac group of lymph nodes. The **coeliac plexus** supplies both sympathetic and parasympathetic fibres to the liver.

THE EXTRAHEPATIC BILIARY APPARATUS (Fig. 13.7)

The extrahepatic biliary apparatus consists of all the structures that concentrate bile and transport it to the second part of the duodenum. Bile enters the gallbladder from the **common hepatic duct**, which is formed by fusion of the right and left

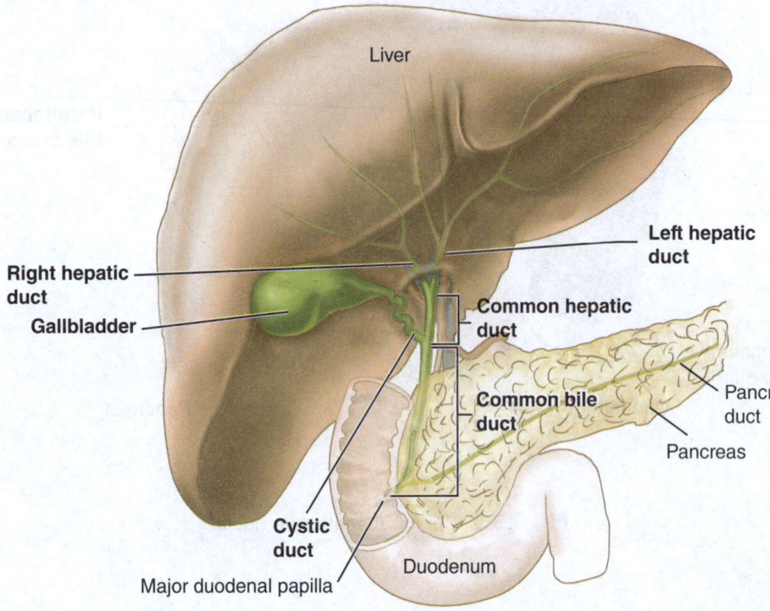

FIG. 13.7 The extrahepatic biliary apparatus.

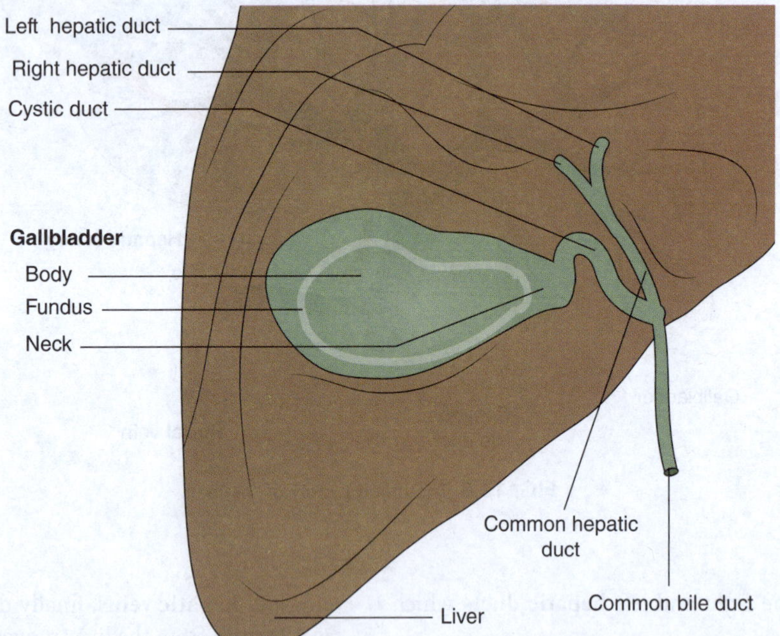

FIG. 13.8 The parts of the gallbladder.

hepatic ducts. It is then concentrated in the **gallbladder**. When it is required to be released, the gallbladder contracts and bile passes through the **cystic duct**, which joins the common hepatic duct to form the **common bile duct**. The common bile duct joins the main pancreatic duct and opens into the second part of the duodenum at the summit of the **major duodenal papilla**.

The **gallbladder** is a hollow, pear-shaped organ that lies in the fossa for the gallbladder on the visceral surface of the liver. It has a **fundus, body** and **neck** (Fig. 13.8). The neck continues as the **cystic duct**. The fundus of the gallbladder lies along the transpyloric plane at the tip of the ninth costal cartilage. The interlobular bile ducts within the liver coalesce to form the left and right hepatic ducts which merge to form the common hepatic duct. The common hepatic duct joins the cystic duct to form the common bile duct. The common bile duct carries bile to the duodenum. Before opening into the second part of the duodenum, it passes along with the hepatic artery and portal vein in the right free margin of the lesser omentum. It then courses inferiorly behind the first part of the duodenum and head of the pancreas before its termination.

Histologically, the wall of the gallbladder is seen to have three layers from within outside, namely the mucosa, fibromuscular layer and serosa or adventitia (Fig. 13.9). Goblet cells, muscularis mucosae and submucosa are absent. The **mucosa** is **extensively folded** and lined by tall, **simple, columnar epithelial cells** with many microvilli giving a brush border appearance. The middle **fibromuscular layer** has variously oriented smooth muscle bundles along with elastic and collagen fibres. The **serosa** contains a mesothelial lining and connective tissue with vessels and nerves. However, where the gallbladder attaches to the liver, only connective tissue is present, the adventitia. The larger ducts of the extrahepatic biliary system are lined by columnar cells and acquire smooth muscle in their walls extrahepatically. **Arterial supply** to the gallbladder is through the cystic artery, venous blood draining into the portal vein. **Lymphatic drainage** is into the cystic nodes. Autonomic **nerve supply** is via the cystic plexus, parasympathetic from the vagus nerve and sympathetic from T7 and T8 segments of the spinal cord.

THE PANCREAS

The pancreas is an elongated, **retroperitoneal gland** which extends from the curve of the duodenum across the midline of the body towards the spleen. It has a **head, neck, body** and **tail** (Fig. 13.10). Structurally, it is a compound, acinar, serous,

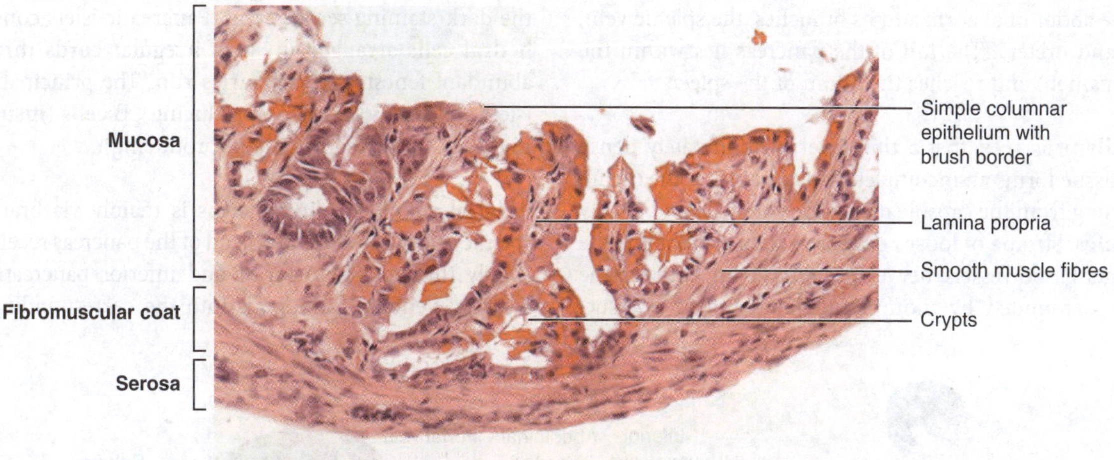

FIG. 13.9 The histology of the gallbladder.

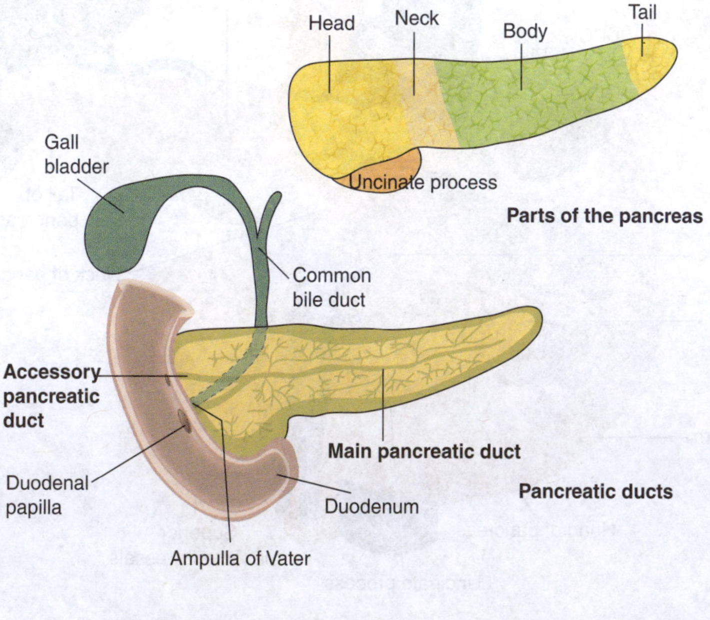

FIG. 13.10 The parts and ducts of the pancreas.

exocrine gland with scattered islets of **endocrine tissue**. The **head** has superior, right and inferior borders and an anterior and posterior surface (Fig. 13.11). The duodenum surrounds the head of the pancreas. Anteriorly, the head of the pancreas provides attachment to the transverse mesocolon, while posteriorly it is related to the bile duct and inferior vena cava. The **uncinate process** is a hook-like extension of the inferior aspect of the head of the pancreas. It is related anteriorly to the superior mesenteric vessels which emerge from behind the body of the pancreas.

The **neck** is the slightly constricted portion of the pancreas between the head and body. It is related posteriorly to the portal vein. The **body** of the pancreas is triangular in cross-section with anterior, superior and inferior **borders** and anterosuperior, anteroinferior and posterior **surfaces**. The anterior border provides attachment to the transverse mesocolon, while the superior border is related to the splenic artery. The anterosuperior surface forms part of the **stomach bed**, while the anteroinferior surface is related to coils of the small intestine. Posteriorly, the body is related to the abdominal aorta and its branches, the splenic vein, left kidney and ureters. The **tail** of the pancreas lies within the lienorenal ligament and reaches the hilum of the spleen.

Histologically, it is seen that a thin layer of moderately dense connective tissue forms an incomplete capsule around the organ. Septa extending from the capsule divide the pancreas into poorly defined **lobules**. Stroma of loose connective tissue surrounds the lobules. Larger blood vessels, nerves and ducts lying between the lobules are surrounded by more abundant connective tissue. Typical **serous acini** which resemble those of the parotid gland are prominently visible (Fig. 13.12). The pancreas differs from the parotid gland by the presence of **centroacinar cells** and reduced fat in the stroma. The duct system in the pancreas begins within the acini. Cells of the smallest ducts, the intercalated ducts, penetrate the centre of the acinus. In sections, they can be identified as centroacinar cells. The lining cells of the intercalated ducts are flattened. The **intercalated ducts** are short and drain into the intralobular collecting ducts. The **intralobular collecting ducts** form a complex, branching network and eventually drain into larger interlobular or excretory ducts. The interlobular ducts drain directly into the **main pancreatic duct**, which runs the length of the pancreas parallel to its long axis and joins the common bile duct before entering the duodenum.

The **islets of Langerhans** constitute only about 2% of the volume of the pancreas. They consist of distinct spherical or ellipsoid masses of cells and are most numerous in the **tail** (Fig. 13.12). Under low power, they appear as **pale-staining islands** among the dark-staining serous acini. Pancreatic islets consist of **polyhedral cells** arranged in short irregular **cords** through which abundant fenestrated capillaries run. The principal cells of the islets are α cells (glucagon producing), β **cells (insulin producing)** and δ cells (somatostatin producing).

Arterial supply to the pancreas is mainly via branches of the splenic artery. However, the head of the pancreas receives its blood supply through the superior and inferior pancreaticoduodenal arteries. **Venous drainage** is into the corresponding veins and

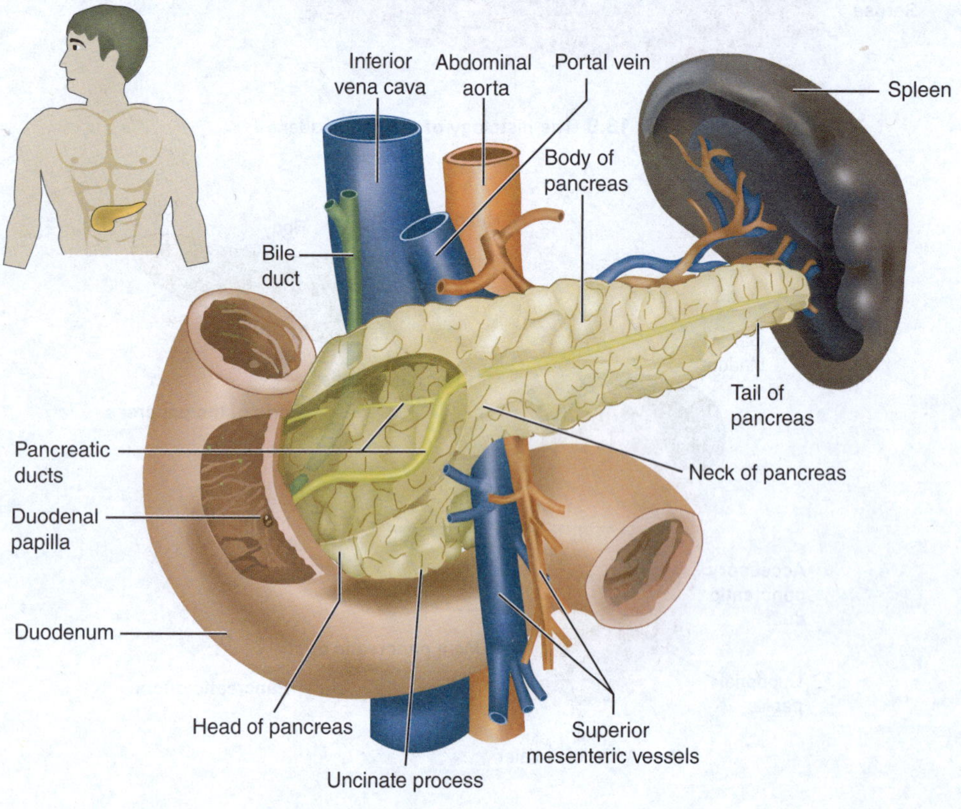

FIG. 13.11 The relations of the pancreas.

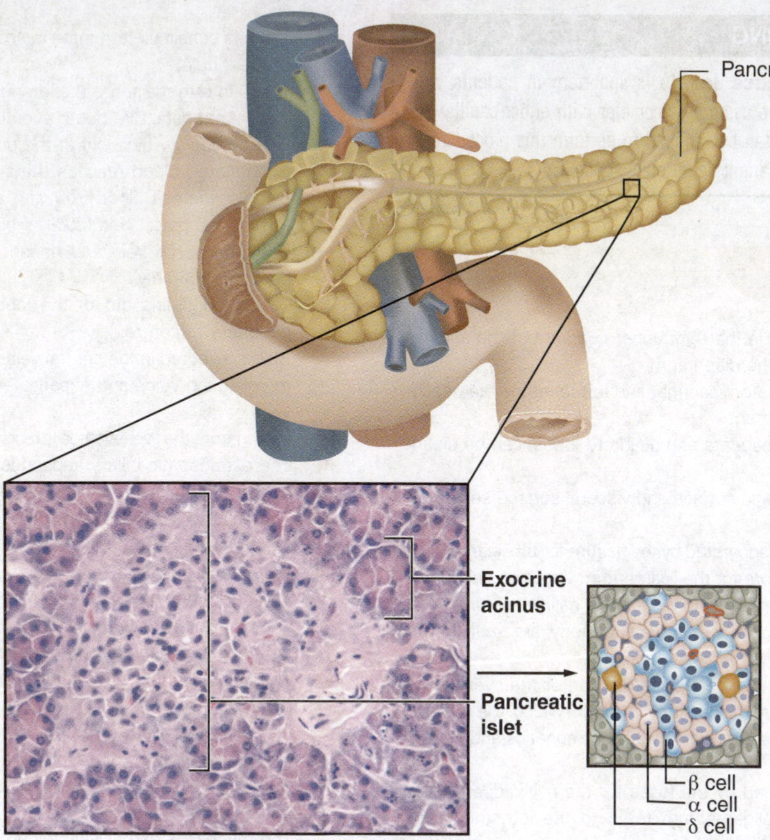

FIG. 13.12 The histology of the pancreas.

eventually into the portal vein. **Lymphatic drainage** of the head of the pancreas is into the pancreaticoduodenal lymph nodes. The pancreatic body and tail drain into the pancreaticosplenic group of lymph nodes. The lymph finally drains into the coeliac and superior mesenteric lymph nodes. **Autonomic nerve supply** of the pancreas is via the coeliac plexus. Parasympathetic fibres are derived from the vagus, while sympathetic supply comes from T6 to T10 segments of the spinal cord.

APPLIED ANATOMY

- Enlargement of the liver is called **hepatomegaly** and may occur due to several disease conditions including fatty liver, viral hepatitis, malaria, abscesses and tumours. In these conditions, the liver is palpable below the right costal margin.
- **Hepatitis** refers to inflammation of the liver. This is commonly due to viral infections and excessive alcohol intake.
- Excessive fibrous deposition and shrinkage of the liver occur in **cirrhosis**. This condition is often caused by chronic excessive alcohol intake and as a complication of certain viral infections.
- **Jaundice** is the externally visible yellowish discolouration of the tissues caused by the passage of bile salts into the bloodstream. This can occur due to excessive destruction of red blood cells in haemolytic anaemias (prehepatic jaundice), destruction of liver cells as in viral hepatitis (intrahepatic jaundice) or blockage of the passage of bile into the duodenum (posthepatic or obstructive jaundice).
- The gallbladder and biliary passages can be visualized radiologically by radio-opaque media that are concentrated in the liver and secreted in the bile. This investigation is known as **cholecystography**.
- **Cholecystitis** refers to inflammation of the gallbladder. In this condition, there may be pain and tenderness at the tip of the ninth costal cartilage on the right side which is related to the fundus of the gallbladder.
- The formation of stones within the gallbladder is termed **cholelithiasis**. The most common type of stones is cholesterol stones.
- The surgical removal of the gallbladder is called cholecystectomy which is commonly performed for cholelithiasis.
- Inflammation of the pancreas is called **pancreatitis**, which may be either acute or chronic. In this condition, pancreatic enzymes are released into the bloodstream.
- **Type I diabetes mellitus** occurs due to the production of antibodies and subsequent destruction of the insulin-secreting beta cells of the pancreas.
- **Carcinomas** of the head of the pancreas can obstruct the passage of bile into the duodenum and cause obstructive jaundice.
- When **splenectomy** is performed, care must be taken not to damage the tail of the pancreas, as the islets of Langerhans are concentrated here. Damage to the tail can subsequently lead to diabetes mellitus.

APPLICATION IN NURSING

- Monitoring of **blood glucose levels** is important in patients with diabetes mellitus. This is done using a glucometer with either capillary or venous blood. Nurses will often be required to perform this procedure in varied settings including outpatient departments and wards.

SUMMARY

- The liver is located mainly in the right upper quadrant of the abdominal cavity just inferior to the diaphragm.
- The liver is divided into anatomical right and left lobes by the attachment of the falciform ligament.
- Two additional lobes, the caudate and quadrate lobes, can be distinguished on the right lobe.
- The liver has a diaphragmatic surface and visceral surface separated by a sharp inferior border.
- The right and left lobes are separated by the fissure for the ligamentum teres inferiorly and the fissure for the ligamentum venosum superiorly.
- Two prominent impressions, the fossa for the gallbladder inferiorly and the groove for the inferior vena cava superiorly, are seen to the right of the fissures.
- The porta hepatis is a transversely placed region of the liver that is situated centrally between the fissures through which the hepatic artery, portal vein, right and left hepatic ducts, lymphatics and nerves pass through.
- The quadrate lobe is defined by the fossa for the gallbladder to the right, the fissure for the ligamentum teres to the left, the hilum superiorly and the inferior border inferiorly.
- The caudate lobe is bounded by the groove for the inferior vena cava on the right, the fissure for the ligamentum venosum on the left and the hilum inferiorly.
- The fundus of the stomach is related to the visceral surface of the left lobe of the liver.
- A prominent impression for the anterior surface of the right kidney is seen on the visceral surface of the right lobe.
- The hepatic flexure of the colon is related to the right of the area related to the superior duodenal flexure.
- The liver is covered by peritoneum, except for an area superiorly known as the bare area, that is directly related to the diaphragm.
- The falciform ligament is attached to the liver between the right and left lobes.
- The coronary ligament attaches the liver to the diaphragm, while the left and right triangular ligaments are the lateral extensions of the coronary ligament.
- The lesser omentum has an L-shaped attachment to the fissure for the ligamentum venosum and porta hepatis.
- Histologically, the liver is surrounded by a capsule of fibrous connective tissue called Glisson's capsule.
- The parenchyma of the liver is divided into lobules, which are incompletely partitioned by septa from Glisson's capsule.
- Lobules consist of plates of hepatocytes in a connective tissue stroma.
- Hepatic lobules are roughly hexagonal in shape and delimited by sparse interlobular connective tissue.
- At the angles of the hexagon are found portal triads.
- The hepatocytes are arranged in stacks of anastomosing plates, one- or two-cell thick, radiating from a central vein at the centre of the lobule towards the periphery.
- The plates of cells are separated by an anastomosing system of sinusoids.
- Bile canaliculi are formed by the separation of cell membranes between adjacent hepatocytes.
- Associated with the sinusoids are Kupffer cells that phagocytose bacteria which enter the blood.
- Bile is secreted into bile canaliculi.
- The bile canaliculi terminate in small bile ductules near the periphery of the lobule.
- These in turn drain into the interlobular bile ducts at the portal areas.
- The intrahepatic bile ducts eventually join to form the right and left hepatic ducts which exit at the porta hepatis.
- Oxygenated blood reaches the liver via the hepatic artery (20% of blood), whereas blood from the abdominal viscera is carried to the liver by the portal vein (80% of blood).
- Both the portal vein and hepatic artery enter the hilum and then branch repeatedly.
- The blood drains out of the lobule through the central vein from periphery to centre.
- Blood collected in the central veins goes to the sublobular veins, then to collecting veins and hepatic veins, finally draining into the inferior vena cava.
- Lymph from the liver eventually reaches the coeliac group of lymph nodes.
- The extrahepatic biliary apparatus consists of all the structures that concentrate bile and transport it to the second part of the duodenum.
- The gallbladder is a hollow, pear-shaped organ that lies in the fossa for the gallbladder on the visceral surface of the liver.
- It has a fundus, body and neck.
- The neck continues as the cystic duct.
- The interlobular bile ducts within the liver coalesce to form the left and right hepatic ducts which merge to form the common hepatic duct.
- The common hepatic duct joins the cystic duct to form the common bile duct.
- The common bile duct carries bile to the duodenum.
- Histologically, the wall of the gallbladder is seen to have three layers from within outside, namely the mucosa, fibromuscular layer and serosa or adventitia.
- The mucosa is extensively folded and lined by tall, simple, columnar epithelial cells with many microvilli giving a brush border appearance.
- Arterial supply to the gallbladder is through the cystic artery, venous blood draining into the portal vein.
- The pancreas is an elongated, retroperitoneal gland which extends from the curve of the duodenum across the midline of the body towards the spleen.
- It has a head, neck, body and tail.
- Structurally, it is a compound, acinar, serous, exocrine gland with scattered islets of endocrine tissue.
- The head has superior, right and inferior borders and an anterior and posterior surface.
- The duodenum surrounds the head of the pancreas.
- The uncinate process is a hook-like extension of the inferior aspect of the head of the pancreas.
- The neck is the slightly constricted portion of the pancreas between the head and body.
- It is related posteriorly to the portal vein.
- The body of the pancreas is triangular in cross-section with anterior, superior and inferior borders and anterosuperior, anteroinferior and posterior surfaces.
- The tail of the pancreas lies within the lienorenal ligament and reaches the hilum of the spleen.
- Histologically, typical serous acini which resemble those of the parotid gland are prominently visible.
- The intralobular collecting ducts form a complex, branching network and eventually drain into larger interlobular or excretory ducts.
- The interlobular ducts drain directly into the main pancreatic duct.
- The islets of Langerhans consist of distinct spherical or ellipsoid masses of cells and are most numerous in the tail.
- Under low power, they appear as pale-staining islands among the dark-staining serous acini.
- The principal cells of the islets are α cells (glucagon producing), β cells (insulin producing) and δ cells (somatostatin producing).
- Arterial supply to the pancreas is mainly via branches of the splenic artery.
- The head of the pancreas receives its blood supply through the superior and inferior pancreaticoduodenal arteries.

4

SECTION

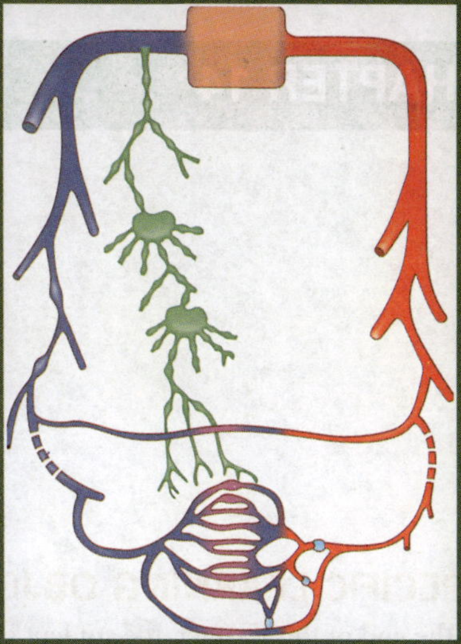

The Circulatory and Lymphatic System

Section Outline

CHAPTER 14

The Vascular System

SPECIFIC LEARNING OBJECTIVES

At the end of this chapter, the student should be able to:

- Describe the structure and functions of the different types of blood vessels.
- Compare and contrast the systemic and pulmonary circulations.
- Name the arteries responsible for supplying blood to the various regions of the body.
- Describe the following arteries in detail: all parts of the aorta; subclavian artery; external carotid artery; axillary, brachial and radial arteries; femoral artery; and coeliac trunk.
- Name the veins responsible for carrying blood from the various regions of the body.
- Describe the following veins: superior and inferior vena cava, superficial veins of the limbs, axillary vein, subclavian vein, internal and external jugular veins, brachiocephalic vein and femoral vein.

GLOSSARY OF TERMS

- **Microcirculation:** arterioles with their associated capillary beds and venules
- **Tunica intima:** the inner layer of blood vessels lined by endothelium
- **Tunica media:** the middle layer of blood vessels containing smooth muscle fibres
- **Tunica adventitia:** the outer layer of blood vessels containing connective tissue
- **Systemic circulation:** high-pressure system carrying blood to and from the tissues of the body excluding the lungs
- **Pulmonary circulation:** low-pressure system carrying blood to and from the lungs for oxygenation
- **Portal circulation:** system of blood vessels that begins and ends in capillaries
- **Anastomosis:** a connection between blood vessels
- **Venae comitans:** double veins that accompany deep arteries

INTRODUCTION

The cardiovascular system includes the heart and blood vessels. The heart is a muscular pump which beats rhythmically throughout the life of an individual. The blood from the heart is pumped into arteries which carry blood away from the heart to all tissues of the body. Diffusion of gases at the level of the tissues occurs through the smallest component of the vascular system known as capillaries. Veins carry blood from the tissues of the body towards the heart. The main functions of the cardiovascular system include ensuring the smooth and adequate flow of blood, delivery of nutrients and oxygen to the tissues and removal of waste products and carbon dioxide from the tissues. Two parallel circulations exist in the body. The systemic circulation carries oxygenated blood from the left ventricle of the heart to the tissues and deoxygenated blood from the tissues to the right atrium. Deoxygenated blood passes from the right ventricle to the lungs, where it gets oxygenated and returns to the left atrium.

GENERAL FEATURES OF BLOOD VESSELS (Fig. 14.1)

Blood flows from the heart into conducting vessels which are **elastic arteries**. The blood then passes into **muscular arteries** which function as distributing vessels. The smallest subdivisions of arteries are **arterioles** which are resistance vessels and regulate blood flow into the tissues. Exchange of gases at the tissue level occurs through **capillaries**. **Venules** then carry blood to **medium-sized veins** which join to form **large veins** that drain into the atria. Veins are capacitance vessels which hold much of the volume of blood in the body. The arterioles, capillaries and venules are together called the **microcirculation**. From the centre to the periphery, blood vessels increase in number, decrease in diameter and decrease in wall thickness. The walls of larger blood vessels have three layers, namely an inner tunica intima, a middle tunica media and an outer tunica adventitia (Fig. 14.2). The **tunica intima** consists of an endothelial layer with a basal lamina, subendothelial connective tissue and the internal elastic lamina. Smooth muscle tissue,

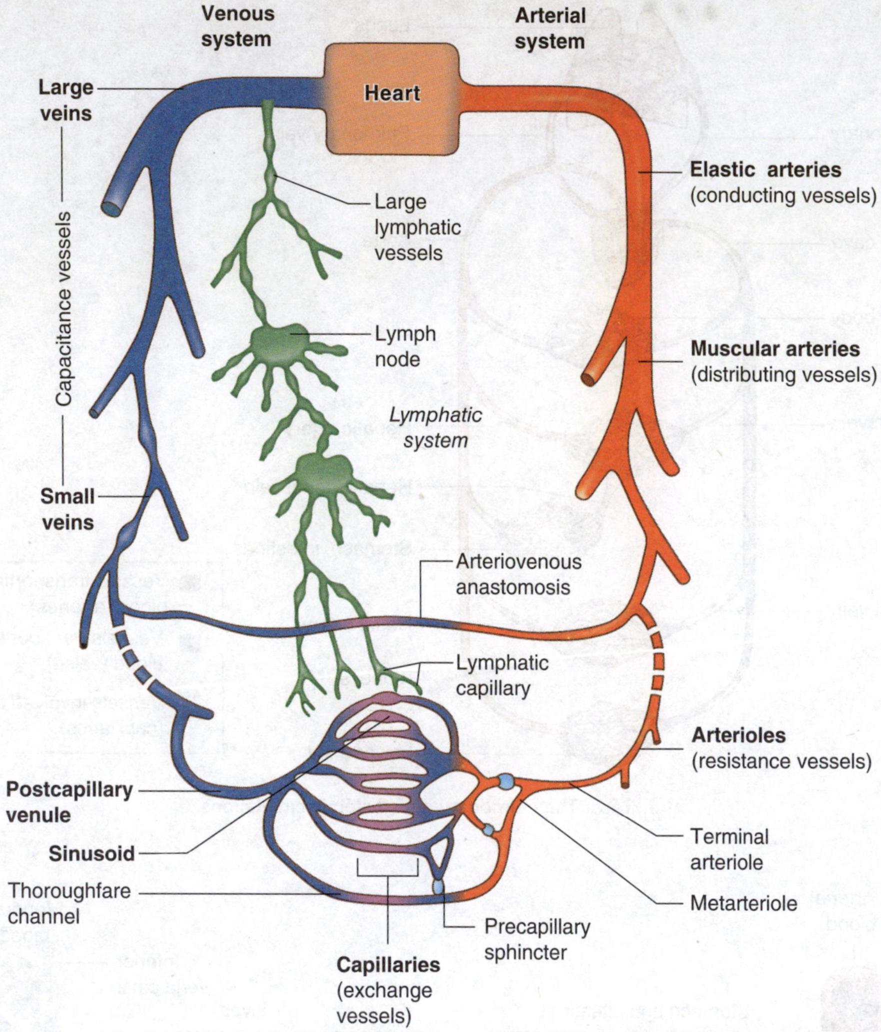

FIG. 14.1 The different types of blood vessels in the body.

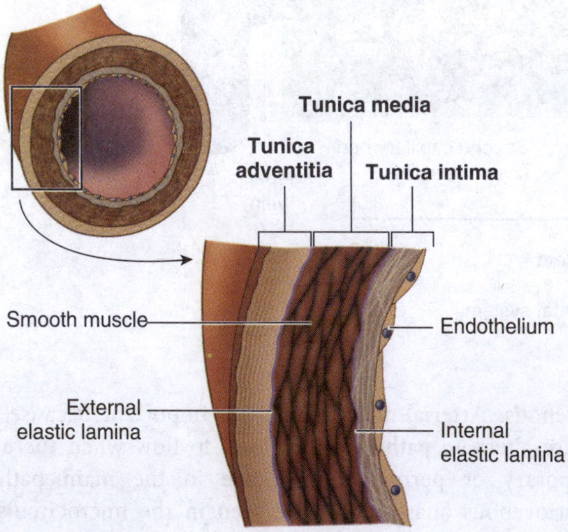

FIG. 14.2 The structure of large blood vessels.

elastic and collagen fibres constitute the **tunica media** which is bounded by the external elastic lamina. The **tunica adventitia** consists of connective tissue which may contain blood vessels (vasa vasorum) and nerves (nervi vascularis). Blood vessels differ in the relative thickness and composition of the layers. In smaller vessels, the number of layers is reduced.

The **systemic circulation** is a high-pressure system that carries blood to all the tissues of the body except the lungs (Fig. 14.3). It begins from the ascending aorta that arises from the left ventricle and carries oxygenated blood. It ends at the superior and inferior venae cavae which carry deoxygenated blood to the right atrium. The **pulmonary circulation** is a low-pressure system that is required for oxygenation of blood. It begins from the pulmonary artery which arises from the right ventricle and carries deoxygenated blood. It ends at the right and left pair of pulmonary veins that carry oxygenated blood to the left atrium. These two circulations always run in parallel to ensure blood supply to the tissues and oxygenation of blood. A **portal**

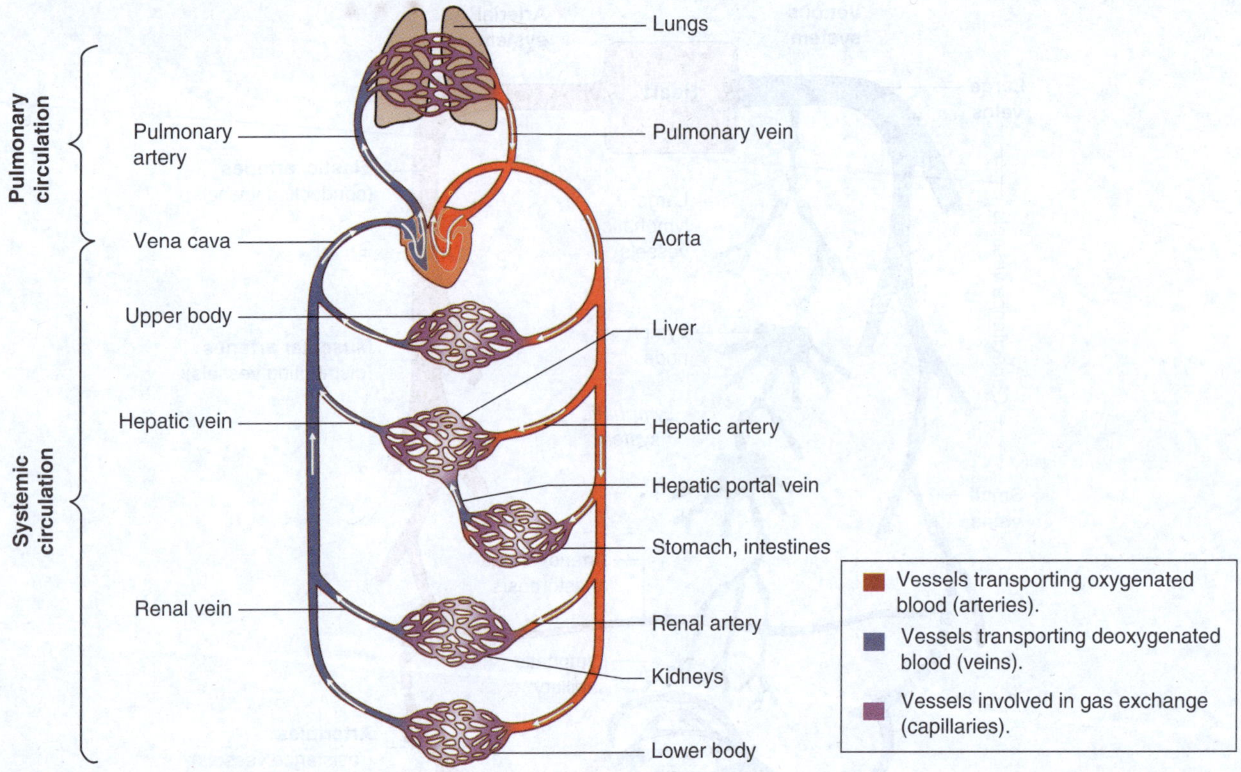

FIG. 14.3 The pulmonary and systemic circulations.

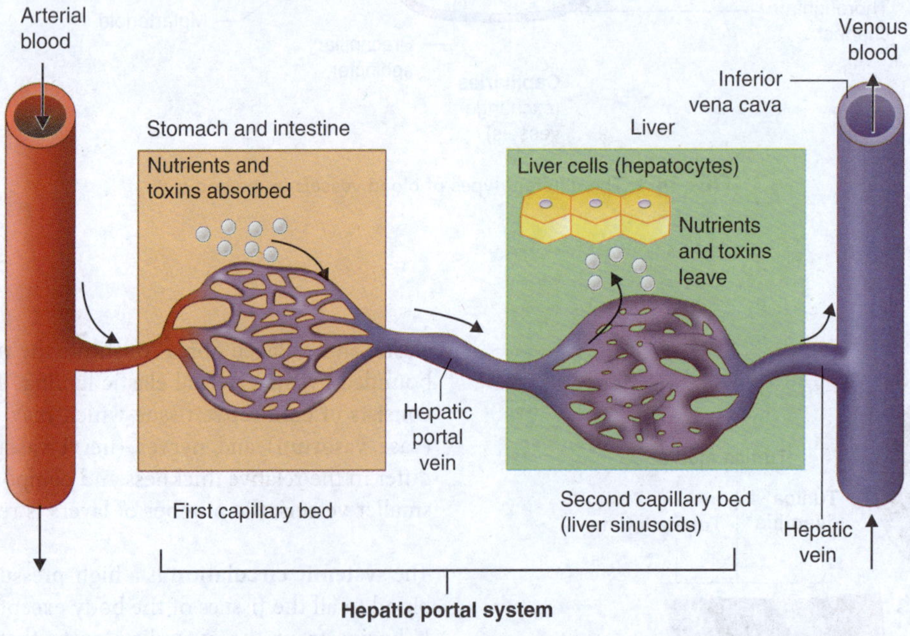

FIG. 14.4 The hepatic portal system.

circulation is one that begins and ends as capillaries (Fig. 14.4). It is found in the liver, pituitary gland and kidneys. In these organs, nutrients, hormones or ions need to be transported by the blood from one site to another necessitating two capillary beds. The connection between two vessels is called an **anastomosis** (Fig. 14.5). Anastomoses may be arterial, arteriovenous or venous. Arterial anastomoses are important because they ensure alternate pathways for blood to flow when there is a temporary or permanent blockage in the main pathway. Arteriovenous anastomoses are seen in the microcirculation and regulate the blood flow through the capillary beds. Venous anastomoses serve a similar purpose to arterial anastomoses.

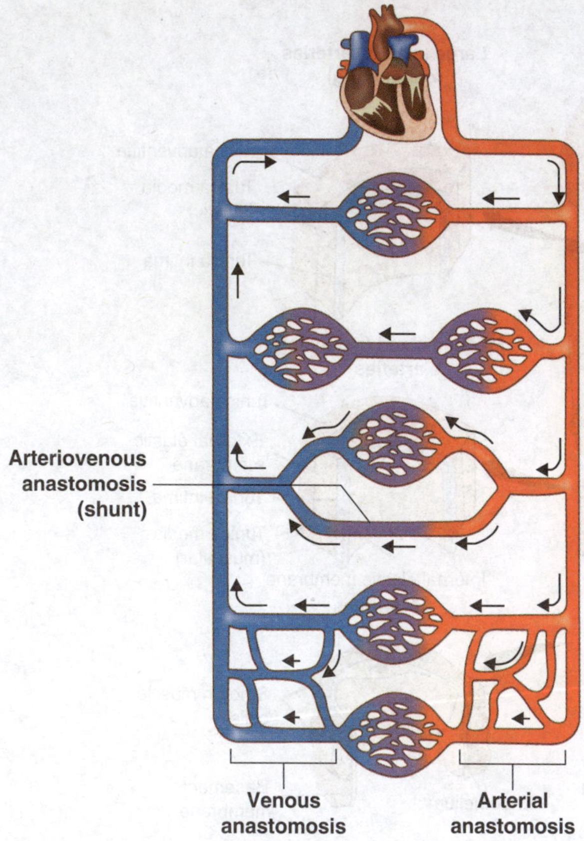

FIG. 14.5 The different types of anastomoses.

Table 14.1 Differences in the Microstructure of Arteries and Veins

	Arteries	Veins
Lumen	Round or oval and well defined	Irregular, sometimes collapsed
Wall thickness	Relatively thicker	Relatively thinner
Valves	Absent	Present
Elastic laminae	Well developed	Poorly developed
Tunica media	Relatively thicker than adventitia with more smooth muscle fibres	Relatively thinner than adventitia with fewer smooth muscle fibres
Tunica adventitia	Relatively thinner than media with connective tissue fibres	Relatively thicker than media with smooth muscle fibres in large veins

HISTOLOGY OF BLOOD VESSELS (Table 14.1; Fig. 14.6)

Arteries can be classified into three types according to their size, namely large or elastic arteries, medium-sized or muscular arteries and small arteries or arterioles. Their characteristic feature, regardless of size, is a well-defined lumen, rounded or oval, maintained by the muscularity of the vessel wall. **Large arteries** like the aorta and pulmonary artery are distinguished by their great elasticity. This helps them smooth out the large fluctuations in blood pressure created by the heartbeat. During systole, their elastic laminae are stretched and reduce blood pressure, while during diastole, the elastic rebound helps maintain arterial pressure. The distinguishing features of large arteries are their large lumen and the presence of abundant elastic fibres in the tunica media. These elastic fibres are produced by smooth muscle cells which are arranged in a spiral around the long axis of the vessel. Most of the named arteries are **medium-sized arteries.** They have a smaller lumen as compared to large arteries and have less elastic tissue in the tunica media. The predominant constituent of the tunica media is smooth muscle. A prominent internal and external elastic lamina can be distinguished. **Arterioles** regulate the flow of blood from the medium-sized arteries to the capillary beds. They are the sites for blood pressure regulation, controlling resistance by changing vessel diameter. Although they are much smaller, their general structure is like that of muscular arteries. The media is muscular and has a few layers of smooth muscle. The other layers become less prominent in more distal branches.

Capillaries are the smallest-diameter exchange vessels located between arteries and veins. They are found in almost every tissue in the body and allow for exchange of nutrients and products of metabolism between the blood and the tissue cells. They are lined by a single layer of endothelial cells and their basement membrane. At intervals, the endothelial cells of capillaries may be surrounded by pericytes which act like supporting cells. Depending on their function, capillaries may be continuous, fenestrated or discontinuous (sinusoids).

Veins are capacitance vessels that return blood to the heart. Like arteries, they are classified as large, medium and small with the sizes blending into one another with no sharp demarcations. Although the same layers (intima, media and adventitia) are present, they are often not as well defined as in arteries. In comparably sized vessels, arteries have thicker walls and a much larger media. In veins, the adventitia is larger than the media. Veins do not retain their shape, the lumen often appearing irregular in sections. They have poorly developed internal and external elastic laminae. Valves are a distinctive feature of veins. Examples of large veins include the venae cavae and portal vein. The tunica adventitia in large veins contains prominent bundles of longitudinally arranged smooth muscle.

THE ARTERIES OF THE BODY

The arteries of the body will be described sequentially from the thorax, abdomen, pelvis, lower limb, upper limb, head, neck and brain. This will be done in a tabular form, summarizing the key anatomical features of the major arteries of each region (Tables 14.2–14.7).

THE VEINS OF THE BODY

The veins of the body usually accompany the arteries. However, in the limbs, a separate set of superficial veins is present.

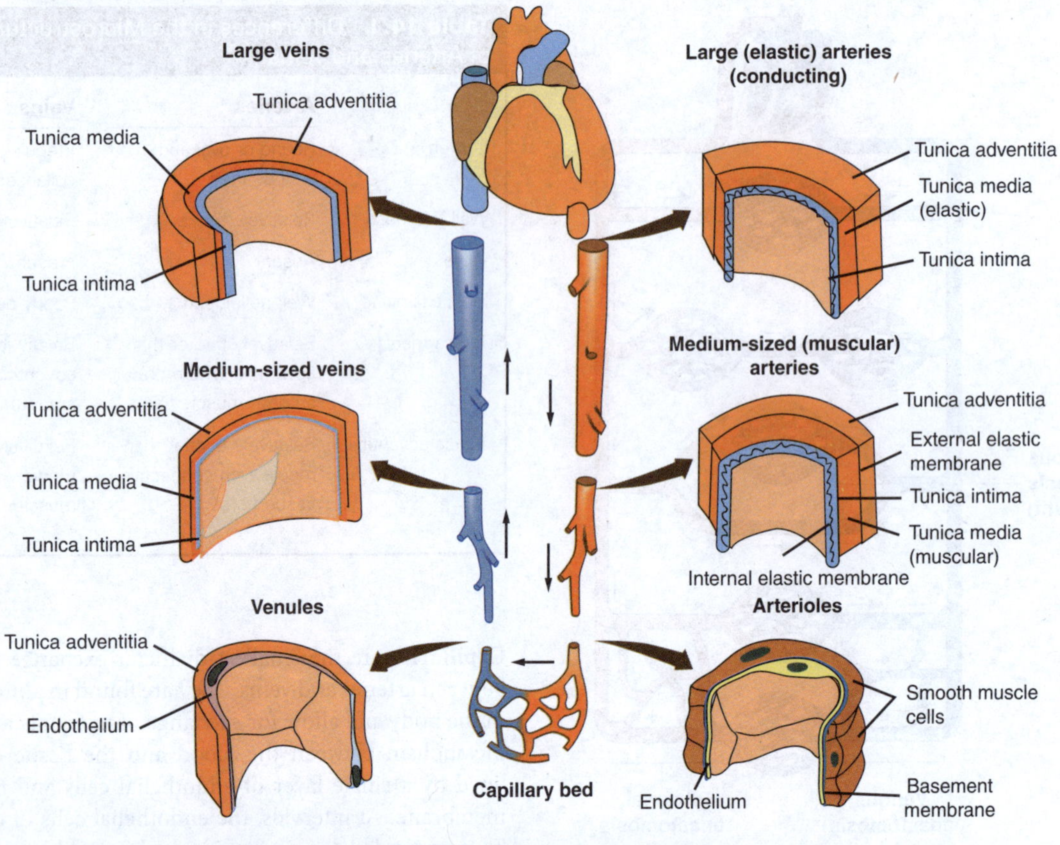

FIG. 14.6 The histology of different types of blood vessels.

Table 14.2 The Arteries of the Thorax (Figs 14.7–14.9)

Artery	Origin	Course	Branches and Distribution	Termination
Pulmonary trunk	• Right ventricle	• Ascends anterior and to the left of the ascending aorta	• Right and left pulmonary arteries • Carries deoxygenated blood to the lungs for oxygenation	• Terminates by dividing into the two pulmonary arteries
Ascending aorta	• Left ventricle	• Ascends posterior and to the right of the pulmonary trunk	• Right and left coronary arteries • Supplies the heart	• Terminates by continuing as the arch of aorta at the level of the sternal angle
Arch of aorta	• Continuation of the ascending aorta at the level of the sternal angle	• Arches backwards and to the left in the superior mediastinum	• Brachiocephalic trunk • Left common carotid artery • Left subclavian artery • Gives rise to the major arteries that supply the head, neck, brain and upper limbs	• Terminates by continuing as the descending thoracic aorta at the level of the sternal angle
Descending thoracic aorta	• Continuation of the arch of the aorta at the level of the sternal angle	• Descends in the posterior mediastinum	• Posterior intercostal arteries • Bronchial arteries • Oesophageal arteries • Supplies the chest wall, lung and oesophagus	• Terminates by passing through the aortic opening in the diaphragm and continuing as the abdominal aorta
Internal thoracic artery	• Branch of the first part of the subclavian artery	• Descends in the anterior mediastinum	• Anterior intercostal arteries • Musculophrenic artery • Superior epigastric artery • Supplies the anterior chest wall, breast, diaphragm and anterior abdominal wall	• Terminates by dividing into its terminal branches, the musculophrenic and superior epigastric arteries

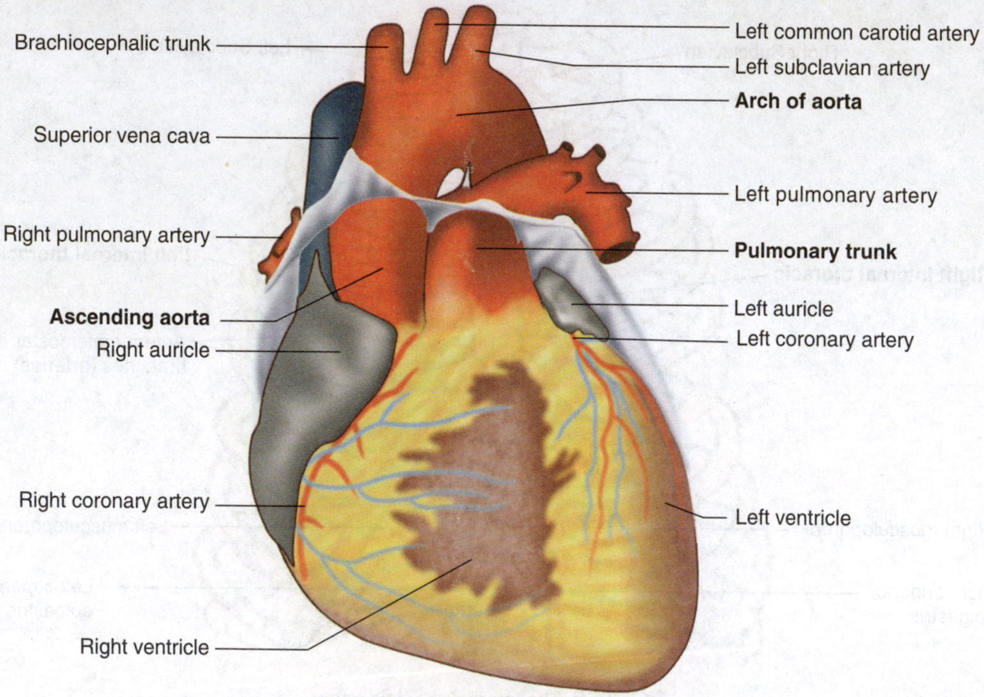

FIG. 14.7 The ascending aorta, arch of aorta and pulmonary trunk.

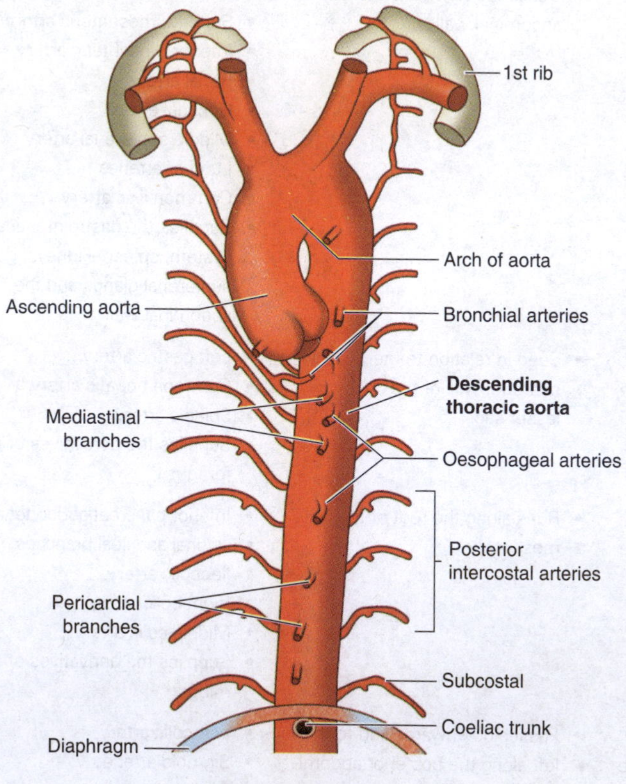

FIG. 14.8 The descending thoracic aorta.

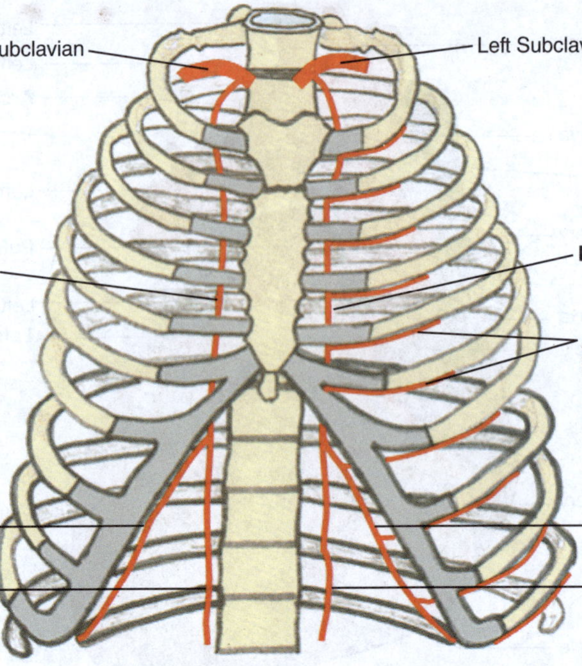

FIG. 14.9 The internal thoracic artery.

Table 14.3 The Arteries of the Abdomen (Fig. 14.10)

Artery	Origin	Course	Branches and Distribution	Termination
Abdominal aorta	• Continuation of the thoracic aorta beyond the aortic opening in the diaphragm	• Descends along the posterior abdominal wall	• Coeliac trunk • Superior mesenteric artery • Inferior mesenteric artery • Renal artery • Gonadal artery • Middle suprarenal artery • Lumbar arteries • Common iliac artery • Supplies the gastrointestinal system, spleen, kidneys, gonads, suprarenal glands and the posterior abdominal wall	• Terminates by dividing into the two common iliac arteries
Coeliac trunk	• Ventral aspect of abdominal aorta at the level of T12 vertebra	• Seen in relation to the posterior wall of the lesser sac	• Left gastric artery • Common hepatic artery • Splenic artery • Supplies the derivatives of the foregut	• After a short course, it splits into its three branches
Superior mesenteric artery	• Ventral aspect of abdominal aorta at the level of L1 vertebra	• Runs along the root of the mesentery	• Inferior pancreaticoduodenal artery • Jejunal and ileal branches • Ileocolic artery • Right colic artery • Middle colic artery • Supplies the derivatives of the midgut	• Ends by anastomosing with the ileal branch of the ileocolic artery, which is its own branch
Inferior mesenteric artery	• Ventral aspect of abdominal aorta at the level of L3 vertebra	• Passes downwards and to the left along the posterior abdominal wall	• Left colic artery • Sigmoid arteries • Superior rectal artery • Supplies derivatives of the hindgut	• The superior rectal artery is the continuation of the inferior mesenteric artery after it gives off the sigmoid branches

Table 14.3 The Arteries of the Abdomen—cont'd

Artery	Origin	Course	Branches and Distribution	Termination
Renal artery	• Lateral branches of the aorta given off just inferior to the superior mesenteric artery	• Passes laterally along the posterior abdominal wall and enters the kidneys at their hila posterior to the renal veins and anterior to the pelvis of the ureter	• Segmental branches to the kidney • Inferior suprarenal artery • Ureteric branches	• Terminates by dividing into branches that enter the kidneys at their hila
Gonadal artery	• Arises from the antero-lateral aspect of the abdominal aorta just inferior to the renal arteries	• Passes downward and laterally along the posterior abdominal wall towards the deep inguinal ring	• Branches to the gonads • Branches to the ureter	• Terminates by giving off branches that enter the mediastinum testis and supply the testes
Lumbar arteries	• Arise from the postero-lateral aspect of the abdominal aorta	• Pass along the muscles of the posterior abdominal wall and enter the muscle layers of the anterior abdominal wall	• Supply the posterior and anterior abdominal walls	• Anastomose with the other arteries supplying the anterior abdominal wall
Common iliac artery	• Terminal branches of the abdominal aorta	• Passes inferolaterally along the posterior abdominal wall towards the sacroiliac joint on each side	• External iliac artery • Internal iliac artery	• Ends by dividing into the external and the internal iliac arteries

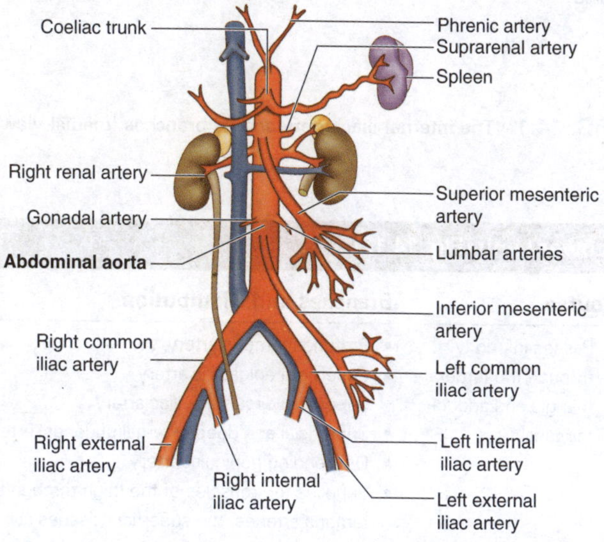

FIG. 14.10 The abdominal aorta and its branches.

Table 14.4 The Arteries of the Pelvis (Fig. 14.11)

Artery	Origin	Course	Branches and Distribution	Termination
Internal iliac artery	• Terminal branch of common iliac artery	• Passes inferolaterally along the lateral pelvic wall	• Superior and inferior vesical arteries • Uterine and vaginal arteries • Middle rectal artery • Internal pudendal artery • Superior and inferior gluteal arteries • Iliolumbar artery • Lateral sacral artery • Obturator artery • Supplies the pelvic viscera, pelvic walls and the perineum	• Terminates by dividing into the inferior gluteal and internal pudendal arteries
External iliac artery	• Terminal branch of common iliac artery	• Passes along the posterior part of the pelvic brim and deep to the inguinal ligament	• Inferior epigastric artery • Deep circumflex iliac artery • Supplies the anterior and posterior abdominal walls	• Terminates by continuing as the femoral artery beyond the inguinal ligament at the mid-inguinal point

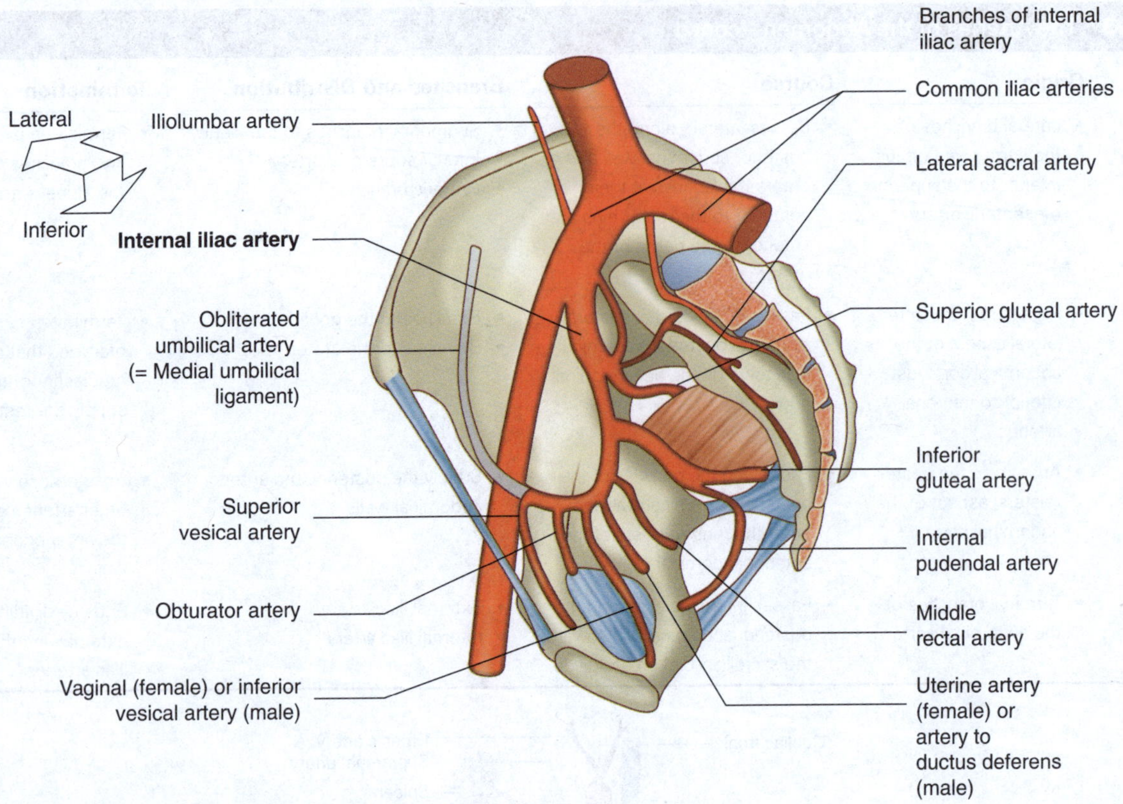

FIG. 14.11 The internal iliac artery and its branches (medial view).

Table 14.5 The Arteries of the Lower Limb (Fig. 14.12)

Artery	Origin	Course	Branches and Distribution	Termination
Femoral artery	• Continuation of the external iliac artery beyond the inguinal ligament at the mid-inguinal point	• Passes inferiorly through the femoral triangle and adductor canal	• Profunda femoris artery • Superficial epigastric artery • Superficial circumflex iliac artery • Superficial and deep external pudendal arteries • Descending genicular artery • Supplies the muscles of the thigh through the profunda femoris arteries, the superficial tissues around the upper part of the thigh and lower part of the anterior abdominal wall and the knee joint	• Terminates by passing through an opening in the adductor magnus muscle and continues as the popliteal artery
Popliteal artery	• Continuation of the femoral artery beyond the opening in the adductor magnus muscle	• Passes inferiorly through the popliteal fossa	• Genicular branches • Anterior tibial artery • Posterior tibial artery • Supplies the knee joint through its genicular branches	• Terminates by dividing in the lower part of the popliteal fossa into the anterior and posterior tibial arteries
Anterior tibial artery	• Terminal branch of the popliteal artery given off near the lower part of the popliteal fossa	• Runs inferiorly through the anterior compartment of the leg	• Anterior and posterior tibial recurrent arteries • Muscular branches • Anterior medial and lateral malleolar arteries • Supplies the knee joint, ankle joint, muscles of the anterior compartment of the leg and the dorsum of the foot through the dorsalis pedis arteries	• Terminates by continuing as the dorsalis pedis artery into the dorsum of the foot
Posterior tibial artery	• Terminal branch of the popliteal artery given off near the lower part of the popliteal fossa	• Runs inferiorly through the posterior compartment of the leg	• Peroneal artery • Muscular branches • Medial plantar artery • Lateral plantar artery • Supplies the muscles of the lateral and posterior compartments of the leg, ankle joint and sole of the foot	• Terminates by dividing into the medial and the lateral plantar arteries near the medial malleolus

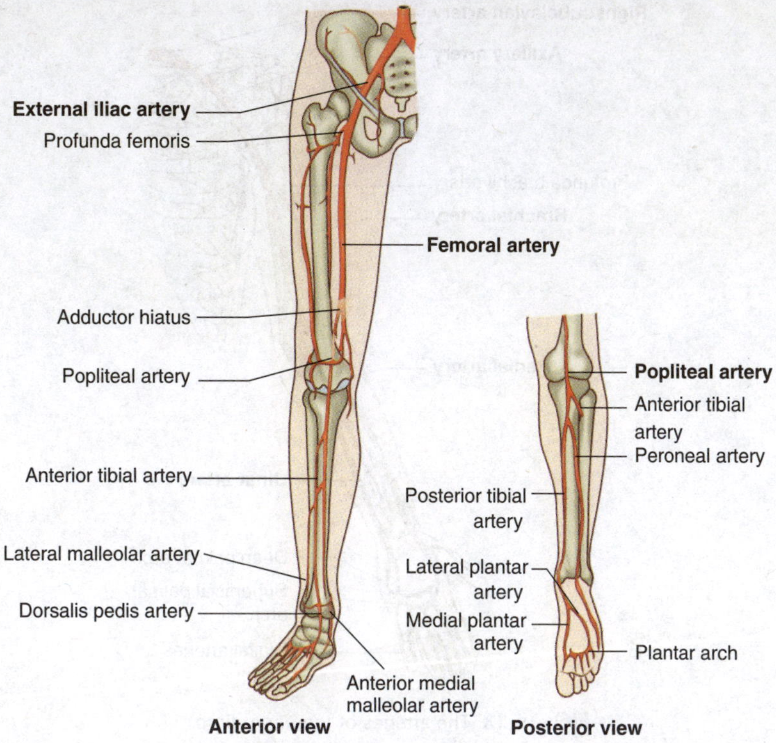

FIG. 14.12 The arteries of the lower limb.

Table 14.6 The Arteries of the Upper Limb (Fig. 14.13)

Artery	Origin	Course	Branches and Distribution	Termination
Axillary artery	• Continuation of the subclavian artery beyond the outer border of the first rib	• Passes infero-laterally through the axilla surrounded by the cords and branches of the brachial plexus	• Superior thoracic artery • Thoracoacromial artery • Lateral thoracic artery • Subscapular artery • Anterior and posterior circumflex humeral arteries • Supplies the walls of the axilla, breast and shoulder joint	• Terminates by continuing as the brachial artery at the lower border of the teres major muscle
Brachial artery	• Continuation of the axillary artery beyond the lower border of the teres major muscle	• Passes along the medial side of the arm to reach the cubital fossa	• Profunda brachii artery • Muscular branches • Superior and inferior ulnar collateral arteries • Radial artery • Ulnar artery • Supplies the muscles of the posterior compartment of the arm through the profunda brachii artery, the muscles of the anterior compartment of the arm and the elbow joint	• Terminate by dividing in the cubital fossa into the radial and the ulnar arteries
Radial artery	• Terminal branch of the brachial artery given off in the cubital fossa	• Passes inferiorly along the lateral aspect of the forearm	• Radial recurrent artery • Superficial palmar branch • Palmar and dorsal carpal branches • First dorsal metacarpal artery • Radialis indicis artery • Princeps pollicis artery • Supplies the elbow joint, wrist joint, muscles of the forearm, palm and the first and second digits	• Terminates by continuing as the deep palmar arch in the palm of the hand
Ulnar artery	• Terminal branch of the brachial artery given off in the cubital fossa	• Passes inferiorly along the medial aspect of the forearm	• Anterior and posterior ulnar recurrent arteries • Common interosseous artery • Muscular branches • Deep palmar branch • Supplies the elbow joint, wrist joint, muscles of the forearm and the palm	• Terminates by continuing as the superficial palmar arch in the palm of the hand

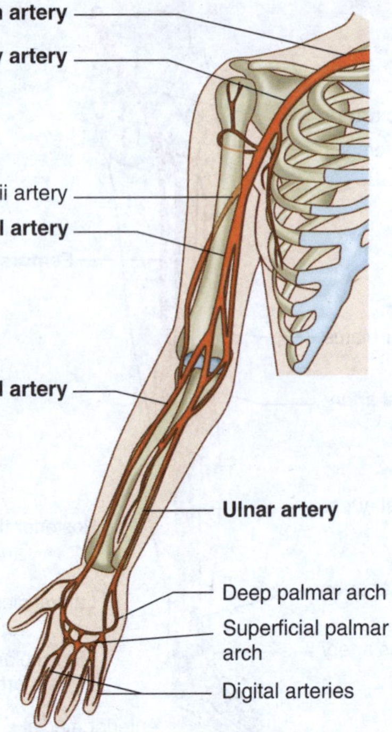

FIG. 14.13 The arteries of the upper limb.

Table 14.7 The Arteries of the Head, Neck and Brain (Figs 14.14 and 14.15)

Artery	Origin	Course	Branches and Distribution	Termination
Common carotid artery	• Arises from the brachiocephalic trunk on the right side and the arch of the aorta on the left side	• Passes superiorly in the carotid sheath accompanied by the internal jugular vein and vagus nerve • Near its bifurcation are seen the carotid sinus and carotid body which have baroreceptors and chemoreceptors, respectively	• External carotid artery • Internal carotid artery	• Terminates at the level of the superior border of the thyroid cartilage (C4 vertebra) by dividing into the internal and external carotid arteries
External carotid artery	• Arises from the common carotid artery at the level of the superior border of the thyroid cartilage (C4 vertebral level)	• Passes superiorly in the carotid triangle and within the parotid gland	• Superior thyroid artery • Ascending pharyngeal artery • Lingual artery • Facial artery • Occipital artery • Posterior auricular artery • Maxillary artery • Superficial temporal artery • Supplies the scalp, face, oral cavity, salivary glands, tongue, pharynx, nasal cavity, thyroid gland, scalp and external ear	• The external carotid artery terminates near the neck of the mandible by dividing into its two terminal branches, the maxillary and the superficial temporal arteries
Internal carotid artery	• Arises from the common carotid artery at the level of the superior border of the thyroid cartilage (C4 vertebral level)	• Ascends from its origin within the carotid sheath and passes into the cranial cavity through the carotid canal	• Superior and inferior hypophyseal arteries • Ophthalmic artery • Posterior communicating artery • Anterior choroidal artery • Anterior cerebral artery • Middle cerebral artery • Meningeal branches • Supplies the brain through the circle of Willis formed by the internal carotid and vertebral arteries, eye, pituitary gland, meninges, forehead and scalp	• The internal carotid artery terminates within the cranial cavity by dividing into its two terminal branches, the anterior and the middle cerebral arteries

Table 14.7 The Arteries of the Head, Neck and Brain—cont'd

Artery	Origin	Course	Branches and Distribution	Termination
Subclavian artery	• Arises from the brachiocephalic trunk on the right side and the arch of the aorta on the left side	• Passes laterally along the root of the neck towards the apex of the axilla	• Vertebral artery • Internal thoracic artery • Thyrocervical trunk • Costocervical trunk • Dorsal scapular artery • Supplies the brain through the circle of Willis formed by the internal carotid and vertebral arteries, thyroid gland, neck, upper back, chest wall, breast and anterior abdominal wall	• Terminates by continuing as the axillary artery at the outer border of the first rib

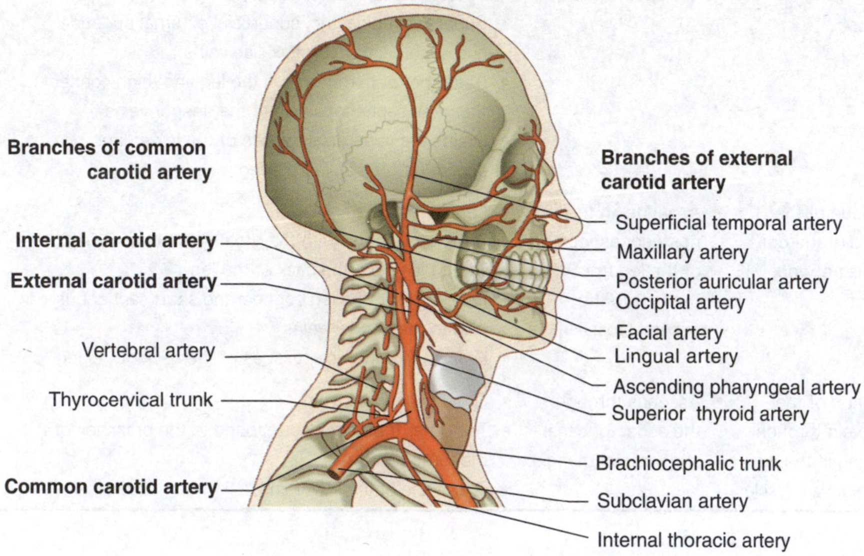

FIG. 14.14 The arteries of the head and neck.

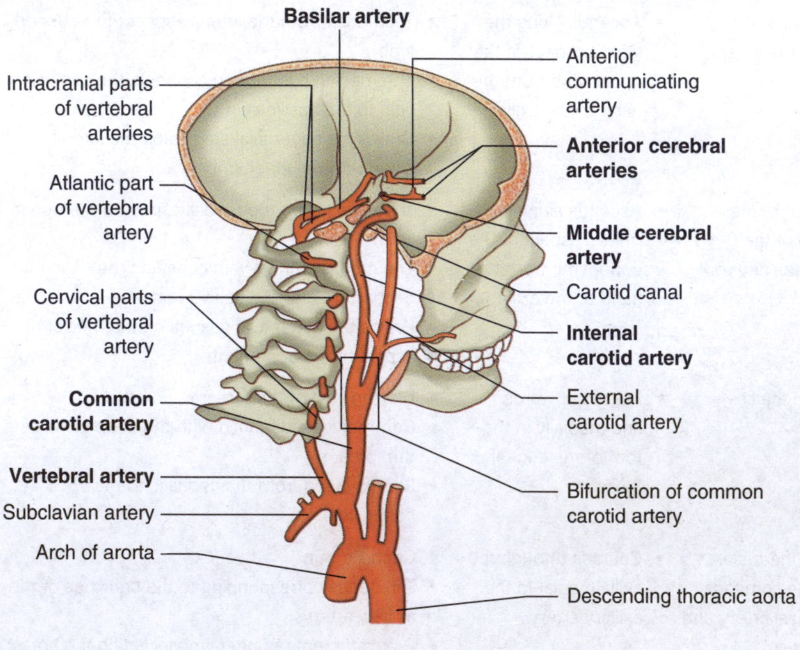

FIG. 14.15 The arteries supplying the brain.

These veins are connected to the deep veins by perforator veins. The deep veins of the limbs are often double and are known as venae comitans. The portal vein is seen in the abdomen and carries blood from the gut and its derivatives to the liver. Venous blood from the brain is drained into dural venous sinuses which are present between the two layers of dura mater. Like the arteries, the major veins will be described with the help of tables (Tables 14.8–14.12).

Table 14.8 Veins of the Lower Limb (Fig. 14.16)

Vein	Formation	Course	Tributaries and Drainage Areas	Termination
Great saphenous vein	• Continuation of the medial end of the dorsal venous network of the foot	• Ascends on the medial aspect of the lower limb from the foot to the upper thigh	• Medial marginal vein • Anterior leg vein • Posterior arch vein • Anterolateral vein of the thigh • Posteromedial vein of the thigh • Superficial epigastric, superficial external pudendal and superficial circumflex iliac veins • A number of perforators in the leg and thigh connect the great saphenous vein to the deeper veins • Drains the superficial tissues of the lower limb except for the back of the leg	• It terminates by passing through the saphenous opening in the fascia lata (deep fascia of the thigh) and drains into the femoral vein
Short saphenous vein	• Continuation of the lateral end of the dorsal venous network of the foot	• Ascends on the posterior aspect of the leg from the foot to the popliteal fossa	• Lateral marginal vein • Communications with the great saphenous vein • Tributaries from the back of the leg • Perforators in the leg connect the short saphenous vein to the deeper veins • Drains the superficial tissues of the back of the leg	• It terminates by passing through the deep fascia of the leg and drains into the popliteal vein
Femoral vein	• Continuation of the popliteal vein through the opening in the adductor magnus muscle	• Ascends through the adductor canal and femoral triangle	• Great saphenous vein • The other tributaries correspond to the branches of the femoral artery • Drains the entire lower limb	• It terminates by continuing as the external iliac vein superior to the inguinal ligament

Table 14.9 Veins of the Upper Limb (Fig. 14.17)

Cephalic vein	• Continuation of the lateral end of the dorsal venous network	• Ascends along the lateral aspect of the upper limb from the hand to the axilla	• Tributaries from the lateral aspect of the upper limb • The median cubital vein connects the cephalic vein to the basilic vein • Drains the superficial tissues on the lateral aspect of the upper limb	• It terminates by piercing the clavipectoral fascia and draining into the axillary vein
Basilic vein	• Continuation of the medial end of the dorsal venous network	• Ascends along the medial aspect of the upper limb from the hand to the axilla	• Tributaries from the medial aspect of the upper limb • The median cubital vein connects the cephalic vein to the basilic vein • Drains the superficial tissues on the medial aspect of the upper limb	• It terminates by fusing with the venae comitans of the brachial artery to form the axillary vein
Median cubital vein	• Arises from the cephalic vein	• Passes upwards and medially in the roof of the cubital fossa	• Median vein of the forearm • Communicating branch with the deep veins of the forearm • Shunts blood from the cephalic to the basilic vein	• Terminates by joining the basilic vein
Axillary vein	• Formed by the fusion of the venae comitans of the brachial artery and the basilic vein	• Courses through the axilla medial to the axillary artery	• Cephalic vein • Tributaries corresponding to the branches of the axillary artery • Drains the entire upper limb including the breast	• It terminates by continuing as the subclavian vein beyond the outer border of the first rib

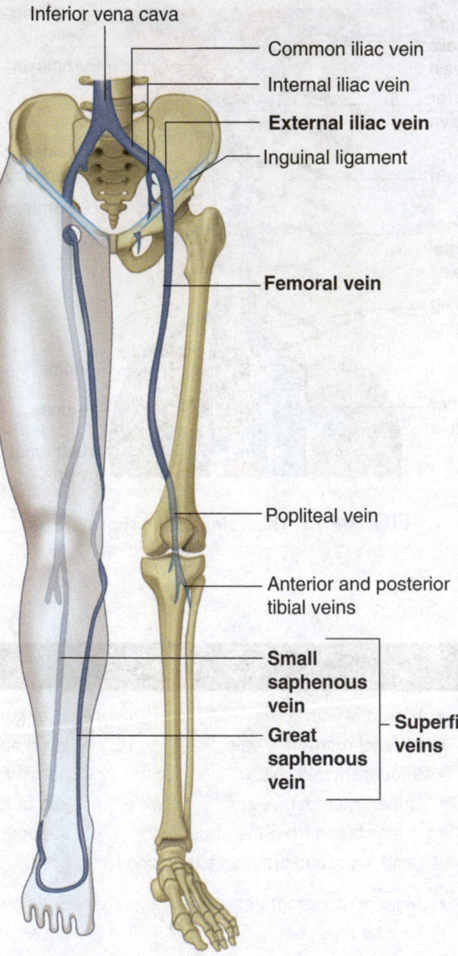

FIG. 14.16 The veins of the lower limb.

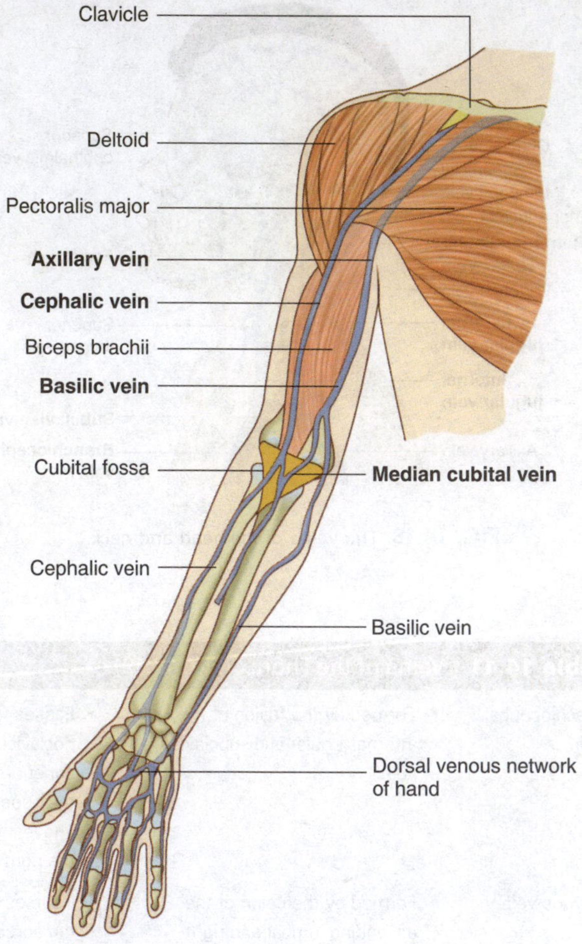

FIG. 14.17 The veins of the upper limb.

Table 14.10 Veins of the Head and Neck (Fig. 14.18)

Internal jugular vein	• Formed by fusion of the sigmoid sinus and inferior petrosal sinus	• Passes inferiorly in the carotid sheath accompanied by the internal or common carotid arteries and the vagus nerve	• Common facial vein • Superior and middle thyroid veins • Lingual vein • Drains the major part of the brain, face, thyroid gland and tongue	• It terminates by joining the subclavian vein to form the brachiocephalic vein
Retromandibular vein	• Formed by the fusion of the maxillary and superficial temporal veins within the parotid gland	• Passes inferiorly within the parotid gland and divides into anterior and posterior divisions	• Anterior division fuses with the facial vein to form the common facial vein • Posterior division fuses with the posterior auricular vein to form the external jugular vein • Drains structures in the temporal region, infratemporal fossa, scalp and face	• It terminates by giving its two divisions within or just outside the parotid gland
External jugular vein	• Formed by the fusion of the posterior division of the retromandibular vein with the posterior auricular vein	• Passes along the roof of the posterior triangle of the neck	• Suprascapular vein • Transverse cervical vein • Anterior jugular vein • Drains the neck and scalp	• It terminates by draining into the subclavian vein at the root of the neck
Subclavian vein	• Formed by the continuation of the axillary vein beyond the outer border of the first rib	• Passes medially in the root of the neck over the first rib	• External jugular vein • The thoracic duct and right lymphatic duct drain into the junction of the subclavian vein and the internal jugular vein on each side • Drains blood from the upper limb, face and scalp	• It terminates by fusing with the internal jugular vein to form the brachiocephalic vein on each side

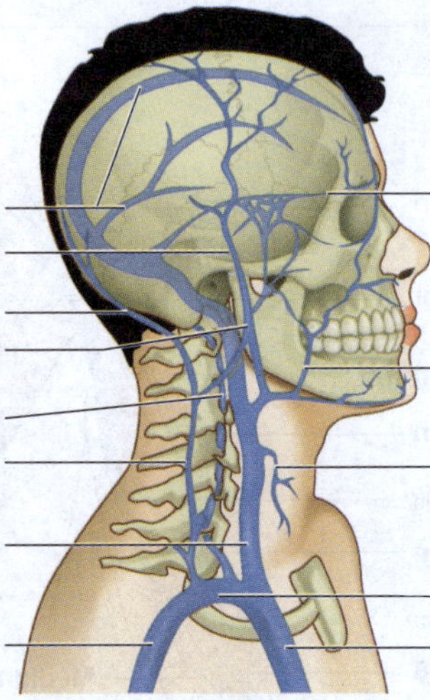

FIG. 14.18 The veins of the head and neck.

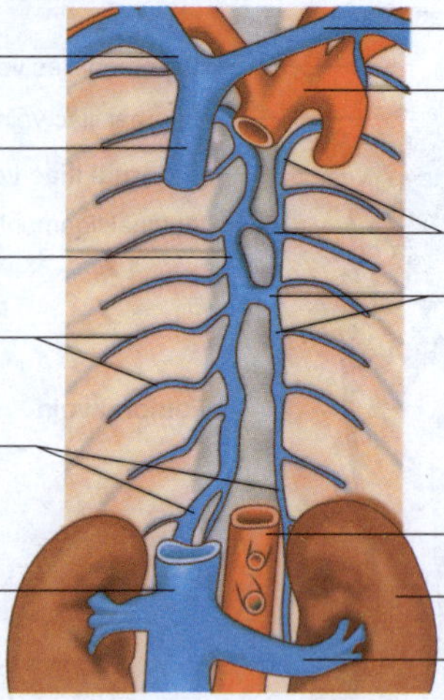

FIG. 14.19 The veins of the thorax.

Table 14.11 Veins of the Thorax (Fig. 14.19)

Brachiocephalic vein	• Formed by the fusion of the internal jugular and subclavian vein	• Passes from behind the sternoclavicular joint towards the superior vena cava within the superior mediastinum • The left vein is longer than the right	• Vertebral vein • Internal mammary vein • Inferior thyroid vein • Upper intercostal veins • Drains blood from the upper limb, head, neck and brain on either side	• The right and left brachiocephalic veins join to form the superior vena cava
Azygos vein	• Formed by the union of the ascending lumbar and right subcostal veins	• Courses upwards through the aortic opening of the diaphragm and then in the posterior mediastinum	• Right posterior intercostal veins • Hemiazygos vein • Accessory hemiazygos vein • Right bronchial vein • Oesophageal, pericardial and mediastinal veins • Drains blood from the chest wall and mediastinal structures	• Ends by forming an arch which drains into the superior vena cava
Superior vena cava	• Formed by the fusion of the two brachiocephalic veins	• Passes behind the right sternal margin from the first to the third ribs	• Azygos vein • Drains blood from the upper limb, head, neck, brain and thorax	• Drains into the right atrium
Pulmonary veins	• The right and left superior and inferior pulmonary veins are formed within the lungs and exit at the hila	• From the hila, each pair of pulmonary veins courses medially	• Carry oxygenated blood to the left atrium	• Terminate in the left atrium

APPLIED ANATOMY

- **Arteriography** is the radiological visualization of arteries by the injection of radiopaque solutions into the vascular system.
- **Venography** is the radiological visualization of veins by the injection of radiopaque solutions into the vascular system.
- **Venepuncture** refers to the puncture of a vein to withdraw blood.
- Muscular spasm of the smooth muscle in the wall of a blood vessel is called **vasospasm**.
- **Atherosclerosis** is the development of plaques (fatty deposits) on the inner lining of the arterial walls. This often produces narrowing of the lumen of the arteries known as **stenosis.**
- An **embolus** is a detachable blood clot which can block blood supply to a region.
- **Thrombosis** is the formation of a blood clot in a vein in response to inflammation of the venous wall or prolonged stasis of blood.
- The pathological weakening of an arterial wall causing dilatation is known as an **aneurysm**.
- Aneurysms of the **arch of the aorta** may produce visible suprasternal pulsations.
- **Renal artery** stenosis may be a cause for hypertension.
- The **femoral artery** is often used for the introduction of a catheter for coronary angiography.

Table 14.12 Veins of the Abdomen and Pelvis (Figs 14.20 and 14.21)

Portal vein	• Formed by fusion of the splenic and superior mesenteric veins	• Formed behind the neck of the pancreas • Ascends in the right free margin of the lesser omentum • Enters the liver at the porta hepatis	• Paraumbilical veins • Cystic vein • Gastric veins • Drains the gut, liver, pancreas and spleen	• Enters the liver and branches repeatedly, finally carrying blood to the sinusoids
Common iliac vein	• Formed by the union of the internal and external iliac veins	• Passes from the level of the sacroiliac joint to the fifth lumbar vertebra to the right of the midline	• Iliolumbar vein • Lateral sacral vein • Median sacral vein • Drains the lower limbs and pelvis	• The two common iliac veins unite to form the inferior vena cava
Inferior vena cava	• Formed by fusion of the two common iliac veins	• Ascends along the posterior abdominal wall to the right of abdominal aorta to reach the caval opening in the diaphragm	• Renal veins • Right suprarenal vein • Inferior phrenic veins • Right gonadal vein • Lumbar veins • Hepatic veins • Drains the lower limbs, abdomen and pelvis	• Drains into the right atrium

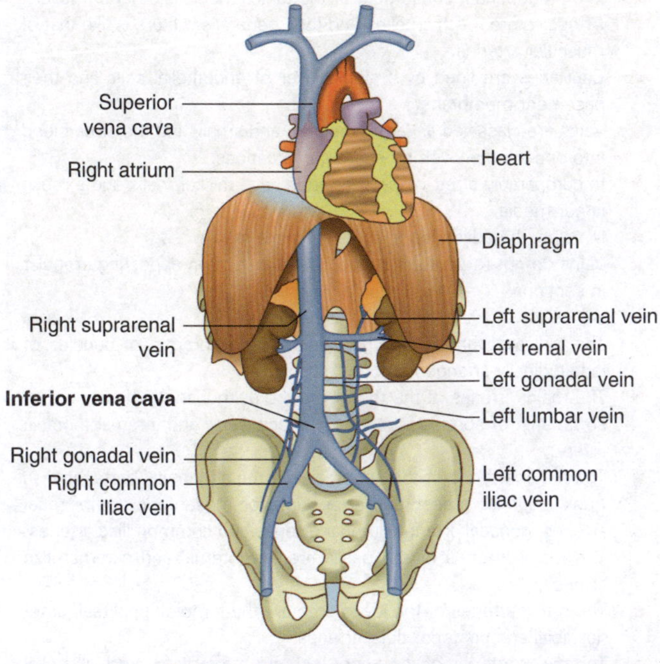

FIG. 14.20 The inferior vena cava.

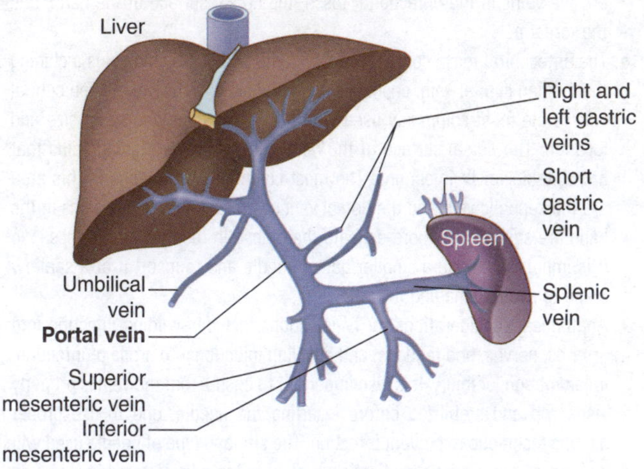

FIG. 14.21 The portal vein.

- Pulsations of the **anterior and posterior tibial arteries** are palpated when there is suspected peripheral vascular disease of the lower limb.
- The **brachial artery** is palpated and auscultated in the cubital fossa when taking blood pressure measurements.
- The **radial artery** is palpated over the lower end of the radius when taking the pulse of a subject.
- Stenosis of the **common carotid or internal carotid artery** due to atherosclerosis can lead to decreased blood supply to the brain and transient ischaemic attacks.
- The **carotid sinus** is massaged to reduce abnormally high heart rates due to supraventricular tachycardias.
- **Varicose veins** refer to the abnormal tortuosity and dilatation of superficial veins of the lower limb due to valve incompetence in the perforator veins.
- The **femoral vein** can be accessed for venepuncture as it is relatively superficial and large.
- The **superficial veins of the upper limb** provide convenient access points for venepuncture.
- A **surgical arteriovenous anastomosis** between the cephalic vein and radial artery is created to provide a convenient location to access the vascular system for renal dialysis.
- The **jugular venous pulse and pressure** are observed in the internal jugular vein, as it reflects the right atrial pressure.
- The **internal jugular and subclavian veins** are used to place central venous lines.
- **Portal hypertension** causes the anastomoses between veins of the portal venous system and systemic veins to open at certain sites. The common sites are the lower end of the oesophagus, the umbilicus and the rectum. Rupture of

dilated veins at the lower end of the oesophagus (oesophageal varices) can cause fatal bleeding.

- When either the superior or the inferior vena cava is blocked, the **azygos** provides a collateral pathway for venous blood to reach the right atrium.

APPLICATIONS IN NURSING

- An important component of monitoring a patient is the recording of the **pulse.** This is most often done using the radial artery. The radial artery is relatively superficial and can be conveniently palpated over the lower end of the radius.
- The recording of **blood pressure** is a common procedure that needs to be mastered by nurses. This involves tying an inflatable cuff around the arm and placing the stethoscope on the brachial artery in the cubital fossa just medial to the tendon of the biceps brachii. The popliteal artery is similarly used for measuring blood pressure in the lower limb.
- Blood is drawn from the superficial veins of the upper limb for various tests. This procedure is termed **phlebotomy** or **venipuncture.** Certain drugs are administered through the intravenous route. Nurses must be proficient in these procedures. The most common sites used for IV injections are the veins in the antecubital fossa, the dorsal surface of the hand, and the forearm.
- The antecubital fossa contains several large and accessible veins including the median cubital vein, cephalic vein, and basilic vein. The median cubital vein is the most commonly used vein for IV injections due to its size and location. The dorsal surface of the hand contains several small veins that are suitable for IV injections. The most commonly used veins in this area are the cephalic vein and the dorsal venous arch. However, the veins in the hand are smaller and more delicate than those in the antecubital fossa, so it is important to use a smaller gauge needle and to insert it at a shallow angle to avoid damaging the vein.
- Anatomical considerations for IV injections include avoiding injection into arteries, nerves, and tendons, and avoiding injection into areas of infection, inflammation, or injury. It is also important to ensure that the vein is properly visualized and stabilized before inserting the needle, and to use proper aseptic technique to prevent infection. The size and type of needle used will depend on the specific medication or fluid being administered, as well as the size and location of the vein.
- **Pulse oximetry** is a simple and painless procedure to noninvasively estimate oxygen saturation in arterial blood by placing a pulse oximeter over the tip of a digit. The oxygen saturation is an important parameter that is routinely monitored by nurses, more so with the COVID-19 pandemic.

SUMMARY

- Blood flows from the heart into the conducting vessels which are elastic arteries.
- The blood then passes into the muscular arteries which function as distributing vessels.
- The smallest subdivisions of arteries are the arterioles which are resistance vessels and regulate blood flow into the tissues.
- Exchange of gases at the tissue level occurs through capillaries.
- Venules then carry blood to the medium-sized veins which unite to form large veins that drain into the atria.
- The arterioles, capillaries and venules are together called the microcirculation.
- The walls of larger blood vessels have three layers, namely an inner tunica intima, a middle tunica media and an outer tunica adventitia.
- The tunica intima consists of an endothelial layer with a basal lamina, subendothelial connective tissue and the internal elastic lamina.
- Muscle tissue, elastic and collagen fibres constitute the tunica media which is bounded by the external elastic lamina.
- The tunica adventitia consists of connective tissue which may contain blood vessels (vasa vasorum) and nerves (nervi vascularis).
- The systemic circulation is a high-pressure system that carries blood to all the tissues of the body except the lungs.
- The pulmonary circulation is a low-pressure system that is required for oxygenation of blood.
- A portal circulation is one that begins and ends as capillaries.
- The connection between two vessels is called an anastomosis.
- Arteries can be classified into three types according to their size, namely large or elastic arteries, medium-sized or muscular arteries and small arteries or arterioles.
- Their characteristic feature, regardless of size, is a well-defined round or oval lumen, maintained by the muscularity of the vessel wall.
- Large arteries like the aorta and pulmonary artery are characterized by their great elasticity.
- The distinguishing features of large arteries are their large lumen and the presence of abundant elastic fibres in the tunica media.
- Most of the named arteries are medium-sized arteries.
- They have a smaller lumen as compared to large arteries and have less elastic tissue in the tunica media.
- The predominant constituent of the tunica media is smooth muscle.
- Arterioles are much smaller, and their general structure is like that of muscular arteries.
- Capillaries are lined by a single layer of endothelial cells and their basement membrane.
- Veins are classified as large, medium and small, and the sizes blend into one another with no sharp demarcations.
- In comparably sized vessels, arteries have thicker walls and a much larger media.
- In veins, the adventitia is larger than the media.
- Veins do not retain their shape, the lumen often appearing irregular in sections.
- Valves are a distinctive feature of veins.
- The tunica adventitia in large veins contains prominent bundles of longitudinally arranged smooth muscle.
- The major arteries of the thorax are the pulmonary trunk, ascending aorta, arch of aorta, descending thoracic aorta and internal thoracic artery.
- The major arteries of the abdomen are the abdominal aorta, coeliac trunk, superior mesenteric artery, inferior mesenteric artery, renal arteries, gonadal arteries, lumbar arteries and common iliac arteries.
- The major arteries of the pelvis are the internal and external iliac arteries.
- The major arteries of the lower limb are the femoral, popliteal, anterior tibial and posterior tibial arteries.
- The major arteries of the upper limb are the axillary, brachial, radial and ulnar arteries.
- The major arteries of the head, neck and brain are the common carotid, internal carotid, external carotid and subclavian arteries.
- The major superficial and deep veins of the lower limb are the great saphenous vein, short saphenous vein and femoral vein.
- The major superficial and deep veins of the upper limb are the cephalic vein, basilic vein, median cubital and axillary vein.
- The major veins of the head and neck are the internal jugular, external jugular and subclavian veins.
- The major veins of the thorax are the right and left brachiocephalic veins, the superior vena cava and the azygos vein.
- The major veins of the abdomen are the common iliac vein, portal vein and inferior vena cava.

CHAPTER 15

The Pericardium, Exterior of the Heart and Its Blood Supply

SPECIFIC LEARNING OBJECTIVES

At the end of this chapter, the student should be able to:

- Describe the gross anatomy of the pericardium.
- Describe the external features of the heart.
- Explain the blood supply of the heart and its clinical importance.

GLOSSARY OF TERMS

- **Fibrous pericardium:** outer layer of the pericardium
- **Serous pericardium:** formed by outer parietal and inner serous parts separated by a pericardial cavity containing pericardial fluid
- **Pericardial sinuses:** spaces formed between prolongations of the serous pericardium over the great blood vessels of the heart
- **Endocardium:** inner layer of the heart lined by simple squamous epithelium
- **Myocardium:** middle thick muscular layer of the heart
- **Epicardium:** outer layer of the heart, otherwise called the visceral layer of serous pericardium
- **Coronary arteries:** arteries supplying the heart
- **Aortic sinuses:** spaces above the leaflets of the aortic valve from where the coronary arteries arise
- **Coronary sinus:** main vein draining blood from the heart

INTRODUCTION

The heart is a hollow muscular organ that functions as a complex pump. It has atria for receiving venous blood and ventricles for driving blood into arteries for distribution to the body. The contraction of the atria and ventricles is regulated by the conduction system of the heart, which in turn is influenced by the autonomic nervous system. The right side of the heart contains deoxygenated blood, whereas oxygenated blood flows through the left side. The interatrial and interventricular septa ensure that deoxygenated and oxygenated blood do not mix. Valves regulate the flow of blood from the atria to the ventricles and from the ventricles into the arteries. The pericardium protects and anchors the heart, prevents overfilling of the heart with blood and allows for the heart to work in a relatively friction-free environment. The heart requires a rich blood supply to perform its functions. This is provided by the coronary arteries and the coronary sinus.

THE PERICARDIUM

The **pericardial cavity** is a double-walled sac around the heart composed of a superficial **fibrous pericardium** and a deep two-layered **serous pericardium** (Figs 15.1 and 15.2). The fibrous pericardium is attached to the diaphragm inferiorly and merges superiorly with the adventitia of the great vessels that emerge from the heart. Anteriorly, it is attached to the sternum by the sternopericardial ligaments. On either side, it is related to the mediastinal surfaces of the lungs. The phrenic nerves run along the lateral aspects of the fibrous pericardium bilaterally. The **parietal layer** of the serous pericardium lines the internal surface of the fibrous pericardium, while the **visceral layer** or epicardium lines the outer surface of the heart. The serous pericardium also encloses the great vessels that emerge from the heart. Two **pericardial sinuses** can be defined between the pericardial prolongations over the great vessels (Fig. 15.3). The **transverse sinus** is seen between the arterial tubes anteriorly and venous tubes posteriorly, while the **oblique sinus** is located between the two pairs of pulmonary veins. A **fluid-filled** pericardial cavity separates the visceral and parietal layers of the serous pericardium. This is a mechanism to reduce the friction during movements of the heart. The fibrous pericardium and parietal layer of serous pericardium are supplied by the **phrenic nerves** which are somatic nerves. **Arterial supply** to these structures is through branches of the internal thoracic, bronchial, oesophageal and superior phrenic arteries. **Venous drainage** is into the internal thoracic and azygos veins. The nerve supply (sympathetic and parasympathetic) and blood supply (coronary vessels) of the visceral pericardium corresponds to that of the heart.

THE EXTERNAL FEATURES OF THE HEART

The heart is approximately the size of a fist and weighs around 300 g. It rests on the thoracoabdominal diaphragm and lies between the two pleural cavities in the **middle mediastinum** (Fig. 15.4). The sternum lies anterior, while the vertebral column is posterior to the heart. As the heart is **rotated** to the **left**, a major part of it lies to the left of the midline. It has **four chambers**, namely the **right atrium** which receives blood from the systemic circuit, the **right ventricle** which pumps blood to the pulmonary circuit, the **left atrium** which receives blood from the pulmonary circuit and the **left ventricle** which pumps blood to the systemic circuit. The atria are located posterior and superior to the ventricles. The chambers of the heart are made up of three layers (Fig. 15.5). Innermost is the **endocardium**, which is lined by simple squamous epithelium underlying which is a thin layer of connective tissue. The middle layer is the **myocardium** which is by far the thickest layer and consists of cardiac muscle fibres arranged in various orientations. External to the myocardium is the **epicardium** which is otherwise called the visceral layer of the serous pericardium.

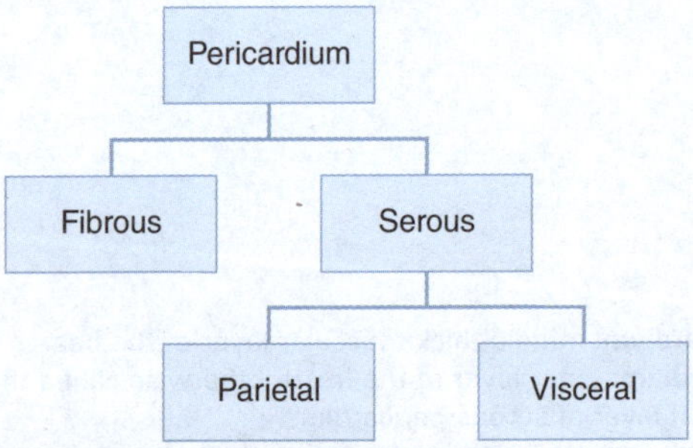

FIG. 15.1 The parts of the pericardium.

The heart has an apex, base, three surfaces and three borders (Fig. 15.6). The **apex** of the heart is formed by the left ventricle. It is situated in the left fifth intercostal space just medial to the mid-clavicular line. The **base** or posterior surface of the heart faces posteriorly and is formed by the left and right atria. Located posterior to the sternum is the anterior or **sternocostal surface.** It is formed mainly by the right ventricle and partially by the left ventricle. The inferior or **diaphragmatic surface** rests on the dome of the diaphragm, formed mainly by the left ventricle and partially by the right ventricle. The **left surface** is related to the mediastinal surface of the left lung and is formed almost entirely by the left ventricle. The surfaces are separated by borders. The **right border** is formed by the right atrium and extends from the opening of the superior vena cava above to the opening of the inferior vena cava below. The sharp **inferior border** extends from the lower end of the right border to the apex of the heart. This border separates the sternocostal surface

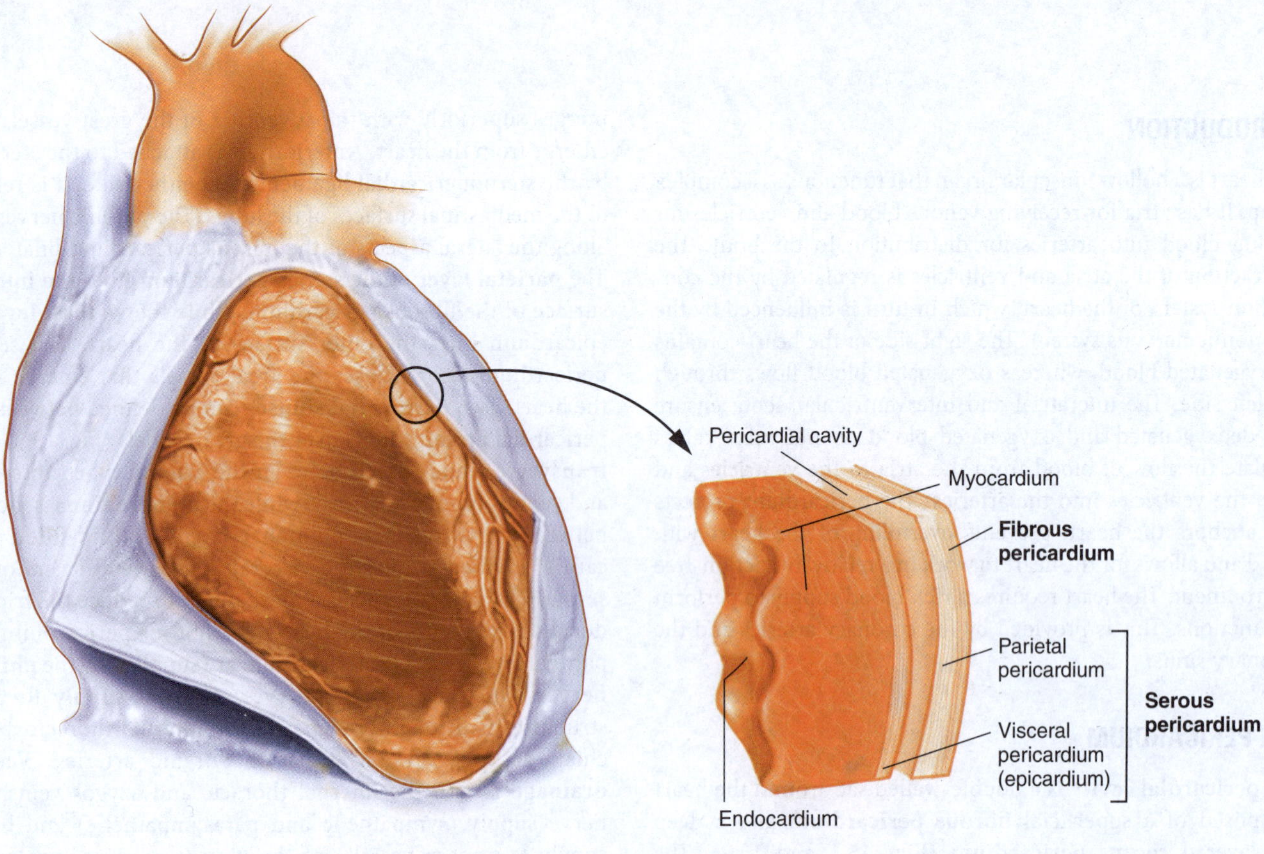

FIG. 15.2 The layers of the pericardium.

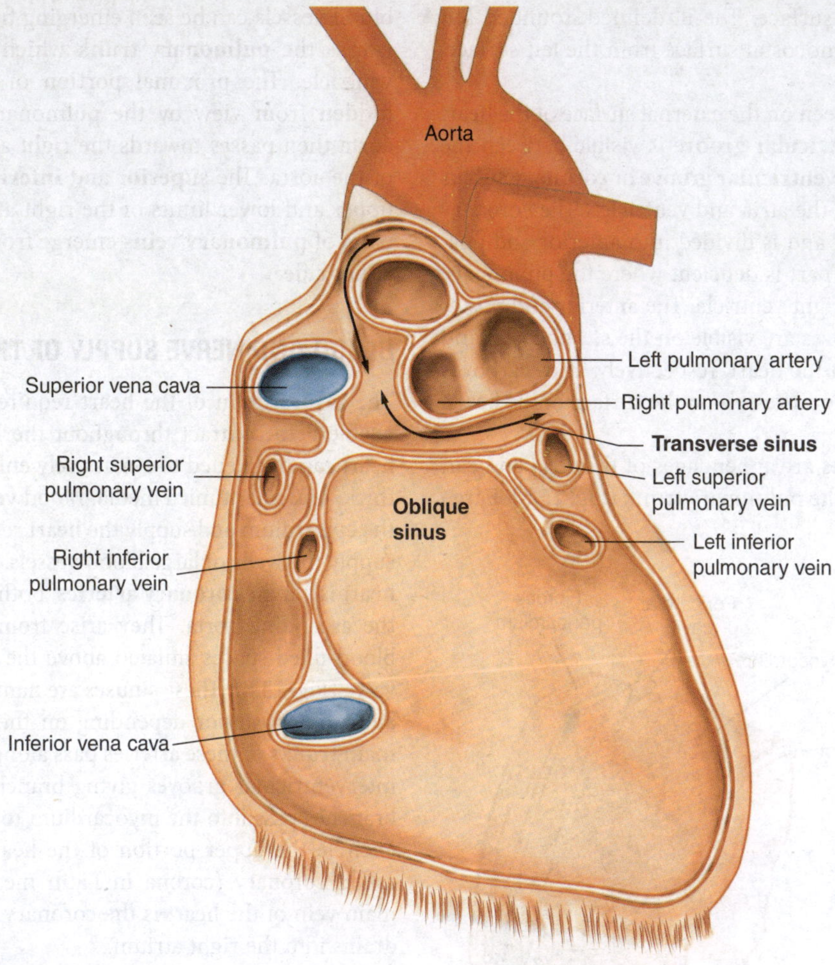

FIG. 15.3 The sinuses of the pericardium.

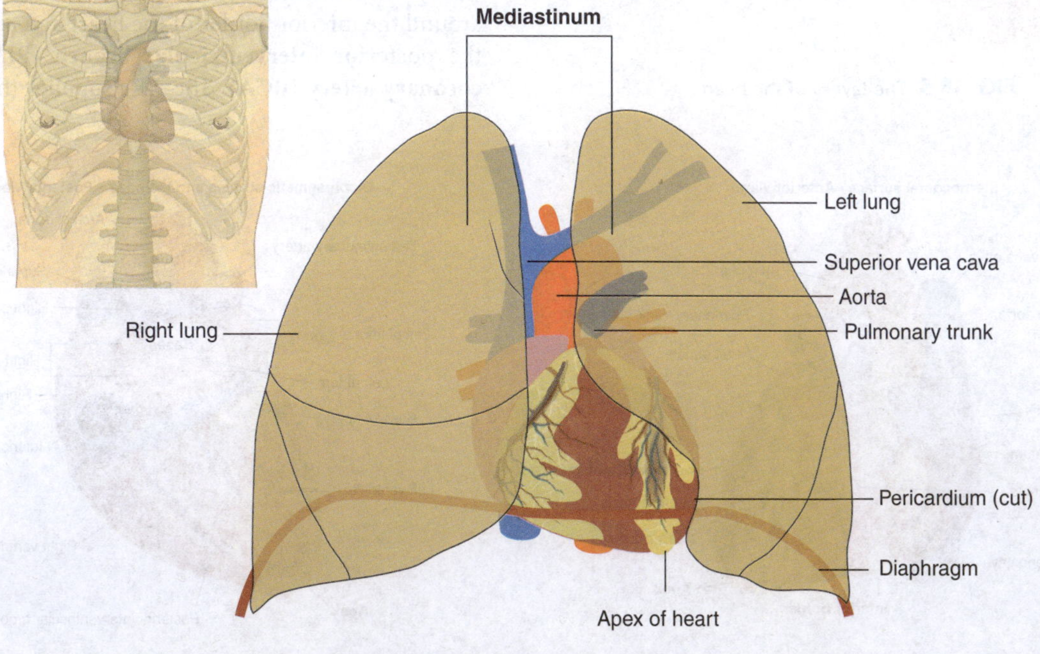

FIG. 15.4 The location of the heart.

from the diaphragmatic surface. The ill-defined, rounded **left border** separates the sternocostal surface from the left surface.

Two grooves or sulci are seen on the external surface of the heart (Fig. 15.7). The **interventricular groove** is visible between the ventricles, while the **atrioventricular groove** or **coronary sulcus** can be observed between the atria and ventricles. The coronary sulcus encircles the heart and is divided into anterior and posterior parts. The anterior part is deficient where the pulmonary trunk emerges from the right ventricle. The anterior and posterior interventricular grooves are visible on the sternocostal and diaphragmatic surfaces of the heart, respectively. These grooves allow for the passage of blood vessels on the surface of the heart.

The right and left **auricles** are appendages of the atria and can be seen on either side of the pulmonary trunk (Fig. 15.6). Large blood vessels can be seen emerging from the heart. Most anterior is the **pulmonary trunk** which emerges from the right ventricle. The proximal portion of the **ascending aorta** is hidden from view by the pulmonary trunk. The ascending aorta then passes towards the right and continues as the arch of the aorta. The **superior** and **inferior venae cavae** enter the upper and lower limits of the right atrium. The **right** and **left** pairs of **pulmonary veins** emerge from behind the auricles on either side.

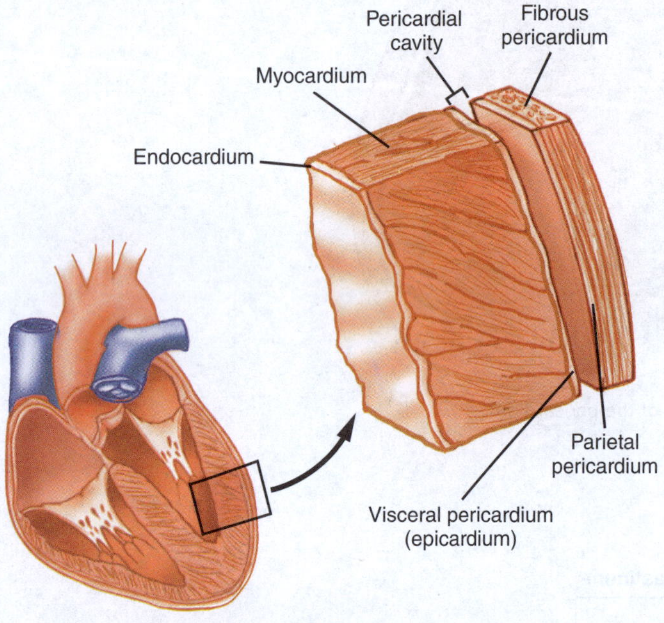

FIG. 15.5 The layers of the heart.

BLOOD AND NERVE SUPPLY OF THE HEART

The myocardium of the heart requires a rich blood supply to enable it to contract throughout the life of an individual. The heart can be likened to a massively enlarged blood vessel with a thick, muscular tunica media. Blood vessels that course through the epicardium and supply the heart resemble vasa vasorum that supply the walls of large blood vessels. The arterial supply of the heart is via the **coronary arteries**, both of which are branches of the ascending aorta. They arise from **aortic sinuses** that are blood-filled spaces situated above the three cusps of the aortic valve (Fig. 15.8). These sinuses are named anterior, left posterior and right posterior depending on their relative locations. The main trunks of these arteries pass along the atrioventricular and interventricular grooves giving branches along the way. These branches pass into the myocardium to supply it. As the arteries encircle the upper portion of the heart like a crown, they are called coronary (corona in Latin means crown) arteries. The main vein of the heart is the coronary sinus, from which blood drains into the right atrium.

The **left coronary artery (LCA)** is the larger of the two coronary arteries (Fig. 15.9). It arises from the left posterior aortic sinus. It soon divides into the anterior interventricular and circumflex arteries. The **anterior interventricular artery (AIA)** passes along the anterior interventricular groove, winds around the inferior border of the heart and anastomoses with the **posterior interventricular branch (PIA)** of the **right coronary artery (RCA)**. The AIA supplies the anterior walls

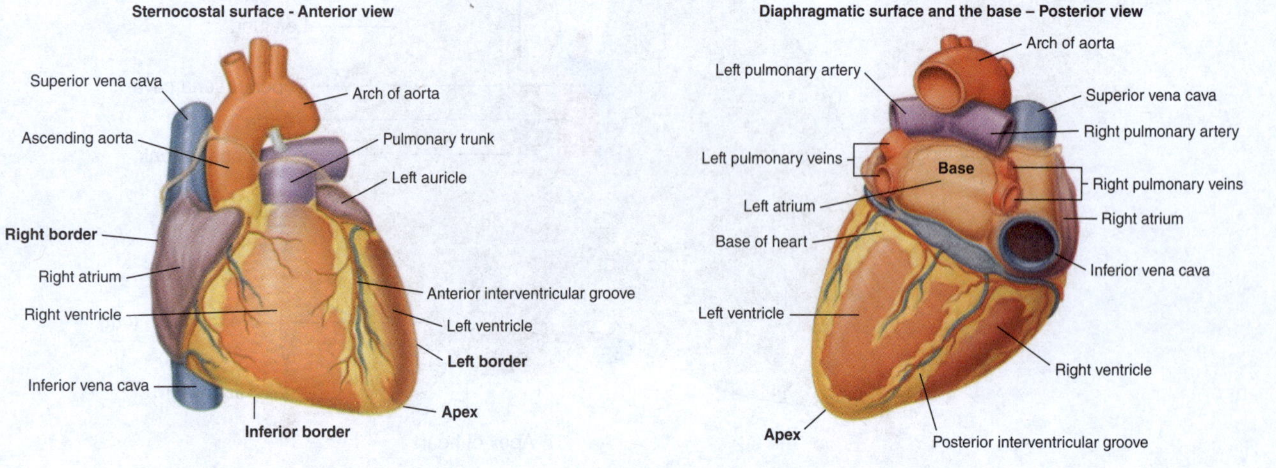

FIG. 15.6 The external features of the heart.

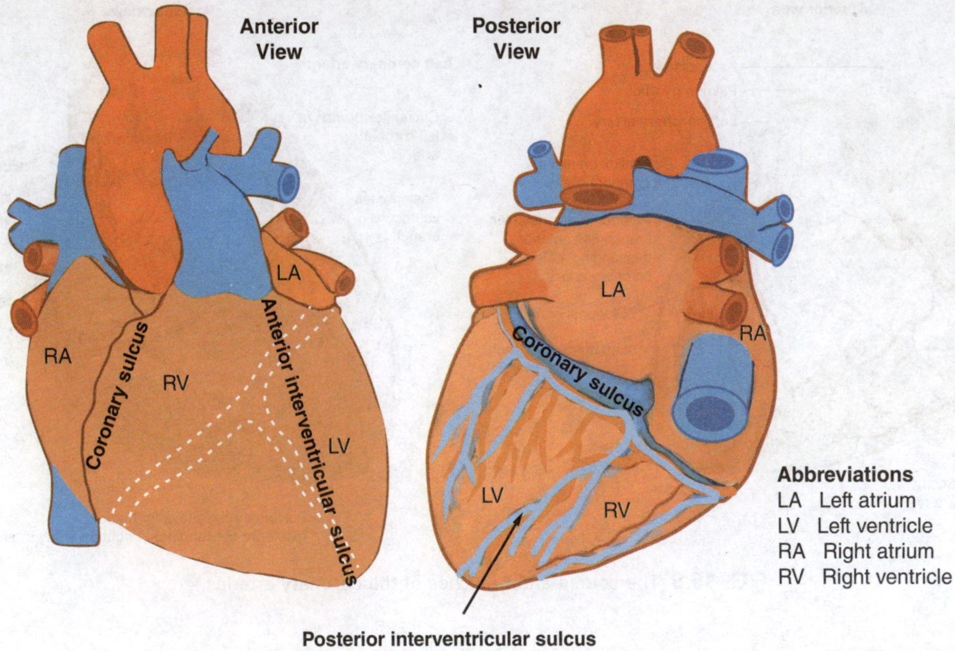

FIG. 15.7 The sulci of the heart.

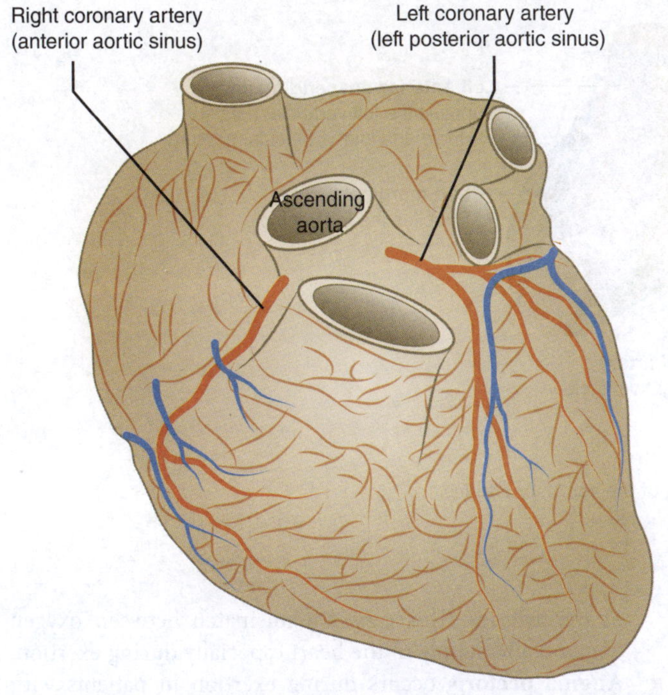

FIG. 15.8 The origin of the coronary arteries from the aortic sinuses.

of both the right and left ventricles and the anterior part of the interventricular septum (Fig. 15.10). After arising from the LCA, the circumflex artery (CA) passes along the left half of the coronary sulcus and ends by anastomosing with the RCA in the posterior part of the coronary sulcus. It gives off the left marginal branch which passes along the left border of the heart. The CA supplies the left ventricle and left atrium (Fig. 15.10).

The **RCA** arises from the anterior aortic sinus and passes along the right half of the coronary sulcus (Fig. 15.9). It terminates in the posterior part of the coronary sulcus by anastomosing with CA. Before its termination, it gives off the **PIA** that passes along the posterior interventricular groove and anastomoses with AIA. It also gives off the **right marginal** artery which passes along the inferior border of the heart. The RCA supplies the right atrium, the right ventricle, a portion of the left ventricle adjoining the posterior interventricular groove, the posterior part of the interventricular septum and most of the conducting system of the heart (Fig. 15.10).

Nearly all venous blood from the heart drains into the **CS** (Fig. 15.11). The CS is situated near the centre of the posterior part of the coronary sulcus. It drains into the posterior part of the **right atrium** near the opening of the inferior vena cava. Its tributaries include the great cardiac, middle cardiac and small cardiac veins which pass along the anterior interventricular, posterior interventricular and atrioventricular grooves, respectively. The posterior vein of the left ventricle and oblique vein of the left atrium also drain into the CS. The anterior cardiac veins are seen on the sternocostal surface of the right ventricle and drain directly into the right atrium. The autonomic **nerve supply** of the heart is through the cardiac plexus. The sympathetic fibres arise from T1 to T4 segments of the spinal cord, whereas parasympathetic fibres arise from the vagus nerve.

APPLIED ANATOMY

- Inflammation of the pericardium is known as **pericarditis.** A common symptom of this condition is the sudden onset of sharp chest pain.

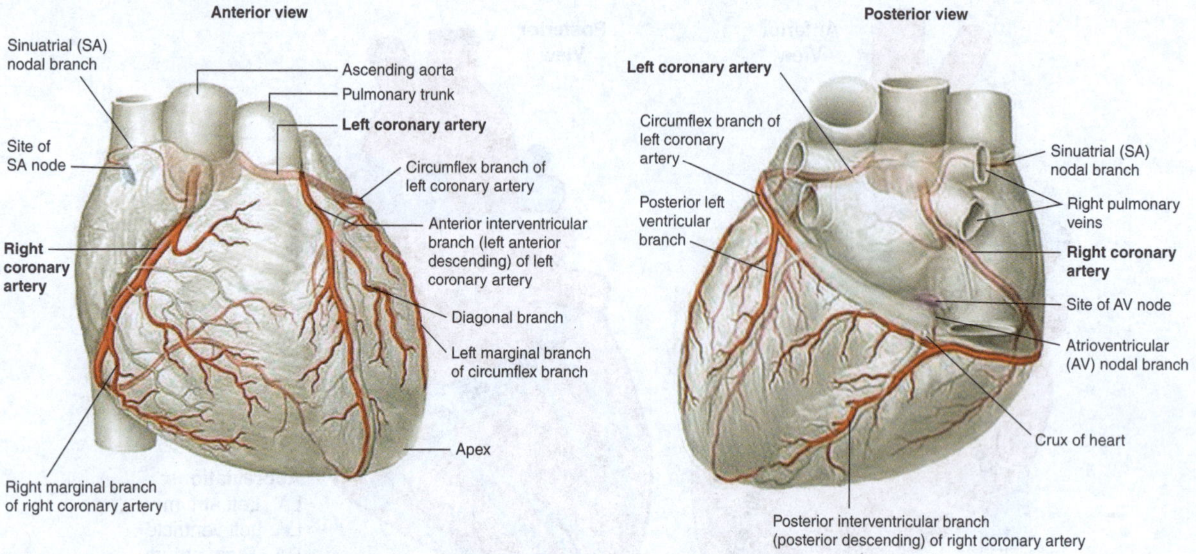

FIG. 15.9 The course and branches of the coronary arteries.

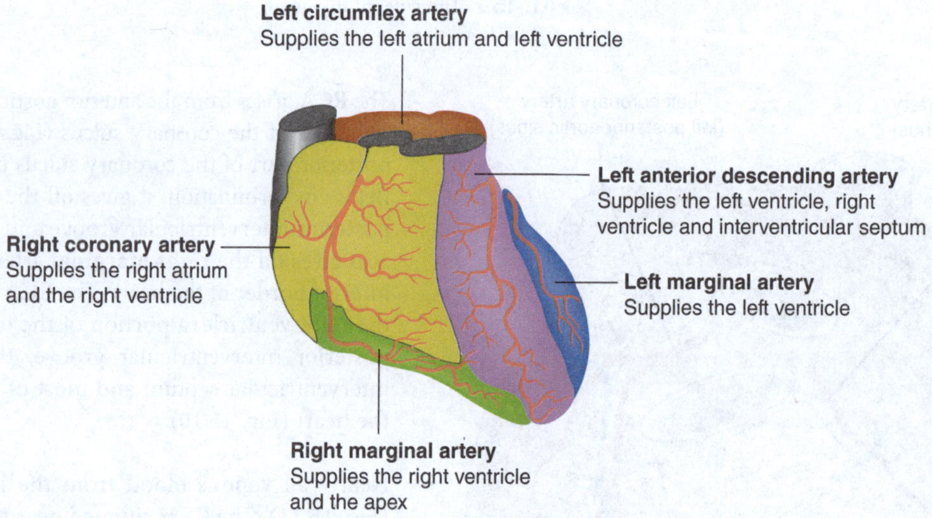

FIG. 15.10 The distribution of the coronary arteries.

- **Pericardial effusion** refers to the excessive collection of fluid in the pericardial cavity. When the volume of fluid is great enough to impair functioning of the heart, the condition is known as cardiac tamponade.
- The removal of fluid through a needle inserted in the fifth or sixth intercostal space or in the infrasternal angle is called **pericardiocentesis.**
- **Cardiomyopathies** are a group of disorders that cause malfunctioning of the myocardium.
- **Myocarditis** refers to inflammation of the heart muscle, most commonly due to viral infections.
- **Ischaemic heart disease** is caused by a narrowing of the coronary arteries or their branches. The most common cause is atherosclerosis or fat deposition in the tunica intima of the arteries. This causes a mismatch between oxygen demand and supply to the heart especially during exertion.
- **Angina pectoris** occurs during exertion in patients with ischaemic heart disease. The pain is retrosternal, constricting in nature and radiates to the left side of the neck and along the medial side of the left upper limb. The pain is relieved on taking rest or nitroglycerin tablets.
- **Myocardial infarction** is commonly known as a 'heart attack'. It is caused by infarction of a portion of the myocardium due to cessation of blood flow to that part. The pain during a myocardial infarction is like that of angina except that it is more severe and is not relieved by rest or nitroglycerin. Sweating, hypotension and arrhythmias sometimes accompany myocardial infarctions.

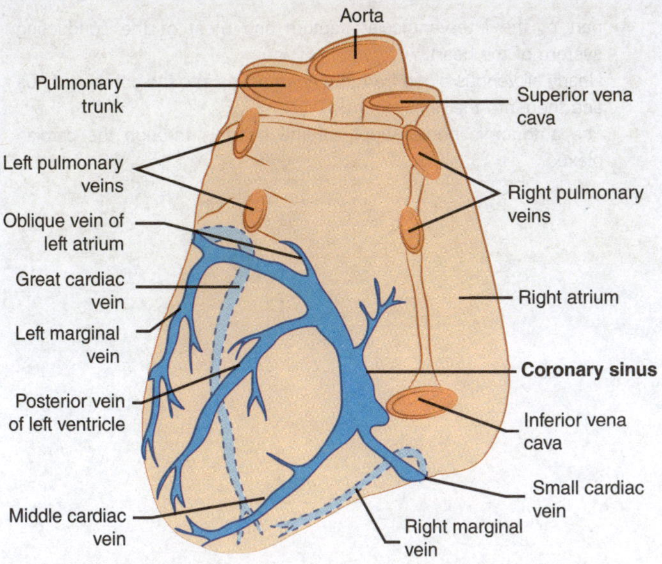

FIG. 15.11 The coronary sinus and its tributaries – view from below and behind.

- The diagnosis of stenosis of coronary arteries by radiopaque dyes injected into the coronary vessels is called **angiography**.
- **Angioplasty** refers to the placement of stents in the narrowed portions of coronary arteries to relieve the stenosis and restore normal blood flow.
- **Coronary bypass surgery** is performed using small lengths of the great saphenous vein or the internal thoracic artery to bypass the stenosed portion of a coronary artery.

APPLICATIONS IN NURSING

- The **heart sounds** can be auscultated by placing the stethoscope over the precordium. The **apex beat** can be palpated in the left fifth intercostal space just medial to the mid-clavicular line.
- Delivering **cardiopulmonary resuscitation** in patients with a cardiac arrest is an essential skill. As part of the resuscitation, cardiac compressions are performed by placing the palm over the precordium and depressing the sternum. This compresses the heart between the sternum and vertebral column.
- Chest leads for **electrocardiography (ECG)** must be placed over the chest wall at six specific locations. The correct placement of these leads is essential for making an accurate diagnosis.

SUMMARY

- The pericardial cavity is a double-walled sac around the heart composed of a superficial fibrous pericardium and deep two-layered serous pericardium.
- The fibrous pericardium is attached to the diaphragm inferiorly and merges superiorly with the adventitia of the great vessels that emerge from the heart.
- The parietal layer of the serous pericardium lines the internal surface of the fibrous pericardium, while the visceral layer or epicardium lines the outer surface of the heart.
- The transverse sinus is seen between the arterial tubes anteriorly and venous tubes posteriorly, while the oblique sinus is located between the two pairs of pulmonary veins.
- A fluid-filled pericardial cavity separates the visceral and parietal layers of the serous pericardium.
- The fibrous pericardium and parietal layer of serous pericardium are supplied by the phrenic nerves which are somatic nerves.
- The nerve (sympathetic and parasympathetic) and blood supply (coronary arteries) of the visceral pericardium corresponds to that of the heart.
- The heart rests on the thoracoabdominal diaphragm and lies between the two pleural cavities in the middle mediastinum.
- As the heart is rotated to the left, a major part of it lies to the left of the midline.
- It has four chambers, namely the right atrium which receives blood from the systemic circuit, the right ventricle which pumps blood to the pulmonary circuit, the left atrium which receives blood from the pulmonary circuit and the left ventricle which pumps blood to the systemic circuit.
- The chambers of the heart are made up of three layers.
- Innermost is the endocardium which is lined by simple squamous epithelium underlying which is a thin layer of connective tissue.
- The middle layer is the myocardium which is by far the thickest layer and consists of cardiac muscle arranged in various orientations.
- External to the myocardium is the epicardium which is otherwise called the visceral layer of serous pericardium.
- The heart has an apex, base, three surfaces and three borders.
- The apex of the heart is formed by the left ventricle and is situated in the left fifth intercostal space just medial to the mid-clavicular line.
- The base or posterior surface of the heart faces posteriorly and is formed by the left and right atria.
- Located posterior to the sternum is the anterior or sternocostal surface, formed mainly by the right ventricle and partially by the left ventricle.
- The inferior or diaphragmatic surface rests on the dome of the diaphragm, formed mainly by the left ventricle and partially by the right ventricle.
- The left surface is related to the mediastinal surface of the left lung and is formed almost entirely by the left ventricle.
- The right border is formed by the right atrium and extends from the opening of the superior vena cava above to the opening of the inferior vena cava below.
- The sharp inferior border extends from the lower end of the right border to the apex of the heart.
- The ill-defined, rounded left border separates the sternocostal from the left surface.
- Two grooves or sulci are seen on the external surface of the heart.
- The interventricular groove is visible between the ventricles, while the atrioventricular groove or coronary sulcus can be observed between the atria and ventricles.
- The right and left auricles are appendages of the atria and can be seen on either side of the pulmonary trunk.
- Large blood vessels can be seen emerging from the heart.
- Most anterior is the pulmonary trunk that emerges from the right ventricle.
- The ascending aorta arises from the left ventricle and passes towards the right behind the pulmonary trunk and continues as the arch of the aorta.
- The superior and inferior venae cavae enter the upper and lower limits of the right atrium.
- The right and left pairs of pulmonary veins emerge from behind the auricles on either side.
- The arterial supply of the heart is via the coronary arteries, both of which are branches of the ascending aorta.
- They arise from the aortic sinuses that are blood-filled spaces above the three cusps of the aortic valve.
- The left coronary artery arises from the left posterior aortic sinus.

- It soon divides into the anterior interventricular and circumflex artery.
- The anterior interventricular artery supplies the anterior walls of both the right and left ventricles and anterior part of the interventricular septum.
- The circumflex artery supplies the left ventricle and left atrium.
- The right coronary artery arises from the anterior aortic sinus and passes along the right half of the coronary sulcus.
- It supplies the right atrium, the right ventricle, a portion of the left ventricle adjoining the posterior interventricular groove, the posterior part of the interventricular septum and most of the conducting system of the heart.
- Nearly all venous blood from the heart drains into the coronary sinus and then into the right atrium.
- The autonomic nerve supply of the heart is through the cardiac plexus.

CHAPTER 16

The Interior of the Heart

SPECIFIC LEARNING OBJECTIVES

At the end of this chapter, the student should be able to:

- Describe the internal features of the atria and ventricles.
- Draw a neat, labelled diagram of the interior of the right atrium.
- Describe the structure of the valves of the heart.
- Describe the anatomical location of the pacemaker cells and conducting system of the heart.
- Name some common clinical conditions that affect the internal structures of the heart.

GLOSSARY OF TERMS

- **Crista terminalis:** a vertical muscular ridge in the right atrium
- **Musculi pectinati:** horizontal muscular ridges extending from the crista terminalis
- **Sinus venarum:** smooth posterior part of the right atrial cavity
- **Fossa ovalis:** depression seen in the interatrial septum
- **Limbus fossa ovalis:** thickened margins of the fossa ovalis
- **Trabeculae carneae:** muscular ridges seen in the ventricles
- **Papillary muscles:** muscular pillars seen in the ventricles
- **Chordae tendineae:** fibrous cords connecting the papillary muscles and valve cusps
- **Infundibulum or conus:** smooth outflow tract of the right ventricle
- **Aortic vestibule:** smooth outflow tract of the left ventricle

INTRODUCTION

In the last chapter, we looked at the external features of the heart. Each of the chambers of the heart has internal features that enable its optimum functioning. The walls of the heart consist of cardiac muscle fibres. The atria are relatively thin-walled chambers which receive venous blood. The ventricles have thicker walls to enable them to pump blood into the arteries. Atrioventricular valves are present at the junction of the atria and ventricles to regulate the flow of blood. Semilunar valves are placed where arteries emerge from the ventricles. The muscles of the atria and ventricles as well as the valves are kept in position by their attachment to the fibrous skeleton of the heart. The pacemaker cells and the conducting system of the heart are modified cardiac muscle fibres which have specific locations within the heart. In this chapter, we will focus on the internal features of the heart and structure of the valves. An overview of the anatomy of the pacemaker cells and conduction system of the heart will be provided.

INTERNAL FEATURES OF THE CHAMBERS OF THE HEART

When the **right atrium** is opened along the two major veins that drain into it, the superior and inferior vena cava, it shows a clear subdivision into a **rough anterior part** and **smooth posterior part, the sinus venarum** (Fig. 16.1). These two regions are divided by a vertical muscular ridge called the **crista terminalis**, which corresponds to the sulcus terminalis seen from the outside. The rough anterior portion has a comb-like appearance due to the presence of several muscular ridges called **musculi pectinati** that run horizontally from the crista terminalis. The posterior **sinus venarum** is smooth walled. Three veins, the superior vena cava, inferior vena cava and coronary sinus, open into it. An **interatrial septum** separates the two atria. When viewed from inside the right atrium, it shows a depression called the **fossa ovalis** and a thickened rim called the **limbus fossa ovalis.** These structures are remnants of the communication between the right and left atrium that exists in foetal life. The right atrium communicates with the right ventricle through the right atrioventricular orifice which is guarded by the **tricuspid valve.** The interior of the **left atrium** is simpler than that of the right atrium (Fig. 16.2). It is entirely **smooth walled** and receives the openings of a pair of **pulmonary veins** on each side. The left atrium communicates with the left ventricle through the left atrioventricular orifice which is guarded by the **mitral valve.**

The **right ventricle** has a rough inflow and smooth outflow tract (Fig. 16.3). The inflow portion has several muscular ridges

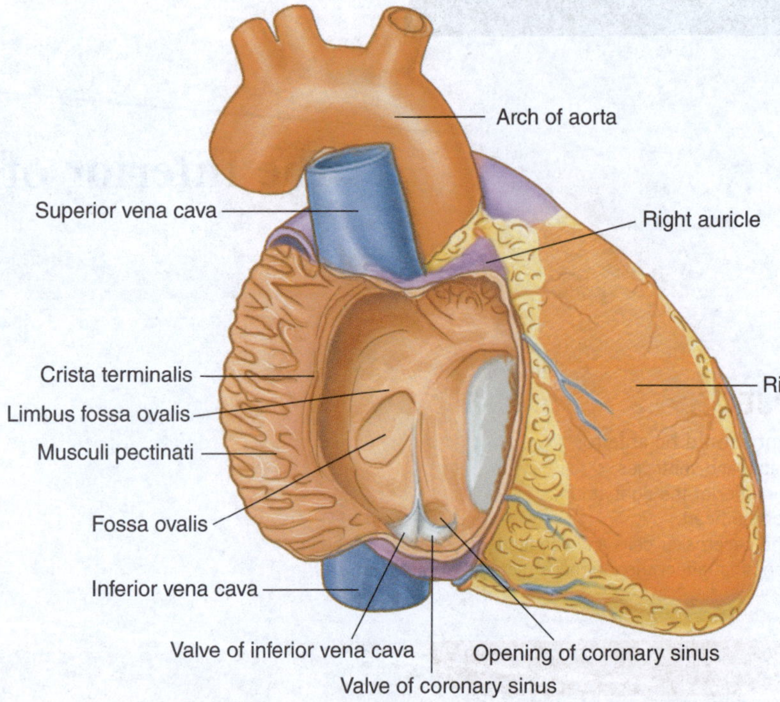

FIG. 16.1 The interior of the right atrium seen from the right.

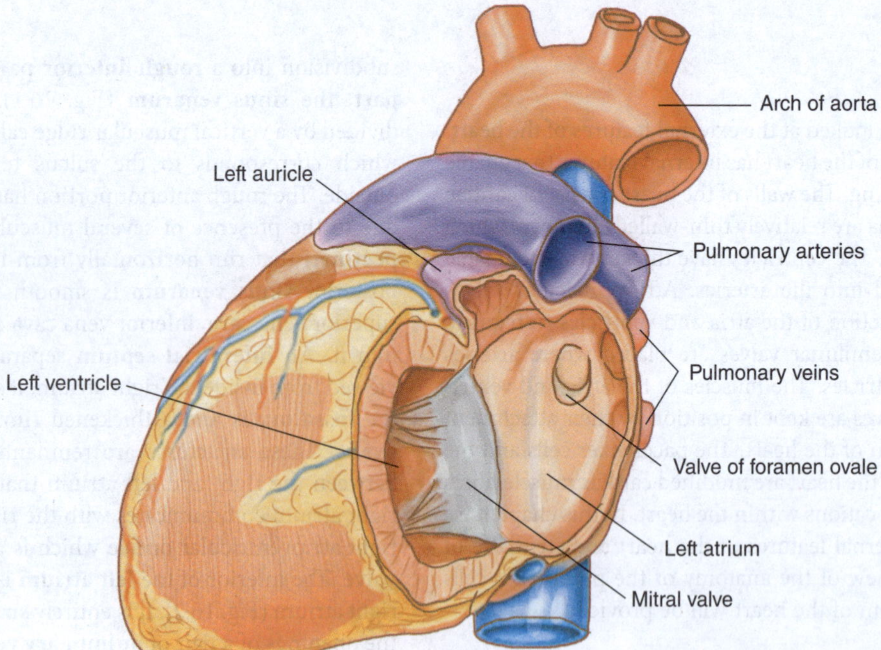

FIG. 16.2 The interior of the left atrium seen from the left.

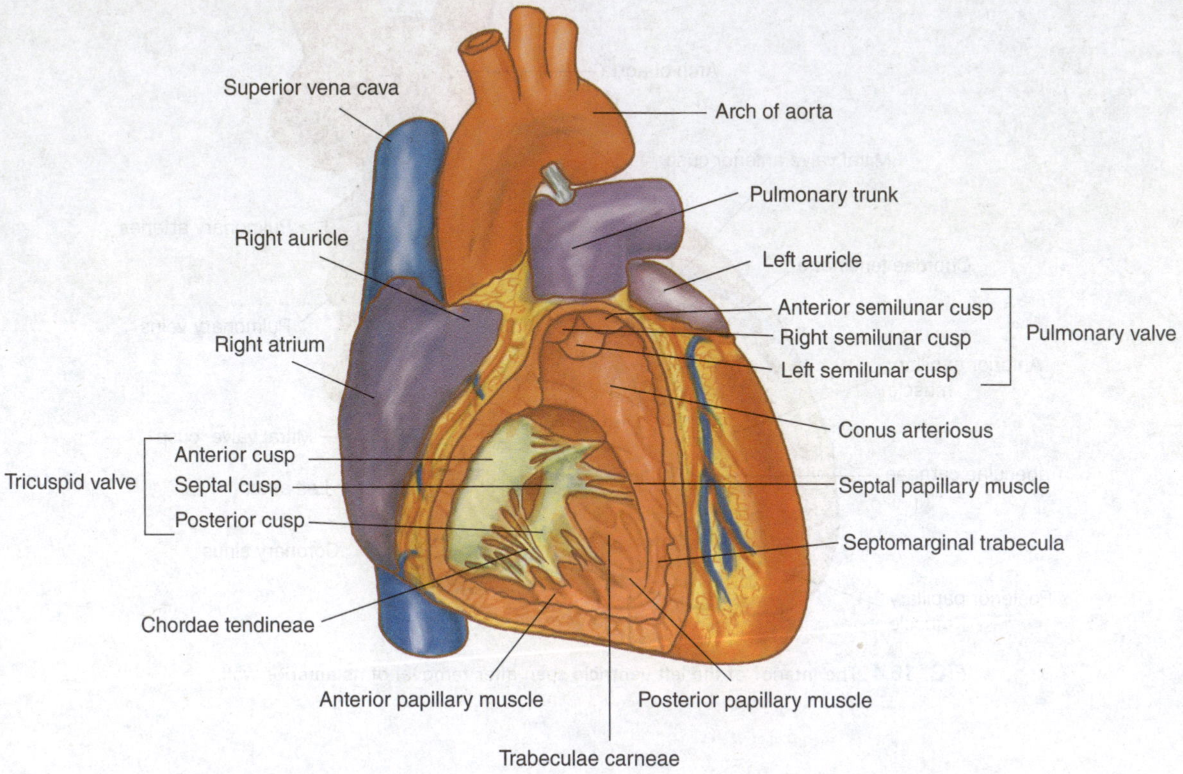

FIG. 16.3 The interior of the right ventricle seen after removal of its anterior wall.

called **trabeculae carneae**. Three **papillary muscles**, which are pillar-like structures, project from the ventricular walls. These **papillary muscles** are named anterior, posterior and septal based on the location of their origin from the ventricular wall. Each papillary muscle has a number of fibrous cords attached to their free end called **chordae tendineae**. The other ends of the **chordae** attach to the leaflets of the tricuspid valve. During ventricular systole, the papillary muscles contract making the chordae taut. This prevents regurgitation of blood into the right atrium. The outflow tract is smooth and is called the **conus** or **infundibulum**. This leads to the pulmonary trunk, guarded by the **pulmonary valve**. The right ventricle is separated from the left ventricle by an **interventricular septum** which is muscular below and membranous above.

The interior of the **left ventricle** is similar to that of the right ventricle (Fig. 16.4). However, the walls of the left ventricle are much thicker because they pump blood to the systemic circulation which operates at a much higher pressure than the pulmonary circulation. The rough inflow tract of the left ventricle has **trabeculae carneae** and **papillary muscles** as in the right ventricle. However, only two **papillary muscles**, anterior and posterior, are seen. The **chordae tendineae** of the left ventricle are attached to the two leaflets of the mitral valve. The smooth outflow tract of the left ventricle is the **aortic vestibule**. This leads to the origin of the ascending aorta, guarded by the **aortic valve**.

The **tricuspid valve** connects the right atrium and ventricle (Fig. 16.3). As its name suggests, it has three leaflets or cusps which are peripherally attached to a fibrous annulus (ring) which is part of the fibrous skeleton of the heart. From this fibrous ring, the three leaflets (anterior, posterior and septal) project inwards. The **tricuspid valvular complex** consists of the fibrous ring, the three leaflets, the **chordae tendineae** and the **papillary muscles**, which have been discussed earlier under the interior of the right ventricle. All these elements together are responsible for ensuring optimum functioning of the valve. The **mitral valve** connects the left atrium and ventricle (Fig. 16.4). The structure and function of the mitral valve are like the tricuspid valve, except that only two leaflets (anterior and posterior) are seen. The mitral valve complex consists of an annulus, leaflets, **papillary muscles** and **chordae tendineae**.

The **pulmonary valve** is situated between the right ventricle and pulmonary trunk. It consists of three semilunar cusps (two anterior and one posterior). Above each of the cusps are spaces called sinuses. During ventricular diastole, blood fills these sinuses causing passive closure of the valve. This is unlike the atrioventricular valves, the closure of which is dependent on the contraction of the **papillary muscles**. The **aortic valve** is located between the left ventricle and ascending aorta (Fig. 16.5). It is similar in structure and function to the pulmonary valve. However, there is one anterior and two posterior cusps. Like the pulmonary valve, sinuses called **aortic sinuses** are seen above

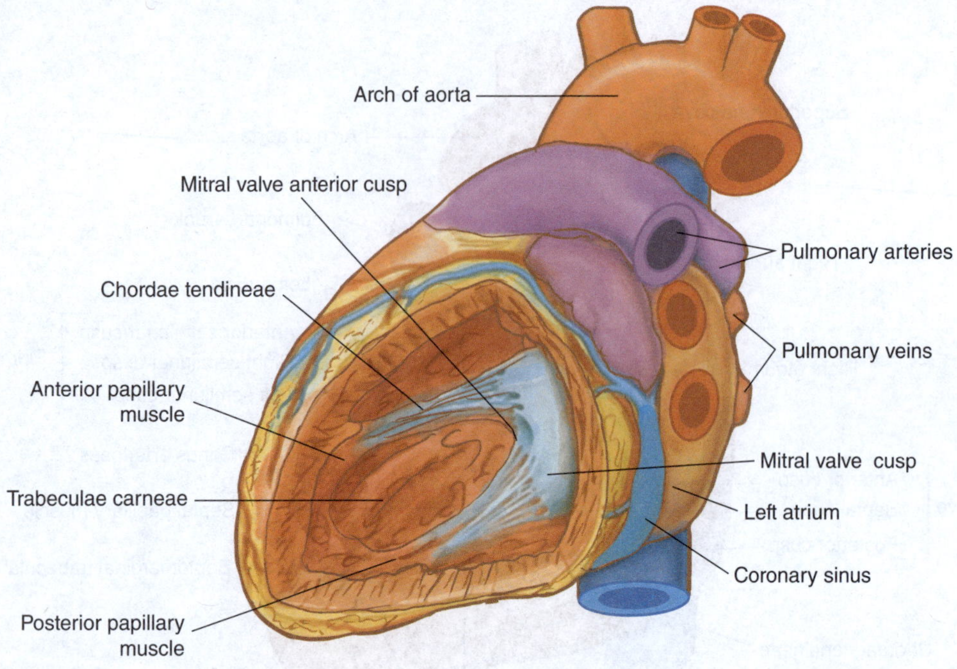

FIG. 16.4 The interior of the left ventricle seen after removal of its anterior wall.

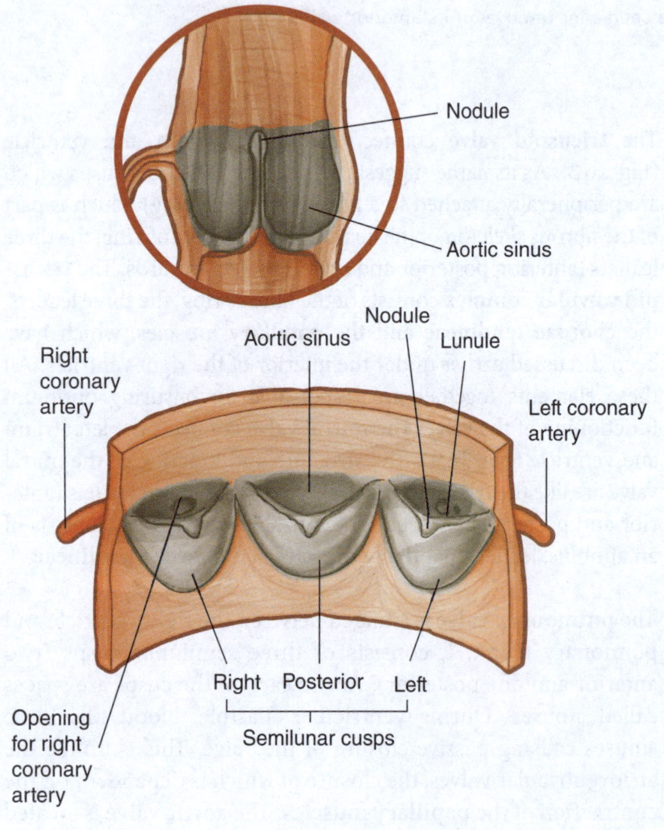

FIG. 16.5 The three semilunar cusps of the aortic valve along with the origins of the right and left coronary arteries from the aortic sinuses.

each leaflet of the aortic valve. The **aortic sinuses** are extremely important structures as they provide origin to the right and left **coronary arteries** from the ascending aorta. The anterior aortic sinus provides origin to the right coronary artery, while the left coronary artery arises from the left posterior aortic sinus.

THE CONDUCTING SYSTEM OF THE HEART (Fig. 16.6)

The rhythmic contraction of the heart is regulated by pacemaker cells and a conducting system. There are two pacemaker centres, the **sinoatrial node** (SAN) and the **atrioventricular node** (AVN). The conducting system consists of the **atrioventricular bundle** (AVB) of His, its right and left branches and the **Purkinje fibres**. The SAN is in the right atrium close to the opening of the superior vena cava. The AVN is situated in the interatrial septum, near the opening of the coronary sinus. The AVB passes through the membranous part of the interventricular septum, after which it divides into a right and left bundle branch which enter the muscular part of the interventricular septum. From here, the Purkinje fibres branch out to supply the heart.

APPLIED ANATOMY

- The communication between the two atria that exists in foetal life may persist. This is called an **atrial septal defect**.
- The ventricular septum may not be fully formed. This defect is called a **ventricular septal defect**. It is the most common congenital malformation of the heart.

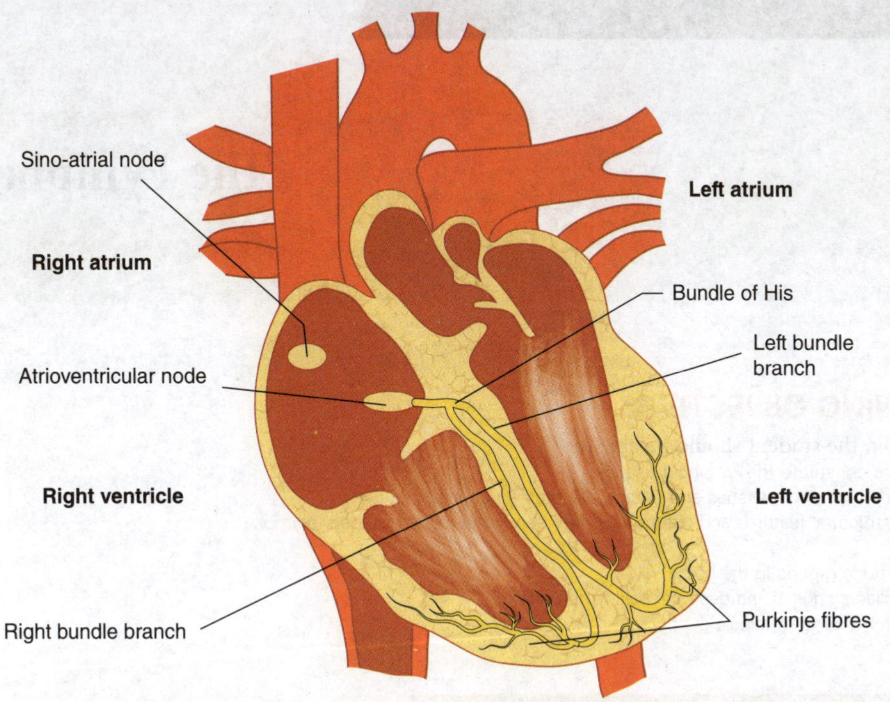

FIG. 16.6 The conducting system of the heart.

- **Fallot's tetralogy** is another congenital malformation of the heart that is relatively common. The cardiac abnormalities seen include pulmonary stenosis, right ventricular hypertrophy, ventricular septal defect and an overriding of the aorta over both ventricles.
- Narrowing (**stenosis**) and incompetence of valves (**regurgitation**) can cause clinical symptoms.

APPLICATIONS IN NURSING

- **Cardiac pacemakers** are battery-operated devices that are placed under the skin of the chest in patients with arrhythmias. They send impulses to the heart to ensure that the heart beats at the correct rate. Nursing personnel should be able to counsel patients with pacemakers about their care. These include the need for regular follow-up, battery replacements when required and taking precautions such as avoiding MRI scans.

SUMMARY

- The right atrium has a rough anterior part with musculi pectinati, a smooth posterior part and an interatrial septum.
- The smooth posterior portion receives the openings of the venae cavae and coronary sinus.
- The left atrium is smooth throughout and receives the openings of two pairs of pulmonary veins.
- The right ventricle has a rough inflow portion with trabeculae carneae and a smooth outflow portion called the conus or infundibulum.
- The left ventricle has a rough inflow portion with trabeculae carneae and a smooth outflow portion called the aortic vestibule.
- Both ventricles have papillary muscles to which are attached chordae tendineae.
- The interventricular septum, partly membranous and partly muscular, separates the two ventricles.
- The atrioventricular valves are the mitral and tricuspid valves.
- The tricuspid valve has three leaflets and separates the right atrium and ventricle.
- The mitral valve has two leaflets and separates the left atrium and ventricle.
- The semilunar valves are the aortic and pulmonary valves, each having three cusps.
- The coronary arteries arise from the aortic sinuses.
- The conducting system of the heart consists of the sinoatrial node, atrioventricular node, bundle of His, right and left bundle branches and Purkinje fibres.

CHAPTER 17

The Lymphatic System

SPECIFIC LEARNING OBJECTIVES

At the end of this chapter, the student should be able to:

- Name the structures that constitute the lymphoid tissues.
- Describe the cells found in lymphoid tissues and enumerate their functions.
- Describe the common structural features and differences between lymph nodes, spleen, thymus and tonsils.
- Name the major lymph node groups in the body.
- Describe in brief the axillary, inguinal and deep cervical lymph nodes.
- Describe the gross anatomy of the thoracic duct.

GLOSSARY OF TERMS

- **Lymphoid tissue:** connective tissue rich in lymphocytes
- **Lymphoid organs:** organs formed by dense aggregations of lymphocytes
- **Lymphocyte:** a type of white blood cell responsible for humoral and cellular immunity
- **B lymphocyte:** a type of lymphocyte responsible for humoral immunity
- **T lymphocyte:** a type of lymphocyte responsible for cellular immunity

INTRODUCTION

Lymphoid tissue is connective tissue which is rich in **lymphocytes.** It either exists free within regular connective tissue or is surrounded by a capsule. Lymphocytes are the most important constituents of this type of tissue. They have very little cytoplasm and therefore stain dark blue with haematoxylin and eosin stain. Between the lymphocytes is a rich network of **reticular fibres** that support the cells. The main function of lymphoid tissue is to generate immunocompetent lymphocytes that respond to a diversity of antigens. To be able to do this, the lymphoid tissue should be able to concentrate antigens that enter the body into **lymphoid organs** and circulate lymphocytes through them. Finally, the products of the immune response (antibodies or effector T cells) need to be delivered to the blood and tissues.

LYMPHOID ORGANS

A **lymph vascular network** permeates all tissues of the body. Lymphoid organs are the group of organs associated with the lymph vascular network, as well as regions of diffuse lymphoid tissue, that may occur anywhere in the body. They may be classified based on the site of **differentiation** or the degree of **encapsulation** (Fig. 17.1).

LYMPH NODES

Lymph nodes are small, **encapsulated** lymphatic organs located along lymphatic vessels (Fig. 17.2). They are **bean shaped**, with a convex and concave surface, and range in size from 1 mm to about 2 cm along their longest dimension. They serve as **filters** through which lymph percolates on its way to the blood and are concentrated in certain areas, such as the neck, axilla and groin (Fig.17.3).

The neck contains lymph nodes along the internal jugular vein called the **deep cervical lymph nodes.** This group of lymph nodes collects lymph from the rest of the nodes of the head and neck. Another collection of lymph nodes is located in the axilla known as the **axillary group of lymph nodes.** These nodes drain the upper limb, upper half of the trunk and mammary gland. The **inguinal group of lymph nodes** is situated in the groin region. They drain the lower limb, lower half of the trunk, external genitalia and anal canal.

When viewed under the microscope, lymph nodes have a connective tissue **capsule** which sends trabeculae into their substance (Fig. 17.2). An outer dark-staining **cortex** and an inner pale-staining **medulla** can be appreciated. The outer

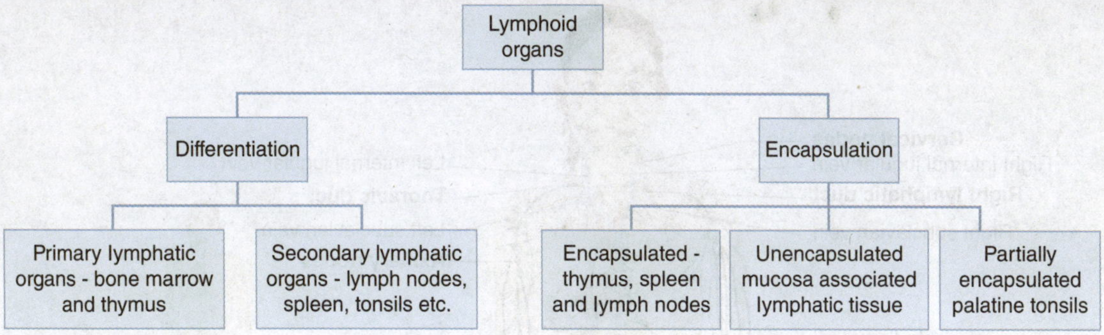

FIG. 17.1 Flowchart showing the classification of lymphatic organs.

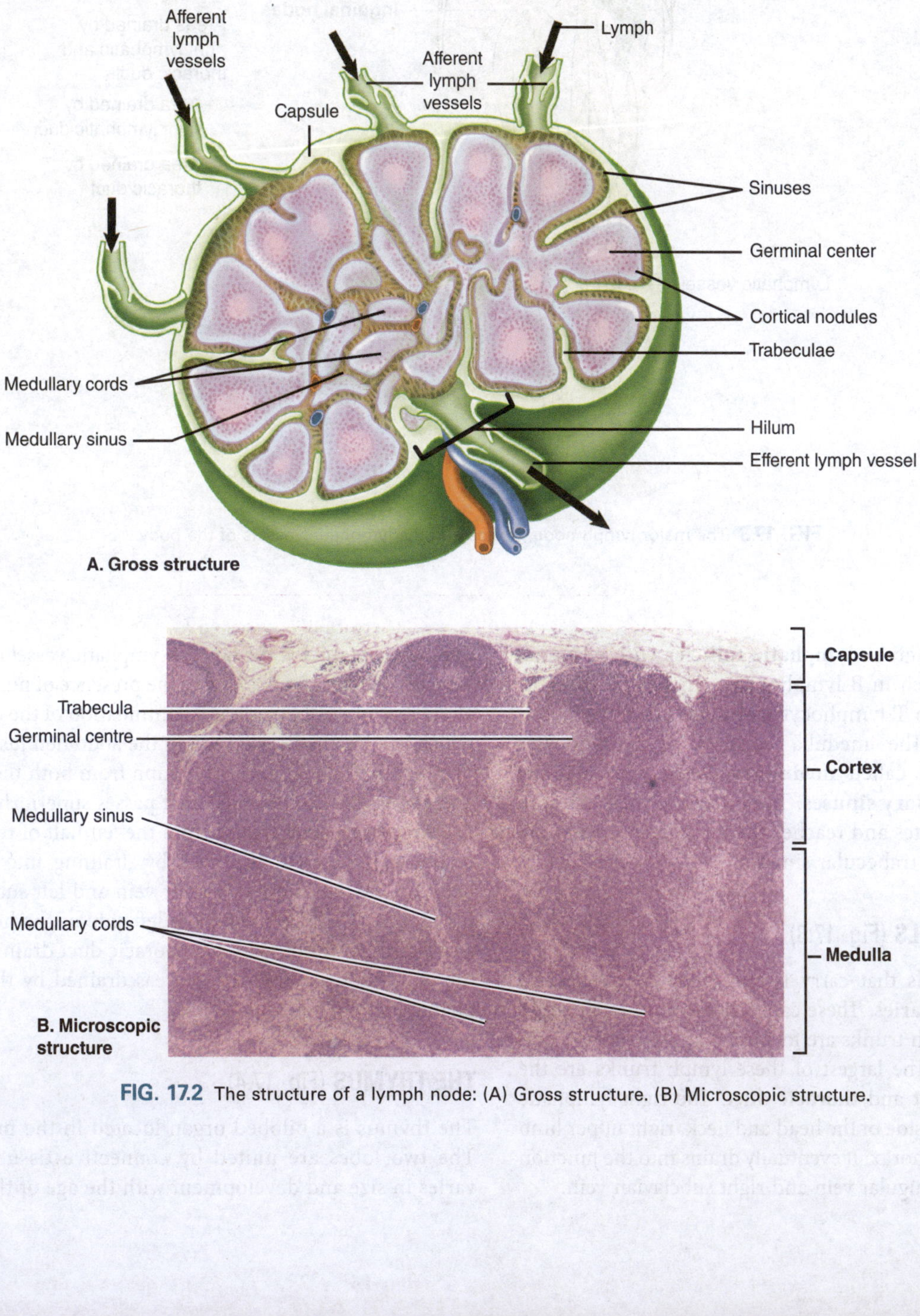

FIG. 17.2 The structure of a lymph node: (A) Gross structure. (B) Microscopic structure.

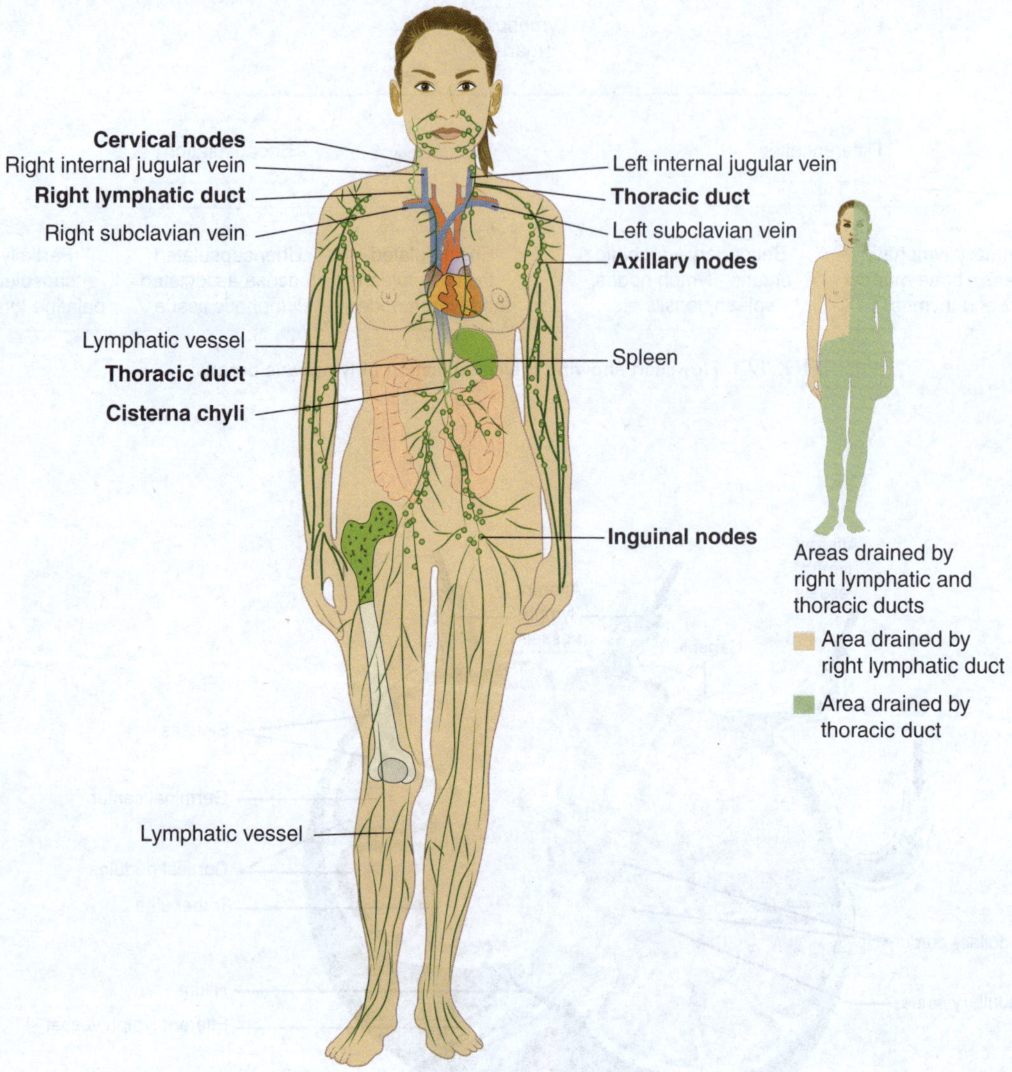

FIG. 17.3 The major lymph node groups and the lymphatic vessels of the body.

cortex contains numerous **lymphatic follicles** with germinal centres which are rich in B lymphocytes. The deep cortex or **paracortex** is rich in T lymphocytes and has a homogeneous dark appearance. The medulla consists of lymphocytes arranged in strands called **medullary cords**, separated by spaces called **medullary sinuses**. The other channels through which lymph circulates and reaches the medullary sinuses are the subcapsular and trabecular sinuses.

LYMPHATIC VESSELS (Fig. 17.3)

The lymphatic vessels that carry lymph from the tissues are termed **lymph capillaries**. These capillaries join to form larger vessels. Finally, lymph trunks are formed that drain lymph into the venous system. The largest of these lymph trunks are the **right lymphatic duct** and **thoracic duct**. The right lymphatic duct drains the right side of the head and neck, right upper limb and right half of the thorax. It eventually drains into the junction of the right internal jugular vein and right subclavian vein.

The **thoracic duct** is the **largest** lymphatic vessel in the body. It is **beaded** in appearance due to the presence of numerous valves along its course. It begins as a continuation of the **cisterna chyli** which is a lymphatic sac seen in the abdomen just beneath the diaphragm. This sac receives lymph from both the lower limbs and abdomen. The thoracic duct passes superiorly through the diaphragm, receives lymph from the left half of the thorax and finally terminates in the neck by draining into the junction between the left internal jugular vein and left subclavian vein. It also receives lymph from the left side of the head and neck and left upper limb. Thus, the thoracic duct drains lymph from the entire body except those areas drained by the right lymphatic duct.

THE THYMUS (Fig. 17.4)

The thymus is a bilobed organ located in the **mediastinum**. The two lobes are united by connective tissue. The organ varies in size and development with the age of the individual

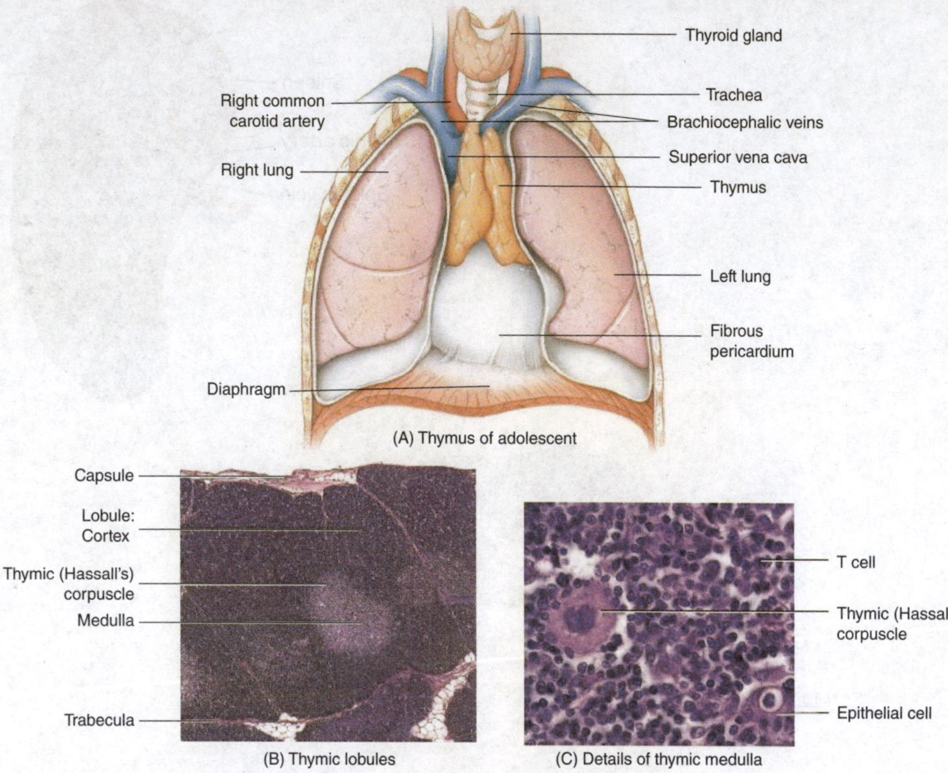

FIG. 17.4 The structure of the thymus.

and attains its maximum development after puberty. Much of the thymic tissue eventually becomes replaced by adipose tissue. It is the site where stem lymphocytes proliferate and differentiate into T cells. Large numbers of **T lymphocytes** are released and carried by the blood to other lymphatic organs and tissues.

Microscopically, the thymus is surrounded by a thin **capsule** that gives off septa defining incompletely separated **lobules**. The principal components of lobules are immature T lymphocytes (thymocytes), epithelial reticular cells and macrophages. The outer zone of the lobules is known as the **cortex** which is dark staining and contains numerous densely packed thymocytes. The central region of the lobules, the **medulla**, is light staining with fewer thymocytes and more epithelial reticular cells. Thymic corpuscles **(Hassall's corpuscles)** are unique to the medulla. They consist of a central, eosinophilic, hyaline core surrounded by concentric layers of reticular cells.

THE SPLEEN (Figs 17.5 and 17.6)

It is the **largest** lymphoid organ and located in the **upper left quadrant** of the **abdominal cavity**. It is closely related to the 9th to 11th ribs, stomach, left kidney and splenic flexure of the colon. It has a **rich blood supply** and is supplied by the splenic artery and vein. While lymph nodes serve as immunological filters of the lymph, the spleen serves as the **immunological filter** of the **blood**. It serves as an important defence against microorganisms that enter the circulation. Another essential function of the spleen is the **destruction** of **old erythrocytes**.

Microscopically, the spleen is surrounded by a **capsule** of dense connective tissue from which branched **trabeculae** extend into the parenchyma. The parenchyma of the spleen is termed the **pulp** and is divided into **white** and **red pulp**. The red pulp consists of cellular cords, called splenic cords or **cords of Billroth**, which form a spongy network of modified lymphatic tissue that gradually merges into the white pulp. Separating the cords are **venous sinuses**. The white pulp forms small, oval or rounded greyish white areas between the splenic cords. It characteristically contains **central arteries** around which are seen aggregations of lymphocytes.

THE TONSILS (Fig. 17.7)

Tonsils are organs composed of aggregates of **incompletely encapsulated** lymphoid tissue. They are characterized by depressions of the surface epithelium around which are seen groups of lymph nodules. The palatine, lingual, pharyngeal and tubal tonsils form a ring of lymphoid tissue, the **Waldeyer's ring**, surrounding the pharynx where the nasal and oral passages unite. The palatine and lingual tonsils lie in relation to the oropharynx, whereas the pharyngeal and tubal tonsils are present in the nasopharynx. The tonsils reach their maximum development in **childhood**.

The **palatine tonsils** are covered on their free surface by **stratified squamous nonkeratinized epithelium** that is

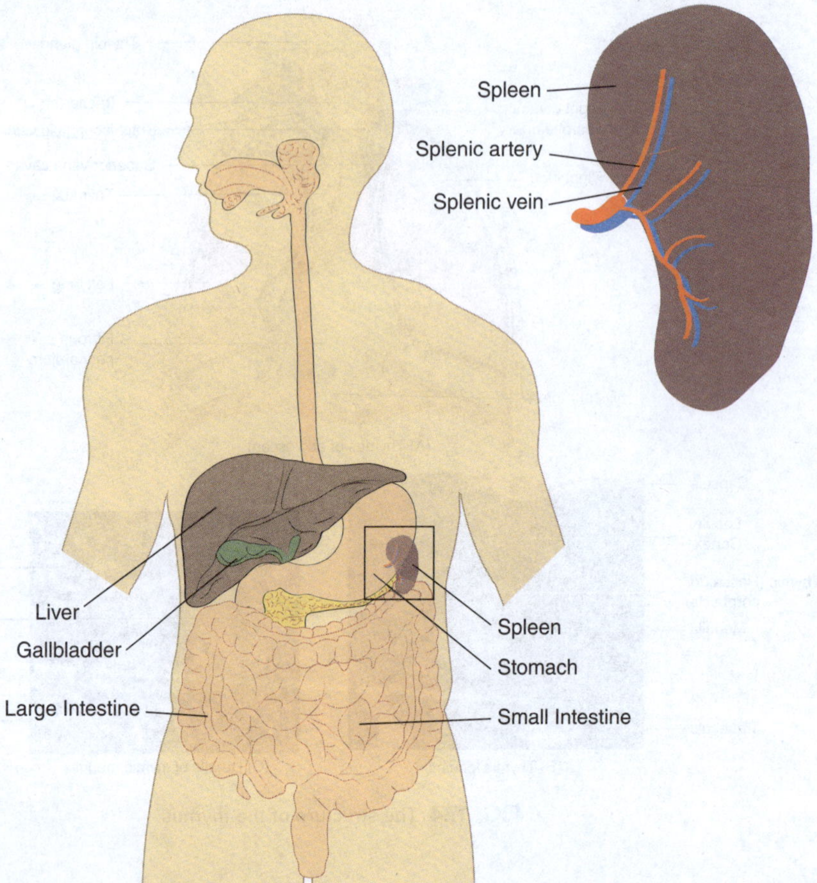

FIG. 17.5 The gross anatomy of the spleen.

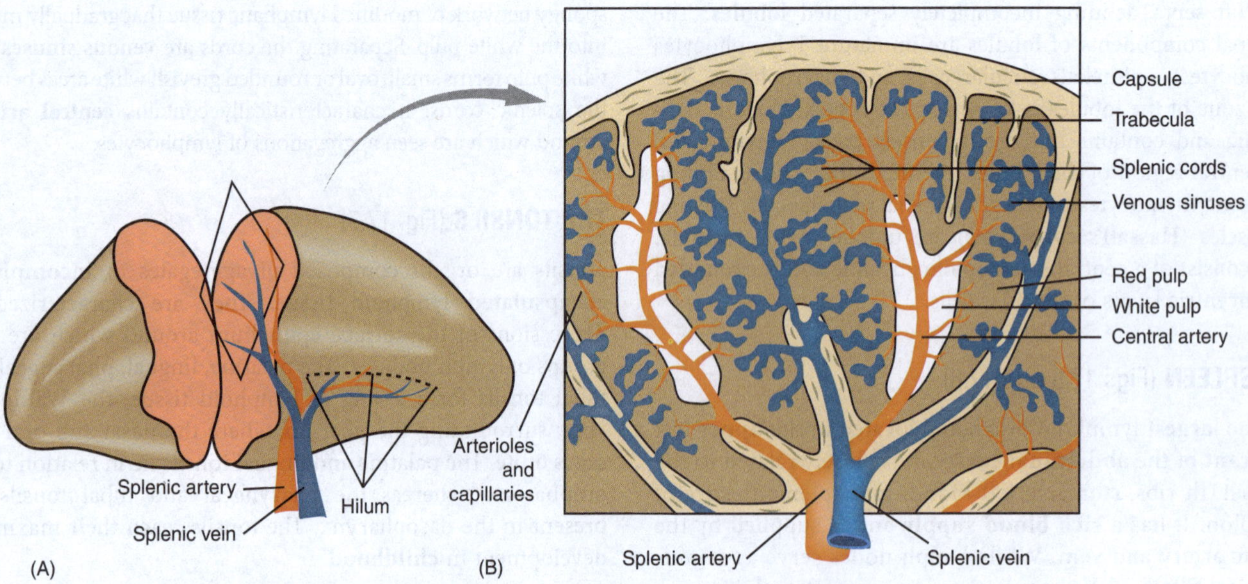

FIG. 17.6 The microscopic anatomy of the spleen.

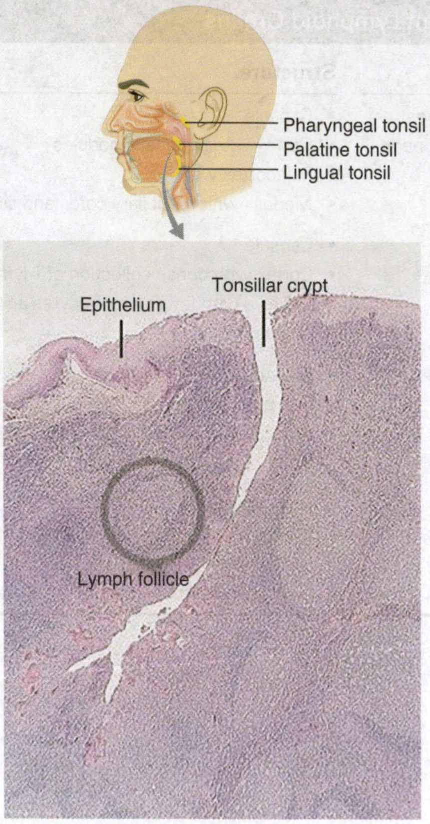

FIG. 17.7 The structure of the tonsils.

continuous with the lining of the mouth and pharynx. The epithelium covering the tonsil dips into the interior of the tonsil, forming **tonsillar crypts**. Lymphoid tissue containing lymph nodules surrounds the crypts. The deepest portion of the palatine tonsil is covered by fibrous tissue which is condensed to form a thin **hemicapsule**. Connective tissue septa extend into the interior of the tonsil from the capsule. Small mucous glands lie in the connective tissue adjacent to the capsule. A comparison of the different lymphoid organs is shown in Table 17.1.

APPLIED ANATOMY

- Enlargement of lymph nodes is called **lymphadenopathy** and occurs most commonly due to infections and malignancies.
- The thymus is sometimes enlarged in patients with **myasthenia gravis.**
- Enlargement of the spleen is called **splenomegaly** and is often caused by infections like malaria.
- The spleen can be injured by trauma to the left lower chest wall and may then have to be surgically removed, a procedure known as **splenectomy**.
- Enlarged pharyngeal tonsils are called **adenoids**, which are a common cause of airway obstruction in young children.
- Infection of the palatine tonsils is common and known as **tonsillitis**.
- Surgical removal of the palatine tonsils is called **tonsillectomy**.

SUMMARY

- The lymphoid organs contain dense aggregations of lymphocytes and serve immunological functions.
- Lymphoid organs may be classified based on differentiation and encapsulation.
- The bone marrow and thymus are primary lymphoid organs which produce B and T lymphocytes, respectively.
- Secondary lymphoid organs like the lymph nodes and spleen receive already differentiated lymphocytes.
- Lymphoid organs may have no capsule, a hemicapsule or a complete capsule.
- Lymph nodes serve as immunological filters of lymph and are aggregated in the neck, axilla, abdomen and groin.
- Lymph nodes have a capsule, a cortex with lymphatic nodules and a medulla with medullary rays and sinuses.
- The thymus is the site for the maturation of T lymphocytes.
- The thymus is enclosed in a capsule and has a cortex with T lymphocytes and a medulla with fewer lymphocytes and Hassall's corpuscles.
- The spleen serves as an immunological filter of blood.
- The spleen is completely encapsulated and contains red pulp with cords of Billroth and white pulp with central arteries and aggregations of lymphocytes.
- The tonsils form a ring around the upper aerodigestive tract known as Waldeyer's ring.
- They have a hemicapsule and crypts which pass into their substance underlying which are seen lymphatic nodules.

Table 17.1 A Comparison of the Different Lymphoid Organs

Lymphoid Organ	Location	Structure	Function
Lymph node	All over the body, the largest aggregations being in the neck, axilla, abdomen and groin	• Capsule • Cortex with lymphatic nodules • Paracortex with T cells • Medulla with medullary cords and sinuses	Serves as an immunological filter of lymph
Thymus	Mediastinum	• Capsule • Cortex with dense collection of T lymphocytes • Medulla with fewer lymphocytes and Hassall's corpuscles	T lymphocytes undergo maturation in the thymus
Spleen	Left upper quadrant of the abdominal cavity	• Capsule • Red pulp with cords of Billroth and venous sinuses • White pulp with central artery surrounded by lymphocytes	Serves as an immunological filter of blood
Tonsils	In the nasopharynx and oropharynx	• Hemicapsule • Crypts lined by stratified squamous nonkeratinized epithelium • Lymphatic nodules underlying the epithelium	Protects the upper aerodigestive tract from pathogens

5 SECTION

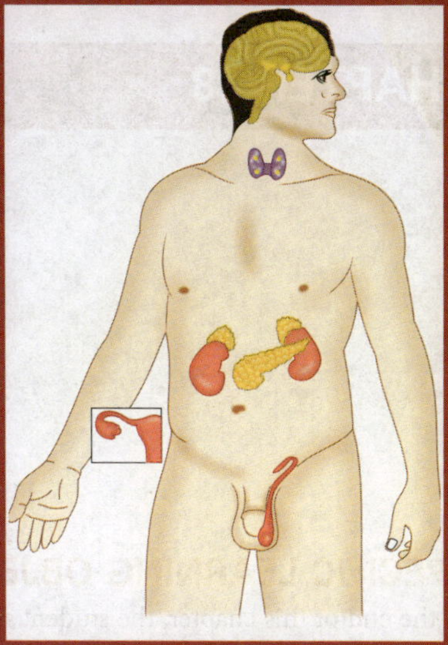

The Endocrine System

Section Outline

CHAPTER 18

The Endocrine System

SPECIFIC LEARNING OBJECTIVES

At the end of this chapter, the student should be able to:

- Name the major endocrine organs.
- Describe the anatomy and functions of the pituitary gland, thyroid gland, adrenal gland and pancreatic islets.
- Describe in brief the anatomy and functions of the hypothalamus, parathyroid and pineal glands.

GLOSSARY OF TERMS

- **Endocrine glands:** ductless glands whose secretions are poured directly into the bloodstream, for example thyroid gland
- **Endocrine tissues:** collections of endocrine cells within an organ that has other functions, for example islets of Langerhans
- **Follicle:** a central spherical space surrounded by cells

INTRODUCTION (Fig. 18.1)

Endocrine glands are **ductless glands** that secrete hormones directly into the bloodstream. The endocrine system consists of endocrine glands and endocrine tissues. The hormones secreted may be steroids, small peptides, proteins, glycoproteins and amino acid analogues or their derivatives. Endocrine cells are specialized for secretion and arranged in **cords, small clumps** or **follicles**. All endocrine glands are richly supplied with **blood vessels**. The vessels associated with endocrine glands have **fenestrated endothelium** to allow the secretions to pass into the circulation. The major **endocrine glands** include the hypothalamus, pituitary, pineal, thyroid, parathyroid and adrenal glands. **Endocrine tissues** are found at numerous sites in the body including the pancreas, testes, ovaries, kidneys, heart and thymus. The functions of the endocrine system include the regulation of growth and development, reproduction, metabolism, circadian rhythms, involuntary muscle contraction and glandular secretion. This chapter will describe the major endocrine glands and the endocrine tissues in the pancreas.

THE HYPOTHALAMUS (Fig. 18.2)

The pituitary gland (or hypophysis) was thought to be the 'master gland' that controlled the functioning of all the other endocrine glands. We now know that they are controlled by the hypothalamus. The hypothalamus is part of the **forebrain**. It **integrates** the activities of the nervous and endocrine systems in three ways. First, it secretes regulatory hormones that act on the pituitary gland. Next, there are hormones that are secreted directly into the bloodstream like other endocrine organs. Finally, it contains autonomic centres that control the functioning of the sympathetic and parasympathetic nervous systems.

THE PITUITARY GLAND (Figs 18.2 and 18.3)

The pituitary gland is a **pea-shaped** structure that is about 0.5 inch in diameter. It lies within a depression in the sphenoid bone called the **sella turcica**. It is constituted by two anatomically and functionally different parts, the **adenohypophysis** and **neurohypophysis**. The major constituents of the adenohypophysis are the **pars distalis** or anterior and pars intermedia. The neurohypophysis mainly consists of the **pars nervosa** or posterior.

The pars anterior consists of glandular epithelial cells arranged in cords and clumps. Abundant fenestrated capillaries (sinusoids) are seen in close relation to the cell aggregations. The cells are divided about evenly into **chromophobes** and **chromophils**. Chromophobes (50% of all cells) take up little or no stain, whereas chromophils are subdivided into **acidophils** (40% of all cells) and **basophils** (10% of all cells).

Chromophobes are relatively small cells with a pale-staining cytoplasm. They are thought to be inactive or undifferentiated

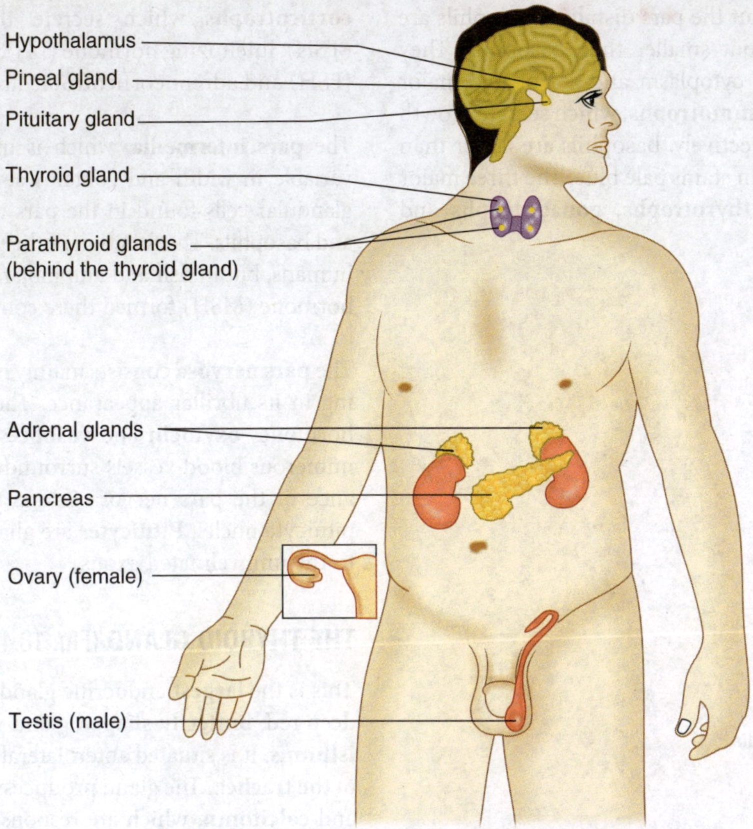

FIG. 18.1 The major endocrine glands and tissues.

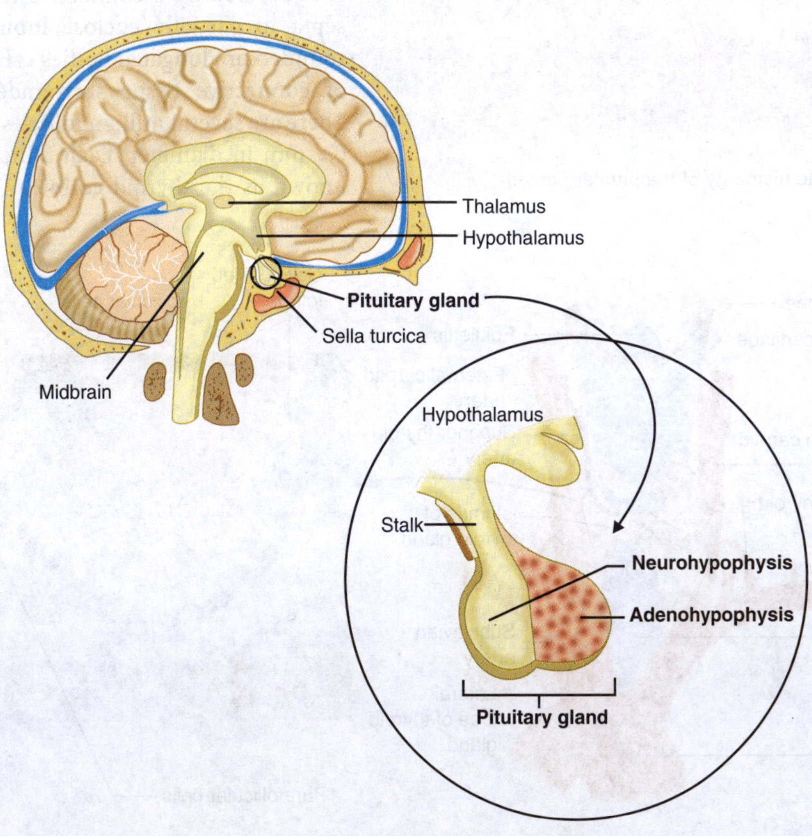

FIG. 18.2 The gross anatomy of the hypothalamus and pituitary gland.

cells and are found throughout the pars distalis. Acidophils are larger than chromophobes but smaller than basophils. They have a strongly eosinophilic cytoplasm and are of two major types, **somatotrophs** and **mammotrophs**, which secrete growth hormone and prolactin, respectively. Basophils are larger than acidophils and their cytoplasm stains pale blue. The three major types of basophils include **thyrotrophs, gonadotrophs** and **corticotrophs** which secrete thyroid-stimulating hormone (TSH), luteinizing hormone (LH), follicle-stimulating hormone (FSH) and adrenocorticotropic hormone (ACTH), respectively.

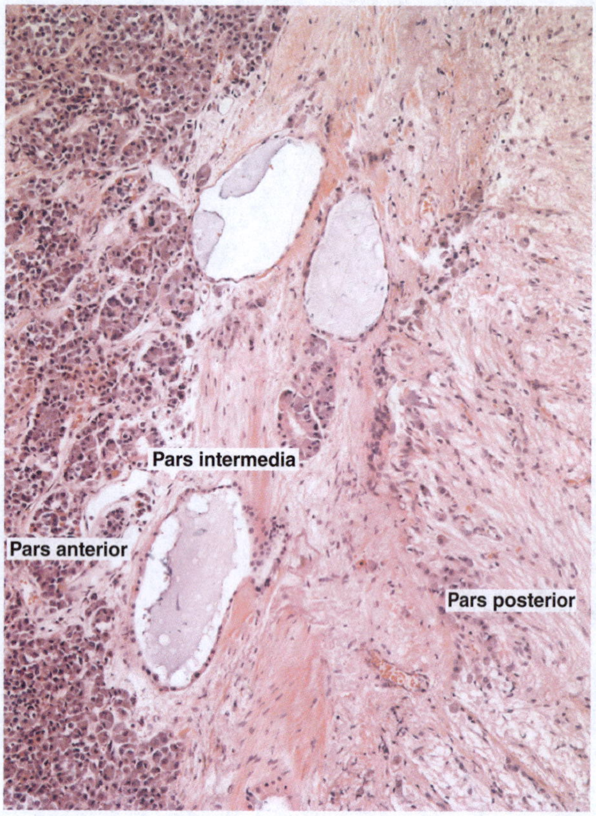

FIG. 18.3 The histology of the pituitary gland.

The **pars intermedia**, which is underdeveloped in humans, is variable in width and contains several **colloid-filled cysts**. The glandular cells found in the pars intermedia are chromophobes and basophils. The function of the pars intermedia is unknown in humans, but in fish and amphibians, the melanocyte-stimulating hormone (MSH) formed there controls skin pigmentation.

The **pars nervosa** consists mainly of **unmyelinated axons** resulting in its fibrillar appearance. The axon terminals contain the hormones **oxytocin** and **vasopressin** that are poured into the numerous blood vessels surrounding them. The grainy appearance of the pars nervosa is due to the presence of abundant pituicyte nuclei. **Pituicytes** are glial cells which provide support to the unmyelinated axons.

THE THYROID GLAND (Fig. 18.4)

This is the **largest** endocrine gland weighing around 30 g. It is a deep red, **butterfly-shaped** gland with two lateral **lobes** and an **isthmus.** It is situated anterolateral to the **larynx** and upper part of the **trachea**. The gland produces **thyroxine, triiodothyronine** and **calcitonin**, which are responsible for increasing the **metabolic rate**, regulation of growth and development and maintenance of **blood calcium** levels.

It is covered by a connective tissue **capsule** which sends in septa to partially enclose **lobules**. Within the lobules are rounded or elongated bodies called **follicles** in a loose stroma of connective tissue surrounded by numerous capillaries. There are several million follicles which vary between 0.02 and 0.9 mm in diameter. Each follicle is filled with viscous fluid known as the thyroid **colloid**. Follicles are lined by a single

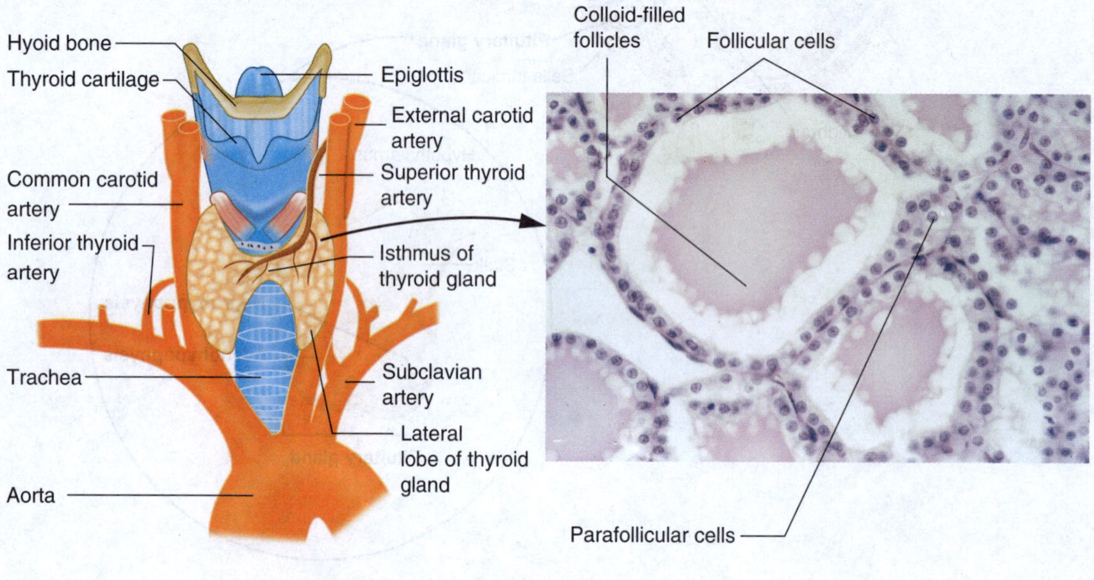

FIG. 18.4 The anatomy of the thyroid gland.

layer of **cuboidal follicular cells**, which vary in height dep ending on the levels of activity of the gland. Follicle cells synthesize and secrete colloid. They then pinocytose colloid, process it and release hormones from the basal surface of the cell to capillaries around the follicle. Calcitonin-secreting **parafollicular cells** lie between the follicular cells and basal lamina and sometimes outside the basal lamina. They occur singly or in small clusters which have no direct access to the follicular lumen.

The thyroid gland is supplied by the **superior** and **inferior thyroid arteries** which arise from the external carotid and subclavian arteries, respectively. It is drained by three pairs of veins, namely the **superior, middle** and **inferior thyroid veins**. These drain into the internal jugular and brachiocephalic veins. The arteries are seen in close relation to the nerves that supply the larynx.

PARATHYROID GLANDS (Fig. 18.5)

These are **four small glands** arranged as superior and inferior pairs situated on the posterior aspect of the thyroid gland. They are adherent to the capsule of the thyroid gland. They are covered by their own thin connective tissue capsule. The cells of the gland are supported by fine reticular fibres and situated near fenestrated capillaries. Two types of glandular cells are described: **chief cells** and **oxyphil cells**. Chief cells are the most numerous type and are relatively small, polygonal cells that synthesize **parathormone**. Oxyphil cells are less frequent, relatively large cells that contain numerous mitochondria. Parathormone increases calcium levels in the blood and along with calcitonin maintains blood calcium levels.

ADRENAL GLANDS (Fig. 18.6)

These are **paired glands** with one placed **above** each **kidney**. They produce both water-soluble and lipid-soluble hormones. Like other endocrine glands, they are enclosed by a connective tissue capsule. The **adrenal cortex** is the larger outer portion of the gland, while the **adrenal medulla** is the smaller inner portion. The outer cortex and inner medulla are two separate organs with different functions. Both areas are highly vascular with sinusoids. The hormones secreted by the adrenal gland help to maintain the sodium and potassium levels in the blood, regulate blood pressure, respond to stressful stimuli, develop secondary sexual characters and initiate the fight-or-flight response to emergency situations.

The **cortex** is divided into three layers: the **outer zona glomerulosa, middle zona fasciculata** and **inner zona reticularis**. The zona glomerulosa constitutes around 15% of the cortical volume and consists of closely packed ovoid clusters of cells surrounded by capillaries. It secretes mineralocorticoids, principally **aldosterone**. The zona fasciculata constitutes around 80% of the cortical volume. It consists of straight, radially oriented cords of cells separated by sinusoids. It secretes **glucocorticoids** and some androgens. The zona reticularis constitutes around 5% of the cortical volume and contains anastomosing cords of cells separated by sinusoids. The cells in this layer secrete **androgens** and some glucocorticoids. The **medulla** contains large cells in ovoid clusters and cords separated by sinusoids. Large veins are characteristic of this layer which secretes **adrenaline** and **noradrenaline** hormones.

The adrenal glands are supplied by three pairs of arteries which arise directly from the **abdominal aorta** or its branches. Each adrenal gland is drained by a single vein which drains into

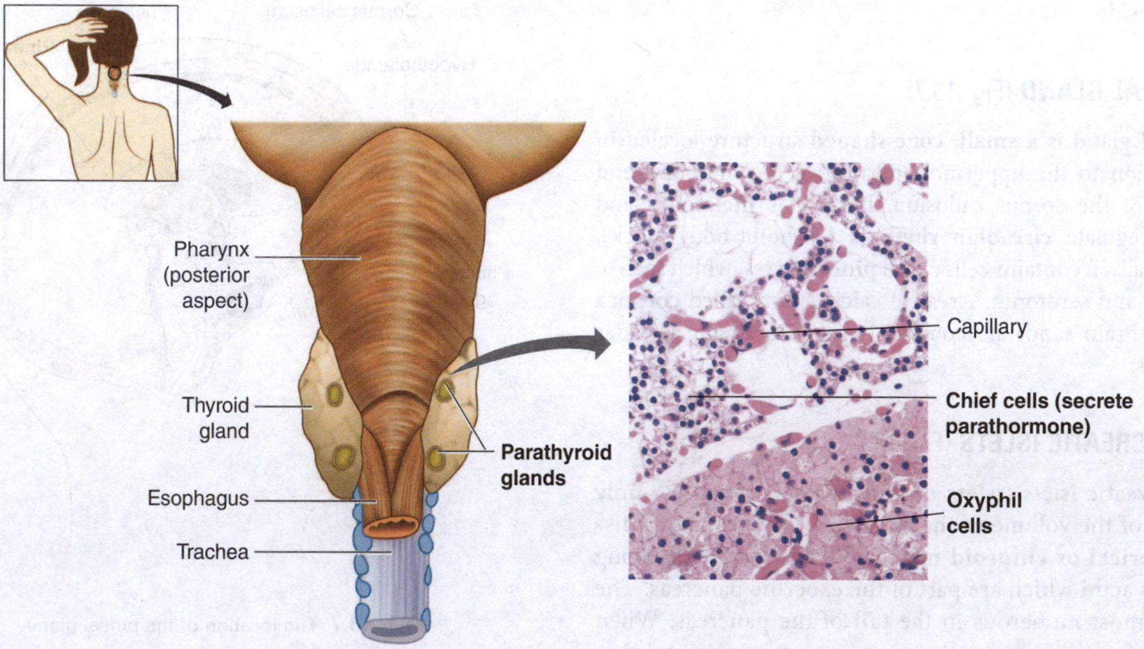

FIG. 18.5 The anatomy of the parathyroid glands (posterior view).

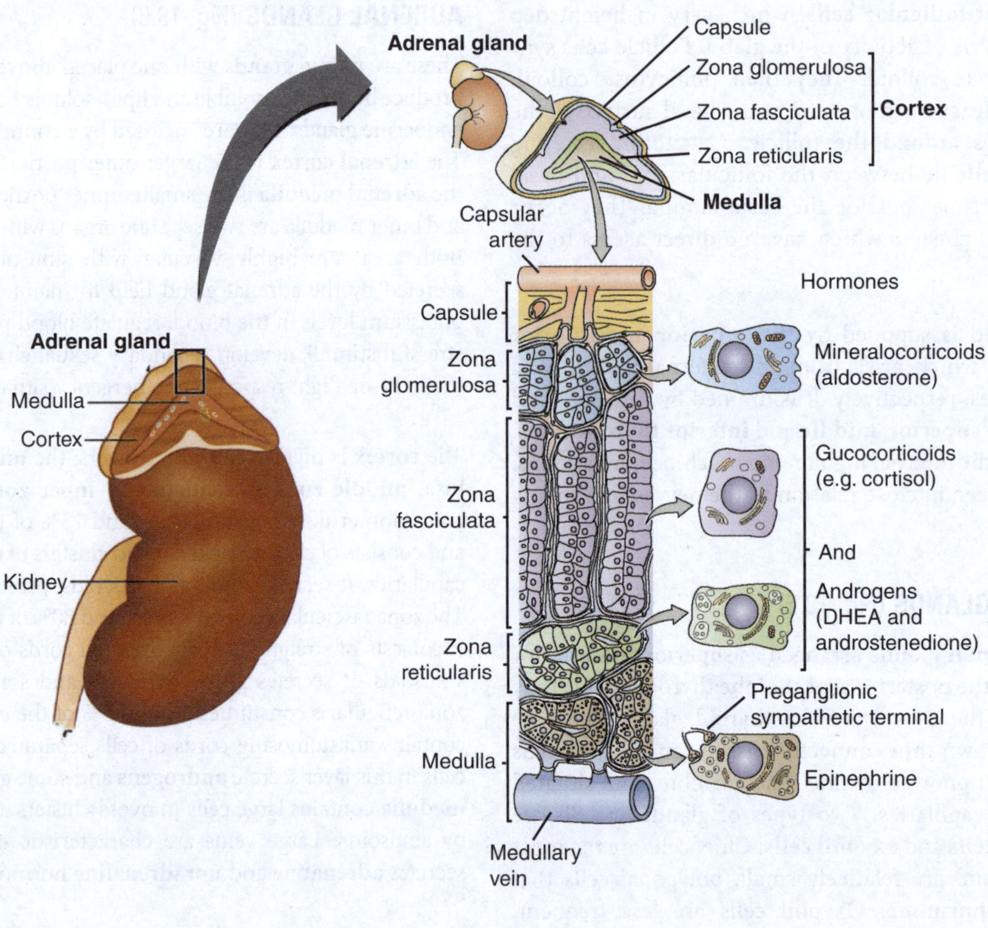

FIG. 18.6 The anatomy of the adrenal gland.

the **inferior vena cava** on the right side and the left renal vein on the left side.

THE PINEAL GLAND (Fig. 18.7)

The pineal gland is a **small, cone-shaped** structure located in close relation to the uppermost portion of the midbrain and splenium of the corpus callosum. It secretes **melatonin** and helps to regulate **circadian rhythms** (24-hour body clock). Histologically, it contains cells called **pinealocytes**, which secrete melatonin and serotonin. Areas of calcification called **corpora arenacea** (brain sand) are commonly seen, especially in older individuals.

THE PANCREATIC ISLETS (Fig. 18.8)

The pancreatic islets **(islets of Langerhans)** constitute only about 2% of the volume of the pancreas. They consist of distinct **spherical or ellipsoid masses** of cells scattered among the serous acini which are part of the exocrine pancreas. The islets are most numerous in the **tail** of the pancreas. When viewed under the microscope, they appear as **pale-staining islands** among the dark-staining serous acini. Pancreatic

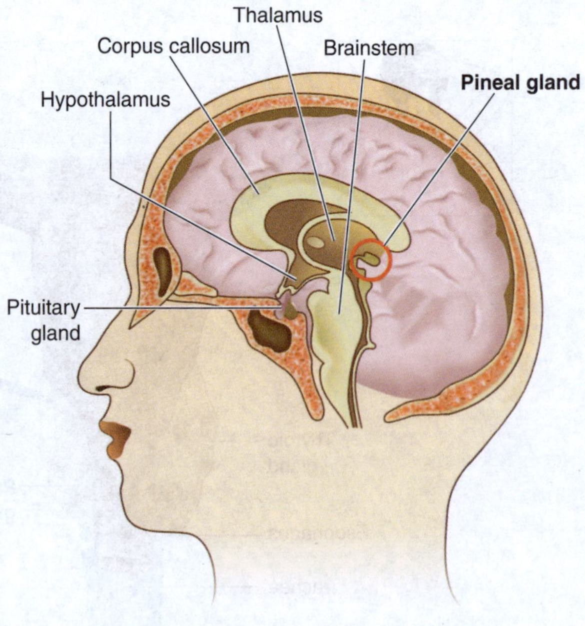

FIG. 18.7 The location of the pineal gland.

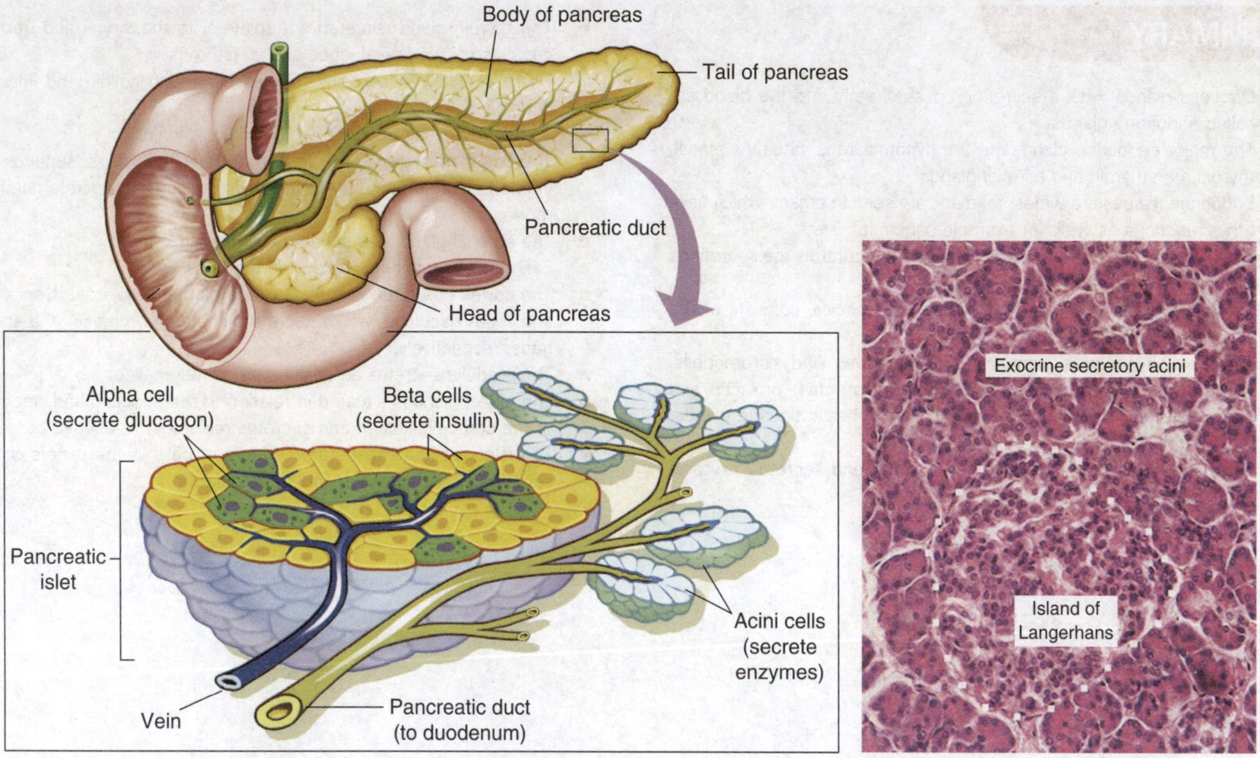

FIG. 18.8 The anatomy of the pancreatic islets.

islets consist of **polyhedral cells** arranged in short irregular cords through which run abundant fenestrated capillaries. The principal types of cells are **α (glucagon-producing), β (insulin-producing)** and **δ (somatostatin-producing) cells**. The β cells make up 60%–70% of the cells in the islets, α cells constitute about 15%–20% of the cells and δ cells constitute 5%–10% of the cells.

APPLIED ANATOMY

- **Pituitary tumours** can cause increased secretion of hormones. When growth hormone secretion is increased, it can cause gigantism (before puberty) and acromegaly (after puberty).
- Visible enlargement of the thyroid gland is called **goitre.** This condition can be associated with both hypothyroidism (decreased secretion) and hyperthyroidism (increased secretion).
- During surgeries for the removal of the thyroid gland (**thyroidectomy**), the nerves passing to the larynx can be damaged leading to hoarseness of voice.
- **Increased secretion of parathormone** due to tumours of the parathyroid gland can cause weakening of bones due to calcium resorption from them.
- The parathyroid glands may be inadvertently removed during thyroidectomy leading to **tetany** due to decreased calcium levels in the blood.
- Increased secretion of aldosterone from the zona glomerulosa occurs in **Conn syndrome** and causes disturbances in the electrolyte balance of sodium and potassium.
- **Cushing syndrome** is caused by an increase in cortisol levels in the body. The clinical manifestations of this condition include weight gain, increase in blood sugar and blood pressure levels, moon-like face and easy bruising.
- **Seasonal affective disorder (SAD)** is seen in individuals living in countries with long winters and little sunlight. This is thought to be related to increased melatonin secretion by the pineal gland due to decreased sunlight.
- **Calcification** in the pineal gland helps in its identification on radiological imaging.
- **Type 1 diabetes mellitus** is caused by decreased insulin secretion due to autoimmune destruction of type β cells in the pancreatic islets.

APPLICATIONS IN NURSING

- Patients with diabetes mellitus require regular monitoring of **blood glucose levels**. This is usually done by placing a drop of blood, obtained after pricking the tip of a finger, on a disposable test strip. The meter then estimates the blood glucose levels from this strip.
- **Foot ulcers** are more common in patients with diabetes mellitus because of diabetic neuropathy and hyperglycaemia. Along with other measures taken to maintain appropriate blood glucose levels, these ulcers need to be periodically dressed. These patients also need to be counselled on appropriate foot care like avoiding walking barefoot, use of appropriate footwear and regular inspection of the feet for cuts, blisters, etc.

SUMMARY

- Ductless glands whose secretions pass directly into the blood are called endocrine glands.
- The major endocrine glands are the hypothalamus, pituitary, pineal, thyroid, parathyroid and adrenal glands.
- Endocrine tissues are widespread and are seen in organs which have other functions as well, for example pancreatic islets.
- The hypothalamus is part of the forebrain and controls the secretions of the pituitary gland.
- The pituitary gland, located within the sella turcica, consists of the adenohypophysis and neurohypophysis.
- The adenohypophysis contains chromophobes and chromophils, which secrete hormones such as growth hormone, prolactin and hormones which control the secretions of other endocrine glands, for example TSH.
- The neurohypophysis contains nerve fibres and secretes oxytocin and vasopressin.
- The thyroid gland, situated anterolateral to the larynx and trachea, consists of two lateral lobes and an isthmus.
- Microscopically, it contains follicles filled with colloid and lined by cuboidal cells.
- The thyroid gland secretes T3, T4 and calcitonin.
- The parathyroid glands are four in number (two pairs, superior and inferior) situated posterior to the thyroid gland and secrete parathormone.
- The adrenal glands are situated above each kidney.
- Each gland contains a cortex and medulla.
- The cortex has three layers, the zona glomerulosa, zona fasciculata and zona reticularis, which secrete aldosterone, cortisol and androgens, respectively.
- The medulla secretes adrenaline and noradrenaline.
- The pineal gland is situated in relation to the midbrain and splenium of the corpus callosum and secretes melatonin.
- The islets of Langerhans are clusters of cells in the pancreas that secrete insulin, glucagon and somatostatin.

6

SECTION

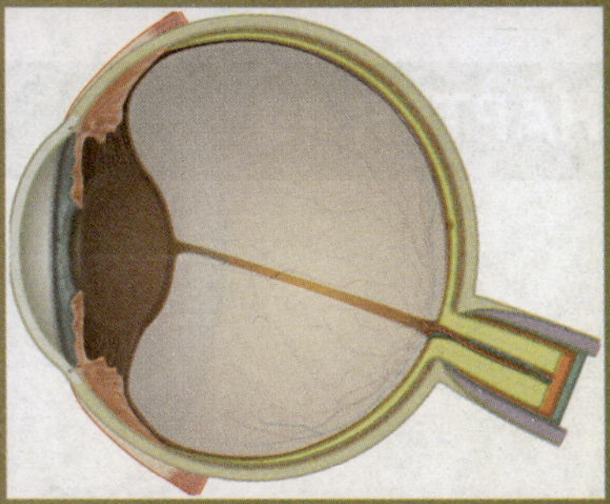

The Sensory Organs

Section Outline

CHAPTER 19

The Integumentary System

SPECIFIC LEARNING OBJECTIVES

At the end of this chapter, the student should be able to:

- Describe the general features of skin.
- Describe the histological features of thick skin including the layers, characteristics of each layer and other associated structures.
- Describe the histological features of thin skin as above, including hair follicles and sebaceous glands.
- Name and describe in brief the appendages of the skin.

GLOSSARY OF TERMS

- **Epidermis:** outer layer of the skin
- **Dermis:** inner layer of the skin
- **Stratified squamous keratinized epithelium:** the multilayered epithelium seen in the epidermis of the skin
- **Keratinocyte:** the most common cell type in the epidermis which produces keratin
- **Melanocyte:** cell responsible for pigmentation of the skin
- **Merkel cells:** sensory cells in the epidermis
- **Langerhans cells:** immune cells in the epidermis
- **Lines of Langer:** tension lines produced by collagen fibre arrangements in the dermis
- **Meissner's corpuscles:** sensory receptors in the papillary dermis that detect light touch
- **Pacinian corpuscles:** sensory receptors in the reticular dermis that respond to vibrations
- **Ruffini endings:** sensory receptors in the reticular dermis that respond to deep pressure
- **Thin skin:** skin containing hair follicles present all over the body except the palms and soles
- **Thick skin:** skin on the palms and soles without hair follicles
- **Hair:** composed of keratinized cells produced by the hair follicles
- **Sebaceous glands:** holocrine glands opening into hair follicles
- **Sweat glands:** coiled tubular glands in the dermis that open onto the surface or into hair follicles
- **Nails:** plates of hard keratin produced by the nail matrix

INTRODUCTION

The skin is the **largest organ** of the body which has a total surface area of 1.5–2 m^2 and a weight of 4–5 kg. It is a good example of epithelial and connective tissues working together for specific purposes. The skin has a variable thickness of 1.5–4 mm. The functions of the skin are manifold and include the regulation of body temperature, protection of deeper structures, sensory perception, excretion (in sweat), immunity, acting as a significant blood reservoir and the synthesis of vitamin D. The appendages of the skin include hair and hair follicles, sweat (sudoriferous) glands, sebaceous glands, nails and mammary glands.

GENERAL FEATURES OF SKIN (Figs 19.1 and 19.2)

The skin consists of an outer **epidermis** and inner **dermis**. The epidermis is the lining epithelium, while the dermis is the dense irregular connective tissue that underlies the epidermis. The hypodermis (superficial fascia or subcutaneous tissue) is a layer of loose connective tissue and fat beneath the dermis. The epidermis consists of a **stratified squamous keratinized epithelium** which serves as a protective barrier. It is about 0.1 mm thick, but on the palms and soles, the thickness can be greater (0.8–1.4 mm). The **keratinocyte** is the principal cell of the epidermis which produces the protein keratin. There are four types of cells that are seen in the epidermis, namely keratinocytes (90%), **melanocytes** (8%), **Langerhans cells** and **Merkel cells.** **Melanocytes** contain melanin and are responsible for pigmentation of the skin. **Langerhans cells** are antigen-presenting cells that serve an immune function. **Merkel's cells** seen in the stratum basale detect sustained pressure.

The **dermis** consists of irregular, moderately dense connective tissue and accommodates nerves, blood vessels, lymphatics, epidermal appendages and a changing population of cells. It provides considerable strength to the skin and consists of a **papillary layer** and **reticular layer**.

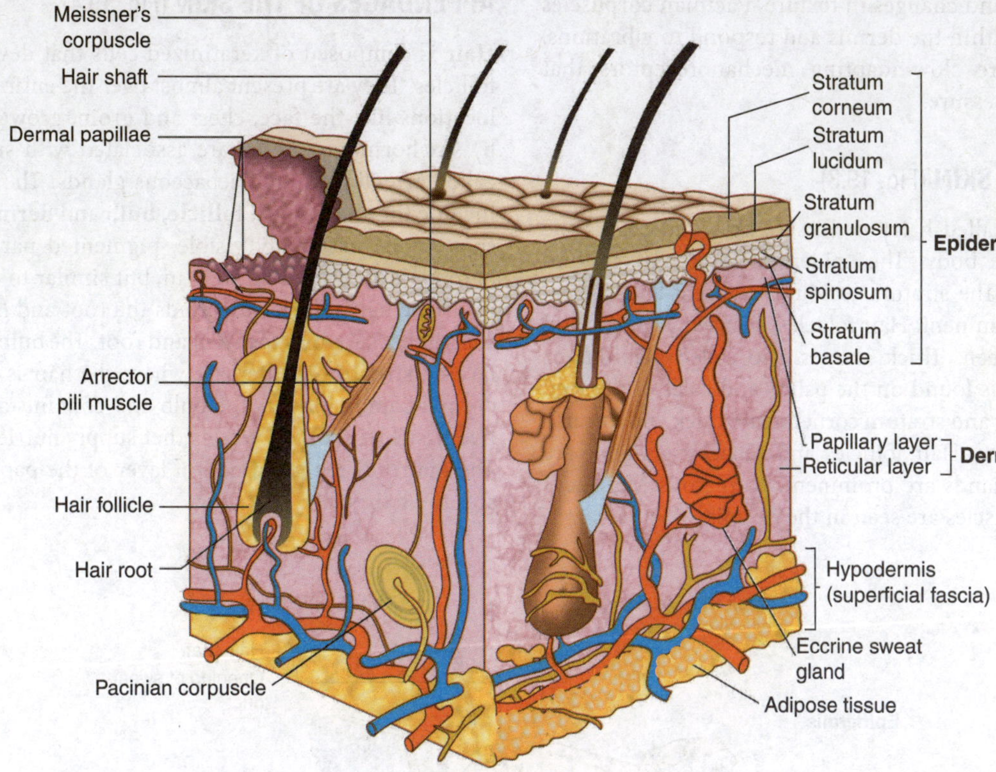

FIG. 19.1 General features of skin.

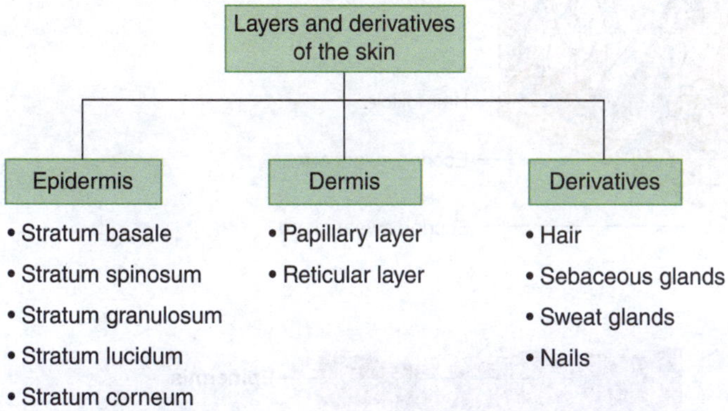

FIG. 19.2 The layers and derivatives of skin.

The epidermis consists of five layers from deep to superficial, namely **stratum basale, stratum spinosum, stratum granulosum, stratum lucidum** and **stratum corneum**. The stratum basale is a single layer of cuboidal to low columnar cells that contains stem cells, melanocytes and Merkel cells. The stem cells give rise to keratinocytes by mitosis and push the other layers to the top. The stratum spinosum contains several layers of closely packed keratinocytes that have irregular, angulated outlines and Langerhans cells. The stratum granulosum is made up of three or four layers of flattened, intensely basophilic cells containing keratohyalin granules. The nuclei of cells in this layer become pyknotic and cell death is initiated. The stratum lucidum is seen only in thick skin (palms and feet). It appears as a clear, eosinophilic layer that has a refractile appearance. This layer, which varies the most in thickness, contains incompletely keratinized, anucleate cells. The most superficial layer, the stratum corneum, comprises closely packed layers of flattened, polyhedral, anucleate squames. These are filled with keratin and are continuously shed and replaced.

The **papillary dermis** is the thin upper layer of the dermis. Numerous dermal papillae (upward projections) interdigitate with epidermal rete pegs (downward projections) in the base of the epidermis. This prevents slipping of the epidermis on the dermis. This layer consists of relatively small, finely textured collagen fibres. Capillary loops are frequently seen in relation to the papillae and sensory receptors called Meissner's corpuscles may also be seen in this layer. The **reticular dermis** is considerably thicker and lies beneath the papillary layer. As compared to the papillary layer, this layer contains larger, coarser collagen fibres and fewer cells. The collagen fibres form an interlacing network forming linear tension **lines of Langer**.

The skin contains **sensory receptors** of various types. It is also well supplied with motor endings to the blood vessels, arrector pili muscles and sweat glands. Sensory nerve endings include **free nerve endings, Meissner's corpuscles, Pacinian corpuscles** and **Ruffini endings**. Free nerve endings detect touch, pain and temperature. Meissner's corpuscles are specialized to detect light touch and changes in texture. Pacinian corpuscles are located deep within the dermis and respond to vibrations. Ruffini endings are slow-adapting mechanoreceptors that respond to deep pressure.

THICK AND THIN SKIN (Fig. 19.3)

Thin skin is also called hairy or hirsute skin and covers the greater part of the body. The epidermal layer and stratum corneum are thin. The stratum lucidum is absent and dermal papillae are not prominent. Hair follicles, sebaceous glands and sweat glands are seen. **Thick skin** is also called glabrous or nonhairy skin and is found on the palms and soles of the feet. The epidermal layer and stratum corneum are thick with prominent dermal papillae. Hair follicles and sebaceous glands are absent but sweat glands are prominent. Numerous Meissner's and Pacinian corpuscles are seen in the dermis.

APPENDAGES OF THE SKIN (Fig. 19.4)

Hair is composed of keratinized cells that develop from hair follicles. They are present almost over the entire body. In some locations like the face, chest and groin, growth is influenced by sex hormones. Hairs are associated with smooth muscles called arrector pili and sebaceous glands. The parts of a hair include the **shaft, root, follicle, bulb** and **dermal papilla**. The shaft is the externally visible, pigmented part composed of hard keratin. Buried in the skin, but similar to the shaft, is the root. The hair follicle surrounds the root and is enclosed by a sheath that supports the shaft and root. The bulb is the enlarged layered structure at the base where the hair is generated. The dermal papilla indents the bulb and contains areolar connective tissue with blood vessels that supply nutrients to the hair. The matrix is the germination layer of the papilla that generates the hair shaft.

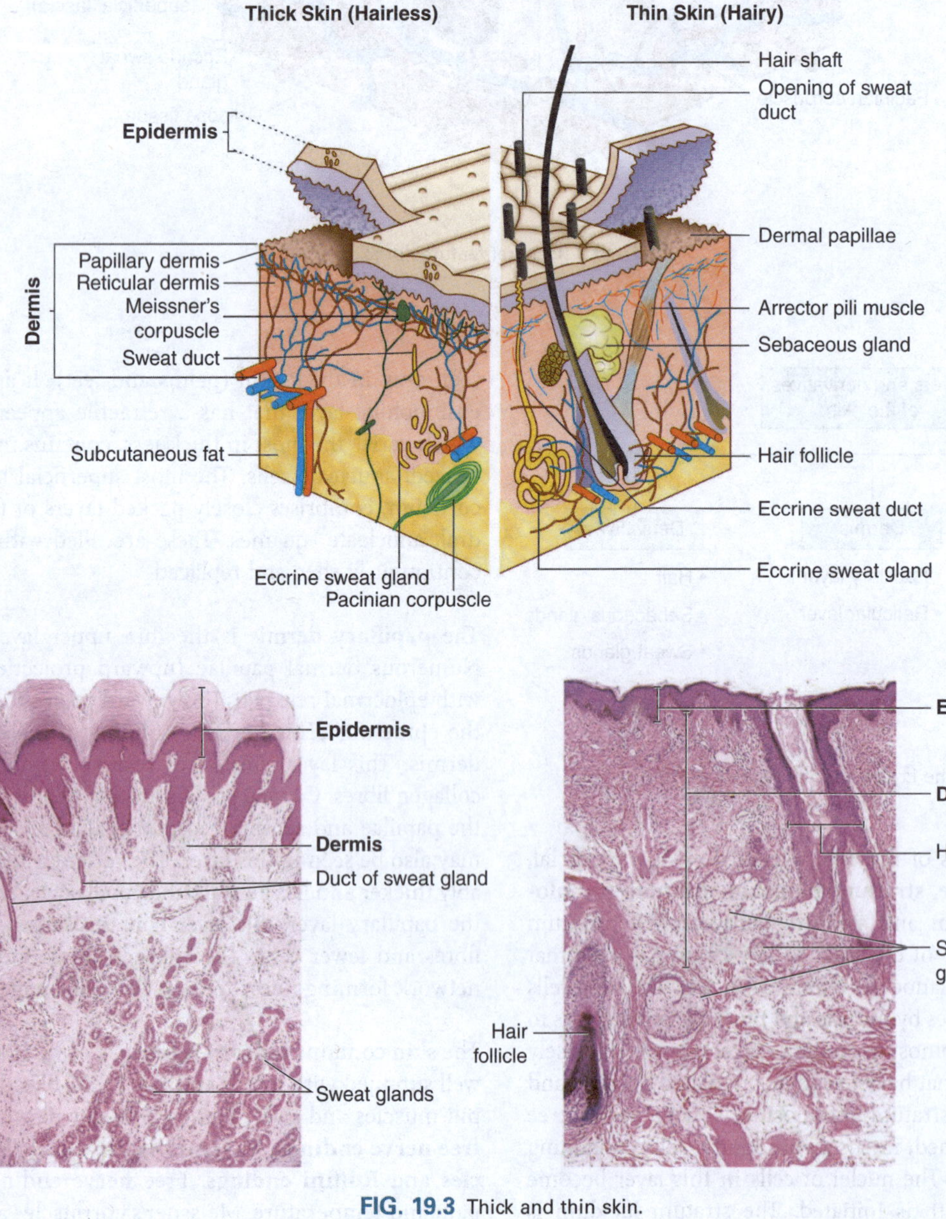

FIG. 19.3 Thick and thin skin.

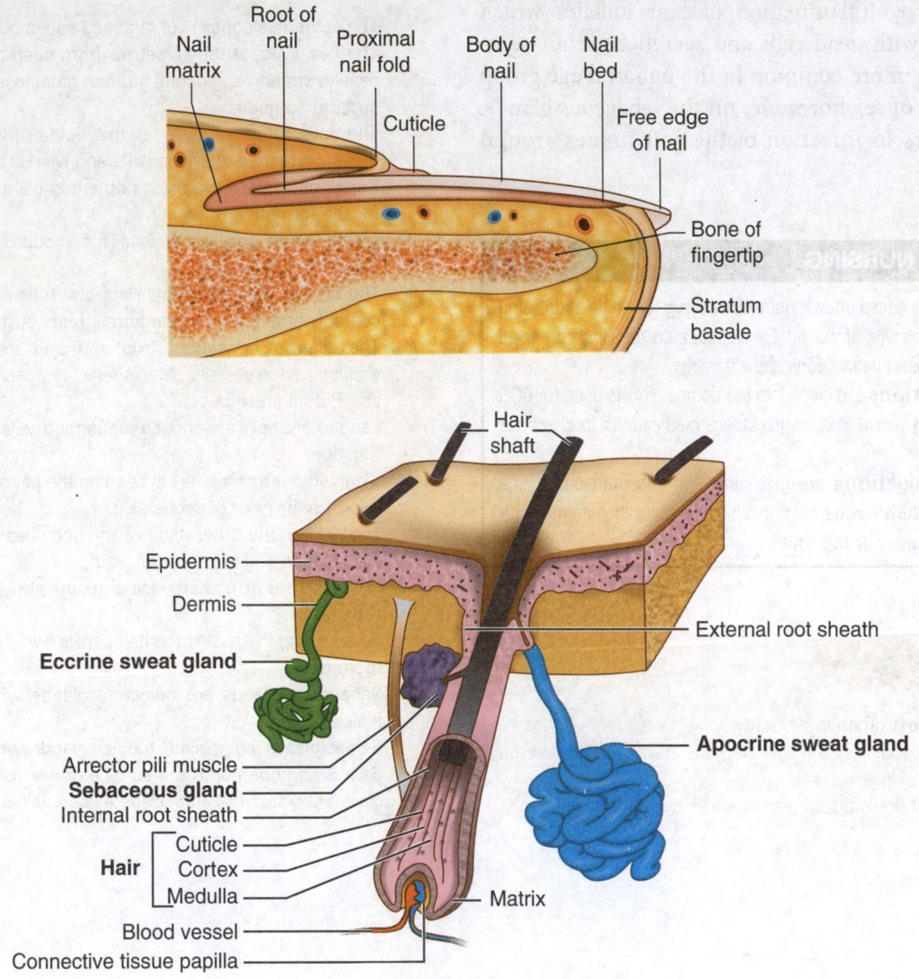

FIG. 19.4 Appendages of skin.

Sebaceous glands are holocrine glands that secrete sebum into the hair follicles and are responsible for preventing the skin from drying. The arrector pili are smooth muscles connecting the hair follicle to the dermis. They function in piloerection and secretion of sebum by pressing on the sebaceous glands. **Sweat glands** are simple, coiled tubular glands that reside in the dermis. There are two types of sweat glands seen in the skin. The eccrine variety opens directly onto the surface via ducts. This type of sweat gland is the most common and seen all over the body. They produce a watery secretion and are stimulated to secrete by sympathetic cholinergic nerve supply. These nerves also supply the arrector pili and smooth muscles of the blood vessels in the skin. Apocrine sweat glands are seen in regions like the groin, perineum and axilla and pour their secretions into the hair follicles. The mammary glands, the ceruminous glands in the external ear and the glands of Moll in the eyelid are all modified apocrine sweat glands. **Nails** are plates of keratinized cells containing hard keratin. The nail consists of a free edge, body and root. The body lies on the nail bed, while the root lies in close relation to the nail matrix. Cells in the nail matrix divide to produce cells that eventually form the nail plate.

APPLIED ANATOMY

- The damage to the skin by external **burns** causes fluid loss and increased risk of infections.
- Congenital absence of skin pigmentation is called **albinism.**
- Patches of skin with increased and decreased pigmentation are called **lentigo** and **vitiligo**, respectively.
- **Skin carcinomas** are more common among light-skinned people. The more common skin carcinomas arise from keratinocytes and melanocytes and are termed squamous cell carcinoma and malignant melanoma, respectively.
- **Psoriasis** is a skin condition caused by increased cell turnover in the epidermis leading to the formation of patches that are scaly, red and itchy.
- **Surgical incisions** made parallel to the lines of Langer are likely to heal with less scarring as compared to those made perpendicular to them.
- **Alopecia** is the term used to describe hair loss. The common form is seen in males and is called male pattern baldness or androgenetic alopecia. Here, there is a characteristic loss of hair in the temporal and central regions of the scalp.

- **Acne** is caused by inflammation of hair follicles which become clogged with dead cells and secretions from sebaceous glands. It is more common in the pubertal age group due to the effects of sex hormones on the sebaceous glands.
- **Paronychia** refers to infection of the soft tissues around the nail.

APPLICATIONS IN NURSING

- Skin wounds due to any cause often require **dressing**. The type of dressing required depends on the type of wound. For example, dry dressings are used for nondraining postoperative incisions and abrasions.
- **Intradermal injections** are given into the dermis. This is done for BCG vaccination and giving test doses for injectable medications to check for allergic reactions.
- **Subcutaneous injections** are given into the subcutaneous tissue (superficial fascia) underlying the skin. Insulin injections in patients with diabetes mellitus are given by this route.

SUMMARY

- The skin is the largest organ in the body.
- Hair, sebaceous glands, sweat glands and nails constitute the appendages of the skin.
- The skin consists of an outer epidermis and inner dermis.
- The epidermis consists of stratified squamous keratinized epithelium.
- The five layers of the epidermis from deep to superficial are stratum basale, stratum spinosum, stratum granulosum, stratum lucidum and stratum corneum.
- The four types of cells in the epidermis are the keratinocytes, melanocytes, Langerhans cells and Merkel cells.
- Keratinocytes are the most numerous cell type and are responsible for the formation of keratin.
- Melanocytes are responsible for producing the pigmentation of the skin.
- The dermis consists of papillary and reticular layers with finely and coarsely arranged collagen fibres, respectively.
- The different sensations from the skin are carried via free nerve endings, Merkel cells, Meissner's corpuscles, Pacinian corpuscles and Ruffini endings.
- Langerhans cells are antigen-presenting cells which serve an immune function.
- Skin without hair follicles is seen on the palms and soles and is called thick, nonhairy or glabrous skin.
- The skin on the other parts of the body has hair follicles and associated glands and is called thin skin.
- Hair consists of a shaft, visible externally, and a root buried within the dermis.
- Surrounding the root is the hair papilla, which is expanded into a bulb more deeply.
- Sebaceous glands are holocrine glands which open into the hair follicle.
- Sweat glands are coiled, tubular glands which are situated in the dermis and open onto the surface or hair follicles.
- Nails are plates of keratinized cells containing hard keratin.

CHAPTER 20

The Special Senses

SPECIFIC LEARNING OBJECTIVES

At the end of this chapter, the student should be able to:

- Name the special sensory organs.
- Draw the eyeball showing the various layers.
- Describe the components of each layer in brief.
- Name the parts of the ear.
- Describe in brief each part of the ear.
- Describe the structure of a taste bud.
- Describe the structure of olfactory epithelium.

GLOSSARY OF TERMS

- **Olfactory:** related to smell
- **Gustatory:** related to taste
- **Visual:** related to sight
- **Auditory:** related to hearing
- **Limbus:** junction between the sclera, cornea and iris from where aqueous humour is drained
- **Macula lutea:** small area on the retina where the cones are concentrated
- **Fovea centralis:** minute area on the macula lutea where only cones are present
- **Optic disc:** area on the retina where fibres of the optic nerve exit
- **Ora serrata:** irregular junctional line between the neural and non-neural parts of the retina
- **Canthi:** angles of the eye at the junction between the upper and lower eyelids
- **Bony labyrinth:** spaces within the petrous part of the temporal bone that contain perilymph
- **Membranous labyrinth:** a system of tube-like structures situated within the bony labyrinth that contain endolymph
- **Vestibule:** part of the bony labyrinth that contains the utricle and saccule
- **Utricle and saccule:** parts of the membranous labyrinth that are responsible for monitoring the position of the head
- **Macula:** end organ that responds to linear changes in the position of the head
- **Crista:** end organ that responds to rotational changes in the position of the head
- **Organ of Corti:** end organ of hearing
- **Taste bud:** end organ of taste
- **Papillae:** elevations on the surface of the tongue containing taste buds
- **Olfactory receptor cells:** bipolar neurons that detect odours and transmit them centrally via the olfactory nerve rootlets
- **Bowman's glands:** glands in the connective tissue underlying the olfactory epithelium that produce serous secretions

INTRODUCTION

The four special senses are **vision, hearing, smell** and **taste. Vision** is the dominant sense in humans. Around 70% of sensory receptors in humans are in the eyes. Nearly 40% of the cerebral cortex is involved in processing visual information. The **ear** is the receptor organ for hearing and equilibrium. **Taste buds** are located mostly on the tongue and carry the sensations of sweet, sour, salty and bitter tastes. There are around 1000 types of **smell receptors** in the roof of the nasal cavity. The convergence of many receptor cell signals registers a signature pattern which the brain recognizes as a particular type of smell. In this chapter, we will be discussing the anatomy of these **special sensory organs** with special emphasis on vision and hearing.

THE EYEBALL AND ITS ACCESSORY STRUCTURES

The eyeball is around 1 inch in diameter. Only the anterior one-sixth is visible externally. It lies within the bony orbit surrounded by a protective cushion of fat. The eyeball has three layers, an **outer fibrous layer**, a **middle vascular layer** and an **inner nervous layer** (Figs 20.1 and 20.2). The fibrous layer is composed of two regions of connective tissue. The **sclera**, which is white and opaque, forms the posterior five-sixths of the layer, provides shape to the eyeball and forms an anchor for the attachment of extraocular muscles. The anterior one-sixth of the fibrous layer is formed by the transparent **cornea**. The **limbus** is the junction between the sclera and cornea and is the site for drainage of aqueous humour into veins around it.

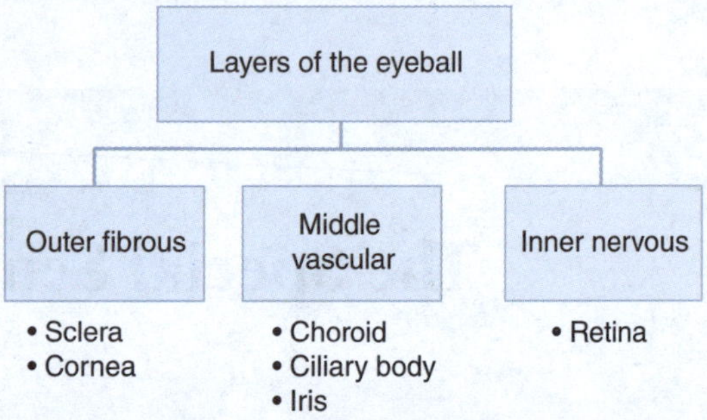

FIG. 20.1 The layers of the eyeball.

The **middle coat** of the eyeball is composed of the **choroid, ciliary body** and **iris**. The **choroid** is a vascular, darkly pigmented membrane which forms the posterior five-sixths of the vascular tunic. Its dark colour is due to the presence of numerous melanocytes. This prevents scattering of light rays within the eye. The choroid corresponds to the arachnoid and pia mater layers of the meninges. The **ciliary body** is the thickened ring of tissue that encircles the lens. It is composed of the ciliaris muscle and ciliary processes. The **suspensory ligaments** pass from the ciliary body to the entire circumference of the lens. The ciliary body is responsible for the production of aqueous humour and regulating the convexity of the lens. The **iris** is the visible coloured part of the eye which is attached to the ciliary body. The **pupil** is the round, central opening in the iris. The iris contains smooth muscles which control the size of the pupil. The **sphincter pupillae** and **dilator pupillae** muscles constrict (miosis) and dilate (mydriasis) the pupil, respectively.

The **retina** is the deepest tunic and is composed of two layers. The **outer pigmented layer** consists of a single layer of melanocytes. The **inner neural layer** contains three main types of neurons, namely photoreceptor cells, bipolar cells and ganglion cells. Synapses occur within the neural layer between the processes of the three types of neurons. The photoreceptor cells are the **rods** and **cones**. Rod cells are more sensitive to light and allow vision in dim light, whereas cone cells function best in bright light and enable high-acuity, colour vision. The cones are especially concentrated at the **macula lutea**, which is a small, oval pigmented area near the centre of the retina. The **fovea centralis** is a minute area within the macula and contains only cones, making it the region of highest visual acuity. The axons of the ganglion cells form the **optic nerve**. The area where these axons exit the retina is called the **optic disc** or blind spot as photoreceptor cells are absent here. The part of the retina that lines the ciliary body and iris is much simpler in its structure and does not contain neurons. The junction between the part of the retina that lines the choroid and the part that lines the ciliary body is called the **ora serrata**, as it has a serrated appearance. The retina receives its blood supply from two sources. Capillaries in the choroid supply the outer third of the retina, while the inner two-thirds of the retina is supplied by the **central artery** and vein of the retina.

The **lens** and suspensory ligament divide the eye into **anterior** and **posterior segments**. **Vitreous humour** which is a clear, jelly-like substance fills the posterior segment. The vitreous allows transmission of light, supports the posterior surface of the lens and helps maintain the intraocular pressure. The anterior segment is divided into **anterior** and **posterior chambers**. The anterior chamber is situated between the cornea and iris, whereas the posterior chamber lies between the iris and lens. **Aqueous humour** fills the anterior chamber and is renewed continuously. It supplies nutrients to the lens and cornea. Aqueous is produced by the **ciliary processes** and absorbed by venules around the limbus. The **lens** is a thick, transparent, biconvex disc that is held in place by the **suspensory ligaments**. The convexity of the lens is controlled by the **ciliaris muscle** located within the ciliary body.

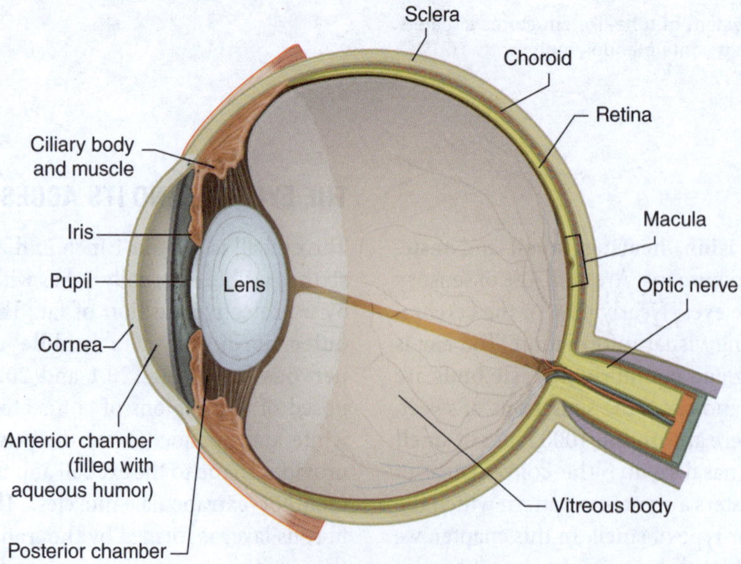

FIG. 20.2 The parts of the eyeball.

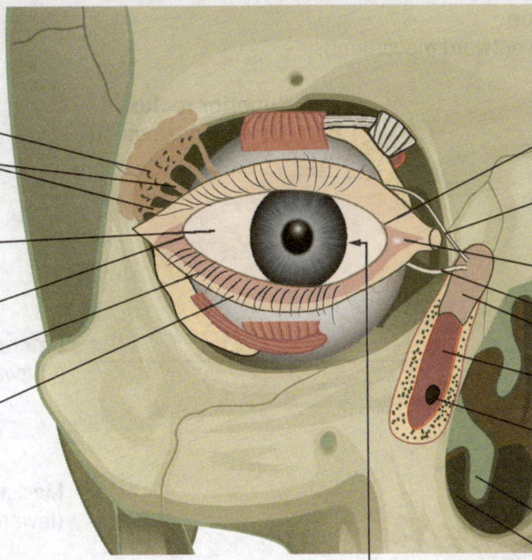

FIG. 20.3 The accessory structures of the eye.

The accessory structures are not directly involved in vision but aid the process (Fig. 20.3). They include the **eyelids, conjunctiva, lacrimal apparatus** and **extraocular muscles**. The upper and lower eyelids or palpebrae are separated by the palpebral fissure. The junctions of the eyelids at either end are known as the **medial** and **lateral canthi**. **Eyelashes** are seen at the margins of the eyelids. Connective tissue plates within the eyelids called **tarsal plates** provide some degree of rigidity to the eyelids. **Tarsal glands** are modified sebaceous glands within the tarsal plates that open at the lid margins. Closure of the eyelids is facilitated by the **orbicularis oculi** muscle, while the **levator palpebrae superioris** muscle acts to lift the upper lid.

The **conjunctiva** is a transparent mucous membrane of stratified columnar epithelium. The **palpebral conjunctiva** lines the eyelids, whereas the **bulbar conjunctiva** covers the white of the eye but not the cornea. Tear production and drainage are performed by the **lacrimal apparatus**. **Tears** contain mucus, antibodies and lysozyme. The lacrimal apparatus consists of the **lacrimal gland, lacrimal puncta, lacrimal canaliculi, lacrimal sac** and **nasolacrimal duct**. The lacrimal gland lies in a depression in the bony orbit superolateral to the eye. It produces tears, which then pass into the conjunctival sac from where the tears pass out successively through the lacrimal puncta, lacrimal canaliculi and lacrimal sac into the nasolacrimal duct. The nasolacrimal duct empties into the nasal cavity.

The eyeball is moved by **extraocular muscles** (Fig. 20.4). There are four **rectus** (straight) muscles, the superior, inferior, medial and lateral, which originate from a common tendinous or annular ring, at the apex of the orbit. There are also two **oblique** muscles: the superior and inferior oblique. The lateral and medial recti **abduct** and **adduct** the eye, respectively. The superior rectus and inferior oblique enable **elevation** of the eyeball, whereas the inferior rectus and superior oblique cause **depression** of the eyeball. All the muscles except the lateral rectus and the superior oblique are supplied by the **oculomotor nerve**. The lateral rectus and the superior oblique are supplied by the **abducent nerve** and **trochlear nerve**, respectively.

THE EAR

The ear is the receptor organ for **hearing** and **equilibrium**. It is composed of three parts, the **outer ear, middle ear** and **inner ear** (Figs 20.5 and 20.6). All three parts function in hearing, whereas the inner ear functions in both hearing and equilibrium. The **external ear** is composed of the **auricle (pinna)** and **external acoustic meatus** or **auditory canal**. It helps to direct sounds towards the middle ear. The pinna is composed of elastic cartilage covered by skin. The major parts of the pinna are the helix, tragus and lobule. The external acoustic meatus is partly cartilaginous and partly bony. It is lined by skin and contains hairs, sebaceous glands and modified sweat glands known as ceruminous glands. The external acoustic meatus runs medially till the **tympanic membrane**, which separates the external and middle ear.

The **middle ear cavity** or tympanic cavity is a small, air-filled space located within the petrous part of the **temporal bone** (Fig. 20.7). Its medial wall contains the oval and round window. Anteriorly, the pharyngotympanic tube (auditory or Eustachian tube) links the middle ear and nasopharynx. The middle ear cavity is connected posteriorly to the mastoid antrum. Superiorly, it is separated from the middle cranial fossa by a plate of bone. The **ear ossicles** are the smallest bones in the body and are contained within the middle ear cavity. The **malleus** attaches to the eardrum. The **incus** lies between the malleus and **stapes**, while the stapes vibrates against the oval window. Two small **skeletal muscles**, the tensor tympani and stapedius, are also seen within the middle ear cavity. Their contraction helps prevent excessive movements of the ear ossicles.

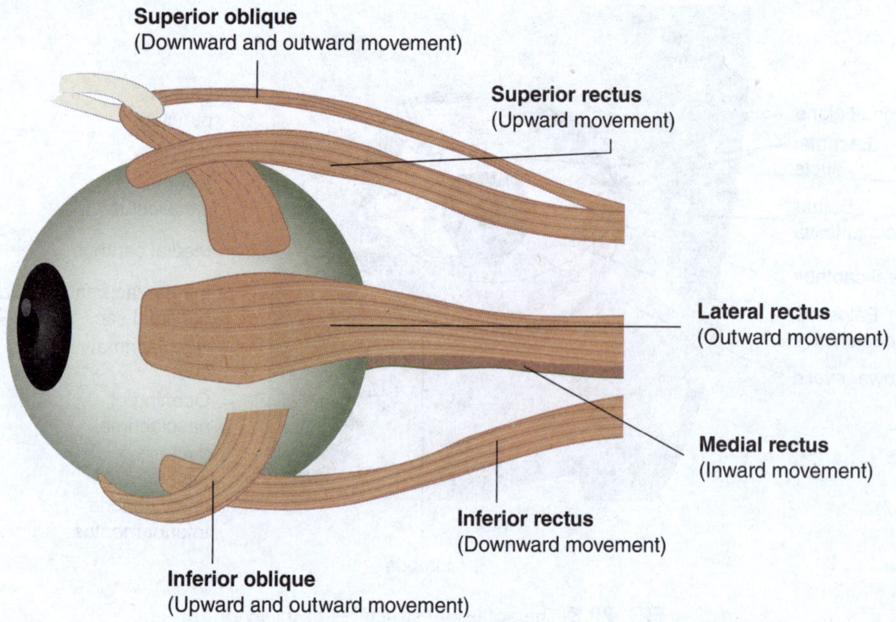

FIG. 20.4 The extraocular muscles.

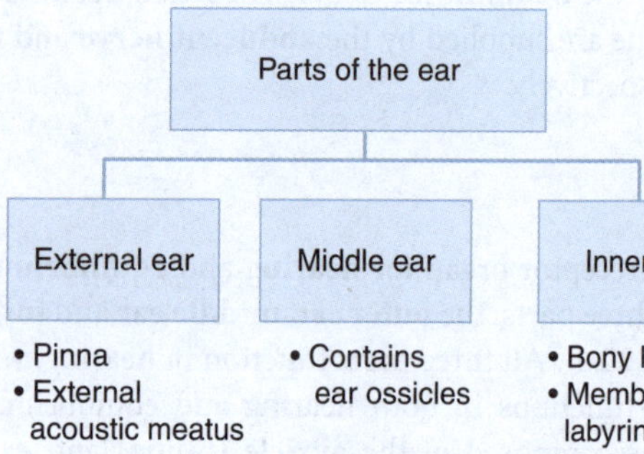

FIG. 20.5 Parts of the ear.

The **inner ear**, also called the **labyrinth**, lies within the petrous part of the temporal bone (Figs 20.8 and 20.9). The **bony labyrinth** is a cavity consisting of three parts: the **semicircular canals**, **vestibule** and **cochlea**. Within the bony labyrinth lies the **membranous labyrinth**. The membranous labyrinth contains a series of membrane-lined sacs and ducts. These include the **semicircular ducts, utricle** and **saccule** and **cochlear duct** which are located within the semicircular canals, vestibule and cochlea, respectively. The membranous labyrinth is filled with a clear fluid known as the **endolymph**, while the bony labyrinth is filled with **perilymph**.

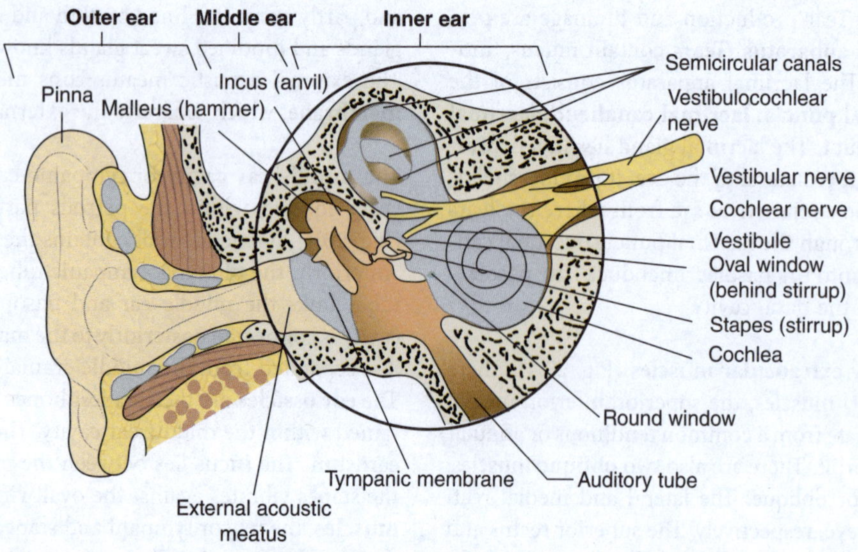

FIG. 20.6 The parts of the ear.

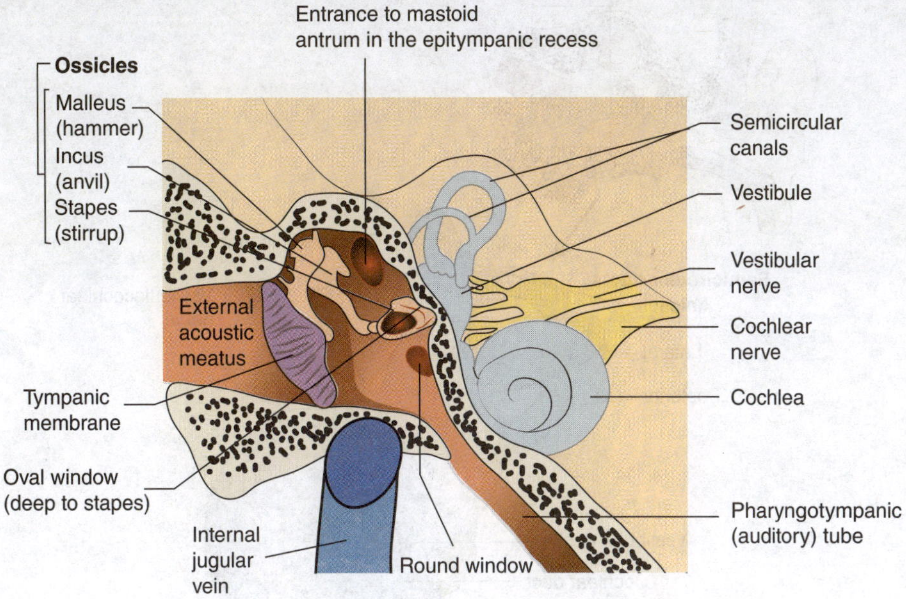

FIG. 20.7 The middle ear cavity.

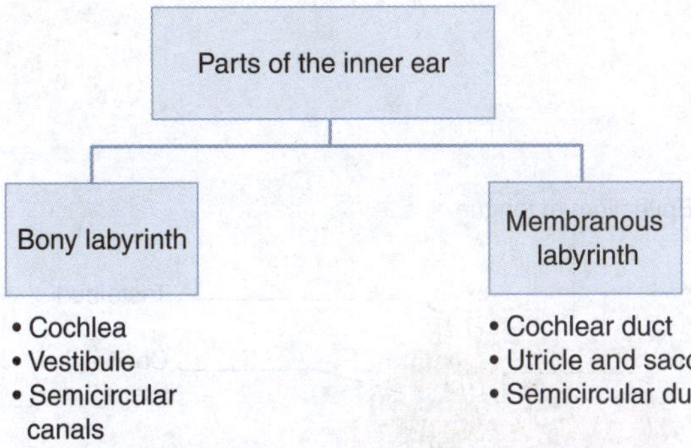

FIG. 20.8 Parts of the inner ear.

The **utricle** and **saccule** are two egg-shaped parts of the membranous labyrinth which house the macula. The **macula** is a sensory epithelium that contains receptor cells. They monitor the position of the head when the head is still. The epithelium contains columnar supporting cells and receptor cells called hair cells which synapse with the vestibular nerve. The **semicircular canals** lie posterior and lateral to the vestibule. The anterior and posterior semicircular canals lie in the vertical plane at right angles to one another, while the lateral semicircular canal lies in the horizontal plane. The semicircular ducts pass through each semicircular canal and contain structures called the **cristae ampullaris**. The cristae contain supporting cells and receptor cells that detect rotational acceleration. The **vestibular division** of the **vestibulocochlear nerve** carries the sensations associated with balance from the macula and crista.

The **cochlea** is a spiral chamber within the bony labyrinth which contains the **cochlear duct**. The end organ of hearing is the **organ of Corti** which contains both sensory hair cells and supporting cells on a membrane called the **basilar membrane**. The hairs of the sensory cells are embedded within a membrane called the **tectorial membrane**. The movement of fluid within the cochlea is caused by forces applied to the oval window by the stapes. This in turn causes movements of the basilar membrane and subsequent stimulation of the hair cells. The sensation of hearing is carried by the **cochlear division** of the **vestibulocochlear nerve**.

ANATOMY OF TASTE (Fig. 20.10)

The sensation of taste is subserved by **taste buds** which are densely aggregated in the **tongue** but also seen on the palate, pharynx and epiglottis. The four basic types of taste are **sweet, sour, salty** and **bitter**. Sweet and salty taste sensations are best perceived near the tip of the tongue, sour tastes along the margins and bitter tastes near the back of the tongue. Taste buds on the tongue are seen in relation to **papillae**, which are minute elevations on its surface. Two types of papillae, **fungiform** and **circumvallate**, possess taste buds. Fungiform papillae are small mushroom-shaped papillae distributed over the entire surface of the tongue but concentrated near its tip. Circumvallate papillae are larger and cylindrical in shape situated as an inverted 'V' near the back of the tongue.

Taste buds consist of **taste cells** and **supporting cells** which are modifications of the surface epithelium. Taste cells possess apical microvilli which serve to increase the receptor surface. Sensory nerve fibres synapse with the bases of taste cells. The gustatory (taste) pathway to the brainstem is carried via three cranial nerves. The **facial nerve** carries taste sensations from the anterior two-thirds of the tongue, while the **glossopharyngeal nerve** does so from the posterior one-third of the tongue and pharynx. Taste sensations from the posterior-most part of the tongue are carried by the **vagus nerve**.

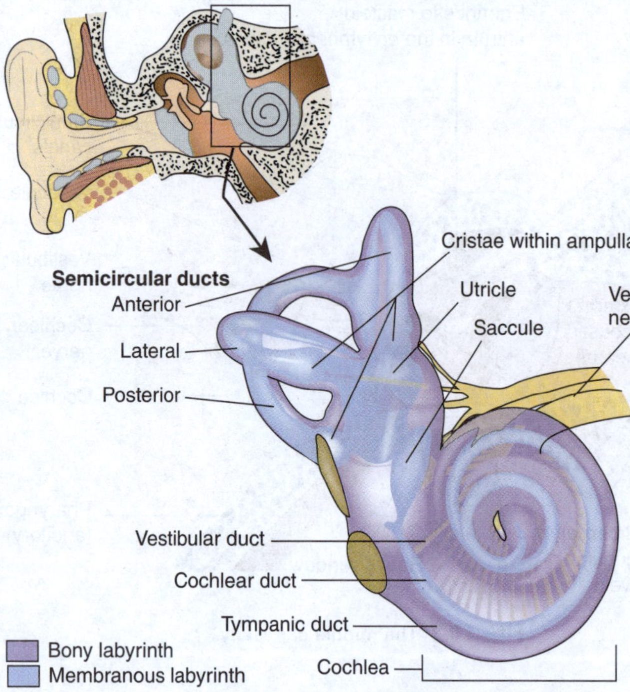

FIG. 20.9 The inner ear.

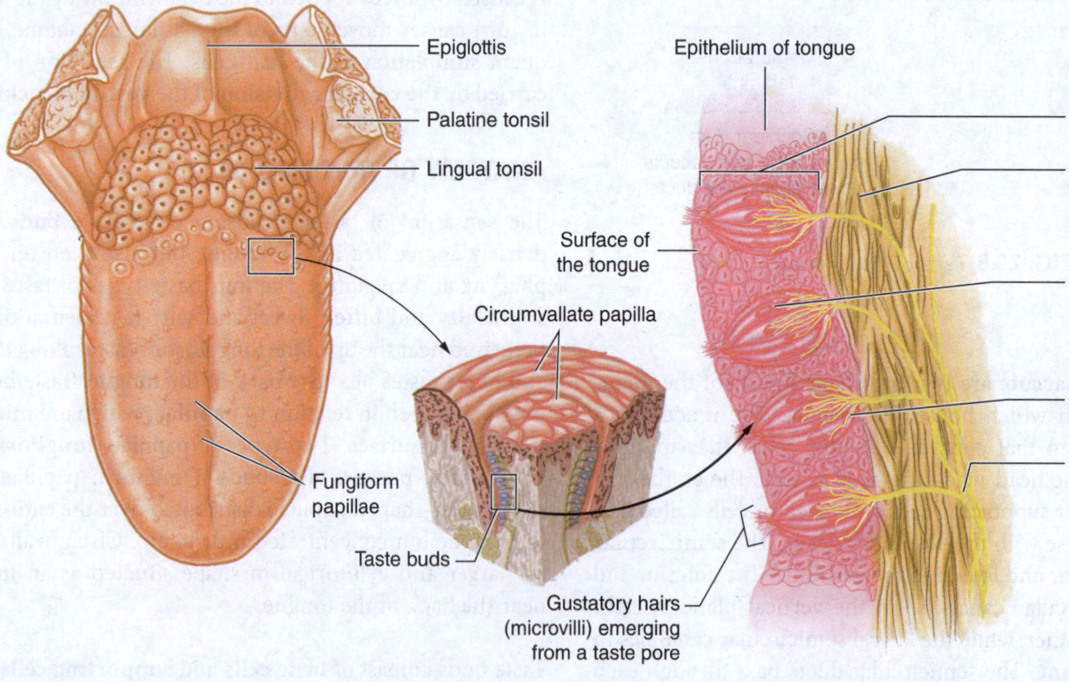

FIG. 20.10 The anatomy of taste.

ANATOMY OF SMELL (Fig. 20.11)

The roof of the nasal cavity contains a **pseudostratified ciliated columnar olfactory epithelium.** This epithelium contains millions of **olfactory receptor cells** which are **bipolar neurons**. These neurons are the only ones in the body that undergo replacement throughout adult life. The peripheral processes of these neurons contain **olfactory cilia** which contain receptors that bind to the odour molecules. The central processes of the neurons are bundled into filaments that constitute the rootlets of the **olfactory nerve**.

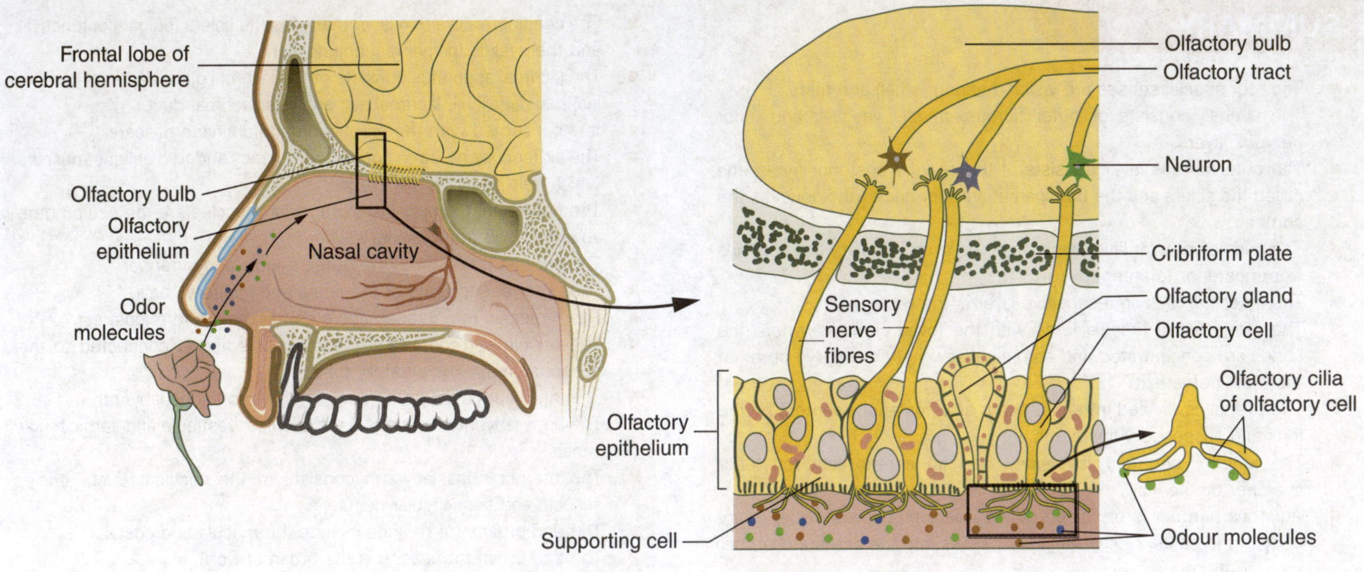

FIG. 20.11 The anatomy of smell.

These rootlets pass through the cribriform plate of the ethmoid bone and synapse with second-order neurons located within the **olfactory bulb**. The **olfactory tract** then carries impulses from the olfactory bulb to the olfactory cortex. **Bowman's glands** are present in the lamina propria underlying the epithelium. The secretions of these serous glands help to dissolve the odorant molecules so that they can then be perceived by the receptor cells. **Supporting cells** are also seen among the olfactory receptor cells.

APPLIED ANATOMY

- A common cause of blindness in elderly individuals is **cataract** which occurs due to opacity of the lens.
- **Glaucoma** occurs due to increased pressure of aqueous humour in the anterior segment of the eye and can lead to visual disturbances and blindness.
- Both diabetes and hypertension can cause morphological changes in the blood vessels of the retina, leading to **diabetic** and **hypertensive retinopathy**, respectively.
- An increase in intracranial pressure can be transmitted via the optic nerve, leading to an oedematous appearance of the optic disc known as **papilloedema**.
- Corneal opacities can be treated by **corneal transplantation.**
- **Styes** are caused due to infection of the hair follicle, its associated sweat or sebaceous glands or the Meibomian glands in the eyelids.
- Malalignment of the visual axes of the eyes is known as strabismus and can cause blurred vision (diplopia).
- Infections of the external ear (**otitis externa**) are extremely painful due to the tight adherence of the skin to the underlying cartilage.
- Excessive **wax** can accumulate in the external acoustic meatus causing decrease in the acuity of hearing.
- The **tympanic membrane** can be **perforated** by forceful blows to the ear or collections of excessive fluid or pus in the middle ear.
- Infection of the middle ear is called **otitis media**, which can spread to the mastoid air cells causing mastoiditis.
- **Deafness** can be sensorineural or conductive. Sensorineural deafness is caused by abnormalities of the organ of Corti or the auditory pathway. Conductive deafness is caused by poor conduction of sound waves to the inner ear because of abnormalities of the external or middle ear.
- Inner ear disorders can cause **vertigo** due to abnormal stimulation of the macula and crista.
- **Hypogeusia, ageusia** and **dysgeusia** refer to decreased taste sensation, loss of taste sensation and distorted taste sensation, respectively.
- **Taste disorders** can be caused by respiratory infections, head injuries, poor oral hygiene, certain medications and lesions of nerves conducting taste sensations.
- Absence of the sense of smell is called **anosmia** and may be caused by trauma, colds or allergies producing excessive mucus, polyps causing blockage or zinc deficiency.

APPLICATIONS IN NURSING

- **Irrigation of the eye** with cool water is required when foreign bodies or irritating solutions enter the eye. The eye is flushed from the medial to the lateral canthus.
- Medications such as drops and **ointments** are introduced into the eye for a variety of reasons such as infections, allergies and glaucoma. The inferior aspect of the conjunctival sac is a convenient location to instill these medications after depressing the lower eyelid.
- **Ear drops** need to be administered in case of infections or for the softening of earwax. To straighten the external auditory meatus when instilling the drops, the pinna needs to be pulled upward and backward in adults and downward and backward in children.

SUMMARY

- The four special senses are vision, hearing, smell and taste.
- The eyeball consists of outer fibrous, middle vascular and inner nervous layers.
- The outer fibrous layer consists of the opaque posterior five-sixths called the sclera and the transparent anterior one-sixth known as the cornea.
- The middle vascular layer consists of the choroid, ciliary body and iris from posterior to anterior.
- The inner nervous light-sensitive layer is the retina.
- The retina has a macula lutea with the fovea centralis where the cones are concentrated and an optic disc where the nerve fibres of the optic nerve exit.
- The eyeball is divided into an anterior and posterior segment by the lens and suspensory ligaments.
- The anterior segment is divided into an anterior and posterior chamber by the iris.
- Aqueous humour is produced by the ciliary processes of the ciliary body in the posterior chamber and passes into the anterior chamber through the pupil.
- Vitreous humour fills the posterior segment of the eyeball.
- The accessory structures of vision are the eyelids, conjunctiva, lacrimal apparatus and extraocular muscles.
- The eyelids are lined on the outside by skin and on the inside by conjunctiva.
- They have a connective tissue core called the tarsal plate in which are embedded Meibomian glands that open at the lid margins in close relation to the eyelashes.
- The eyelids are separated by the action of the levator palpebrae superioris and closed by the orbicularis oculi.
- The conjunctiva is a thin layer that lines the sclera (bulbar conjunctiva) and the eyelids (palpebral conjunctiva).
- The lacrimal apparatus consists of the lacrimal gland, lacrimal puncta, lacrimal canaliculi, lacrimal sac and nasolacrimal duct.
- It is concerned with the production and drainage of tears.
- The extraocular muscles consist of four recti and two oblique muscles which help to move the eyeball.
- The nerves that supply the extraocular muscles are the oculomotor, abducent and trochlear nerves.
- The ear has three parts, the outer, middle and inner ear.
- The outer ear consists of the pinna and auditory canal.
- The tympanic membrane separates the outer and middle ear.
- The middle ear contains the ear ossicles and is connected to the nasopharynx by the auditory tube.
- The inner ear contains the bony and membranous labyrinth.
- The bony labyrinth consists of the cochlea, vestibule and semicircular canals.
- The membranous labyrinth consists of the cochlear duct, utricle, saccule and semicircular ducts.
- The end organs for balance include the macula and crista.
- The end organ for hearing is the organ of Corti.
- The vestibulocochlear nerve carries impulses from the inner ear.
- The end organs of taste are taste buds seen mainly on the tongue and also on the palate, pharynx and epiglottis.
- On the tongue, taste buds are seen in relation to fungiform and circumvallate papillae.
- The facial, glossopharyngeal and vagus nerves carry the sensation of taste.
- Olfaction is mediated by the olfactory receptor cells which are bipolar neurons seen in relation to the olfactory epithelium.
- The olfactory nerve rootlets carry sensations to the olfactory bulb, from where impulses are conducted to the olfactory cortex.

7.1
SECTION

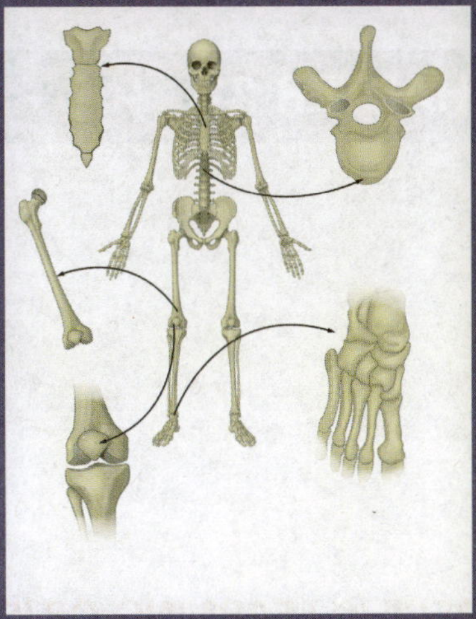

The Skeletal System

Section Outline

CHAPTER 21

Classification, General Features and Microstructure

SPECIFIC LEARNING OBJECTIVES

At the end of this chapter, the student should be able to:

- Classify the bones of the body based on their location and structure.
- Describe the general features of bone tissue.
- Compare and contrast the microstructure of compact and spongy bones.
- Describe in brief the mechanisms of bone growth and development.

GLOSSARY OF TERMS

- **Bone:** specialized connective tissue with a mineralized matrix
- **Axial skeleton:** bones that form the central axis of the body such as the vertebrae and skull
- **Appendicular skeleton:** bones of the extremities
- **Woven bone:** type of bone seen in the developing foetus
- **Lamellar bone:** type of bone seen in adults which is arranged in layers
- **Compact bone:** type of lamellar bone containing osteons
- **Spongy bone:** type of lamellar bone with trabeculae separated by marrow spaces
- **Osteon (Haversian system):** unit of compact bone with central Haversian canal and surrounding concentric lamellae
- **Osteoblast:** bone-forming cell
- **Osteocyte:** bone-maintaining cell
- **Osteoclast:** bone-destroying cell
- **Periosteum:** outer lining of bones
- **Endosteum:** inner lining of bones
- **Membranous ossification:** development of a bone from a membranous precursor
- **Endochondral ossification:** development of a bone from a cartilaginous precursor

INTRODUCTION

Bone is a specialized connective tissue characterized by a mineralized extracellular matrix. It is a highly dynamic tissue, second only to blood in its capacity for regeneration. Unlike cartilage, bone is highly vascular. Its functions are numerous. Bones serve as scaffolds for the soft tissues of the body. They protect important vital organs such as the brain and heart. The bone marrow is the site for the production of cellular components of the blood. Bone tissue serves as a reservoir of calcium and phosphorus to help maintain constant concentrations in body fluids. The long bones serve an important function of providing attachment to skeletal muscles, acting as levers for movements of the body and locomotion. This chapter will focus on the classification, general features and histology of bone tissue.

CLASSIFICATION OF BONES (Fig. 21.1)

Bones can be classified based on the following:

a. **Position** (Fig. 21.2): Bones can be part of either the **axial** or **appendicular** skeleton. The bones of the axial skeleton lie along the central axis of the body and consist of the skull, vertebrae, sternum and ribs. The appendicular skeleton consists of the bones of the upper and lower limbs.

b. **Shape** (Fig. 21.3): Depending on their shape, bones can be classified as **long, short, flat, irregular or sesamoid**. Long bones are seen in the upper and lower limbs. The femur and humerus are typical examples of long bones. Examples of short bones include the carpal and tarsal bones seen in the wrist and foot, respectively. The bones forming the skull cap or calvaria like the parietal bone are examples of flat bones, along with the ribs, sternum and scapulae. Irregular bones usually have a number of projections such as the vertebrae and bones forming the skeleton of the face. Sesamoid bones form within tendons of muscles. Examples are the patella and pisiform.

c. **Structure: Lamellar bone** consists of layers of bone tissue called lamellae. All bones found in adults are of this type. Lamellar bone is usually heavily mineralized and has relatively less cellular elements as compared to **woven bone**. Woven bone is typically seen in the developing foetus.

d. **Development:** Bones may develop from either membranes or cartilage. Those that develop from membranes are said to develop by **intramembranous ossification**. Examples include the bones forming the calvaria of the skull, such as the parietal bone. In the process of **endochondral ossification**, a cartilaginous model of the bone is replaced by bone tissue. This type of ossification is seen in a majority of the bones of the limbs.

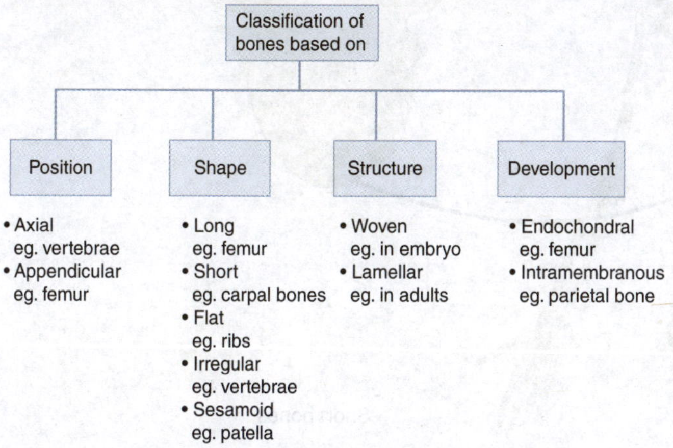

FIG. 21.1 Classification of bones.

TERMS USED TO DESCRIBE THE GROSS ANATOMY OF BONES

A number of terms are used to describe the gross features of bones. Some of the more commonly used terms are listed as follows:

- Condyle – rounded articular area
- Crest – ridge
- Epicondyle – nonarticular eminence superior to a condyle
- Facet – smooth, flat area
- Foramen – hole
- Fossa – depression
- Groove – linear depression or furrow
- Line – linear elevation
- Malleolus – rounded process
- Notch – indentation
- Protuberance – projection
- Spine – thorn-like process
- Spinous process – projecting spine-like part
- Trochanter – large, blunt elevation
- Tubercle – small, raised eminence
- Tuberosity – large, rounded elevation

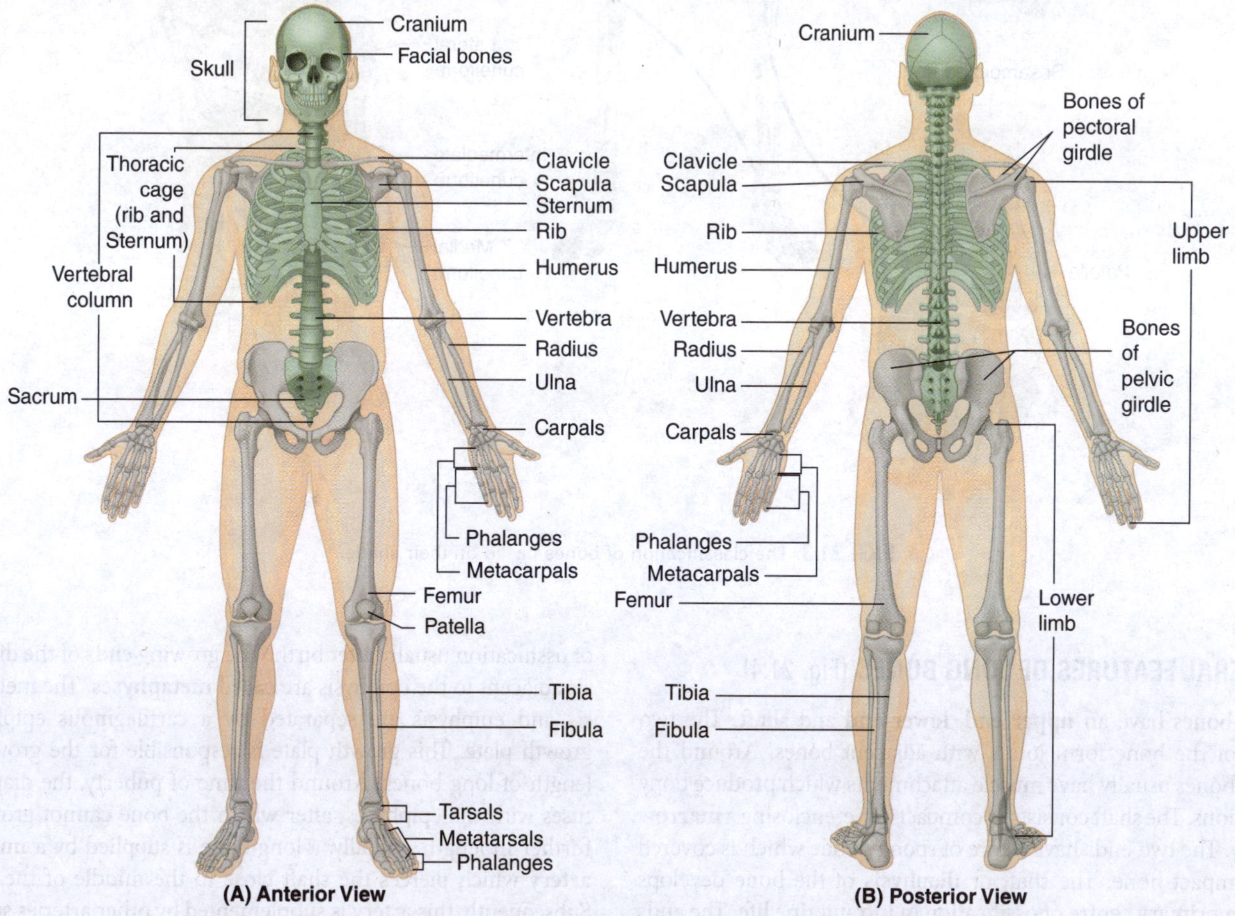

FIG. 21.2 The axial and appendicular skeleton shown in green and grey colour, respectively.

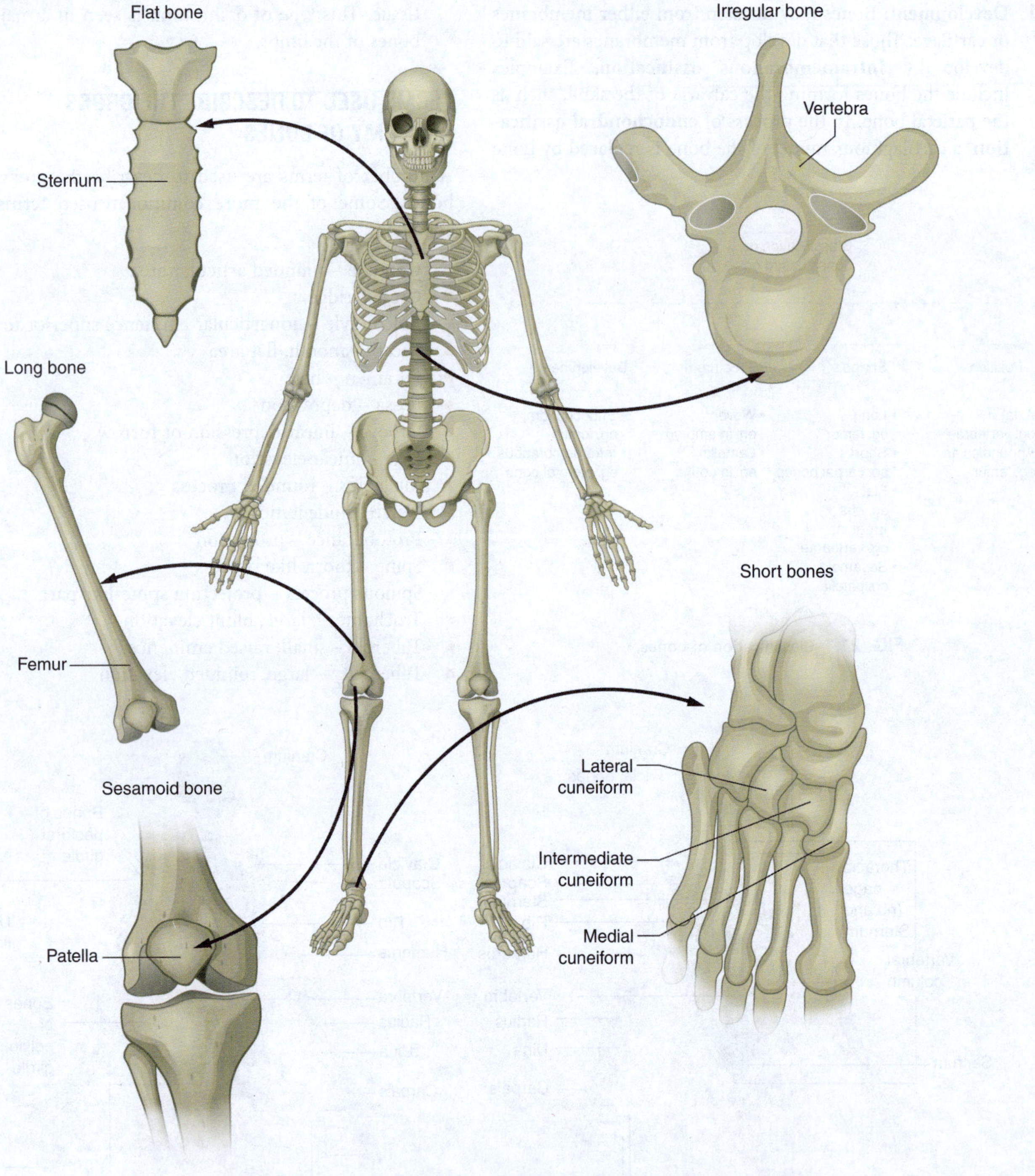

FIG. 21.3 The classification of bones based on their shape.

GENERAL FEATURES OF LONG BONES (Fig. 21.4)

Long bones have an **upper end**, **lower end** and **shaft**. The two ends of the bone form joints with adjacent bones. Around the ends, bones usually have muscle attachments which produce bony elevations. The shaft consists of compact bone, enclosing a **marrow cavity**. The two ends have a core of spongy bone which is covered by compact bone. The shaft or **diaphysis** of the bone develops from a primary centre of ossification in intrauterine life. The ends of long bones, called **epiphyses**, develop from secondary centres of ossification usually after birth. The growing ends of the diaphysis adjacent to the epiphysis are called **metaphyses**. The metaphysis and epiphysis are separated by a cartilaginous epiphyseal growth plate. This growth plate is responsible for the growth in length of long bones. Around the time of puberty, the diaphysis fuses with the epiphyses, after which the bone cannot grow any further in length. Initially, a long bone is supplied by a **nutrient artery** which pierces the shaft close to the middle of the bone. Subsequently this artery is supplemented by other arteries such as metaphyseal, epiphyseal and periosteal arteries.

GENERAL MICROSCOPIC FEATURES OF BONES

Like other types of connective tissue, bone contains widely separated cells surrounded by large amounts of matrix. The four principal types of cells in bone tissue that have been described include **osteogenic cells**, **osteoblasts**, **osteocytes** and **osteoclasts** (Fig. 21.5). **Osteogenic cells** are resting cells that can transform into osteoblasts. They are flattened, resemble fibroblasts and are found on the external and internal surfaces of bones (bone lining cells) as well as in growing bones. They have the capacity to divide and proliferate on stimulation. **Osteoblasts** are the cells that are responsible for laying down the bone matrix and are derived from osteogenic cells. They are basophilic, roughly cuboidal in shape and show all features of typical protein-secreting cells. They form a covering monolayer on the forming surfaces of growing and remodelling bone and are responsible for the synthesis of osteoid (bone matrix) and its mineralization. Once embedded in the matrix, they change to osteocytes.

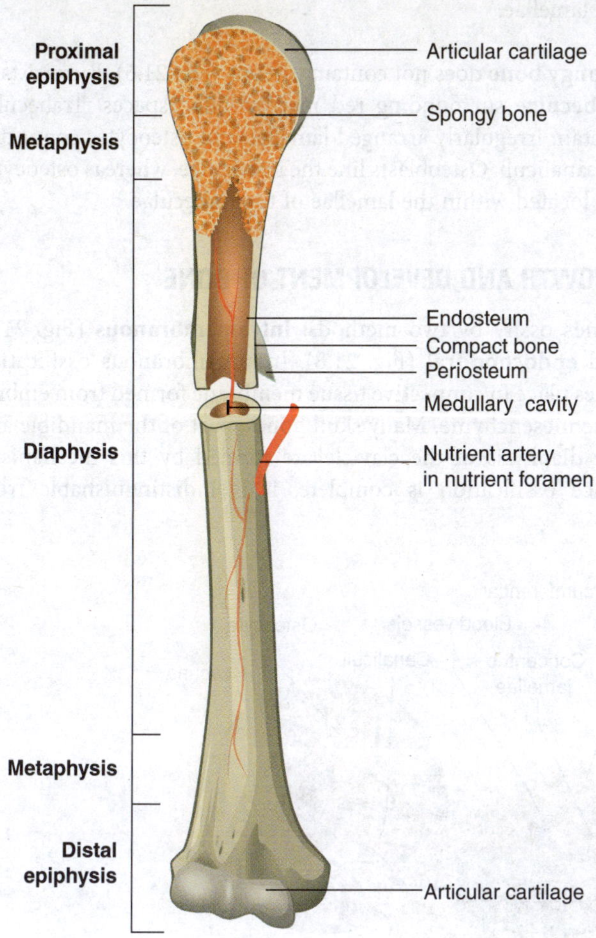

FIG. 21.4 The essential anatomical features of a long bone.

Osteocytes are mature bone cells that actively maintain the bone matrix that has already been laid down. They are smaller than osteoblasts with a less basophilic cytoplasm and sit within spaces called lacunae. Stellate in shape, they possess numerous interconnected dendritic processes located within canaliculi. These serve as gap junctions between osteocytes, providing electrical and metabolic continuity. **Osteoclasts** break down bone matrix by the release of enzymes that digest the bone. They are derived from monocytes and are multinucleated. They are large, motile and polymorphic cells with a variable number of oval, closely packed nuclei. Located in close contact with bone, they lie in resorption bays (Howship lacunae) and have a ruffled border.

The **matrix** of bone is special as it contains mineral salts that confer it with its characteristic hardness. These mineral salts are found primarily as calcium hydroxyapatite crystals. Calcium carbonate and phosphate are also seen in smaller quantities. These mineral deposits are seen amidst a framework of type 1 collagen fibres, which provide the bone with tensile strength. Small amounts of noncollagenous organic components like glycoproteins and proteoglycans also contribute to the matrix. The **periosteum** is a double-layered membrane covering the outer surfaces of bones.

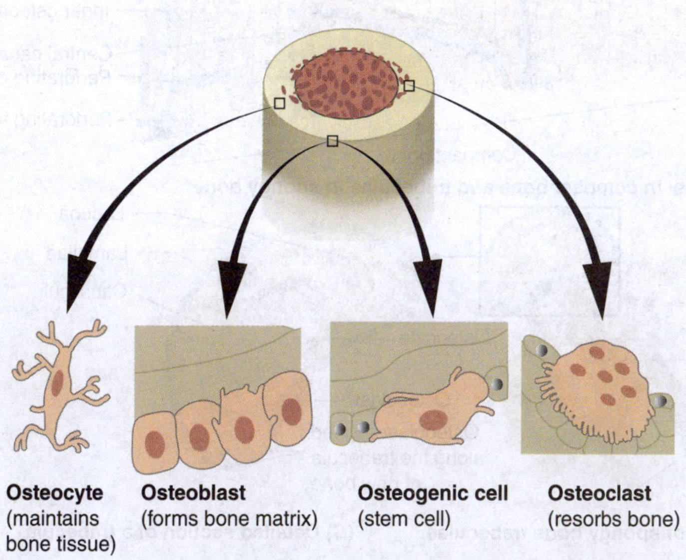

FIG. 21.5 The four types of bone cells.

It consists of an outer fibrous layer and inner cellular layer containing osteogenic cells. The **endosteum**, which lines all internal cavities of bone, is thinner and more cellular.

MICROSTRUCTURE OF LAMELLAR BONE

Lamellar bone is the type of bone tissue found in adults. The following types of lamellar bone have been described: (1) **compact bone** and (2) **spongy bone**. Compact bone is hard and found in the shafts of long bones and outer and inner surfaces of the bones forming the skull cap or calvaria and ribs. It provides the structural rigidity required at these locations. Spongy bone is porous and found at the ends of long bones and within bones such as the ribs. The marrow spaces in spongy bone are important sites of haematopoiesis.

Compact bone is organized into **osteons**, also called **Haversian systems** (Fig. 21.6). An osteon consists of concentric lamellae arranged around a centrally placed **Haversian canal**. Blood vessels run within the Haversian canals and serve to nourish the surrounding bone tissue. **Osteocytes** occupy small cavities called **lacunae** and are arranged along the **concentric lamellae**. **Canaliculi** connect lacunae and contain processes of osteocytes. This mechanism serves to provide intercellular communication between the osteocytes. **Volkmann's canals** are situated at right angles to the long axis of the Haversian canals and serve to connect adjacent Haversian canals. Other lamellae found in compact bones include interstitial, inner and outer circumferential lamellae.

Spongy bone does not contain osteons (Fig. 21.6). It consists of **trabeculae** surrounding red marrow-filled spaces. Trabeculae contain irregularly arranged lamellae and osteocytes connected by canaliculi. Osteoblasts line the trabeculae, whereas osteocytes are located within the lamellae of the trabeculae.

GROWTH AND DEVELOPMENT OF BONE

Bones ossify by two methods: **intramembranous** (Fig. 21.7) and **endochondral** (Fig. 21.8). Intramembranous ossification takes place in connective tissue membrane formed from embryonic mesenchyme. Many skull bones, part of the mandible and the diaphysis of the clavicle are formed by this mechanism. Once ossification is complete, it is indistinguishable from

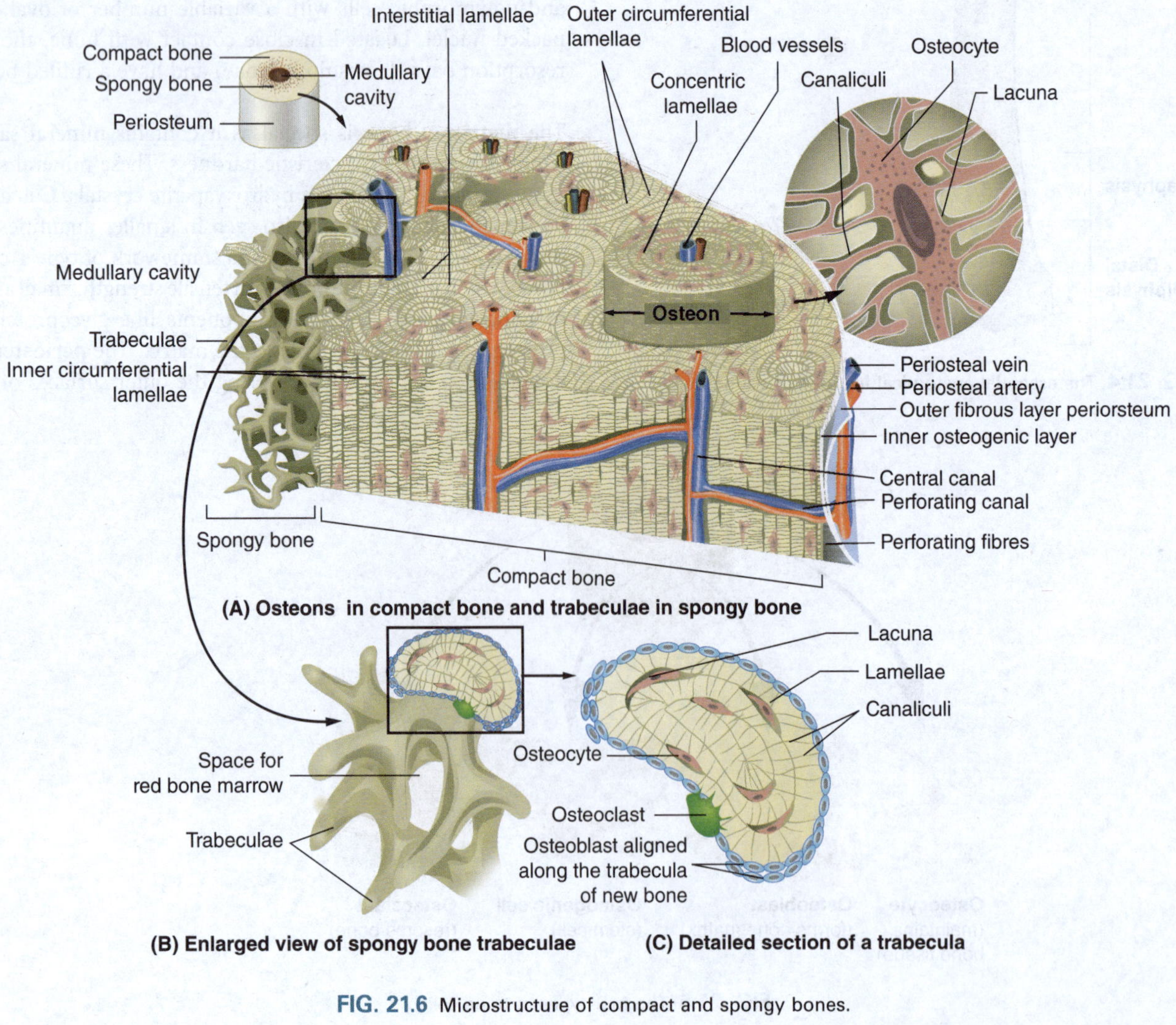

FIG. 21.6 Microstructure of compact and spongy bones.

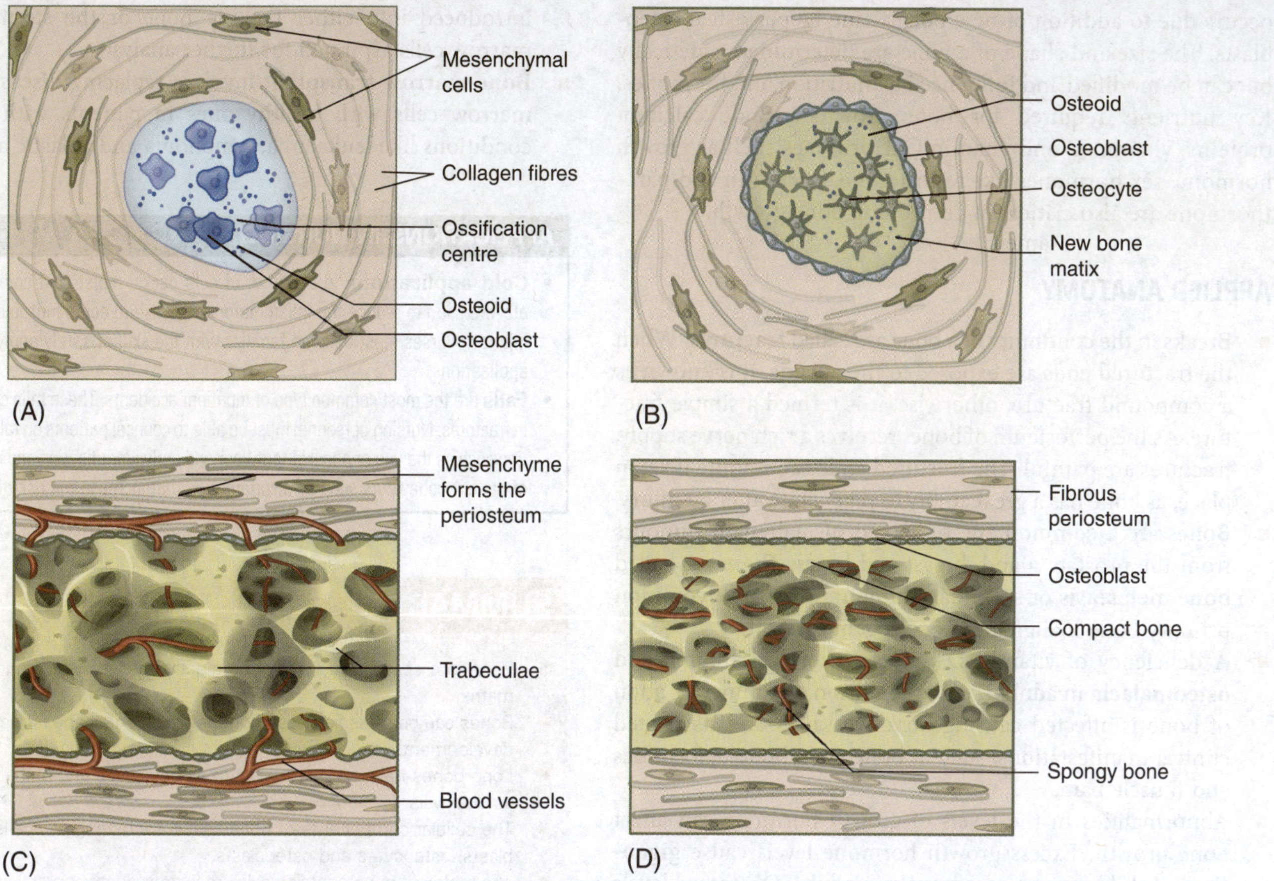

FIG. 21.7 Intramembranous ossification.

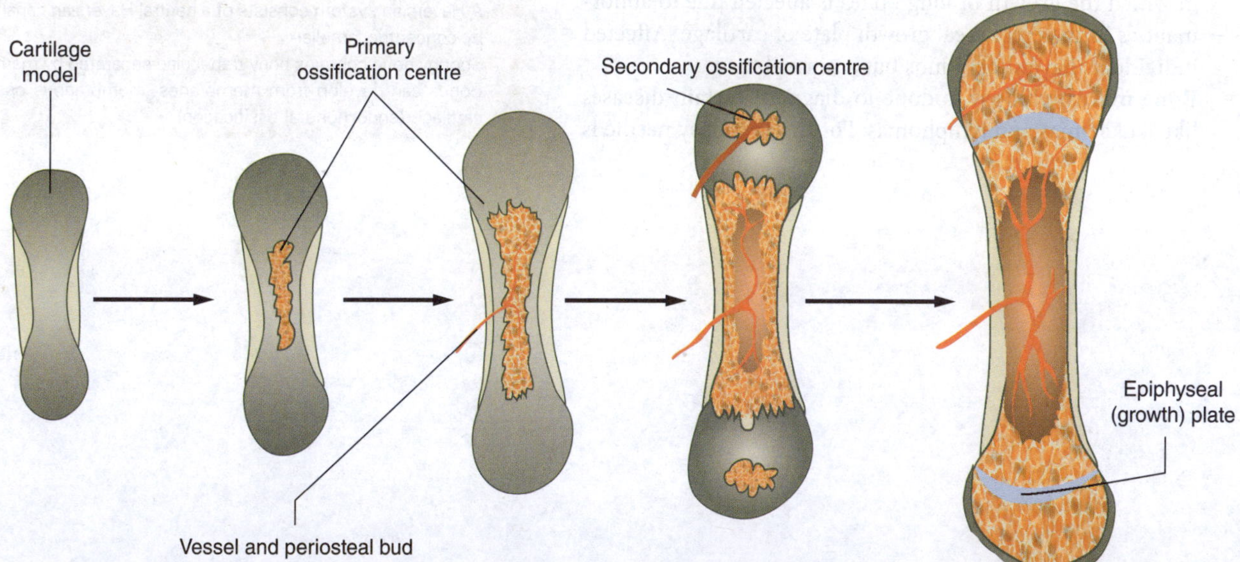

FIG. 21.8 Endochondral ossification.

endochondral bone. Endochondral ossification is seen in bones of the base of the skull, part of the mandible, epiphyses of the clavicles and most of the remaining bones of the skeletal system. Cartilage formation begins at the end of the fourth week of development. Primary ossification centres start appearing at around the second month of intrauterine life. Growth in length occurs at the epiphyseal plate which involves the formation of new cartilage by interstitial growth or appositional growth. Interstitial growth occurs from within the cartilage by proliferation of cells, whereas in appositional growth, growth in diameter occurs due to addition of new bone tissue by periosteal osteoblasts. The size and shape of a bone are determined genetically but can be modified and influenced by nutrition and hormones. Key nutrients required for bone growth include calcium, proteins, vitamin D and vitamin C. Hormones such as growth hormone, sex hormones like testosterone, calcitonin and parathormone are also critical in controlling bone growth.

APPLIED ANATOMY

- Breaks in the continuity of a bone are called **fractures.** When the fractured ends are exposed to the outside, it is known as a compound fracture; otherwise, it is termed a simple fracture. As the periosteum of bones receives a rich nerve supply, fractures are painful. The fractured ends can reunite if set in place, as bone has a great ability to regenerate after an injury.
- Bones are a common site of spread of malignant tumours from the prostate gland, breast and lungs. These are called **bone metastasis** or secondary tumours. The most common primary bone malignancy is osteogenic sarcoma.
- A deficiency of vitamin D causes **rickets** in children and **osteomalacia** in adults. In this condition, the mineralization of bone is affected causing bone weakness and its related clinical manifestations, such as bone pain, bone deformities and muscle pain.
- Abnormalities in the levels of growth hormone can affect bone growth. Excess growth hormone levels cause **gigantism** in children and **acromegaly** in adults. Decreased levels in childhood can cause **dwarfism.**
- **Achondroplasia** is a genetic disease (autosomal dominant) in which the growth of long bones is affected due to abnormalities in the epiphyseal growth plate of cartilage. Affected individuals have short limbs but a normal torso.
- **Bone marrow biopsy** is done to diagnose certain diseases like leukaemias and lymphomas. For this, a biopsy needle is introduced into either the hip bone or the sternum and marrow cells aspirated for further analysis.
- **Bone marrow transplant** involves replacing diseased bone marrow cells with healthy ones in patients with clinical conditions like leukaemia, lymphoma and aplastic anaemia.

APPLICATIONS IN NURSING

- **Cold applications** in the form of cold packs, moist cold compresses, etc. are used to reduce the inflammatory response to acute musculoskeletal injuries. Nurses must become familiar with the skill of safely applying cold applications.
- **Falls** are the most common type of inpatient accidents. These falls can result in fractures. Nursing personnel must be able to counsel patients on fall prevention such as the use of nonskid footwear and early identification and reporting of patient behaviours such as disorientation that increase the risk of falls.

SUMMARY

- Bone is a specialized form of connective tissue with a mineralized matrix.
- Bones can be classified based on their location, shape, structure and development.
- Long bones have two ends known as epiphyses and a shaft known as diaphysis.
- The cellular components of bone tissue are osteogenic cells, osteoblasts, osteocytes and osteoclasts.
- The matrix of bone contains calcium hydroxyapatite crystals and type 1 collagen fibres.
- Lamellar bone is of two types, compact and spongy.
- Compact bone is made up of Haversian systems, also called osteons.
- A Haversian system consists of a central Haversian canal surrounded by concentric lamellae.
- Spongy bone contains bony trabeculae separated by marrow cavities.
- Bones can develop from membranes (membranous ossification) or cartilage (endochondral ossification).

CHAPTER 22

The Axial Skeleton

SPECIFIC LEARNING OBJECTIVES

At the end of this chapter, the student should be able to:

- Name the components of the axial skeleton.
- Describe the main anatomical features of the skull, vertebral column and bony thorax.

GLOSSARY OF TERMS

- **Axial skeleton:** bones that form the axis of the body and support and protect the organs of the head, neck and trunk
- **Calvaria:** part of the skull that forms the dome-like covering of the brain
- **Vertebral column:** the composite pillar-like structure formed by the cervical, thoracic, lumbar, sacral and coccygeal vertebrae enclosing the spinal cord
- **Bony thorax:** the skeletal framework of the thorax formed by the 12 pairs of ribs and sternum

INTRODUCTION

There are 206 bones in the adult human skeleton. The axial skeleton consists of bones that form the axis of the body and support and protect the organs of the head, neck and trunk, whereas the appendicular skeleton is composed of the bones of the limbs. The axial skeleton consists of 80 bones in three regions, namely the skull, vertebral column and bony thorax (Fig. 22.1). Smaller bones that are included in the axial skeleton are the ear ossicles and hyoid bone.

THE SKULL

The skull is a complex skeletal structure consisting of 22 bones. It has two parts called the **cranium** and **facial skeleton** (Fig. 22.2). The cranium consists of 8 bones fused together, while the facial skeleton has 14 bones (Fig. 22.3). Except for the mandible, all skull bones are connected to each other through sutures. The cranium protects the brain, houses ear ossicles and provides muscle attachments for the jaw, neck and face. The dome-shaped part of the cranium that covers the brain is called the **calvaria**. The facial bones form the facial features, contain special sense organs, surround passages for air and food, support the teeth and provide sites of attachment for facial muscles. The skull contains many cavities which hold organs and foramina which allow passage of nerves and blood vessels.

Among the eight bones forming the cranium, two are paired, parietal and temporal, whereas four are unpaired, frontal, occipital, sphenoid and ethmoid. The **frontal bone** forms the forehead, the roof of the orbit and part of the cranial floor. The **parietal bones** form most of the sides and roof of the cranial cavity. The sides and floor of the cranial cavity are formed by the **temporal bones**. The rear and most of the base of the cranium are formed by the **occipital bone**. The **sphenoid bone** forms the middle part of the base of the skull. It is like the keystone of the cranial floor because it articulates with many other cranial bones. The **ethmoid bone** is a light, sponge-like bone that forms the cranial floor between the orbits. It has projections called the superior nasal conchae and middle nasal conchae, which extend into the nasal cavity.

The floor of the cranial cavity is divided into three **cranial fossae** which can be seen after removal of the calvaria (Fig. 22.4). The **anterior cranial fossa** lodges the frontal lobe of the cerebral hemisphere. The **middle cranial fossa** lodges the pituitary gland and temporal lobe of the cerebral hemisphere, whereas the **posterior cranial fossa** lodges the occipital lobe of the cerebral hemisphere and the lobes of the cerebellum.

The **facial skeleton** consists of 14 bones of which 6 are paired and 2 are unpaired. The paired bones include the nasal, maxilla,

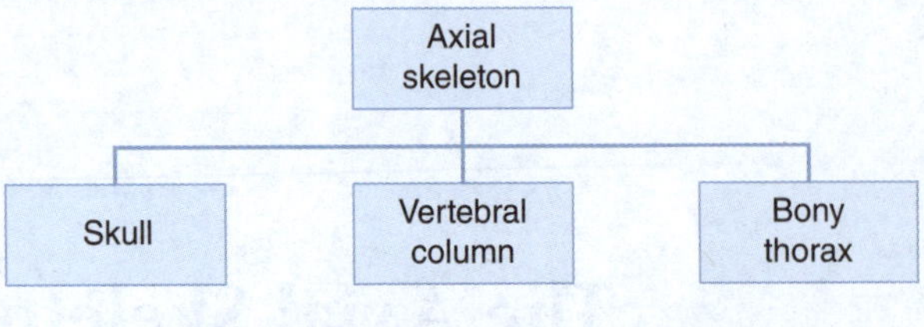

FIG. 22.1 Parts of the axial skeleton.

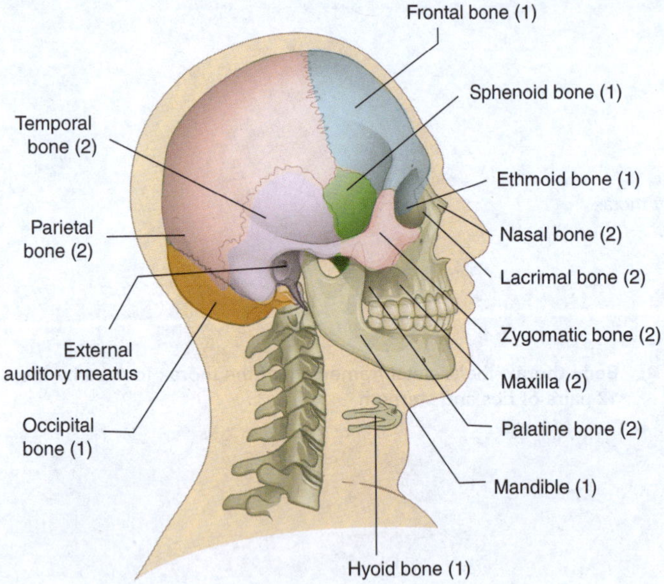

FIG. 22.2 Bones forming the cranium and facial skeleton.

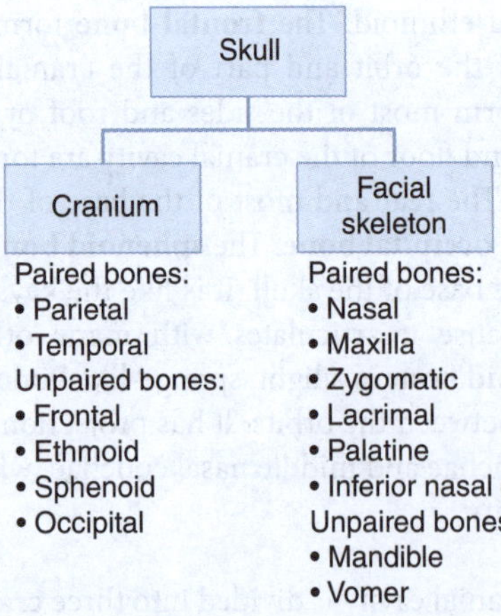

FIG. 22.3 Parts of the skull.

zygomatic, lacrimal, palatine and inferior nasal concha. The mandible and vomer are the two unpaired bones. The **nasal bones** form part of the bridge of the nose. The **maxillae** form the upper jawbone. The cheekbones are formed by the **zygomatic bones**. The smallest bones of the face are the **lacrimal**

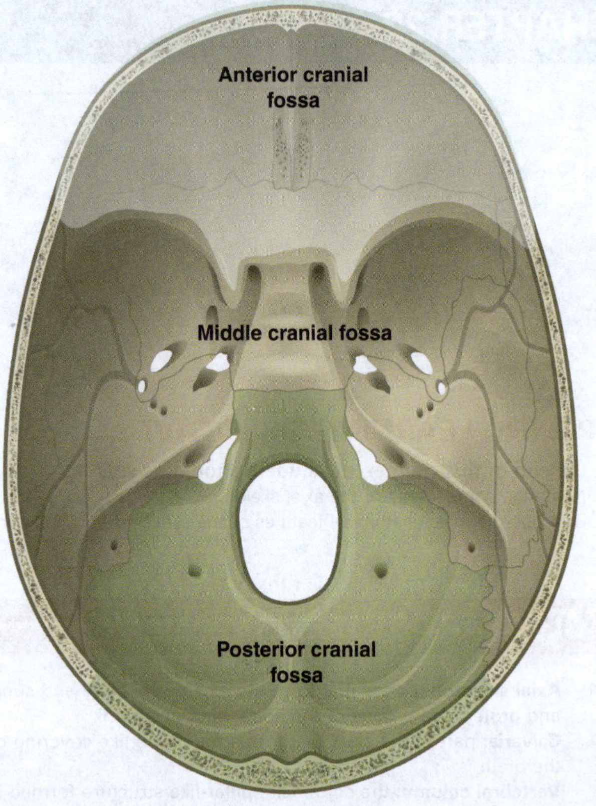

FIG. 22.4 Superior view of the skull after removal of the calvaria showing the three cranial fossae.

bones which are the size of fingernails. They form part of the medial walls of the orbits. The rear part of the hard palate, which separates the nasal cavity from the oral cavity, is formed by the **palatine bones**. The **inferior nasal conchae** form part of the inferior lateral walls of the nasal cavity. The **vomer** makes up the lower part of the nasal septum, which is the partition that divides the nasal cavity into right and left sides. The **mandible** forms the lower jawbone and is the largest and strongest facial bone. It is the only movable skull bone. It articulates with the temporal bone at a synovial joint known as the temporomandibular joint. Important features of the mandible include the body, ramus, angle, condylar process, coronoid processes, alveolar processes for lower teeth and mandibular and mental foramen.

OTHER BONES

The **hyoid bone** is a single U-shaped bone situated between the mandible and larynx. It does not articulate with any other bone of the body. It is suspended by ligaments and muscles from the skull. The tongue, neck and pharyngeal muscles are attached to the hyoid bone. It consists of a horizontal body and paired projections, the lesser and greater horns. The **ear ossicles** will be discussed in the chapter describing the anatomy of the ear.

THE VERTEBRAL COLUMN

The vertebral column is made up of 26 bones. It forms the central axis of the body and protects the spinal cord. All the 12 pairs of

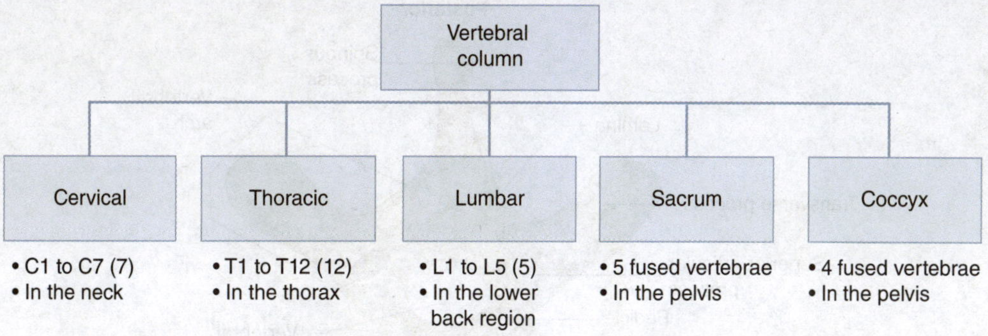

FIG. 22.5 Regions of the vertebral column.

ribs articulate with the thoracic vertebrae. The vertebral column is stabilized by numerous ligaments and provides attachment for the dorsal muscles of the body. The five regions of the vertebral column are shown in Figs 22.5 and 22.6.

When viewed from the side, the vertebral column shows four normal curves (Fig. 22.7). The curves increase the strength of the spine, help maintain balance, absorb shock and prevent fractures. The cervical and lumbar curves are convex forwards, while the thoracic and sacral curves are concave forwards.

All vertebrae except the first two cervical vertebrae (atlas and axis) share common characteristics. They consist of a **body** and **vertebral arch** formed by the pedicles and laminae. The opening between the vertebral arch and body is called the vertebral foramen. Seven processes arise from the vertebral arch, namely the **spinous process (1), transverse process (2), superior articular process (2) and inferior articular process (2)** (Fig. 22.8). The **vertebral canal** is the complete passageway formed by the vertebral foramina when the vertebrae are stacked upon one another to form the backbone. Spinal nerves from the spinal cord emerge from the **intervertebral foramina** which are formed between adjacent vertebrae.

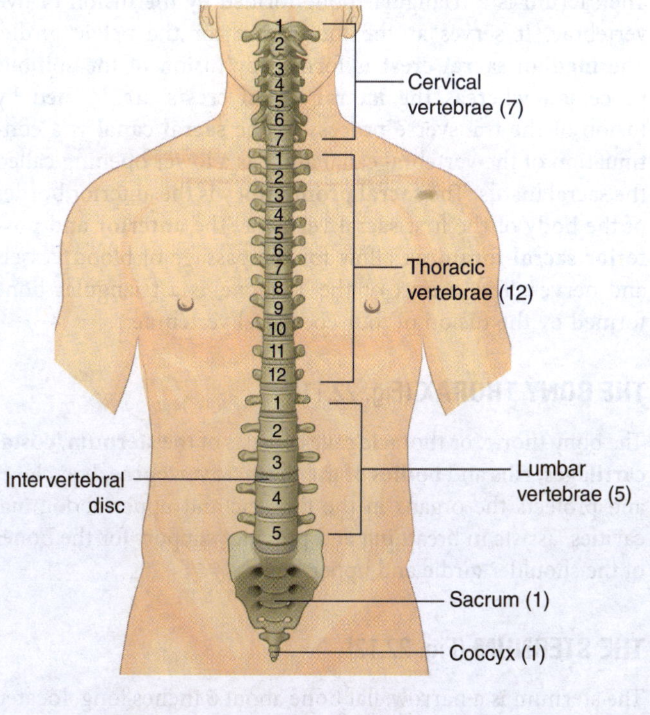

FIG. 22.6 Parts of the vertebral column.

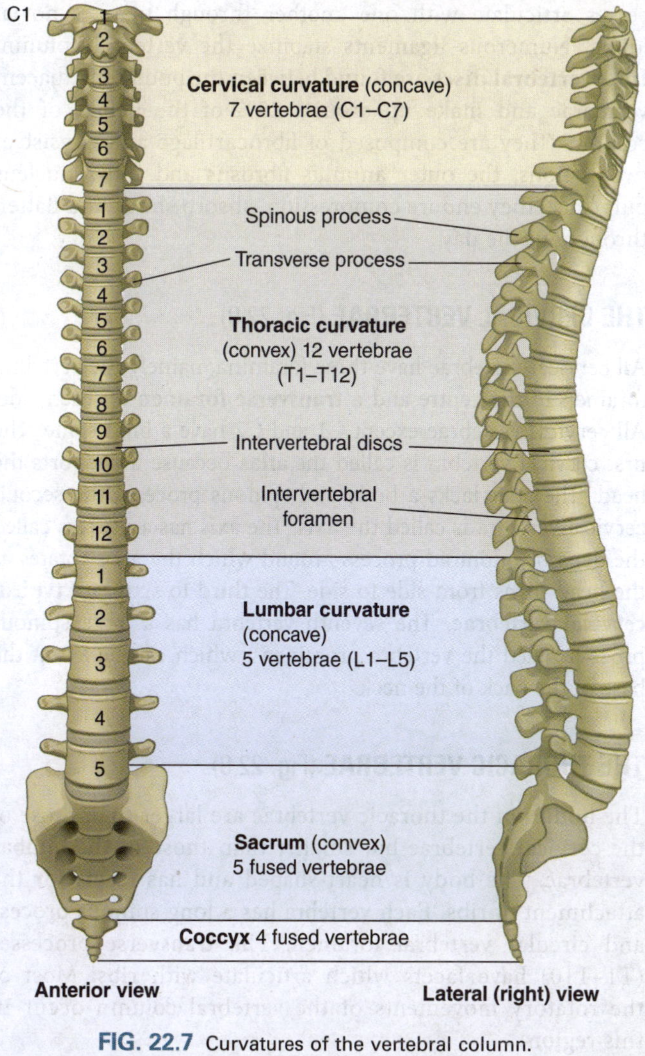

FIG. 22.7 Curvatures of the vertebral column.

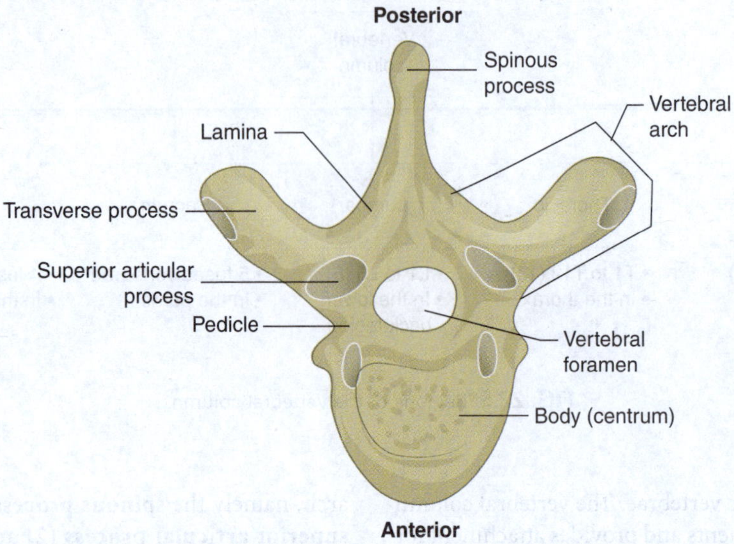

FIG. 22.8 Parts of a vertebra.

The bodies of adjacent vertebrae articulate with each other through symphyses. The superior and inferior articular processes articulate with one another through plane synovial joints. Numerous ligaments stabilize the vertebral column. **Intervertebral discs** are found between the bodies of adjacent vertebrae and make up around 25% of the height of the column. They are composed of fibrocartilage and consist of two regions, the outer annulus fibrosus and inner nucleus pulposus. They endure compression, absorb shock and flatten throughout the day.

THE CERVICAL VERTEBRAE (Fig. 22.9)

All cervical vertebrae have three foramina, namely the vertebral foramen in the centre and a **transverse foramen** on each side. All cervical vertebrae except C1 and C7 have a bifid spine. The first cervical vertebra is called the **atlas** because it supports the head. The atlas lacks a body and spinous process. The second cervical vertebra is called the **axis**. The axis has a process called the dens or odontoid process around which the atlas rotates as the head turns from side to side. The third to sixth are **typical cervical vertebrae**. The seventh vertebra has a large spinous process called the vertebra prominens, which can be felt at the base of the back of the neck.

THE THORACIC VERTEBRAE (Fig. 22.9)

The bodies of the thoracic vertebrae are larger than those of the cervical vertebrae but smaller than those of the lumbar vertebrae. The body is heart-shaped and has facets for the attachment of ribs. Each vertebra has a long spinous process and circular vertebral foramen. The transverse processes (T1–T10) have facets which articulate with ribs. Most of the rotatory movements of the vertebral column occur in this region.

THE LUMBAR VERTEBRAE (Fig. 22.9)

These are the largest and strongest vertebrae in the vertebral column. They bear most of the weight of the body explaining the massive size of their bodies. The pedicles and laminae are short and thick. The vertebral foramina are triangular in shape. Their articular facets are suitably oriented to prevent rotation. The vertebrae have short and thick spinous processes.

THE SACRUM AND COCCYX (Fig. 22.10)

The sacrum is a triangular bone formed by the fusion of five vertebrae. It serves as the foundation for the pelvic girdle. The **median sacral crest** is formed by fusion of the spinous processes, whereas the **lateral sacral crests** are formed by fusion of the transverse processes. The **sacral canal** is a continuation of the vertebral canal and has a lower opening called the sacral hiatus. The **sacral promontory** is the anterior border of the body of the first sacral vertebra. The **anterior** and **posterior sacral foramina** allow for the passage of blood vessels and nerves. The **coccyx** or the 'tailbone' is a triangular bone formed by the fusion of four coccygeal vertebrae.

THE BONY THORAX (Fig. 22.11)

The bony thorax or thoracic cage consists of the **sternum**, **costal cartilages, ribs** and **bodies of the thoracic vertebrae.** It encloses and protects the organs in the thoracic and upper abdominal cavities, assists in breathing and provides support for the bones of the shoulder girdle and upper limbs.

THE STERNUM (Fig. 22.12)

The sternum is a narrow, flat bone about 6 inches long, located in the centre of the chest. It consists of three parts, namely

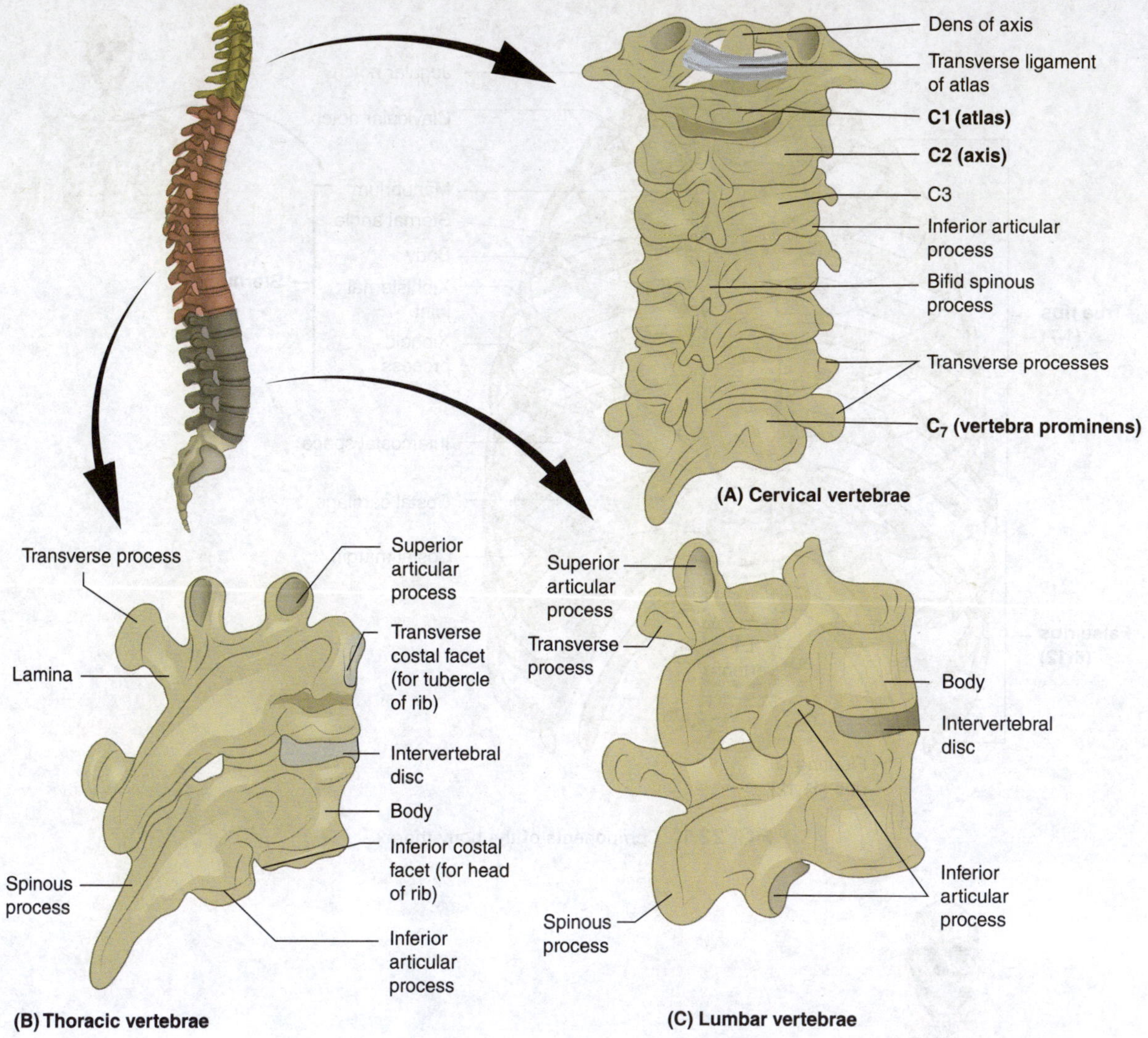

FIG. 22.9 Features of the different regions of the vertebral column.

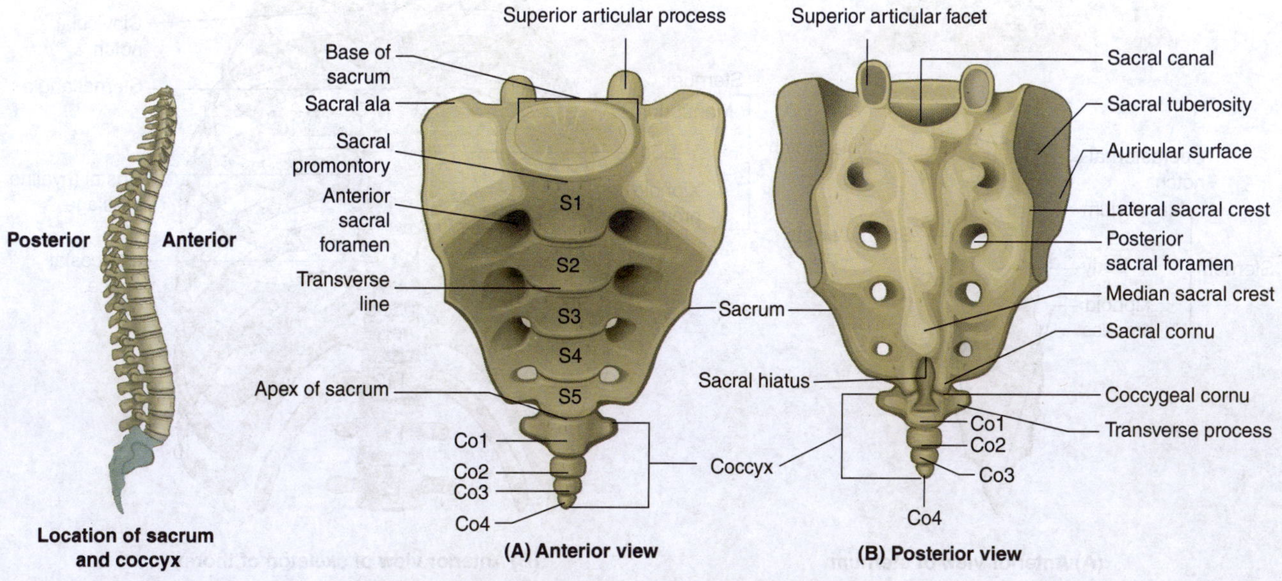

FIG. 22.10 Features of the sacrum and coccyx.

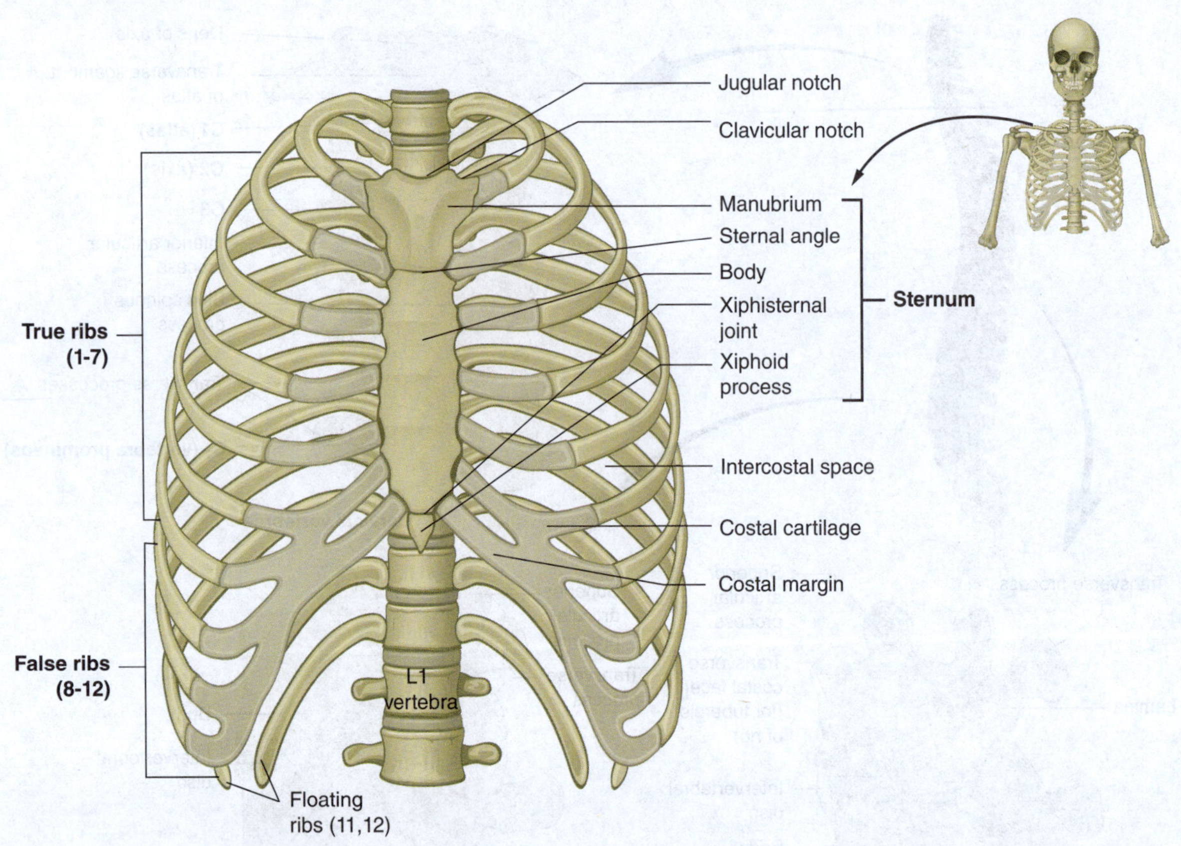

FIG. 22.11 Components of the bony thorax.

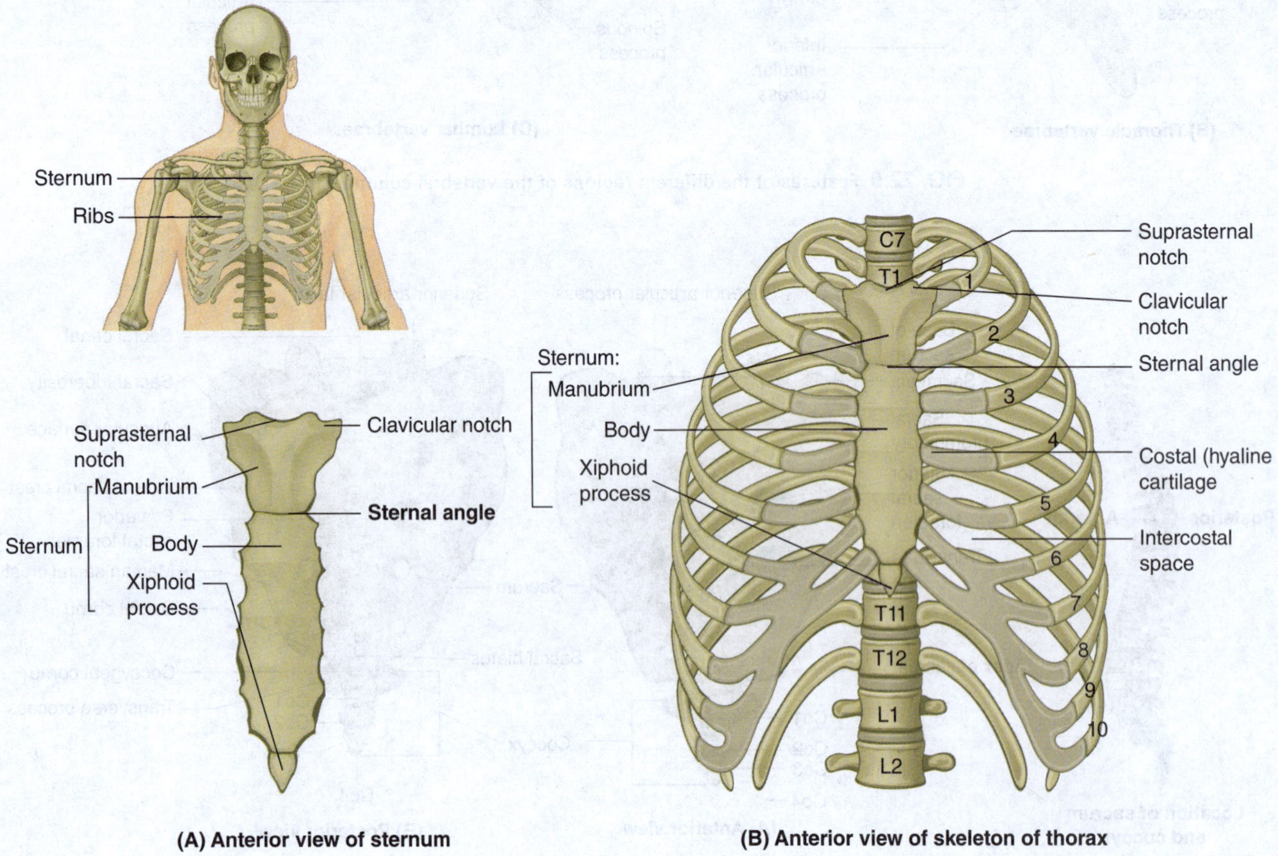

FIG. 22.12 The sternum and its articulations.

manubrium, body and **xiphoid process**. The manubrium articulates with the clavicle and first two ribs. The junction of the body and manubrium is called the **sternal angle** and is an important landmark. It lies at the level of the intervertebral disc between T4 and T5. The body of the sternum articulates with costal cartilages of the second to seventh ribs. The sternum gives attachment to muscles of the abdomen, neck and upper limb.

THE RIBS (Fig. 22.13)

There are 12 pairs of ribs which give structural support to the sides of the thoracic cavity. They articulate posteriorly with the thoracic vertebrae. The third to ninth ribs are called **typical ribs**, whereas the others are **atypical**. The first seven pairs of ribs attach directly to the sternum by costal cartilages and are called **true ribs**. The other five pairs of ribs are called **false ribs**. The 8th to 10th pairs do not attach directly to the sternum. The 11th and 12th pairs are called **floating ribs**. The 11 spaces between ribs are called **intercostal spaces** which contain intercostal muscles and vessels with nerves. Each rib has an **anterior** and **posterior end**. The posterior end has a **head** which articulates with the vertebral bodies of the thoracic vertebrae. The constricted **neck** separates the head from the **tubercle** which articulates with the transverse process of the corresponding thoracic vertebra. The **shaft** contains a **costal groove** in which run the intercostal nerves and vessels.

APPLIED ANATOMY

- **Fracture** of the **hyoid bone** is of medicolegal importance for confirming the cause of death due to strangulation.
- During certain trauma situations involving **whiplash injury** or **hanging**, the dens may be pushed up into the medulla oblongata of the brain and cause death.
- **Herniated (slipped) discs** occur most often in the lumbar region. This condition is called intervertebral disc prolapse. The prolapsed disc can press on the adjacent spinal nerves and cause pain radiating along the lower limbs called sciatica.
- The sacral promontory is one of the important landmarks used to take measurements of the pelvis. These measurements are important for obstetricians to diagnose certain types of **obstructed labour**.
- Abnormal lateral curvature of the spine is called **scoliosis**. **Kyphosis** is an abnormal curvature of the spine which gives the back a rounded appearance. These defects may be developmental or acquired.
- Sometimes the vertebral arch fails to develop normally, leaving a defect through which the meninges and spinal cord can protrude. This condition is called **spina bifida**.
- The sternum is used as a site for **bone marrow biopsy** and the procedure is called sternal puncture.
- The sternum needs to be divided while performing any major thoracic surgeries such as open-heart surgeries. This procedure is called **sternotomy**.
- **Rib fractures** are among the most common types of chest injuries.

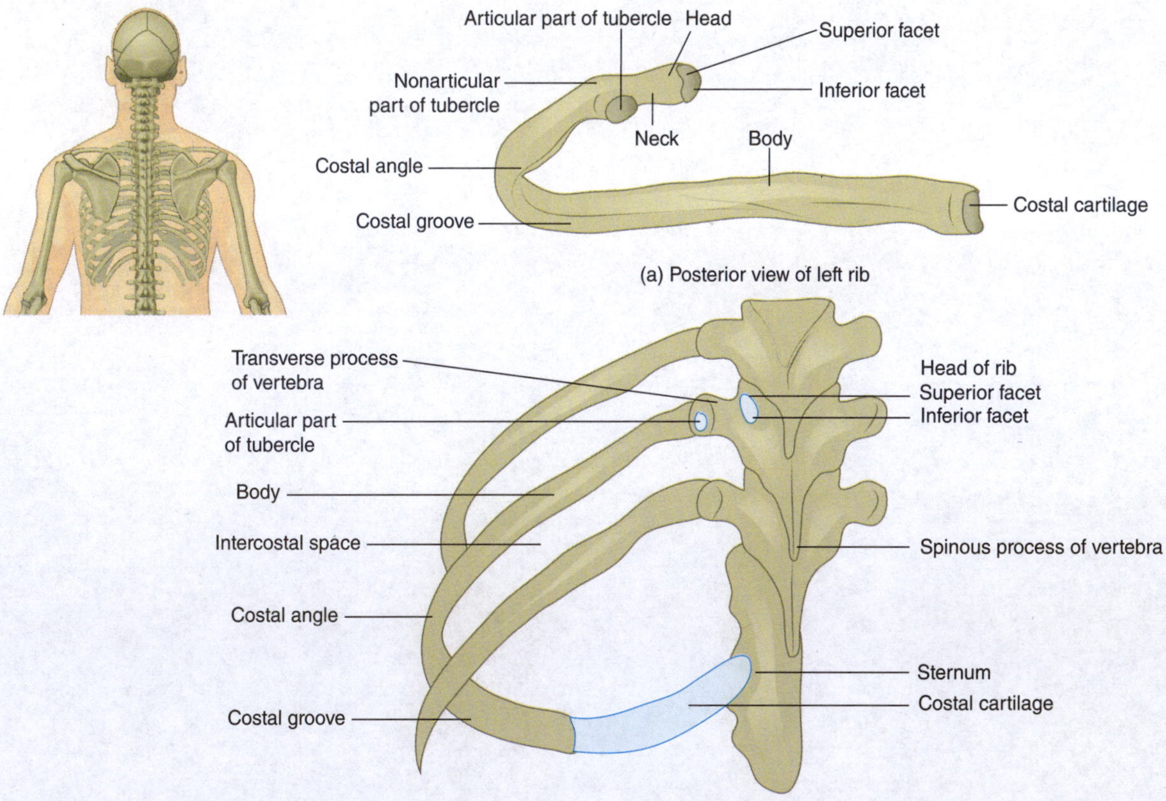

FIG. 22.13 The ribs and their articulations.

APPLICATIONS IN NURSING

- Nurses may have to assist in **safely moving patients** who have suspected or confirmed vertebral instability. The log-rolling technique is used in these situations to prevent excessive relative movement between the different parts of the vertebral column.

SUMMARY

- The axial skeleton forms the central axis of the body.
- The three parts of the axial skeleton are the skull, vertebral column and bony thorax.
- The skull consists of the cranium and facial skeleton.
- The dome-shaped part of the cranium covering the brain is the calvaria.
- The facial skeleton supports the structures of the face.
- With the exception of the mandible, all skull bones are connected to each other through sutures.
- The floor of the cranial cavity is divided into anterior, middle and posterior cranial fossae which can be seen after removal of the calvaria.
- The hyoid bone is located in the neck and is held in place by muscles and ligaments.
- The vertebral column has the following five parts: cervical, thoracic, lumbar, sacral and coccygeal.
- The two parts of a vertebra are the body and vertebral arch, between which is located the vertebral foramen.
- The vertebral arch consists of the pedicle, lamina and processes, namely spinous, transverse, superior and inferior articular.
- The bodies of adjacent vertebrae are connected by intervertebral discs.
- Intervertebral foramina are seen between adjacent vertebrae and provide passage to the spinal nerves.
- The sacrum forms the foundation of the pelvic girdle.
- The bony thorax or thoracic cage consists of the sternum, costal cartilages, ribs and bodies of the thoracic vertebrae.
- The parts of the sternum are the manubrium, body and xiphoid process.
- There are 12 pairs of ribs separated by intercostal spaces.
- All ribs articulate with the thoracic vertebrae posteriorly.
- The first 7 ribs are true ribs, 3rd to 9th typical ribs, and 11th and 12th floating ribs.
- Intercostal spaces contain intercostal muscles, vessels and nerves.

CHAPTER 23

The Appendicular Skeleton

SPECIFIC LEARNING OBJECTIVES

At the end of this chapter, the student should be able to:

- Name the components of the appendicular skeleton.
- Describe the main anatomical features of the skeleton of the upper limb.
- Describe the main anatomical features of the skeleton of the lower limb.

GLOSSARY OF TERMS

- **Appendages:** the upper and lower limbs
- **Appendicular skeleton:** the skeletal framework of the appendages and bones that anchor the appendages to the axial skeleton
- **Pectoral girdle:** the clavicle and scapula
- **Clavicle:** the collar bone
- **Scapula:** the shoulder blade
- **Humerus:** the arm bone
- **Radius:** the lateral bone of the forearm
- **Ulna:** the medial bone of the forearm
- **Carpal bones:** the small bones of the wrist
- **Metacarpals:** the bones of the palm
- **Phalanges:** the bones of the fingers and toes
- **Pelvic girdle:** the hip bones, sacrum and coccyx
- **Femur:** the thigh bone
- **Tibia:** the medial leg bone
- **Fibula:** the lateral leg bone
- **Tarsal bones:** the proximal bones of the foot
- **Metatarsals:** the distal bones of the foot

INTRODUCTION

The appendicular skeleton consists of 126 bones (Fig. 23.1). It consists of the skeletal framework of the appendages and bones that anchor the appendages to the axial skeleton. The main function of the appendicular skeleton is to provide lever arms to facilitate movements of the limbs at joints by the contraction of skeletal muscles. The anatomy of the skeleton of the upper and lower limbs shows both similarities and differences. Both the upper and lower limbs have girdles that anchor them to the axial skeleton, the pectoral and pelvic girdles, respectively. Each free limb shows three segments, the arm, forearm and hand in the upper limb and the thigh, leg and foot in the lower limb. The differences in the anatomy between the upper and lower limb among these three segments are related to their difference in function. The lower limb bones are larger and stronger as they must support the weight of the body.

THE UPPER LIMB

The Clavicle

The clavicle and scapula together constitute the pectoral girdle (Fig. 23.2). The clavicle or collar bone is double curved and horizontally placed (Fig. 23.3). It is unusual in that it is subcutaneous throughout. It has **two ends**, **medial** and **lateral**, and a **shaft**. The medial end articulates with the sternum at the **sternoclavicular joint**. The lateral end articulates with the acromion process of the scapula at the **acromioclavicular joint**. The deltoid, trapezius and sternocleidomastoid are three large muscles that take origin from the clavicle. The weight of the upper limb is transmitted to the trunk via the clavicle. It prevents drooping of the shoulder and serves as a mobile support for the upper limb. It is the first bone in the body to ossify.

The Scapula

The scapula or shoulder blade is a large triangular flat bone that lies on the posterolateral part of the chest wall opposite the second to seventh ribs (Fig. 23.4). It has **two surfaces**, costal and dorsal; **three borders**, superior, lateral and medial; **three angles**, superior, inferior and lateral; and **three processes**, spinous, acromion and coracoid. The lateral angle of the bone contains the glenoid cavity which articulates with the head of the humerus to form the **shoulder joint**. The acromion articulates with the lateral end of the clavicle at the **acromioclavicular joint**. The scapula is held in place by several muscles that are attached to either the axial skeleton or the bones of the upper limb. The serratus anterior is an important muscle attached to the medial border of the scapula that helps to keep it in firm contact with the chest wall.

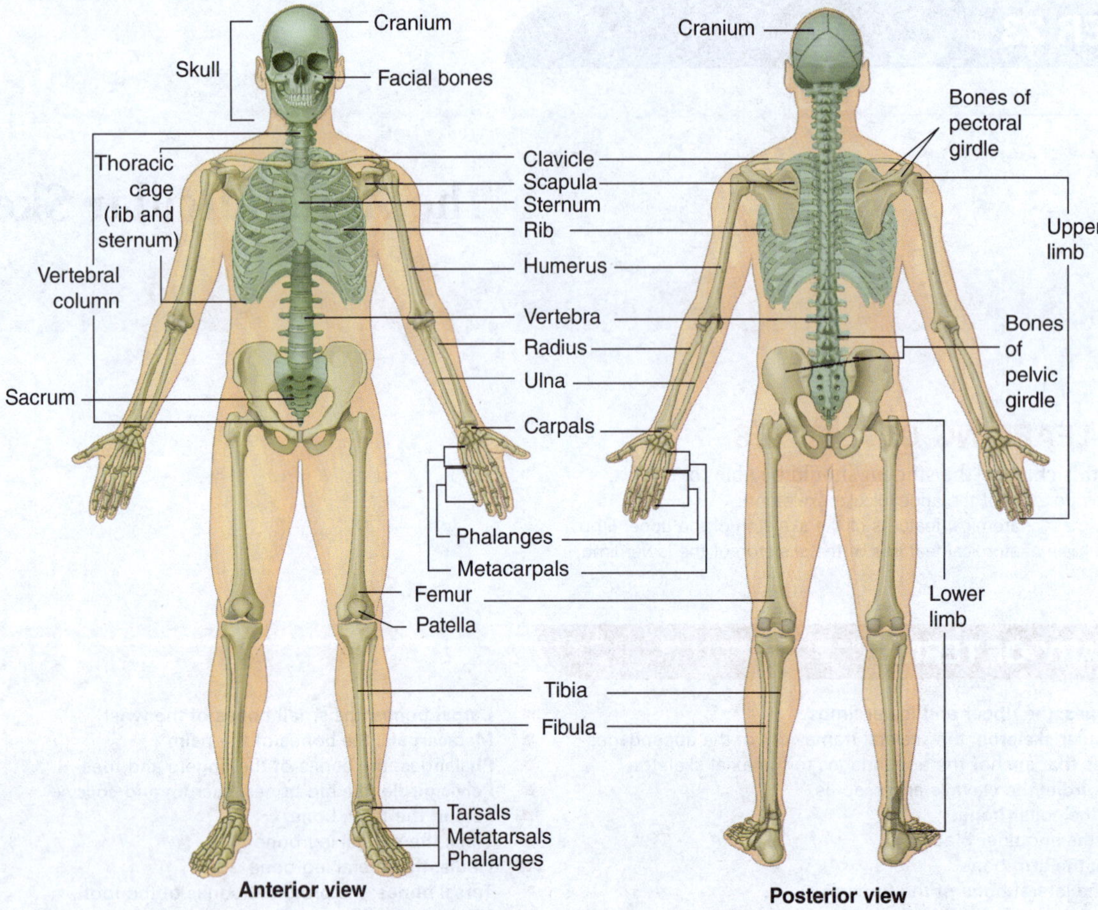

FIG. 23.1 The appendicular skeleton.

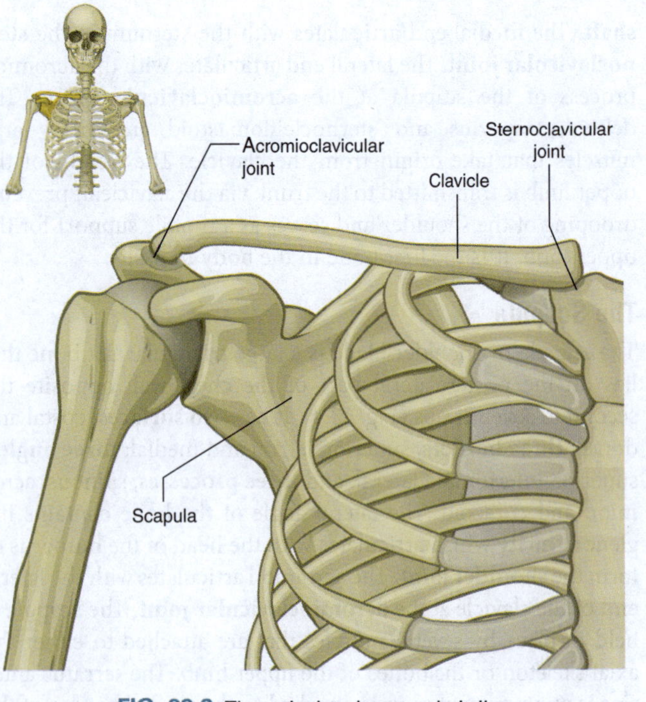

FIG. 23.2 The articulated pectoral girdle.

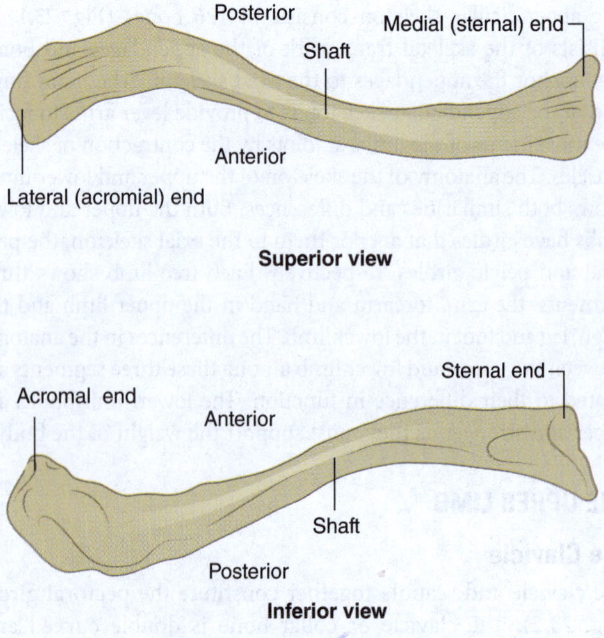

FIG. 23.3 The right clavicle.

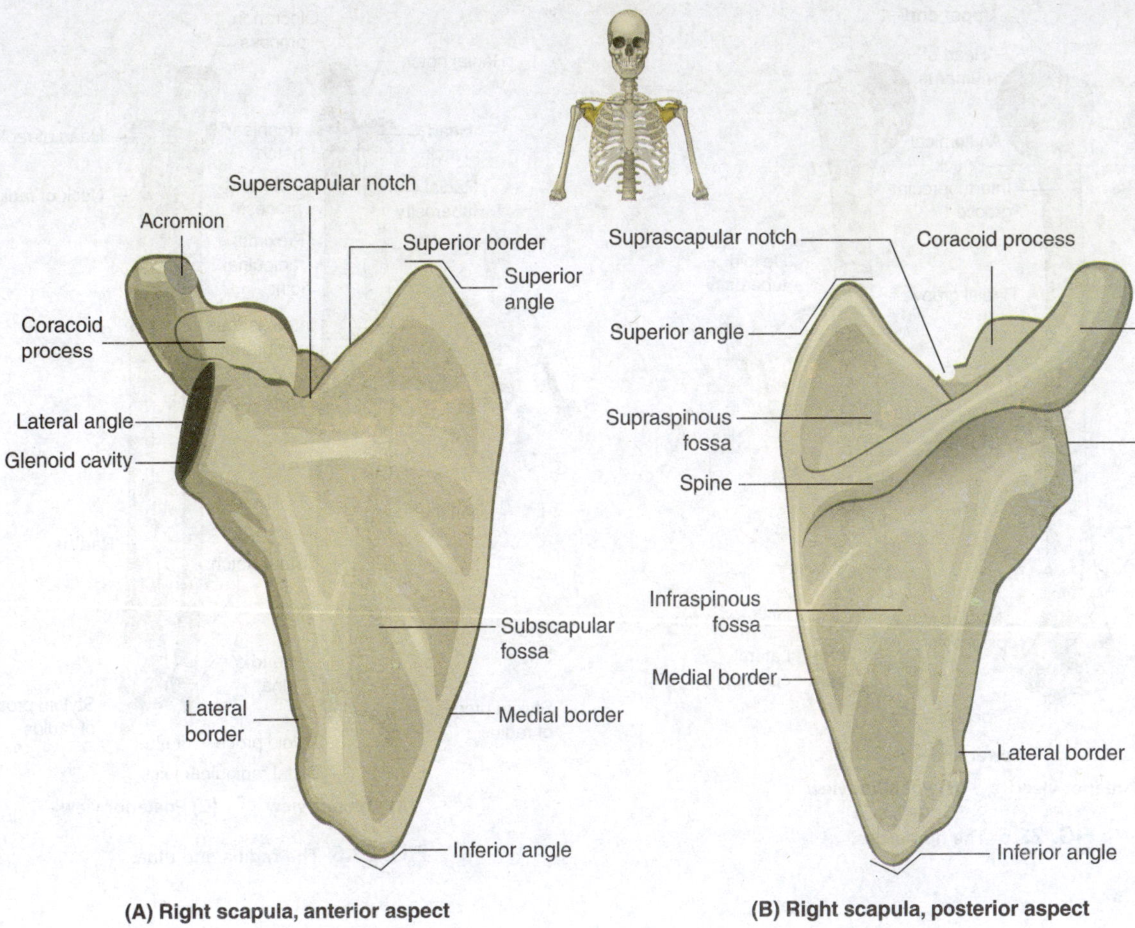

FIG. 23.4 The scapula.

The Humerus

The humerus is the bone of the arm (Fig. 23.5). Like most other long bones, it has an **upper end, lower end** and **shaft**. The upper end has a head, neck and greater and lesser tubercles. The head articulates with the glenoid cavity of the scapula at the **shoulder joint**. The greater and lesser tubercles provide insertion to muscles arising from the scapula. The upper end is separated from the shaft by a constricted part of the bone called the surgical neck. The surgical neck is related to the axillary nerve. The shaft of the humerus provides attachment to the deltoid muscle and is surrounded by muscles of the flexor and extensor compartments. The radial nerve lies in direct contact with the humerus posteriorly. The lower end presents articular and nonarticular parts. The articular parts are the capitulum and trochlea. The capitulum articulates with the head of the radius, while the trochlea articulates with the trochlear notch of the ulna at the **elbow joint**. The nonarticular parts are the medial and lateral epicondyles. The ulnar nerve lies in direct contact with the posterior aspect of the medial epicondyle. The medial and lateral epicondyles provide attachment to the muscles of the flexor and extensor compartment of the forearm, respectively.

The Radius

The radius is the lateral bone of the forearm (Fig. 23.6). It is shorter than the ulna. The **upper end** has a disc-like head and radial tuberosity. The head articulates with the capitulum of the humerus to form part of the **elbow joint**. On the medial side, the head articulates with the radial notch of the ulna at the **superior radioulnar joint**. The radial tuberosity provides attachment to the biceps brachii muscle. The **shaft** is convex laterally and widens at its lower end. The **lower end** is larger than the upper end and presents an ulnar notch that articulates with the lower end of the ulna at the inferior radioulnar joint. The inferior surface of the radius articulates with the proximal row of carpal bones at the **wrist joint**. The lower end presents a conical bony projection from its lateral part called the styloid process.

The Ulna

The ulna is the medial bone of the forearm (Fig. 23.6). The **upper end** presents the coronoid and olecranon processes. The olecranon process forms the tip of the elbow. The coronoid process provides insertion to the brachialis muscle. The two processes present two articular areas, the trochlear and radial notches. The trochlear notch is a hook-like projection which articulates with the trochlea of the humerus at the **elbow joint**. The radial notch articulates with the head of the radius at the **superior radioulnar joint**. Unlike the radius, the shaft of the ulna tapers distally. The **lower end** is smaller and presents a rounded head and a short styloid process. The head articulates with the ulnar notch

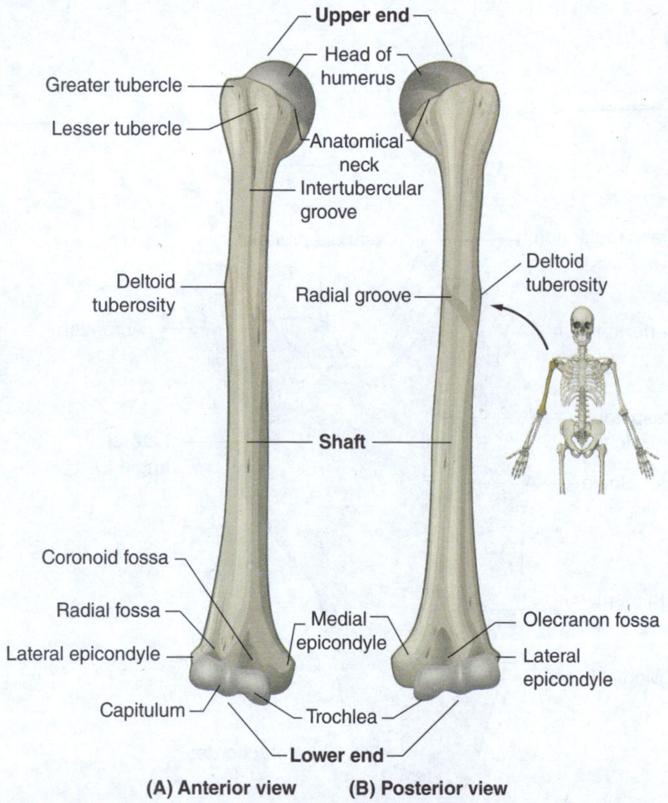

FIG. 23.5 The humerus.

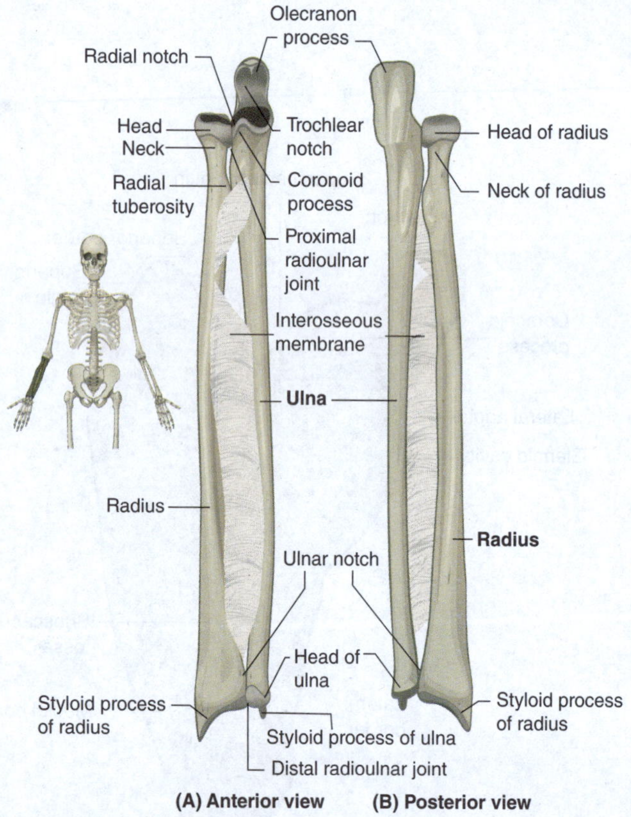

FIG. 23.6 The radius and ulna.

of the radius at the **inferior radioulnar joint**. The inferior surface of the head is separated from the carpal bones by the articular disc of the inferior radioulnar joint.

The Carpal Bones

The carpal bones are arranged as a proximal row and distal row (Fig. 23.7). The bones of the proximal row include the **scaphoid, lunate, triquetral** and **pisiform**. The distal row contains the **trapezium, trapezoid, capitate** and **hamate**. The proximal row of bones articulates with the lower end of the radius at the **wrist joint**. The distal row of bones articulates with the metacarpal bones at the **carpometacarpal joints.**

The Metacarpal Bones and Phalanges (Fig. 23.7)

The five metacarpal bones are numbered from the lateral to the medial side. Each metacarpal bone has a **base, shaft** and **head**. The **bases** of the metacarpal bones articulate with the carpal bones at the **carpometacarpal joints**. The carpometacarpal joints allow little movement except for the first joint. The first carpometacarpal joint is formed between the base of the first metacarpal bone and trapezium. The mobility of this joint is responsible for the wide range of movements of the thumb. The **heads** articulate with the bases of the proximal phalanges at the **metacarpophalangeal joints**. Each digit has three **phalanges** except for the first digit. The phalanges are named **proximal, middle** and **distal**. The first digit has only proximal and distal phalanges. The phalanges articulate with one another at the **interphalangeal joints**.

THE LOWER LIMB

The Hip Bone

The pelvic girdle is formed by the two hip bones, sacrum and coccyx (Fig. 23.8). The total weight of the upper body rests on the pelvis. It protects several organs such as the reproductive organs, urinary bladder and part of the large intestine. The hip bone is an irregular bone which is composed of three fused bones: the **ilium, ischium** and **pubis** (Fig. 23.9). The **ilium** is the upper expanded portion of the bone. The **ischium** is the portion of the bone that bears the weight of the body in the sitting position. The **pubis** is the anterior portion of the bone. All three components come together at the acetabulum which is a large cup-shaped depression that receives the head of the femur at the **hip joint**. Anteroinferior to the acetabulum is a prominent foramen called the obturator foramen. The pubis of one hip bone articulates with the pubis of the other side at the **pubic symphysis**. Each hip bone also articulates with the vertebral column at the right and left **sacroiliac joints.**

The Femur

The femur is the bone of the thigh (Fig. 23.10). It is the longest bone of the body. The **upper end** has a head, neck and greater and lesser trochanters. The head articulates with the acetabulum of the hip bone at the hip joint. The neck of the femur is long and narrow. The greater and lesser trochanters provide insertion to muscles that act on the hip joint. The **shaft** of the femur presents a sharp posterior border called the linea aspera, which

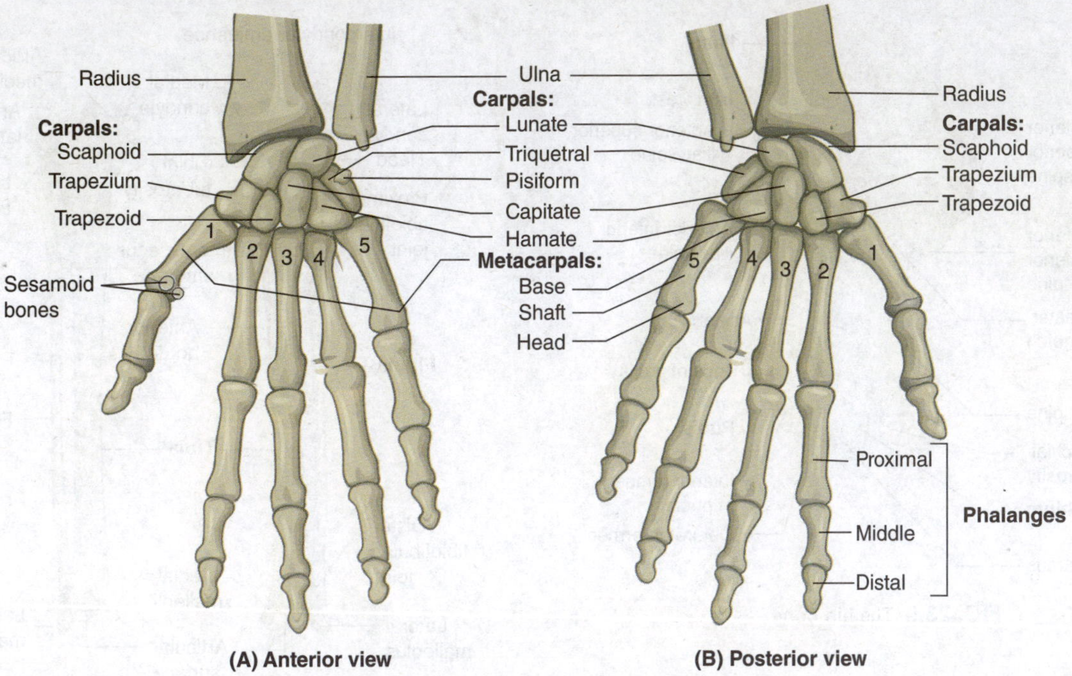

FIG. 23.7 The articulated hand (right side).

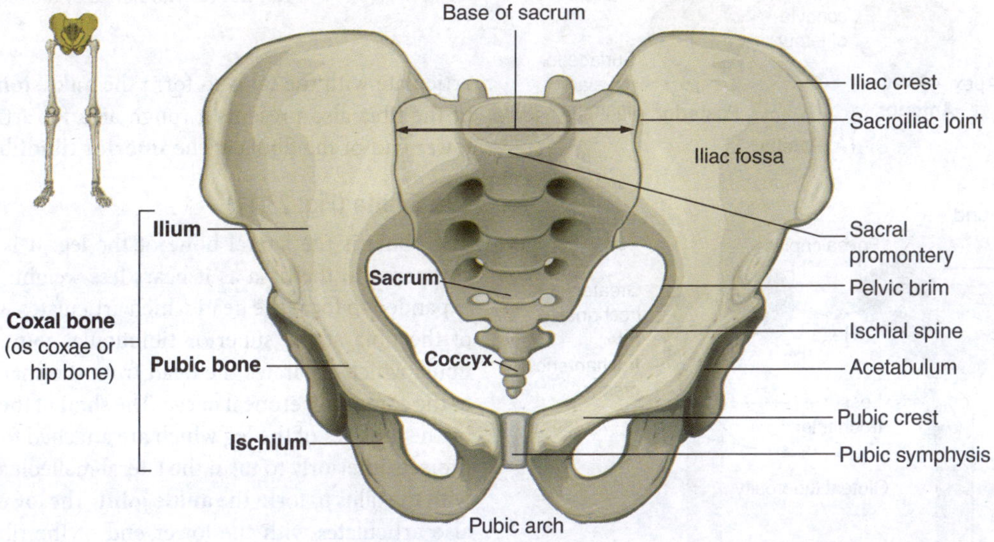

FIG. 23.8 The pelvic girdle.

provides attachment to several thigh muscles. The **lower end** has curved and expanded medial and lateral condyles. The condyles articulate with the corresponding condyles of the tibia at the **knee joint**. The lower end also has a facet that articulates with the patella.

The Patella (Fig. 23.10)

The patella is the largest sesamoid bone in the body and is located within the tendon of the quadriceps femoris muscle. It articulates with the lower end of the femur at the **knee joint**. It straightens the line of pull of the quadriceps femoris muscle and reduces friction.

The Tibia (Fig. 23.11)

The tibia is the larger medial bone of the leg. The **upper end** is expanded to form two condyles whose slightly concave surfaces receive the femoral condyles at the **knee joint**. It also presents a tibial tuberosity that provides attachment to the tendon of the quadriceps femoris muscle. The lateral aspect of the upper end has a facet for articulation with the upper end of the fibula to form the **superior tibiofibular joint**. The **shaft** has a sharp anterior border, commonly called the shin, and a subcutaneous medial surface that is easily palpable. The **lower end** presents a bony projection from its medial part called the medial malleolus. The inferior surface of the lower end and medial malleolus

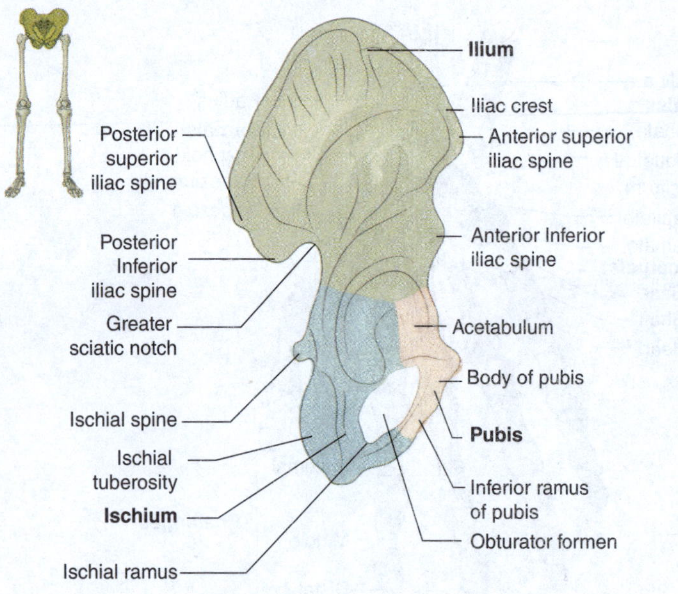

FIG. 23.9 The hip bone.

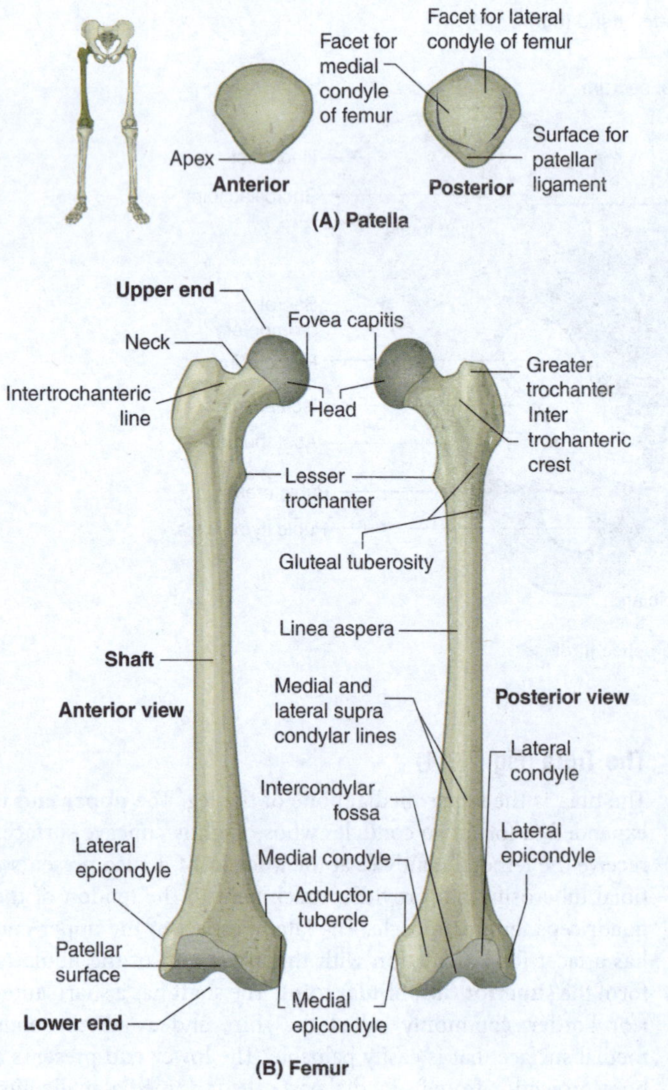

FIG. 23.10 The femur and patella.

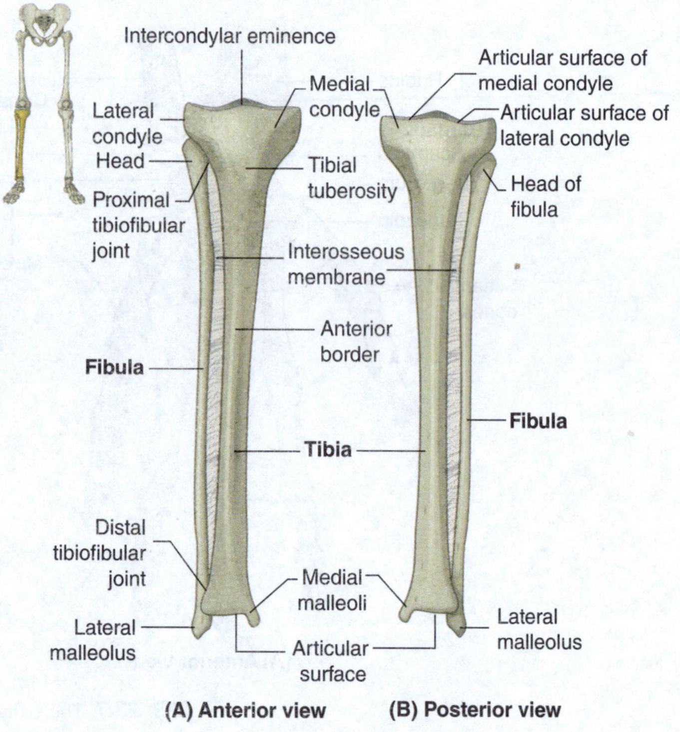

FIG. 23.11 The bones of the leg.

articulate with the talus to form the **ankle joint**. The lower end of the tibia also presents a rough area for articulation with the lower end of the fibula at the **inferior tibiofibular joint**.

The Fibula (Fig. 23.11)

The fibula is the lateral bone of the leg. It is much thinner as compared to the tibia as it bears less weight. The **upper end** is expanded to form the head which articulates with the upper end of the tibia at the superior tibiofibular joint. The neck of the fibula which separates the head from the shaft is closely related to the common peroneal nerve. The **shaft** of the fibula is moulded by the muscles of the leg which are attached to it. The **lower end** projects inferiorly to form the lateral malleolus which articulates with the talus to form the **ankle joint**. The lower end of the fibula also articulates with the lower end of the tibia at the **inferior tibiofibular joint**.

The Tarsal Bones (Fig. 23.12)

The tarsal bones correspond to the carpals of the wrist. However, they are much larger because they have to support the weight of the body. They are seven in number arranged in two rows. The proximal row contains the **talus, calcaneus** and **navicular**. The **medial cuneiform, intermediate cuneiform, lateral cuneiform** and **cuboid** form the distal row. The talus articulates with the tibia and fibula at the **ankle joint**. The calcaneum provides attachment to the Achilles tendon. The distal row of bones articulates with the metatarsal bones at the **tarsometatarsal joints**.

The Metatarsal Bones and Phalanges (Fig. 23.12)

The five metatarsal bones are numbered from the medial to lateral side. Each metatarsal bone has a **base, shaft** and **head**.

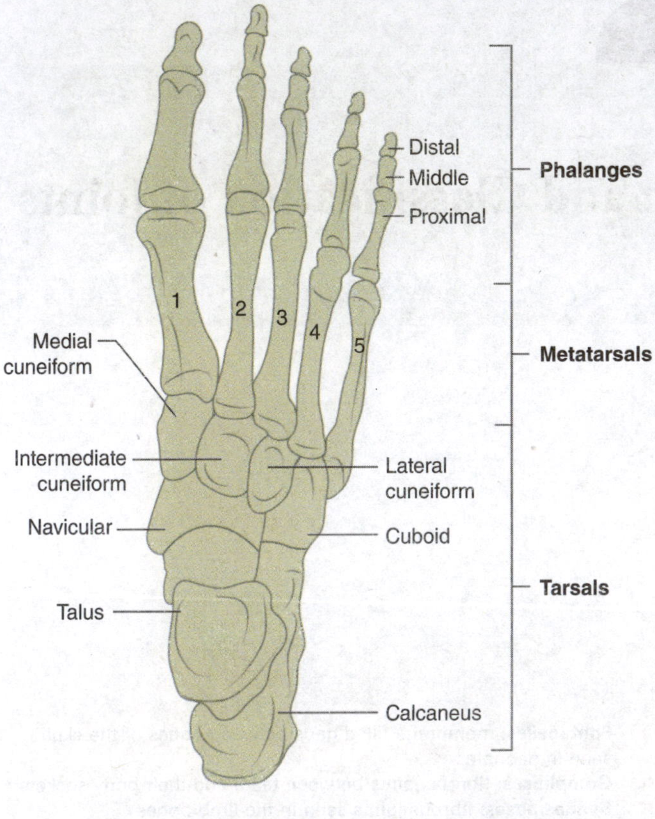

FIG. 23.12 The articulated foot (superior view).

The **bases** of the metatarsal bones articulate with the tarsal bones at the **tarsometatarsal joints**. The **heads** articulate with the bases of the proximal phalanges to form the **metatarsophalangeal joints**. Each digit has three phalanges except for the first digit. The phalanges are named **proximal, middle** and **distal**. The first digit has only proximal and distal phalanges. The phalanges articulate with one another at the **interphalangeal joints**.

APPLIED ANATOMY

- **Fracture** of the **clavicle** is common and occurs due to a fall on the shoulder or outstretched hand.
- **Fracture** of the **surgical neck** of the **humerus** may injure the axillary nerve.
- The radial nerve may be injured due to **fractures** of the **shaft** of the **humerus**.
- **Supracondylar fractures** of the lower end of the humerus are common in children due to a fall on the outstretched hand with the elbow slightly flexed. The median and ulnar nerves can be injured in this type of fracture.
- A common fracture of the lower end of the radius is called **Colles' fracture**. It occurs due to a fall on the outstretched hand and is particularly common in elderly individuals with osteoporosis.
- The **neck** of the **femur** is a common site of **fracture** in the lower limb. This is more common in elderly individuals and leads to immobility.
- **Fracture** of the **upper end** of the **fibula** is likely to injure the common peroneal nerve leading to 'foot drop'. In this condition, there is inability to dorsiflex the foot at the ankle.
- The fibula and hip bone are common donor sites for **bone grafts**.
- The **anterior border** and **medial surface** of the **tibia** are more **prone** to **fractures** due to their subcutaneous location.

APPLICATIONS IN NURSING

- Fractures involving the appendicular skeleton commonly occur due to falls or accidents. First aid measures that need to be taken include splinting of the limb, which ensures that the fractured parts of the bone are kept in place till treatment is started.

SUMMARY

- The appendicular skeleton forms the skeleton of the upper and lower limbs.
- The pectoral and pelvic girdle anchor the bones of the upper and lower limbs, respectively, to the axial skeleton.
- The clavicle or collar bone lies horizontally and acts like a mobile support for the upper limb.
- The scapula or shoulder blade is triangular and articulates with the head of the humerus at the shoulder joint.
- The humerus is the bone of the arm which forms the shoulder joint above and the elbow joint below.
- The radius is the lateral bone of the forearm that forms the elbow joint above and the wrist joint below.
- The ulna is the medial bone of the forearm that forms the elbow joint above and articulates with the radius at the superior and inferior radioulnar joints.
- The carpal bones are eight in number and arranged in proximal and distal rows forming the wrist and carpometacarpal joints, respectively.
- The metacarpal bones are five in number and articulate proximally with the carpal bones at the carpometacarpal joints and distally with the phalanges at the metacarpophalangeal joints.
- The phalanges are bones of the digits and named proximal, middle and distal.
- The hip bone has three parts named the ilium, ischium and pubis.
- It articulates with the opposite hip bone at the pubic symphysis, the sacrum at the sacroiliac joint and the femur at the hip joint.
- The femur is the bone of the thigh which forms the hip joint above and knee joint below.
- The patella is a sesamoid bone located within the tendon of the quadriceps femoris muscle.
- The tibia is the medial bone of the leg that forms the knee joint above and the ankle joint below.
- The fibula is the lateral bone of the leg that forms the ankle joint below and articulates with the tibia at the superior and inferior tibiofibular joints.
- The tarsal bones are seven in number and arranged in proximal and distal rows.
- The metatarsal bones are five in number and articulate proximally with the tarsal bones at the tarsometatarsal joints and distally with the phalanges at the metatarsophalangeal joints.

CHAPTER 24

Introduction and Classification of Joints

SPECIFIC LEARNING OBJECTIVES

At the end of this chapter, the student should be able to:

- Define a joint.
- Classify joints based on their structure and function with suitable examples.
- Describe the features of a typical synovial joint.
- Classify synovial joints with suitable examples.

GLOSSARY OF TERMS

- **Joint:** a junction between two or more skeletal elements
- **Fibrous joint:** a type of joint where fibrous connective tissue connects adjacent skeletal elements
- **Cartilaginous joint:** a type of joint where cartilage connects adjacent skeletal elements
- **Synovial joint:** a type of joint where a cavity filled with synovial fluid separates adjacent bony surfaces
- **Synarthroses:** immovable joints
- **Amphiarthroses:** partially movable joints
- **Diarthroses:** freely movable joints
- **Sutures:** fibrous joints seen between bones of the skull
- **Fontanelles:** membrane-filled gaps between bones of the skull seen in neonates
- **Gomphoses:** fibrous joints between teeth and their bony sockets
- **Syndesmoses:** fibrous joints seen in the limb bones
- **Synchondroses:** primary cartilaginous joints
- **Symphyses:** secondary cartilaginous joints
- **Uniaxial joints:** synovial joints allowing movement around one axis
- **Biaxial joints:** synovial joints allowing movements around two axes
- **Multiaxial joints:** synovial joints allowing movements around more than two axes

INTRODUCTION

The previous two sections dealt with the skeletal structures of the body. As a natural continuation, this section will describe the joints of the body. Muscle contractions move the bony levers of the body at joints, which act as the pivots. Joints serve other functions as well such as shock absorption, providing rigidity combined with a required amount of laxity, facilitation of growth and protection of vital structures. The mobility and stability of a joint are inversely correlated and are determined by the function of the joint. This chapter will provide a broad overview of the joints of the body including their definition and classification. Synovial joints will be discussed in more detail in view of their functional importance.

DEFINITION

A joint is the **junction** between two or more **skeletal elements**. Skeletal elements include bones, cartilages and teeth. **Arthrology** is the study of joints and is derived from the Greek word 'arthron' meaning joint.

CLASSIFICATION

Joints can be classified based on their **structure** and **function**. The **structural classification** is based on the **type of tissue** that lies between the ends of two or more skeletal elements (Fig. 24.1). This may be **connective tissue fibres, cartilage** or **synovial fluid**. The **functional classification** on the other hand is based on the **amount of movement** possible at a joint (Fig. 24.2). Joints at which no movements occur are called **synarthroses**, whereas **diarthroses** are freely movable joints. **Amphiarthroses** permit restricted movement. Fibrous, cartilaginous and synovial joints will now be dealt with in detail.

FIBROUS JOINTS (Fig. 24.3)

In these joints, the adjacent surfaces of the bones are connected by **fibrous connective tissue.** These joints are further classified into **sutures, gomphoses** and **syndesmoses.** While sutures and gomphoses permit very little movement, syndesmoses permit slight movement. **Sutures** are the predominant type of joints seen in the skull. The articular surfaces are connected by a thin layer of tough connective tissue. Based on the shape of the interlocking elements of the bones, sutures may be classified into plane, squamous, serrate or denticulate. Sutures permit the growth of the skull to accommodate the growing brain in children while at the same time providing the rigidity required to protect the brain. Fontanelles are membranous gaps seen in neonates where more than two skull bones meet.

Gomphoses, also called peg and socket joints, are seen between teeth and their bony sockets within the mandible and maxilla. The periodontal ligaments firmly attach the roots of the teeth to their bony sockets. **Syndesmoses** are joints where bones are connected by an interosseous ligament. Examples include the middle radioulnar joint between the radius and ulna and the inferior tibiofibular joint between the tibia and fibula.

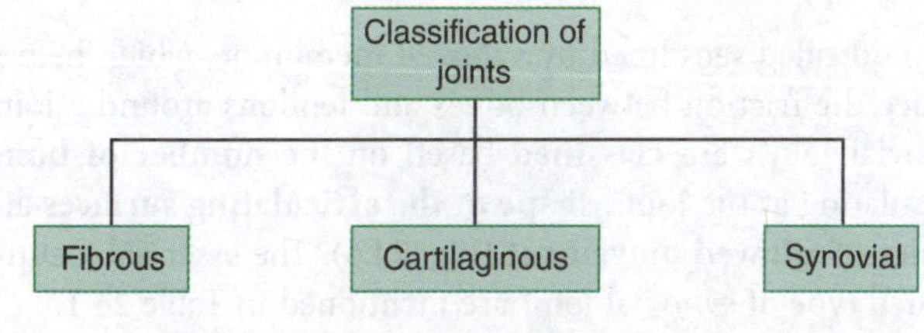

FIG. 24.1 Structural classification of joints.

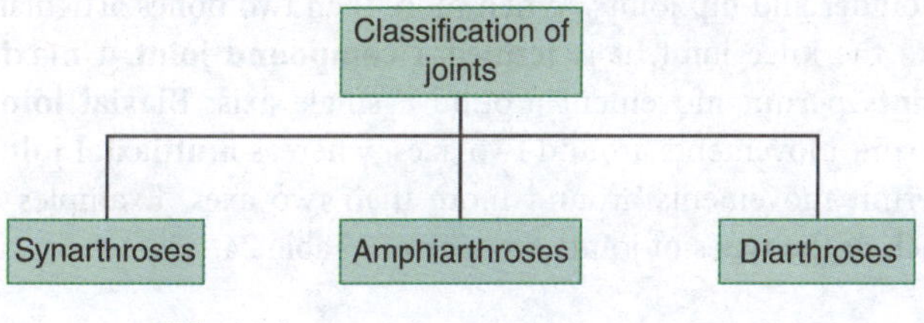

FIG. 24.2 Functional classification of joints.

CARTILAGINOUS JOINTS (Fig. 24.4)

In this type of joint, the bones forming the joint are united by means of hyaline cartilage or fibrocartilage. They lack a joint cavity. Two types of cartilaginous joints have been described, namely **synchondroses** (primary cartilaginous joints) and **symphyses** (secondary cartilaginous joints). In **primary cartilaginous joints**, the bones are united by a plate of hyaline cartilage. These joints are immovable and temporary in nature. The cartilaginous epiphyseal plate which separates the epiphysis from the diaphysis in long bones during growth is a typical example. They are obliterated by bone in the adult. The function of these joints is to provide for growth of the bones.

In **secondary cartilaginous joints**, the articular surfaces are covered by a thin plate of hyaline cartilage, which are connected by a disc of fibrocartilage. Unlike primary cartilaginous joints, these joints are permanent. These joints are seen in the midline, for example pubic symphysis and intervertebral discs. These joints act as shock absorbers and provide for some movement.

SYNOVIAL JOINTS (Fig. 24.5)

These are freely movable joints. The ends of bones forming synovial joints are covered by a smooth layer of hyaline cartilage **(articular cartilage)** that reduces the friction produced by movement. Between the articular surfaces, there is a **joint cavity** which is filled with **synovial fluid** which acts as a lubricant. The joint cavity is enclosed by a **fibrous capsule**. The interior of the joint is lined by **synovial membrane**, except over the articular cartilages. **Ligaments** bind the bones together. Additional structures that may be seen in relation to a synovial joint include articular discs, menisci and bursae. Articular discs and menisci are fibrocartilaginous structures seen in the joint cavity. Bursae

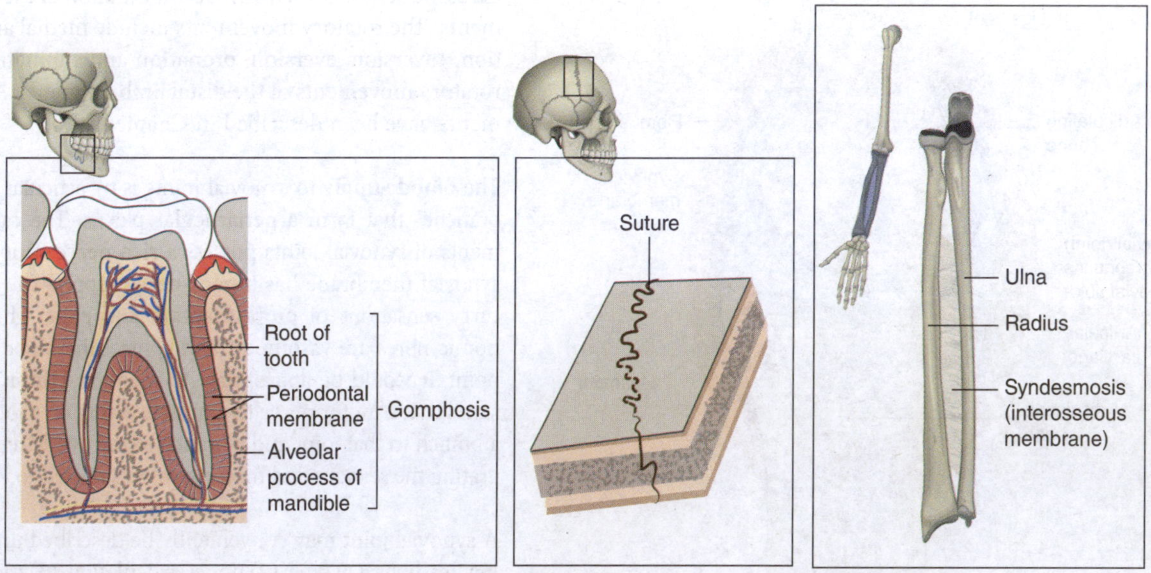

FIG. 24.3 Types of fibrous joints.

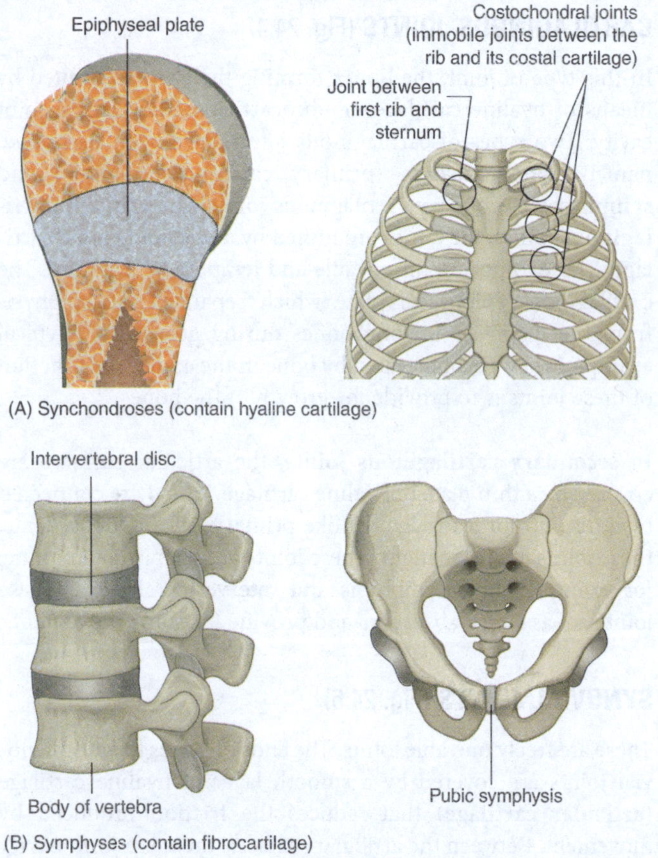

FIG. 24.4 Types of cartilaginous joints.

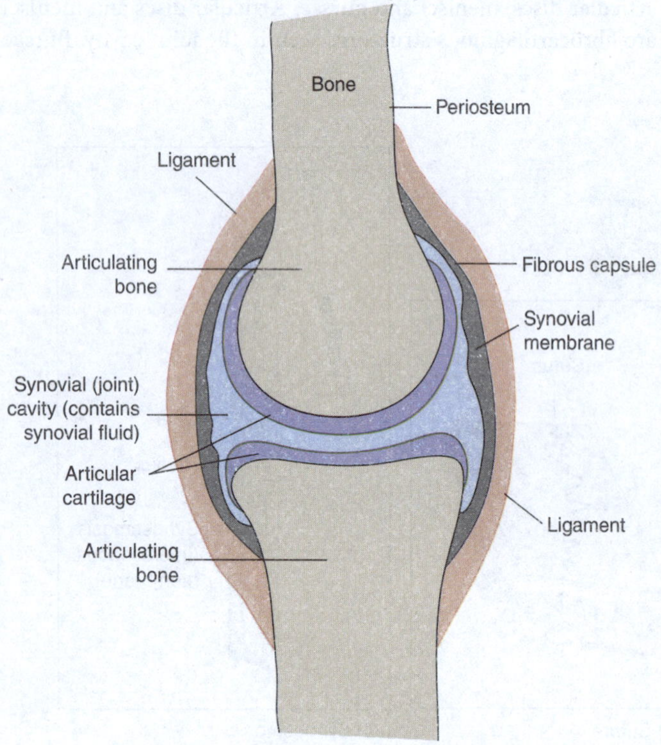

FIG. 24.5 Features of a typical synovial joint.

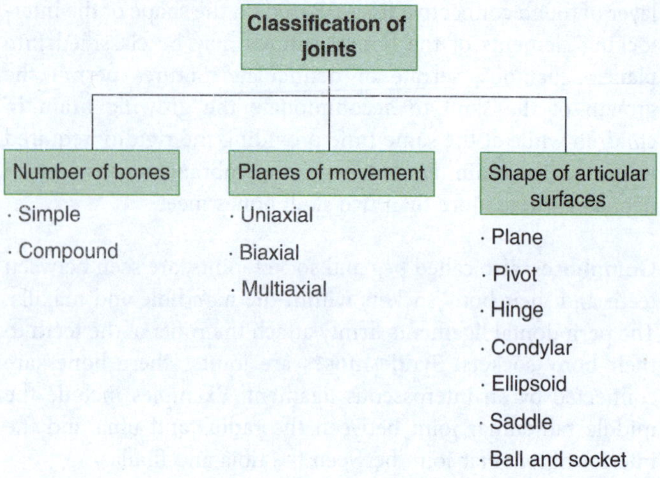

FIG. 24.6 Classification of synovial joints.

are fluid-filled sacs lined by synovial membrane, which help to reduce the friction between bones and tendons around a joint. Synovial joints are **classified** based on the **number of bones** articulating at the joint, **shape of the articulating surfaces** and **planes of allowed movement** (Fig. 24.6). The essential features of each type of synovial joint are mentioned in Table 24.1.

Simple joints are joints where two bones articulate, like the shoulder and hip joints. When more than two bones articulate, like the knee joint, it is termed a **compound joint**. **Uniaxial joints** permit movement around a single axis. **Biaxial joints** permit movements around two axes, whereas **multiaxial joints** permit movements around more than two axes. Examples of each of the types of joints are given in Table 24.1.

Movements that occur at synovial joints can be classified into **gliding, angular, rotatory** and **special**. The angular movements include flexion, extension, abduction and adduction. Circumduction is a sequential combination of the angular movements. The rotatory movements include medial and lateral rotation. Inversion, eversion, pronation and supination are specific rotatory movements of the distal limb segments. All these movements have been described in Chapter 2.

The **blood supply** to synovial joints is by articular and epiphyseal branches that form a periarticular plexus. The capsule and ligaments of synovial joints possess a rich **nerve supply**, whereas the synovial membrane has a poor nerve supply. The somatic nerves carry sensations of proprioception and pain, whereas the autonomic fibres are vasomotor and control the blood supply. At this point, it would be appropriate to mention **Hilton's law**. This law states that a motor nerve to a muscle acting on a joint tends to give a branch to that joint and a branch to the overlying skin, thus integrating the sensory and motor elements related to joint movement.

A synovial joint may conveniently be described under the following headings: (1) type, (2) bones articulating, (3) capsule and synovial membrane, (4) ligaments, (5) movements with muscles causing them, (6) nerve supply, (7) blood supply and (8) applied aspects.

Table 24.1 Salient Features of Each Type of Synovial Joint (Fig. 24.7)

S. No.	Type of Joint	Shape of Articulating Ends	Type of Movement Permitted	Examples
1.	• Plane	• Articular surfaces are nearly flat	• Permit gliding movements in various directions	• Carpal and tarsal joints
2.	• Pivot	• Articular surface comprises a central bony pivot surrounded by an osteoligamentous ring	• Uniaxial • Permits movement around vertical axis	• Superior and inferior radioulnar joints
3.	• Hinge	• Articular surfaces are pulley shaped	• Uniaxial • Permits movements around a transverse axis	• Elbow and ankle joints
4.	• Condylar	• Round articular surface of one bone fits into the articular surface of the other bone	• Biaxial • Permits movements in transverse and vertical axes	• Temporomandibular and knee joints
5.	• Ellipsoid	• Elliptical convex surface of one bone articulates with the elliptical concave surface of the other bone	• Biaxial • Permits movements in transverse and anteroposterior axes • Combination of movements produces circumduction	• Wrist joint
6.	• Saddle	• Articular surfaces are concavo-convex	• Multiaxial • Allows wide range of movements	• First carpometacarpal joint
7.	• Ball and socket	• Rounded convex surface of one bone fits into the cup-like socket of another bone	• Multiaxial • Provides greatest range of movements	• Shoulder joint and hip joints

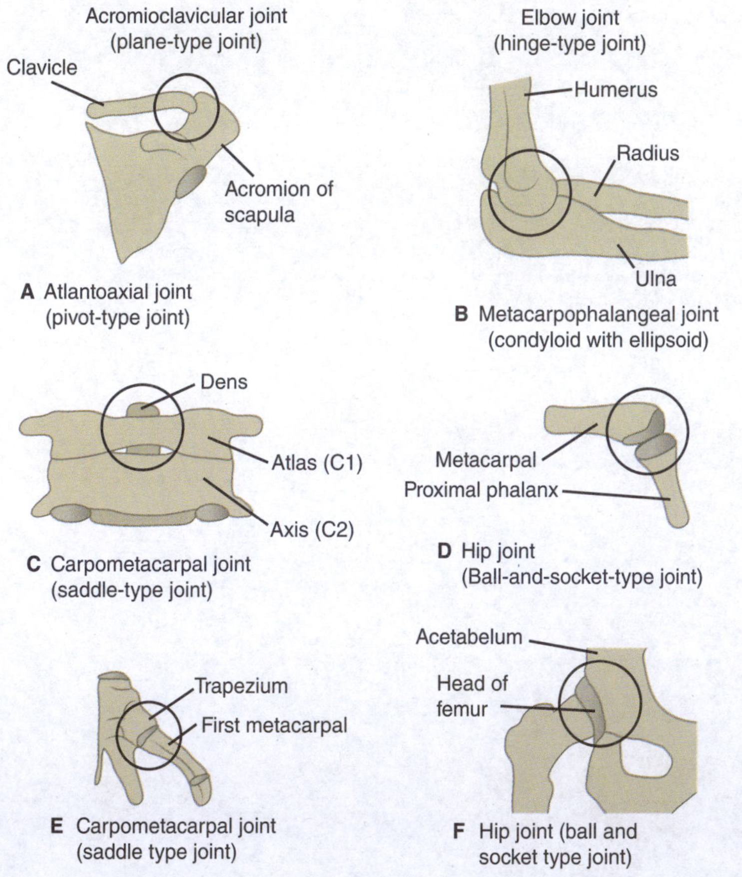

FIG. 24.7 Types of synovial joints: **(A)** plane; **(B)** hinge; **(C)** pivot; **(D)** ellipsoid; **(E)** saddle; and **(F)** ball and socket.

APPLIED ANATOMY

- **Fontanelles** are used in neonates and infants to diagnose certain clinical conditions. They appear excessively bulged in meningitis but sunken in dehydration.
- Joint pain is called **arthralgia** and is caused by a variety of conditions.
- Inflammation of joints is called **arthritis**.
- When the articulating bones in synovial joints partially lose contact, it is termed **subluxation**.
- **Dislocation** is a clinical condition in which the articulating bones in synovial joints are completely separated.

APPLICATIONS IN NURSING

- Patients with chronic arthritis have pain and stiffness of the joints. These symptoms can be relieved by the application of **heat pads** or **hot packs** over the affected joint.

SUMMARY

- A joint is a junction between two or more skeletal elements.
- Joints are functionally classified into immovable, partially movable and freely movable joints.
- Joints are structurally classified into fibrous, cartilaginous and synovial joints, based on the intervening tissue between the adjacent skeletal elements.
- Fibrous joints are further classified into sutures, gomphoses and syndesmoses.
- Cartilaginous joints may be either primary or secondary.
- Synovial joints are classified based on the number of bones articulating, the number of axes of permissible movement and the shape of the articulating surfaces.
- Synovial joints have a cavity filled with synovial fluid and lined by synovial membrane.
- Other features of synovial joints are the presence of articular cartilage, a fibrous capsule and strong ligaments that connect the adjacent bones.
- The movements that can occur at synovial joints include gliding, angular, rotatory and special movements.
- Hilton's law states that a motor nerve to a muscle acting on a joint tends to give a branch to that joint and a branch to the overlying skin.

CHAPTER 25

Major Joints of the Body

SPECIFIC LEARNING OBJECTIVES

At the end of this chapter, the student should be able to:

- Name the large joints of the axial and appendicular skeleton.
- Describe the essential features of the temporomandibular, atlanto-occipital, atlantoaxial, intervertebral and sacroiliac joints.
- Describe the essential features of the shoulder, elbow and wrist joints.
- Describe the essential features of the hip, knee and ankle joints.

GLOSSARY OF TERMS

- **Uniaxial joints:** synovial joints allowing movement around one axis
- **Biaxial joints:** synovial joints allowing movements around two axes
- **Multiaxial joints:** synovial joints allowing movements around more than two axes

INTRODUCTION

The joints of the axial skeleton are designed to allow for movements and yet not compromise the safety of the essential structures contained within it. The movements of the head, neck, jaw, vertebrae, ribs and pelvis are all essential for receiving and responding to visual and auditory stimuli, chewing, respiration, parturition and movements of the trunk. In contrast, the joints of the limbs allow for a considerable range of movement. This is necessary for locomotion and movements of the upper limb such as grasping, throwing, climbing and fine movements of the fingers.

JOINTS OF THE AXIAL SKELETON

Joints of the Head

As described in the previous chapter, the bones of the skull are connected by **sutures**. Some of the other important synovial joints in this region include the **temporomandibular**, **atlanto-occipital** and **atlantoaxial joints**. These joints are responsible for the movements of the jaw and the head. They are described in Table 25.1.

Joints Between the Vertebrae

Although the vertebral column encloses the spinal cord, it is still a mobile structure due to the movements allowed between adjacent vertebrae. These movements occur at joints both between the **bodies** and **vertebral arches** of adjacent vertebrae and include flexion, extension, lateral flexion and rotation. Flexion and extension occur mainly in the cervical and lumbar segments of the vertebral column, whereas rotation occurs in the thoracic segments. While movements between adjacent vertebrae are small, the cumulative effect of movements occurring at a number of these joints produces a considerable range of motion. These joints are described in Table 25.2.

Joints of the Ribs and Sternum (Table 25.2)

These joints are important for the **'pump-handle'** and **'bucket-handle' movements** that occur during movements of the chest wall during respiration. These movements are described in Chapter 9 on respiration in the physiology section of this book. The ribs articulate anteriorly with the sternum or other ribs and posteriorly with the vertebrae. Typical ribs have a head with two facets. The upper facet articulates with the body of the numerically higher vertebra and the lower facet with the numerically corresponding vertebra. For example, the sixth rib articulates with the fifth and sixth thoracic vertebrae. The tubercle of the rib articulates with the transverse process of the numerically corresponding vertebra. The anterior end of the rib articulates with a costal cartilage, which in turn articulates with the sternum or the costal cartilage of a higher rib.

The three parts of the sternum articulate with one another at two secondary cartilaginous joints: the **manubriosternal** and

Table 25.1 Salient Features of Synovial Joints of the Head (Figs 25.1 and 25.2)

S. No.	Name of Joint	Type of Synovial Joint	Articulating Bones	Movements	Muscles Causing These Movements	Nerve Supply
1.	• Temporomandibular	• Bicondylar	• Head of the mandible • Articular fossa of the temporal bone	Movements of the mandible • Elevation • Depression • Protrusion • Retraction • Side-to-side movements	• Muscles of mastication	• Trigeminal nerve (fifth cranial nerve)
2.	• Atlanto-occipital joint	• Ellipsoid	• Occipital condyles • Superior articular facets of C1 vertebra (atlas)	Movements of the head • Flexion • Extension • Lateral flexion	• Prevertebral and suboccipital group of muscles	• C1 spinal nerve
3.	• Median atlantoaxial joint	• Pivot	• Dens of axis (C2 vertebra) • Anterior arch of atlas	• Rotatory movements of the head around a vertical axis	• Suboccipital group of muscles	• C2 spinal nerve

Table 25.2 Salient Features of the Joints Between the Vertebrae, Ribs and Sternum (Figs 25.3–25.5)

S. No.	Name of Joint	Type of Joint	Articulating Bones	Movements	Muscles Causing These Movements	Nerve Supply
1.	• Intervertebral cartilaginous joints	• Secondary cartilaginous	• Body of one vertebra with bodies of adjacent vertebrae	• Permits compression and torsion	• Erector spinae, prevertebral and paravertebral muscles	• Corresponding spinal nerves
2.	• Intervertebral synovial joints	• Plane synovial	• Superior and inferior articular facets of adjacent vertebrae	• Gliding movements	• Erector spinae, prevertebral and paravertebral muscles	• Corresponding spinal nerves
3.	• Costovertebral joints	• Plane synovial	• Bodies of numerically corresponding vertebra and vertebra above • Demifacets on the head of the rib	• Gliding movements	• Intercostal muscles	• Corresponding spinal nerves
4.	• Costotransverse joints	• Plane synovial	• Transverse process of numerically corresponding vertebra • Tubercle of the rib	• Gliding movements	• Intercostal muscles	• Corresponding spinal nerves
5.	• Costochondral joints	• Primary cartilaginous	• Anterior end of rib • Costal cartilage	• No movements		
6.	• Chondrosternal joints	• Plane synovial	• Costal cartilage • Sternum	• Gliding movements	• Intercostal muscles	• Corresponding spinal nerves
7.	• Manubriosternal joint	• Secondary cartilaginous	• Manubrium of sternum • Body of sternum	• 'Pump-handle' movements during respiration		
8.	• Xiphisternal joint	• Secondary cartilaginous	• Xiphoid process • Body of sternum	• Small amounts of movement		

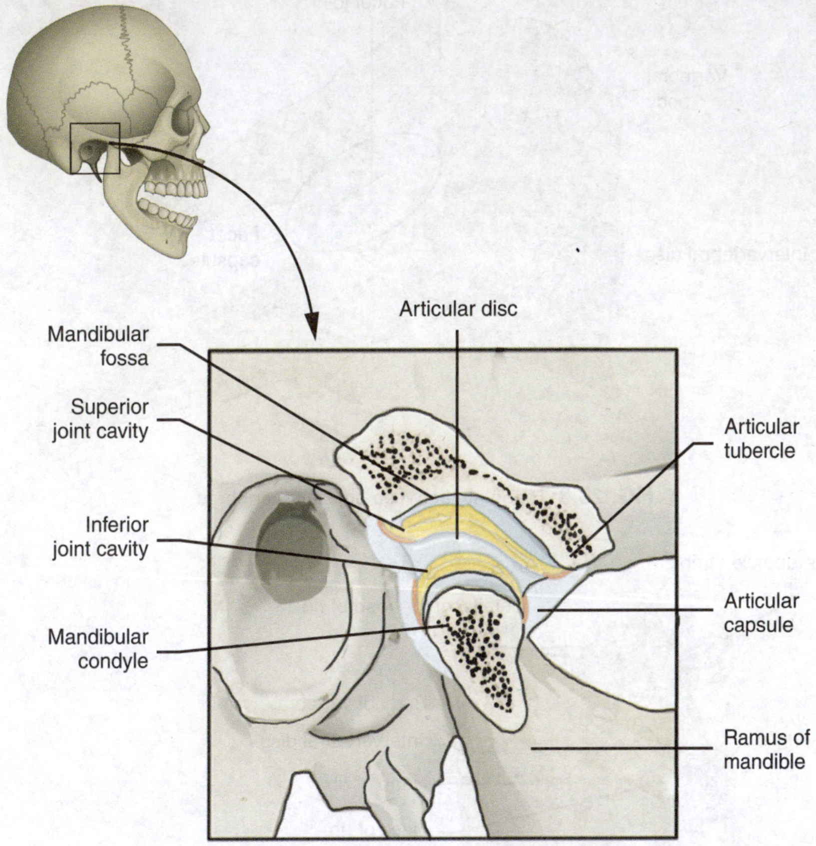

FIG. 25.1 The temporomandibular joint.

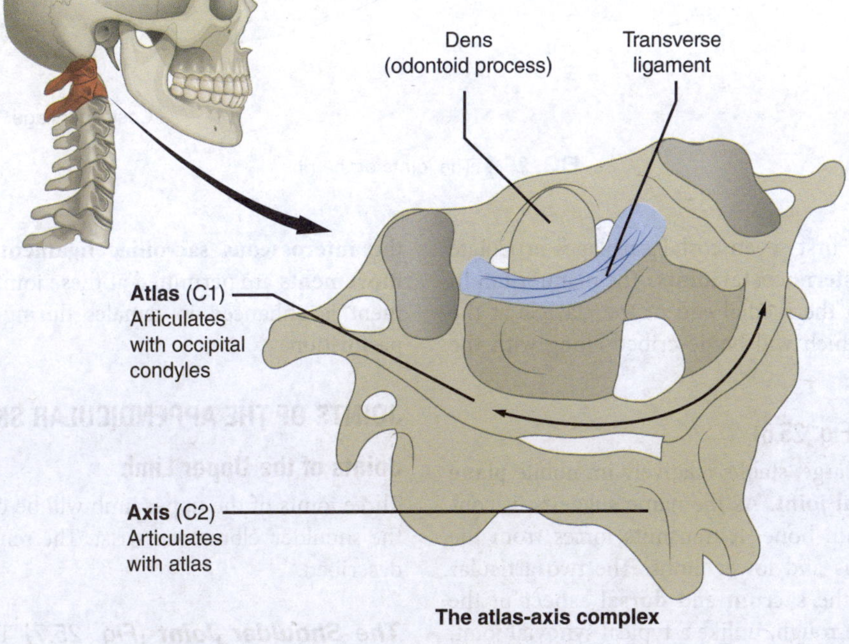

FIG. 25.2 The atlanto-occipital and atlantoaxial joints.

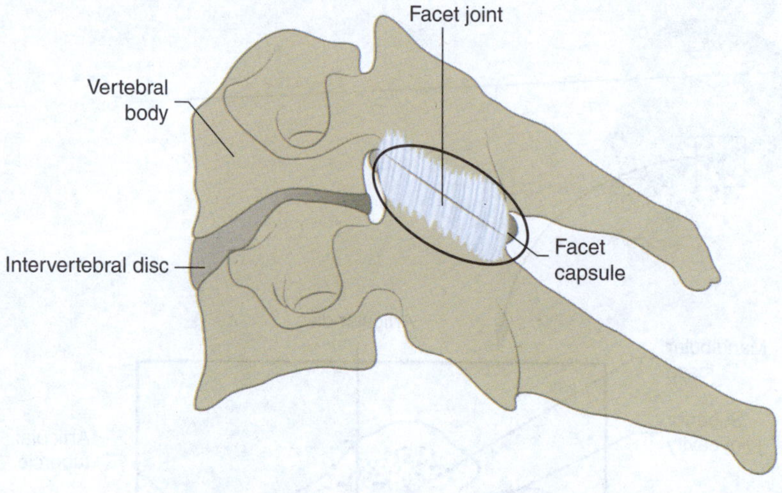

FIG. 25.3 The joints between adjacent vertebrae.

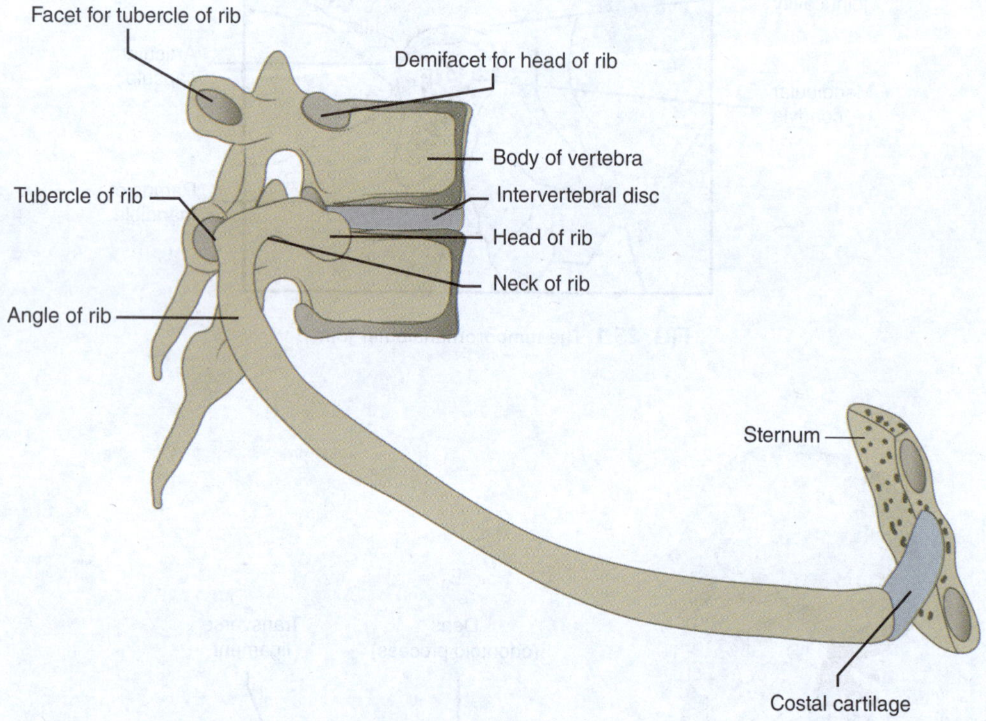

FIG. 25.4 The joints of the ribs.

xiphisternal joints. The first seven costal cartilages articulate with the sternum at the **sternocostal joints**. The manubrium in addition articulates with the medial end of the clavicle at the sternoclavicular joint, which will be described along with the joints of the upper limb.

The Sacroiliac Joint (Fig. 25.6)

The sacroiliac joint is a large, stable, relatively immobile **plane type** of **atypical synovial joint**. As the name suggests, it connects the sacrum and hip bone. It transmits forces from the upper body to the pelvis and lower limbs. The two articular surfaces are the **ala** of the **sacrum** and **dorsal aspect** of the **ileum**. Both surfaces are rough, unlike a typical synovial joint. Several ligaments connect the bones, the strongest of which is the **interosseous sacroiliac ligament**. Only limited **gliding movements** are permitted at these joints. The amount of movement is enhanced in females during pregnancy to facilitate parturition.

JOINTS OF THE APPENDICULAR SKELETON

Joints of the Upper Limb

Three joints of the upper limb will be described in more detail, the shoulder, elbow and wrist. The remaining joints are briefly described.

***The Shoulder Joint** (Fig. 25.7)* The shoulder joint is the most freely movable joint in the body. It is a **ball-and-socket**

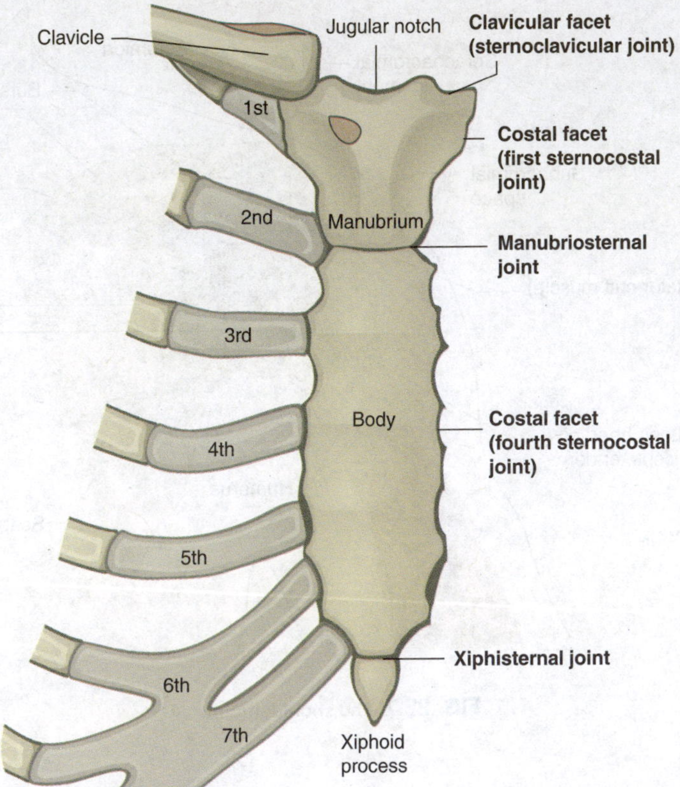

FIG. 25.5 The joints of the sternum.

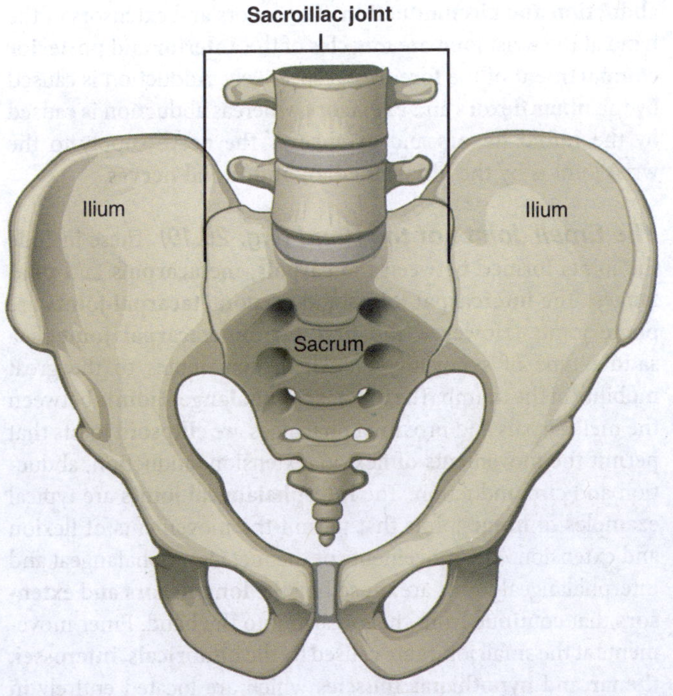

FIG. 25.6 The sacroiliac joint.

type of **synovial joint**. The articulating bones are the **head** of the **humerus** and **glenoid cavity** of the **scapula**. The mobility of the joint is facilitated by the shallowness of the glenoid cavity and looseness of the capsular attachment. The glenoid cavity is deepened by the attachment of a fibrocartilaginous rim around it called the **glenoid labrum**. The joint is supported by several ligaments such as the **glenohumeral**, **coracohumeral** and **transverse humeral ligaments**. The capsule of the joint is reinforced superiorly by the **rotator cuff**, formed by the tendons of four muscles that fuse with and strengthen it. The four muscles are the supraspinatus, infraspinatus, teres minor and subscapularis. A large bursa, the **subacromial bursa**, is present superior to the capsule of the shoulder joint.

The movements that occur at the shoulder joint include flexion, extension, adduction, abduction, medial rotation, lateral rotation and circumduction. The movements and the muscles causing them are shown in Table 25.3. The nerve supply to the shoulder joint is by the **axillary**, **suprascapular** and **lateral pectoral nerves**.

***The Elbow Joint** (Fig. 25.8)* The elbow joint is a **hinge type** of **synovial joint**. It is a **compound joint** as three bones take part

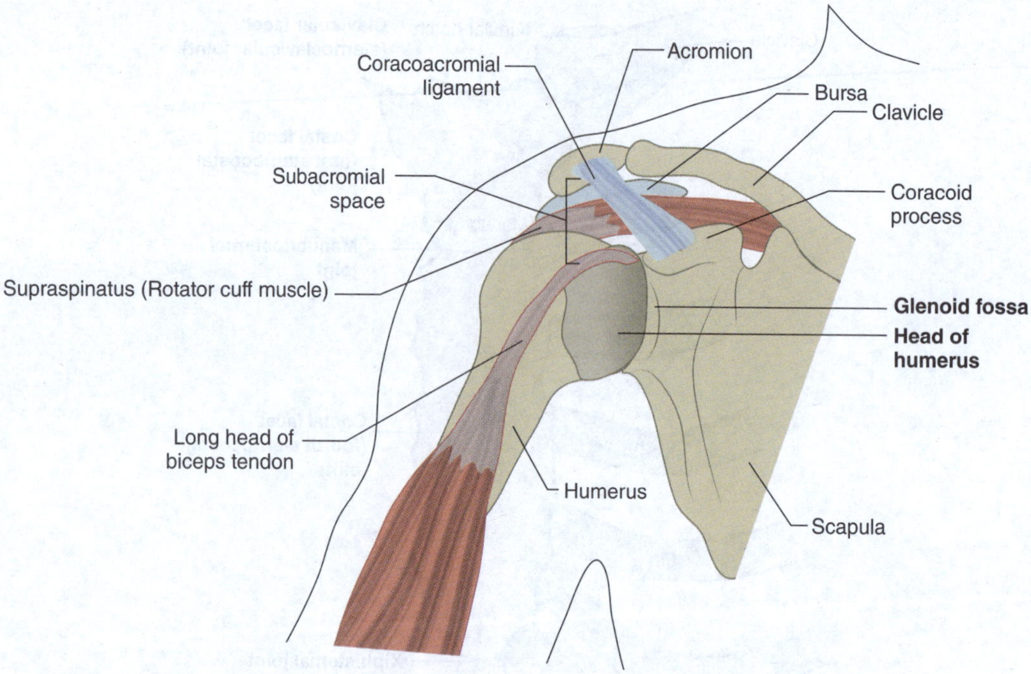

FIG. 25.7 The shoulder joint.

Table 25.3 Movements at the Shoulder Joint and Muscles Causing Them

S. No.	Name of Movement	Important Muscles Causing It
1.	Flexion	• Pectoralis major • Deltoid
2.	Extension	• Latissimus dorsi • Deltoid
3.	Adduction	• Pectoralis major • Latissimus dorsi
4.	Abduction	• Supraspinatus • Deltoid
5.	Medial rotation	• Pectoralis major • Subscapularis
6.	Lateral rotation	• Infraspinatus • Teres minor

in forming it. The articulating bones are the **humerus**, **radius** and **ulna**. The **capitulum** of the **humerus** articulates with the **head** of the **radius**, while the **trochlea** articulates with the **trochlear notch** of the **ulna**. The capsule of the joint is reinforced medially and laterally by the **medial** and **lateral collateral ligaments**. The movements that occur at the joint are **flexion** and **extension**. The flexors of the forearm at the elbow joint are the **biceps brachii** and **brachialis muscles**. Extension at the joint occurs mainly due to the action of the **triceps brachii**. The nerve supply to the elbow joint is by the **ulnar**, **median**, **radial** and **musculocutaneous nerves**.

The Wrist Joint *(Fig. 25.9)* The wrist joint is an **ellipsoid type** of **synovial joint**. It is also a **compound joint** as four bones take part in forming it. The articulating bones are the **radius** and **proximal row** of **carpal bones** except the pisiform. The **lower end** of the **radius** and an **articular disc** superiorly articulate with the proximal surfaces of the **scaphoid**, **lunate** and **triquetral bones**. The capsule of the joint is reinforced medially and laterally by the **medial and lateral collateral ligaments**. The movements that occur at the joint are **flexion, extension, adduction, abduction and circumduction**. The flexors and extensors of the hand at the wrist joint are **muscles** of the **anterior** and **posterior compartment** of the **forearm**, respectively. Adduction is caused by the **ulnar flexors** and **extensors**, whereas abduction is caused by the **radial flexors** and **extensors**. The nerve supply to the wrist joint is by the **ulnar, median and radial nerves**.

The Small Joints of the Hand *(Fig. 25.10)* These include the joints formed between the **carpals, metacarpals** and **phalanges**. The **intercarpal joints** and **carpometacarpal joints** are **plane** joints. However, the **first carpometacarpal joint** is a **saddle** type of synovial joint which contributes to the great mobility of the thumb. The **metacarpophalangeal joints** between the metacarpals and proximal phalanges are **ellipsoid** joints that permit the movements of flexion, extension, adduction, abduction and circumduction. The **interphalangeal joints** are typical examples of **hinge** joints that permit the movements of flexion and extension. The movements of the metacarpophalangeal and interphalangeal joints are caused by the **long flexors** and **extensors** that continue from the forearm into the hand. Finer movements at the small joints are caused by the **lumbricals, interossei, thenar** and **hypothenar muscles** which are located entirely in the hand.

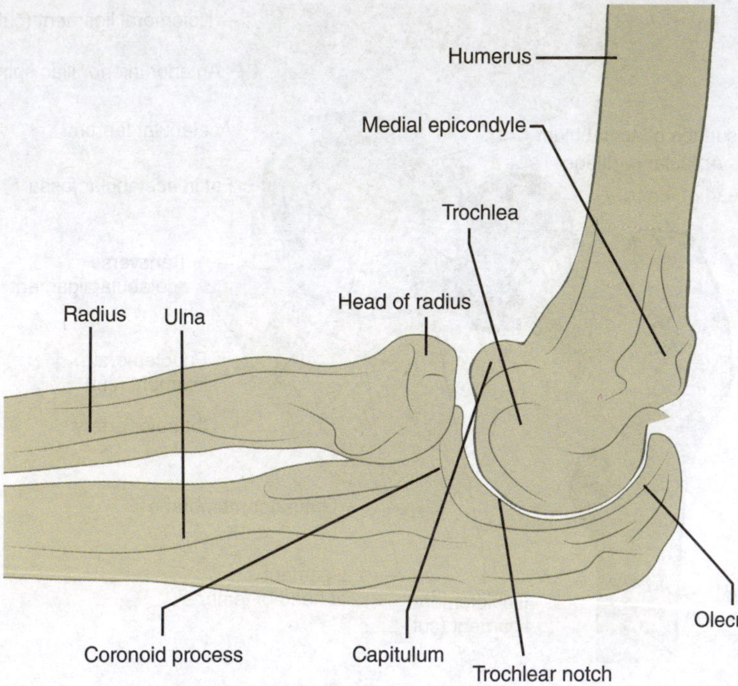

FIG. 25.8 The elbow joint.

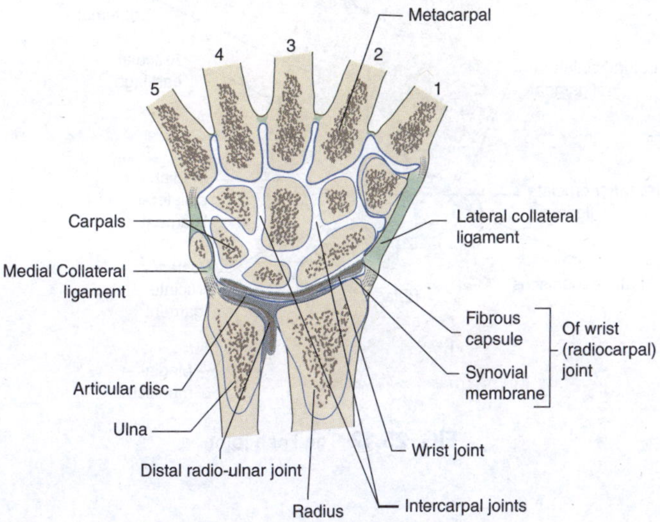

FIG. 25.9 The wrist joint.

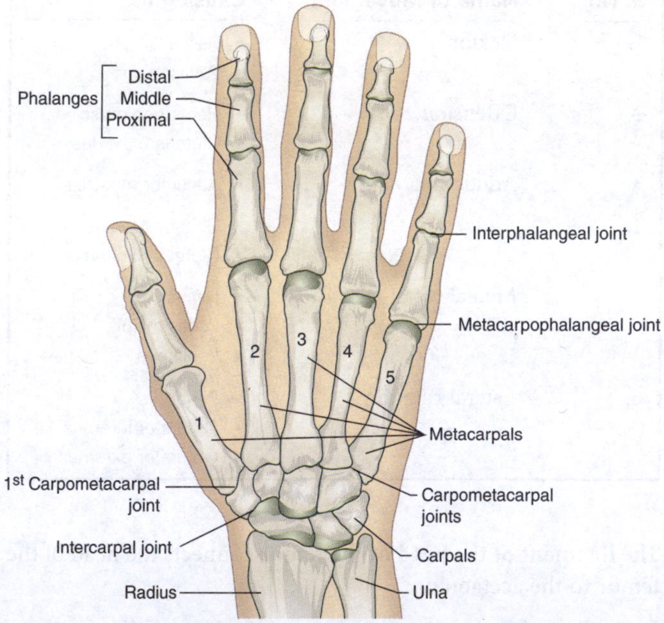

FIG. 25.10 The small joints of the hand.

Joints of the Lower Limb

Three joints of the lower limb will be described in more detail, namely the hip, knee and ankle. The remaining joints are briefly described.

***The Hip Joint** (Fig. 25.11)* The hip joint is the most freely movable joint of the lower limb. It is a **ball-and-socket** type of synovial joint. The articulating bones are the **head** of the **femur** and **acetabulum** of the **hip bone**. In contrast to the shoulder joint, the stability of the hip joint is facilitated by the depth of the acetabulum and the snug fit of the head of the femur into the acetabulum. The acetabulum is deepened by the attachment of a fibrocartilaginous rim around it called the **acetabular labrum**. The joint is supported by several strong ligaments such as the **pubofemoral**, **iliofemoral** and **ischiofemoral ligaments**.

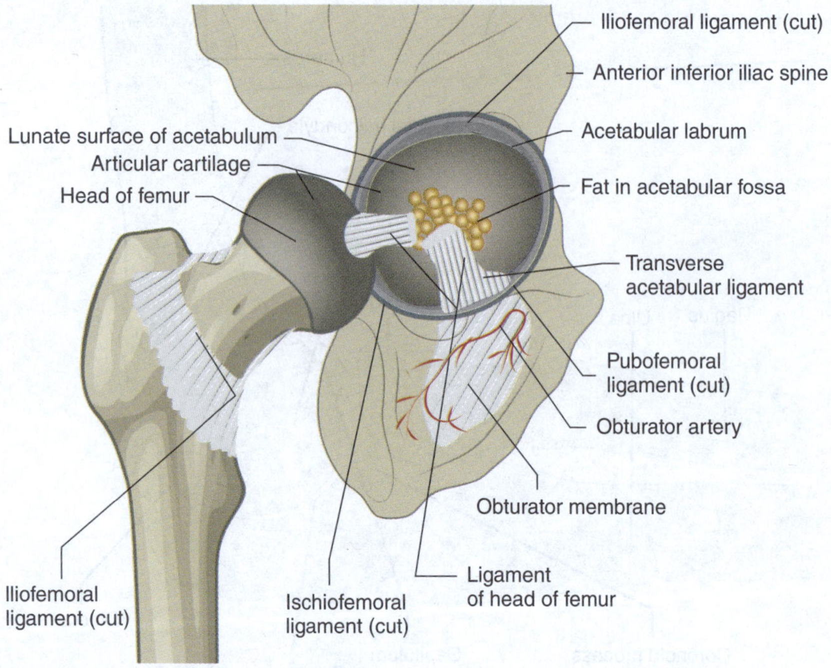

FIG. 25.11 The hip joint.

Table 25.4 Movements at the Hip Joint and Muscles Causing Them

S. No.	Name of Movement	Important Muscles Causing It
1.	Flexion	• Iliacus • Psoas major
2.	Extension	• Hamstring muscles • Gluteus maximus
3.	Adduction	• Adductor muscles
4.	Abduction	• Gluteus medius • Gluteus minimus
5.	Medial rotation	• Iliacus • Psoas major • Pectineus
6.	Lateral rotation	• Piriformis • Obturator internus • Obturator externus

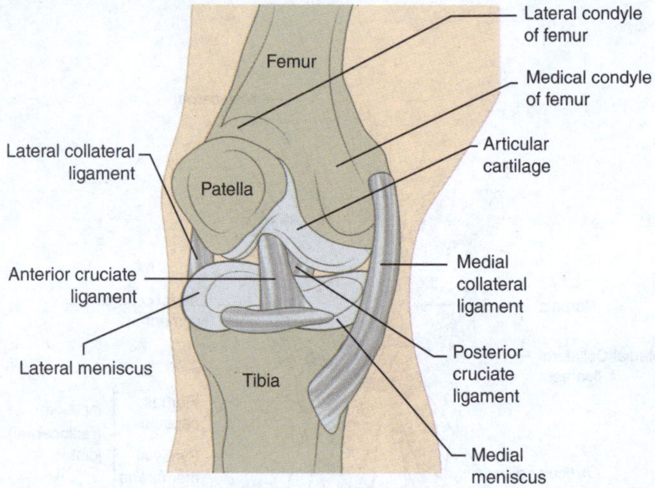

FIG. 25.12 The knee joint.

The **ligament of the head of the femur** connects the head of the femur to the acetabulum.

The movements that occur at the hip joint include flexion, extension, adduction, abduction, medial rotation, lateral rotation and circumduction. The movements and muscles causing them are shown in Table 25.4. The nerve supply to the hip joint is by the **sciatic, femoral, obturator** and **superior gluteal nerves.**

The Knee Joint *(Fig. 25.12)* The knee joint is a **modified hinge (bicondylar) type** of **synovial joint**. It is a **compound joint** as three bones take part in forming it. The articulating bones are the **femur, tibia** and **patella**. The **medial and lateral condyles** of the **femur** articulate with the corresponding **condyles** of the **tibia.** The **patella** articulates with a facet on the anterior aspect of the lower end of the **femur**. The tibial condyles are deepened by fibrocartilaginous structures called **medial** and **lateral menisci**. The capsule of the joint is reinforced medially and laterally by strong ligaments called **medial** and **lateral collateral ligaments**. The anteroposterior stability of the joint is maintained by tough **anterior** and **posterior cruciate ligaments.** The movements that occur at the joint are **flexion** and **extension**. The flexors of the leg at the knee joint are the **hamstring muscles**. Extension at the joint occurs mainly by the action of the **quadriceps femoris** muscle.

The nerve supply to the knee joint is by the **femoral, tibial, common peroneal** and **obturator nerves.**

***The Ankle Joint** (Fig. 25.13)* The ankle joint is a **hinge type** of **synovial joint**. It is a **compound joint** as three bones take part in forming it. The articulating bones are the **tibia, fibula** and **talus**. The **medial** and **lateral malleoli** of the tibia and fibula, respectively, articulate with facets on either side of the **talus**. The trochlear (upper) surface of the **talus** articulates with the inferior surface of the lower end of the **tibia**. The capsule of the joint is reinforced medially and laterally by strong ligaments called the **deltoid** and **lateral ligament**, respectively. The movements that occur at the joint are **plantar flexion** and **dorsiflexion**. The **gastrocnemius** and **soleus** muscles are important plantar flexors. Dorsiflexion at the joint occurs mainly due to the action of the muscles of the **anterior compartment** of the leg. The nerve supply to the ankle joint is by the **deep peroneal** and **tibial nerves.**

***The Joints of the Foot** (Fig. 25.14)* These include the joints formed between the **tarsals, metatarsals** and **phalanges**. Among

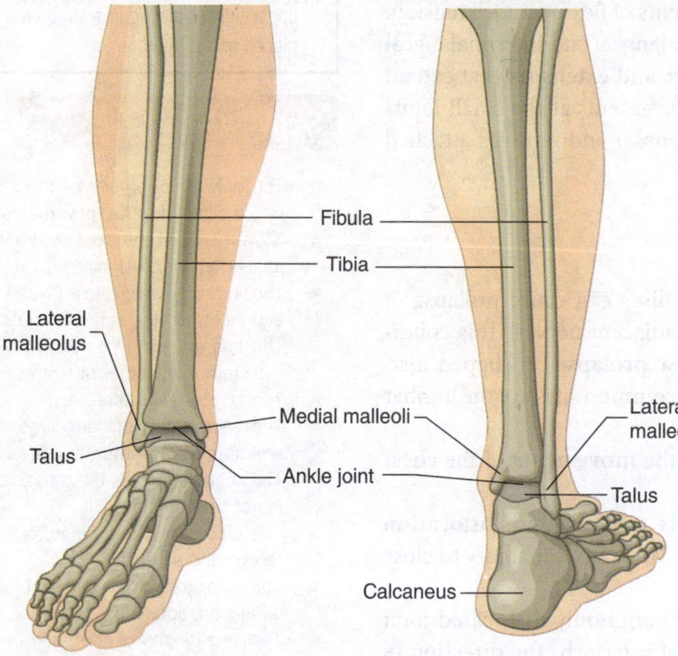

FIG. 25.13 The ankle joint.

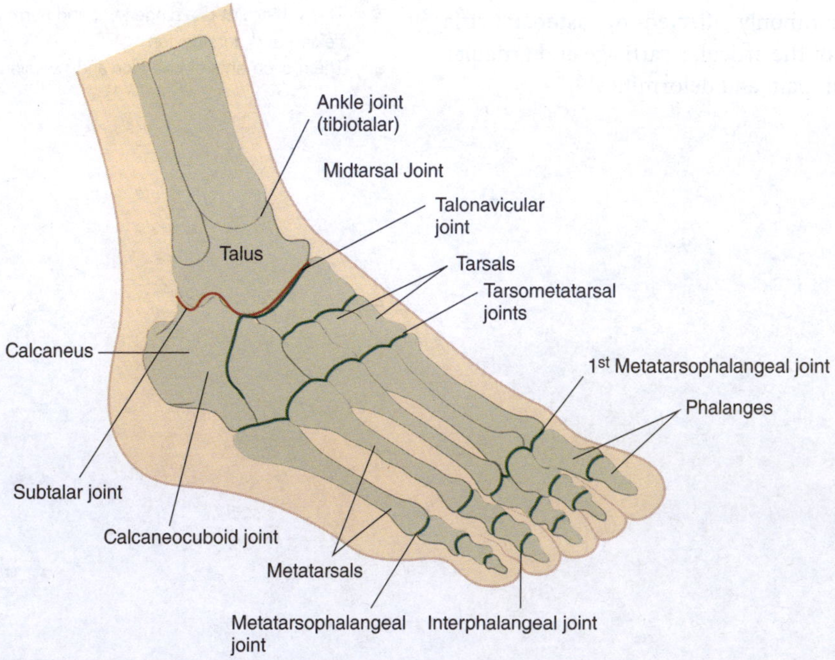

FIG. 25.14 The joints of the foot.

the intertarsal joints, the **subtalar**, talocalcaneonavicular and calcaneocuboid joints are large and allow for the movements of inversion and eversion of the foot. The talocalcaneonavicular and calcaneocuboid joints are together called the **midtarsal joints.** The movements of inversion and eversion are caused by the tibialis group of muscles and peroneal muscles, respectively. The other **intertarsal** and **tarsometatarsal joints** are **plane** joints. The **metatarsophalangeal joints** between the metatarsals and proximal phalanges are **ellipsoid** joints that permit the movements of flexion, extension, adduction, abduction and circumduction. The **interphalangeal joints** are typical examples of **hinge** joints that permit the movements of flexion and extension. The movements of the metatarsophalangeal and interphalangeal joints are caused by the **long flexors** and **extensors** that extend from the leg into the foot. Finer movements at the small joints are caused by the **lumbricals, interossei** and muscles attached to the first and fifth digits.

APPLIED ANATOMY

- Degeneration of intervertebral discs can cause prolapse of their contents and pressure on adjacent nerves. This condition is called **intervertebral disc prolapse** or 'slipped disc' in common language. The most common sites are the lumbar and cervical regions.
- The joints of the ribs allow for the **movements** of the **chest wall** that aid respiration.
- The **temporomandibular joints** can undergo **dislocation** when the jaws are opened wide. This causes inability to close the mouth.
- The **shoulder joint** is the most commonly **dislocated** joint in the body. The joint is weakest inferiorly, the direction in which the dislocation most often occurs.
- Long-standing **rheumatoid arthritis** can cause deformities of the small joints of the hand.
- The knee joint is commonly affected by **osteoarthritis** causing degeneration of the articular cartilage and articular surfaces. This results in pain and deformities.
- **Sports injuries** of the knee joint frequently damage the anterior cruciate ligament, medial meniscus and medial collateral ligament.
- **Sprains** of the **ankle joint** are common and involve various degrees of tears in either the deltoid or lateral ligament.
- **Gout** affects the **first metacarpophalangeal joint** causing pain and swelling.

APPLICATIONS IN NURSING

- **Slings** are used to raise, support and immobilize the arm, forearm and hand. For example, after the treatment of a dislocated shoulder joint, the upper limb is placed in a sling with the forearm flexed at the elbow and placed across the body.

SUMMARY

- The only synovial joint of the skull is the temporomandibular joint, which allows for the movements of mastication.
- Movements of the skull on the vertebrae occur at the atlanto-occipital and atlantoaxial joints.
- The vertebrae articulate with one another through intervertebral discs and facets on the superior and inferior articular processes.
- The ribs articulate posteriorly with the thoracic vertebrae and with the sternum or other ribs or not at all anteriorly.
- The sternum has three parts which articulate via fibrous joints.
- The sacroiliac joints are large synovial joints that allow for small amounts of movement but are very stable.
- The shoulder joint is the most mobile joint in the body but as a result is not very stable.
- The elbow joint is a hinge joint that allows for the movements of flexion and extension.
- The wrist joint is an ellipsoid joint in which movements of flexion, extension, adduction, abduction and circumduction occur.
- The small joints of the hand permit both powerful and fine movements of the fingers.
- The hip joint is both a mobile and stable joint.
- The knee joint is a bicondylar joint that allows for the movements of flexion and extension of the leg.
- The ankle joint is a hinge joint and permits the movements of plantar flexion and dorsiflexion.
- The movements of inversion and inversion occur at the intertarsal joints.

7.2

SECTION

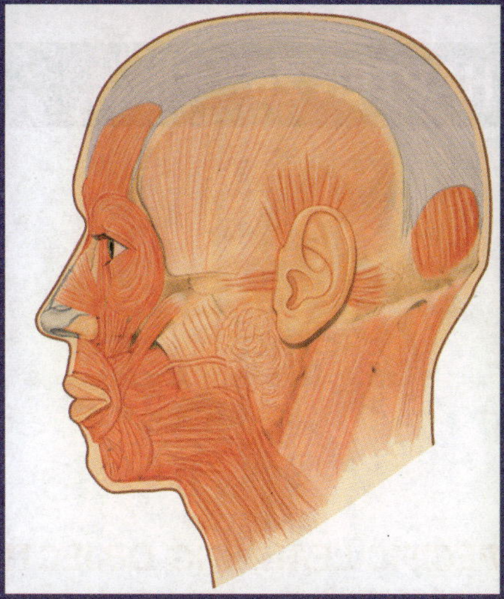

The Muscular System

Section Outline

CHAPTER 26

The Skeletal Muscles Above the Diaphragm Including Diaphragm

SPECIFIC LEARNING OBJECTIVES

At the end of this chapter, the student should be able to:

- Describe the gross anatomy of the major muscle groups of the head and neck.
- Describe the gross anatomy of the major muscle groups of the upper limb.
- Describe the gross anatomy of the major muscle groups of the thorax, including the thoracoabdominal diaphragm.

GLOSSARY OF TERMS

- **Muscles of mastication:** muscles that are responsible for chewing movements of the mandible
- **Extraocular muscles:** muscles that move the eyeball
- **Infrahyoid muscles:** muscles that extend from the sternum and larynx to the hyoid bone
- **Sternocleidomastoid muscle:** muscle of the neck that divides it into anterior and posterior triangles
- **Intercostal muscles:** muscles located in the intercostal spaces between ribs
- **Pectoral muscles:** muscles of the upper limb that arise from the front of the chest wall
- **Deltoid:** an important muscle of the shoulder region which is a common site for administration of intramuscular injections
- **Thoracoabdominal diaphragm:** the musculoaponeurotic partition between the thoracic and abdominal cavities

INTRODUCTION

As mentioned in the previous chapter, all skeletal muscles are attached to bones. Skeletal muscles are usually described with respect to their origin, insertion, nerve supply and action. Muscles of different regions are arranged in functional groups with common actions and nerve supply. For convenience of description, the muscles have been described as muscles of the head and neck, muscles of the upper limb, muscles of the thorax and the thoracoabdominal diaphragm.

MUSCLES OF THE HEAD AND NECK

The muscles of the head and neck are described as mentioned in Fig. 26.1. The muscle groups mentioned in Fig. 26.1 are described in Table 26.1.

MUSCLES OF THE THORAX (Fig. 26.9)

The important muscles of the thoracic cage are the **intercostal muscles**. They are arranged in three layers. From outside to inside, they are the **external intercostal**, **internal intercostal** and **innermost intercostal muscles**. All these muscles are attached to **adjacent ribs** and fill the intercostal spaces. Thus, there are 11 intercostal spaces between the 12 ribs. The intercostal spaces contain the intercostal nerves and vessels in addition to the muscles. The **intercostal nerves** of a particular space supply the muscles of that space. The intercostal muscles serve to **move the ribs**, thus suitably altering the volume of the ribcage during the process of inspiration and expiration. They also serve to provide a degree of **rigidity** to the intercostal spaces, preventing their in-drawing during inspiration and puffing out during expiration.

MUSCLES OF THE UPPER LIMB

The muscles of the upper limb are described as mentioned in Fig. 26.10. The muscle groups mentioned in Fig. 26.10 are described in Table 26.2.

THE DELTOID MUSCLE (Fig. 26.12)

The deltoid muscle is described in more detail in view of its clinical importance. It arises from the **lateral one-third of the clavicle, acromion process** and **spine of the scapula**. The insertion is onto the **deltoid tuberosity of the humerus** located near

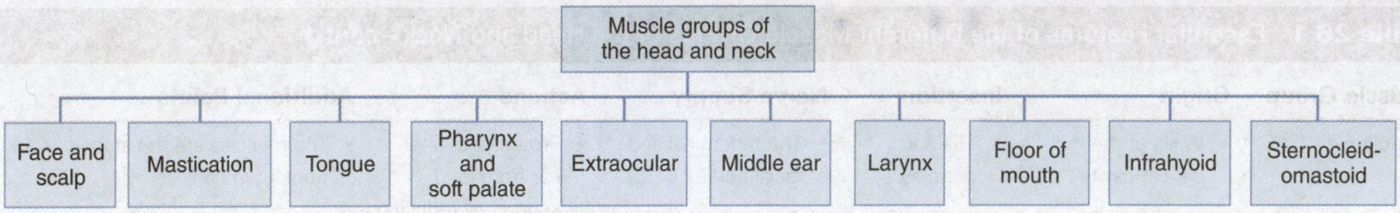

FIG. 26.1 The different muscle groups of the head and neck.

Table 26.1 Essential Features of the Different Muscle Groups of the Head and Neck

Muscle Group	Origin	Insertion	Nerve Supply	Actions	Additional Points
Face and scalp (Figure 26.2a)	• Facial skeleton	• Skin of the face	• Facial nerve, the seventh cranial nerve	• Adjust the dimensions of the orifices of the face such as the eyes, mouth and nose • Control facial expressions	• These muscles are unusual in that they are superficially located in the subcutaneous tissue • Orbicularis oris and orbicularis oculi are two important muscles which help to close the orifices of the mouth and eye, respectively
Mastication (Fig. 26.2b)	• Bones of the base and side of the skull	• Mandible	• Trigeminal nerve, the fifth cranial nerve	• Move the mandible to enable movements required for chewing food	• The individual muscles are the masseter, temporalis, lateral and medial pterygoid muscles
Tongue (Fig. 26.3)	• Bones of the base of the skull, the mandible and hyoid bones • Some muscles are restricted entirely to the tongue alone	• Different parts of the tongue	• Hypoglossal nerve, the 12th cranial nerve	• Adjust the shape and position of the tongue for manipulation of food particles and for articulation during speech	• The muscles of the tongue can be divided into intrinsic and extrinsic • Intrinsic muscles do not have any bony attachment and can alter the shape of the tongue • Extrinsic muscles are the genioglossus, styloglossus, palatoglossus and hyoglossus which can alter both the shape and position of the tongue
Pharynx (Fig. 26.4) Constrictors	• The base of the skull, hyoid bone and larynx	• A median raphe	• Pharyngeal plexus formed by the 9th, 10th and 11th cranial nerves	• Movement of the bolus during the second phase of deglutition	• There are three constrictors, superior, middle and inferior
Longitudinal muscles	• The base of the skull	• The larynx	• Pharyngeal plexus formed by the 9th, 10th and 11th cranial nerves	• Helps to shorten the pharynx during deglutition	• The three longitudinal muscles are the salpingopharyngeus, palatopharyngeus and stylopharyngeus
Soft palate (Fig. 26.5)	• Base of the skull, palatine bone and palatine aponeurosis	• Palatine aponeurosis, tongue and larynx	• Pharyngeal plexus formed by the 9th, 10th, and 11th cranial nerves	• Enable the soft palate to close off the pharyngeal isthmus during deglutition, thus preventing nasal regurgitation of food	• The muscles of the soft palate are the tensor palati, levator palati, palatoglossus, palatopharyngeus and musculus uvulae • The tensor palati forms the palatine aponeurosis to which all the other muscles are attached
Extraocular (Fig. 26.6)	• Bony orbit	• Sclera close to the sclerocorneal junction and upper eyelid	• Oculomotor, trochlear and abducent nerves (third, fourth and sixth cranial nerves)	• Move the eyeball in various directions • Elevate the upper eyelid	• The muscles that move the eyeball are the superior rectus, inferior rectus, lateral rectus, medial rectus, superior oblique and inferior oblique • The levator palpebrae superioris elevates the upper eyelid

Continued

Table 26.1 Essential Features of the Different Muscle Groups of the Head and Neck—cont'd

Muscle Group	Origin	Insertion	Nerve Supply	Actions	Additional Points
Middle ear	• Walls of the middle ear cavity	• The ear ossicles	• The trigeminal and facial nerves	• Protect the inner ear from loud sounds by reducing excessive vibrations of the ossicles	• The muscles are the stapedius and tensor tympani
Larynx (Fig. 26.7)	• Cartilages of the larynx	• Cartilages of the larynx	• The vagus, the 10th cranial nerve	• Phonation • Control the movement of air into the trachea and thence into the lungs	• The most important laryngeal muscle is the posterior cricoarytenoid which opens the laryngeal inlet and maintains the airway
Floor of mouth	• Mandible	• Hyoid bone	• Trigeminal nerve	• Enables the first phase of deglutition	• The mylohyoid is the important muscle that forms the floor of the mouth, the 'oral diaphragm'
Infrahyoid	• Larynx and sternum	• Hyoid bone	• Cervical plexus	• Adjust the position of the hyoid bone during deglutition	• These muscles are also called the strap muscles and cover the thyroid gland
Sternocleidomastoid (Fig. 26.8)	• Sternum and clavicle	• Mastoid process of temporal bone	• Spinal accessory component of 11th cranial nerve	• Turns the head to the side	• This is a key muscle of the neck region that helps to divide the neck into anterior and posterior triangles

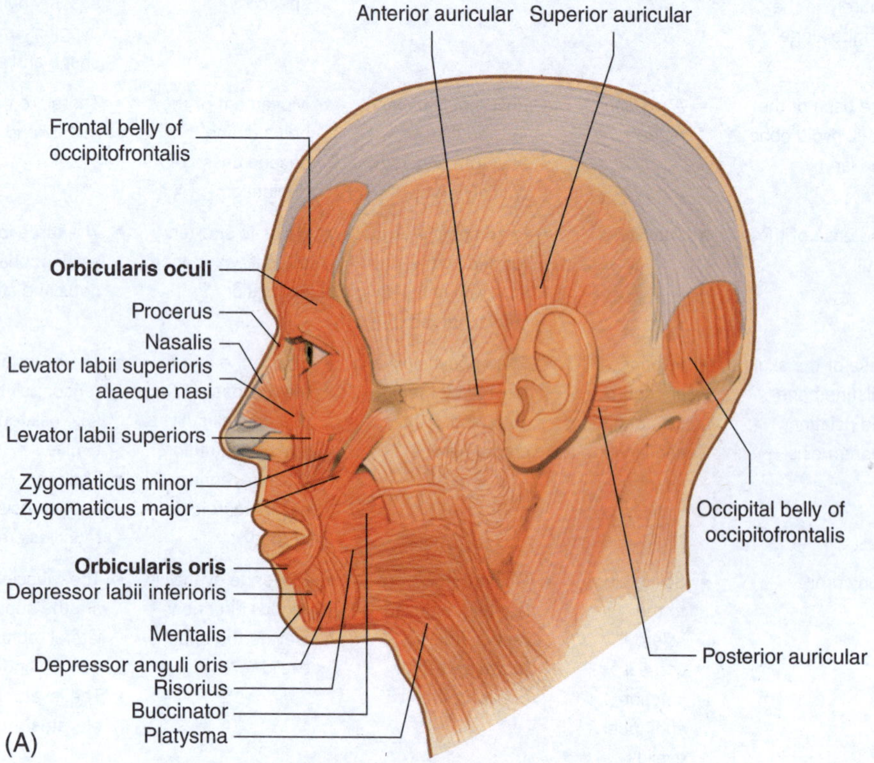

FIG. 26.2 (A) Muscles of the face and scalp (Lateral view).

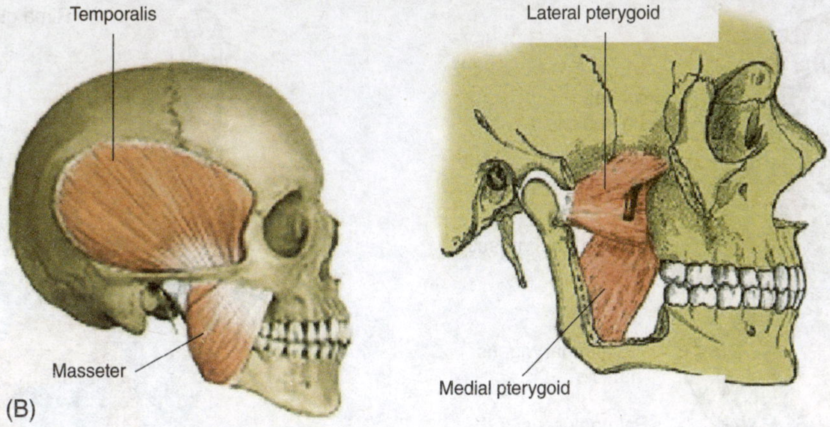

FIG. 26.2 (B) Muscles of Mastication (Lateral view).

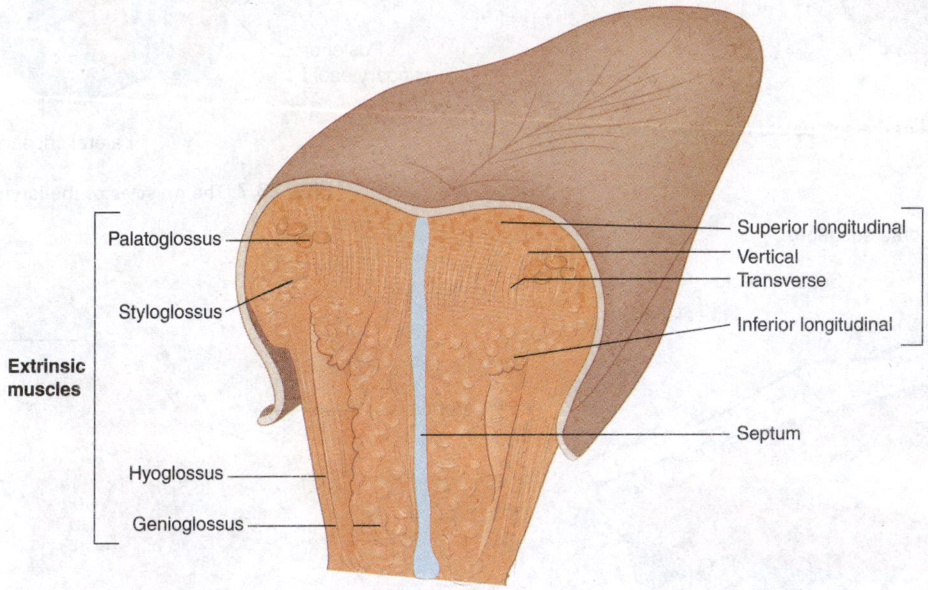

FIG. 26.3 Muscles of the tongue. (Source: Drake et al; Gray's Anatomy for students.)

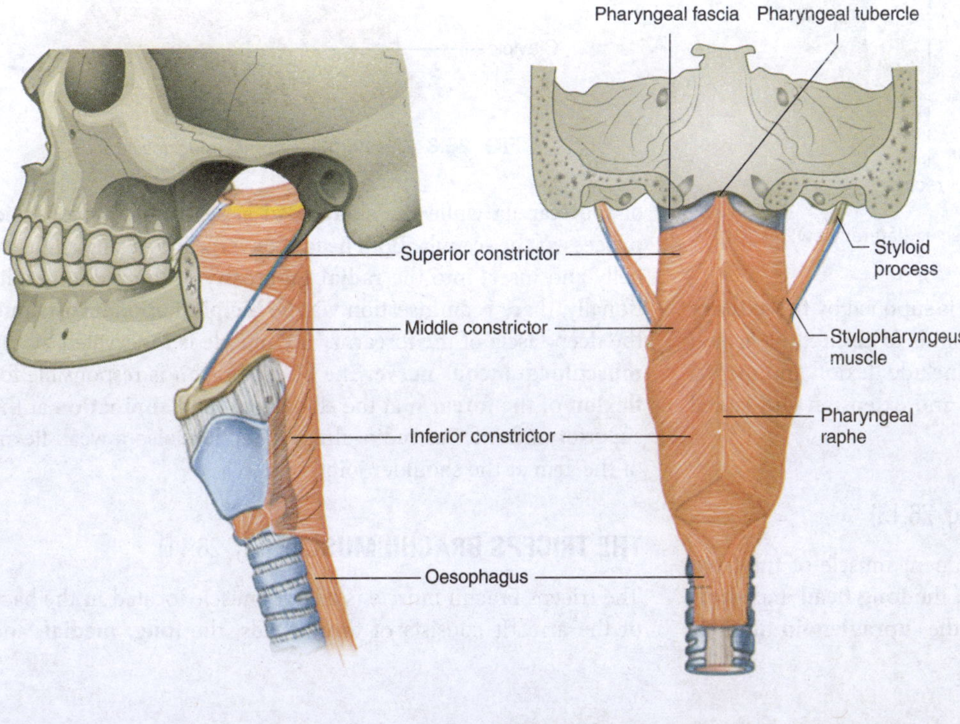

FIG. 26.4 Muscles of the pharynx.

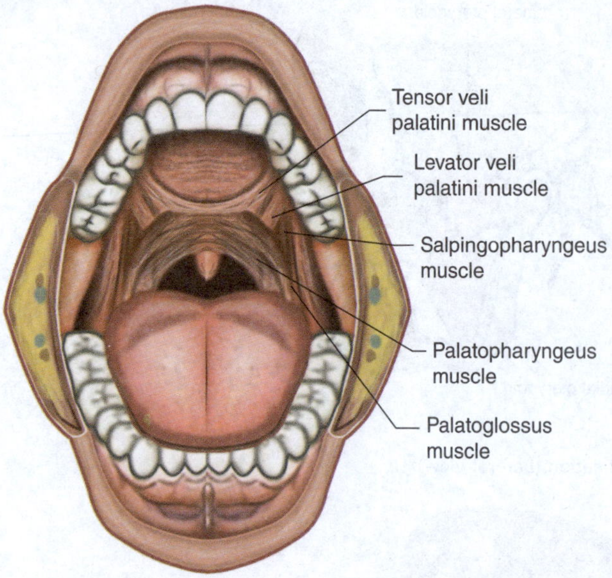

FIG. 26.5 Muscles of the soft palate (anterior view).

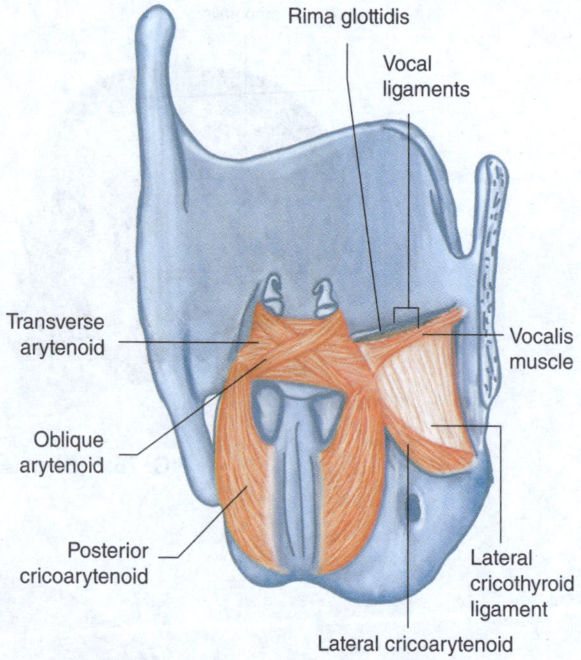

FIG. 26.7 The muscles of the larynx.

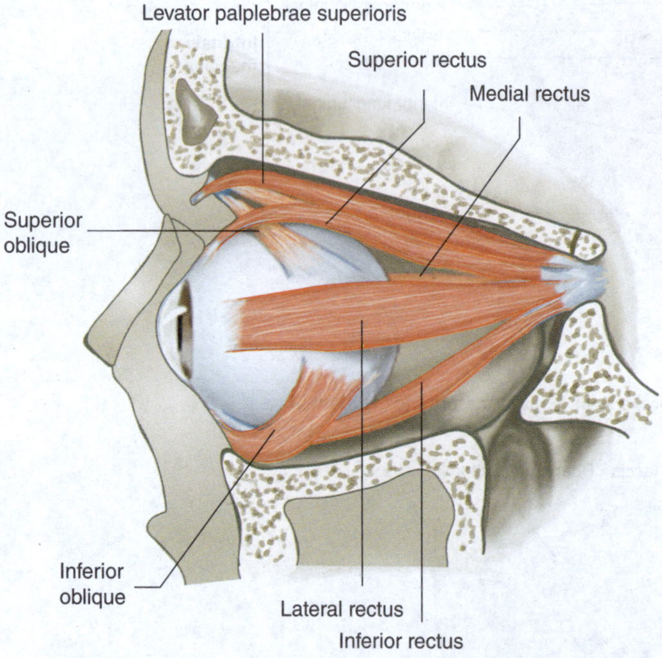

FIG. 26.6 The extraocular muscles (lateral view).

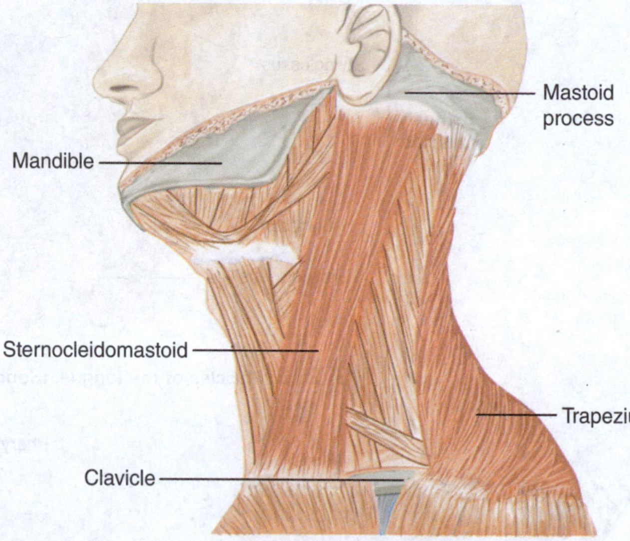

FIG. 26.8 The sternocleidomastoid muscle.

the middle of the shaft of the bone. It is supplied by the **axillary nerve**. The main function of the deltoid is to **abduct** the arm at the **shoulder joint**. Its other actions include flexion and medial rotation of the arm (anterior fibres), and extension and lateral rotation of the arm (posterior fibres).

THE BICEPS BRACHII MUSCLE (Fig. 26.13)

The biceps brachii muscle is a prominent muscle of the front of the arm with two heads of origin, the **long head** and **short head**. The long head originates from the **supraglenoid tubercle** of the scapula while the short head arises from the **coracoid process** of the scapula. Both heads converge into a single muscle belly and insert into the **radial tuberosity** of the radius. Additionally, there is an insertion via the **bicipital aponeurosis** into the deep fascia of the forearm. The muscle is innervated by the **musculocutaneous nerve.** The biceps brachii is responsible for **flexion** of the **forearm** at the elbow joint and **supination** at the superior and inferior radio-ulnar joints. It is also a weak flexor of the arm at the shoulder joint.

THE TRICEPS BRACHII MUSCLE (Fig. 26.11)

The triceps brachii muscle is a large muscle located in the back of the arm. It consists of three heads, the **long, medial**, and

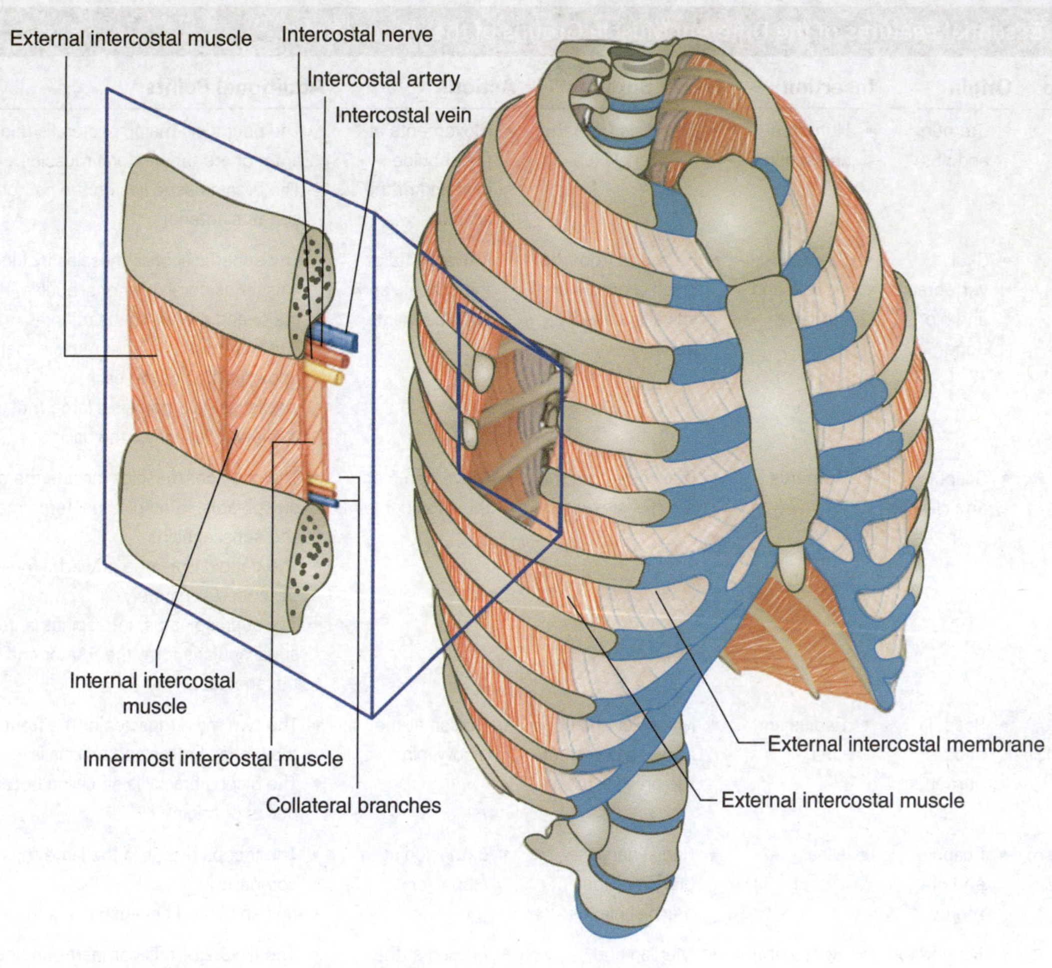

FIG. 26.9 The intercostal muscles.

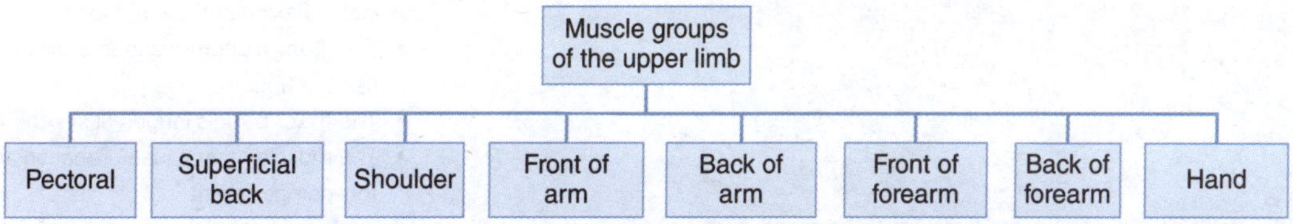

FIG. 26.10 Names of the different muscle groups of the upper limb.

lateral heads. The heads arise from the shaft of the **humerus** and **infraglenoid tubercle** of the **scapula**. All three heads converge to a common tendon that inserts onto the **olecranon** of the **ulna.** The triceps brachii is innervated by the **radial nerve.** The muscle is the main **extensor** of the forearm at the **elbow joint.**

THE THORACOABDOMINAL DIAPHRAGM (Fig. 26.17)

This is the musculoaponeurotic partition between the thorax and abdomen. Its peripheral part is muscular while the central part is tendinous. It arises from the **sternum, ribs** and **vertebrae**. From these origins, the muscle fibres converge to a **central tendon**. The main motor nerve supply to the muscle fibres of the diaphragm is the **phrenic nerve**. The diaphragm is the principal **muscle of inspiration.** It also helps to increase the intra-abdominal pressure when required. It contains **three major openings**, vena caval, oesophageal and aortic, which transmit the **inferior vena cava, oesophagus** and **abdominal aorta**, respectively.

APPLIED ANATOMY

- Damage to the facial nerve or strokes cause paralysis of the muscles of facial expression. A relatively common, usually self-limiting clinical condition causing this is **Bell palsy**.
- Spasm of the sternocleidomastoid muscle can cause **torticollis** in which the head is tilted to one side.

Table 26.2 Essential Features of the Different Muscle Groups of the Upper Limb

Muscle Group	Origin	Insertion	Nerve Supply	Actions	Additional Points
• Pectoral	• Sternum and ribs	• Humerus and scapula	• Branches from the brachial plexus	• Movements at the shoulder joint and of the scapula	• The pectoralis major, pectoralis minor and serratus anterior are the pectoral muscles • The breast tissue lies on the pectoralis major and serratus anterior
• Superficial back	• Skull, vertebrae and hip bone	• Scapula, clavicle and humerus	• Branches from the brachial plexus and spinal accessory nerve	• Movements of the scapula and shoulder joint	• The superficial back muscles include the trapezius, latissimus dorsi, levator scapulae, rhomboideus major and rhomboideus minor • The trapezius is a large muscle that covers the upper portion of the back • The latissimus dorsi is a large muscle that covers the lower portion of the back
• Shoulder (Figs 26.11 and 26.12)	• Scapula and clavicle	• Humerus	• Branches from the brachial plexus	• Movements at the shoulder joint	• The shoulder muscles include the deltoid, supraspinatus, infraspinatus, teres major, teres minor and subscapularis • The deltoid is a large powerful muscle that is described separately • The supraspinatus, infraspinatus, teres minor and subscapularis form the rotator cuff which stabilizes the shoulder joint
• Front of the arm (Fig. 26.13)	• Scapula and humerus	• Radius and ulna	• Musculocutaneous nerve, a branch of the brachial plexus	• Flexion at the elbow joint	• The two main muscles of the front of the arm are the biceps brachii and brachialis • The biceps brachii is so called because it has two heads of origin
• Back of the arm	• Scapula and humerus	• Ulna	• Radial nerve, a branch of the brachial plexus	• Extension at the elbow joint	• The triceps brachii is the large muscle of this compartment • It is so named because it has three heads of origin
• Front of the forearm (Fig. 26.14)	• Humerus, radius and ulna	• Bones of the hand	• Median and ulnar nerves, both branches of the brachial plexus	• Flexion at the wrist, metacarpophalangeal and interphalangeal joints	• The flexors of this compartment include the flexor carpi radialis, flexor carpi ulnaris, flexor digitorum superficialis, flexor digitorum profundus and flexor pollicis longus • The flexor carpi radialis and flexor carpi ulnaris cause flexion at the wrist joint • The flexor digitorum superficialis and profundus flex the fingers • The flexor pollicis longus flexes the thumb • The muscles that cause pronation are also seen in this compartment
• Back of the forearm (Fig. 26.15)	• Humerus, radius and ulna	• Bones of the hand	• Radial nerve, a branch of the brachial plexus	• Extension at the wrist, metacarpophalangeal and interphalangeal joints	• The extensors of this compartment include the extensor digitorum, extensor carpi ulnaris, extensor carpi radialis longus and brevis, extensor pollicis longus and brevis • The extensor carpi ulnaris, extensor carpi radialis longus and brevis cause extension at the wrist joint • The extensor digitorum extends the fingers • The extensor pollicis longus and brevis extend the thumb • The supinator muscle, having the same function as its name suggests, is seen in this compartment
• The hand (Fig. 26.16)	• Carpal and metacarpal bones	• Phalanges	• Median and ulnar nerves, both branches of the brachial plexus	• Fine movements of the thumb and other digits	• The muscles of the hand are the thenar muscles, hypothenar muscles, lumbricals and interossei • The thenar and hypothenar muscles move the thumb and little finger, respectively • The lumbricals and interossei are responsible for fine movements of the other digits

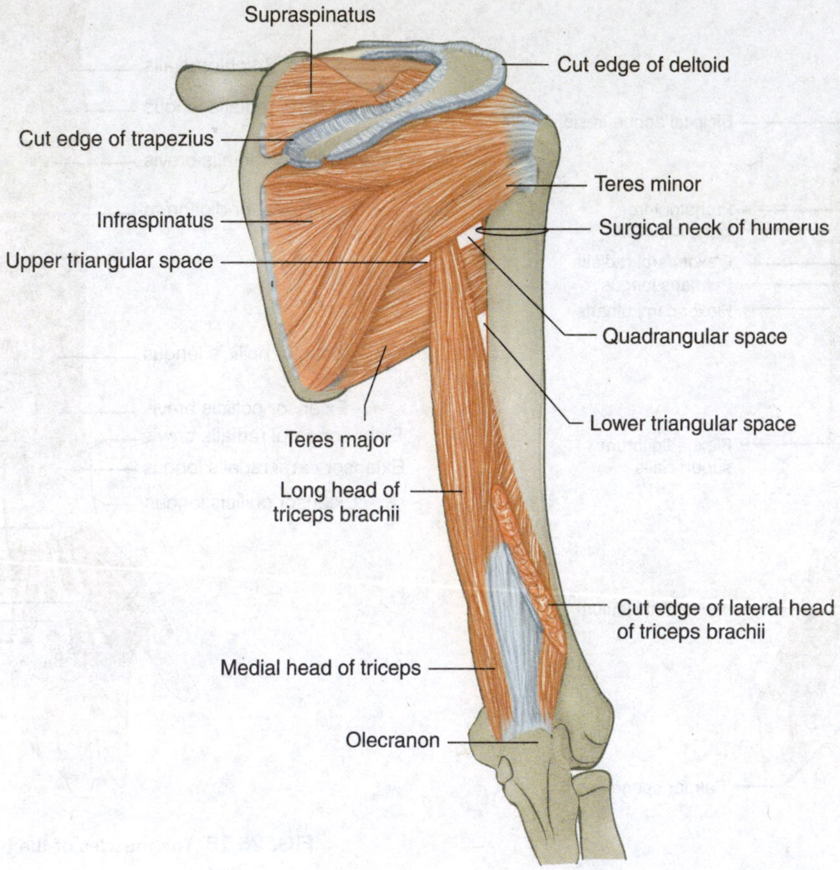

FIG. 26.11 The muscles of the shoulder region and back of the arm (posterior view).

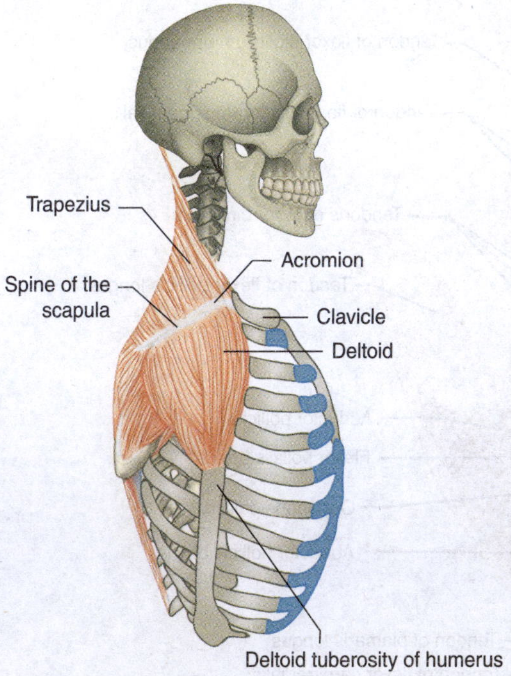

FIG. 26.12 The deltoid muscle.

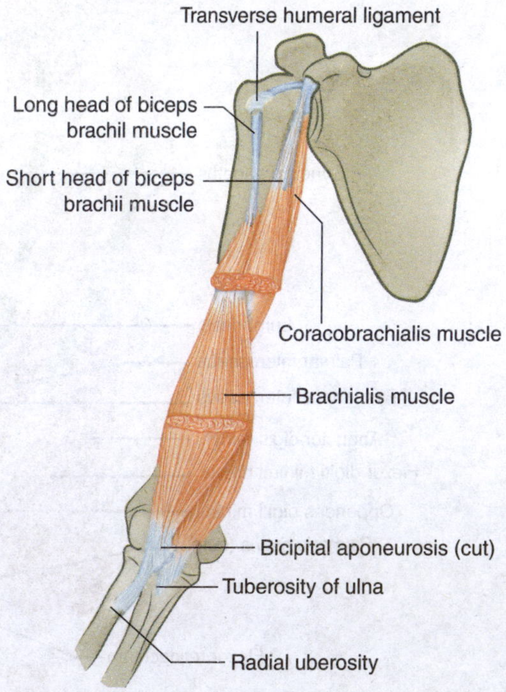

FIG. 26.13 The muscles of the front of the arm.

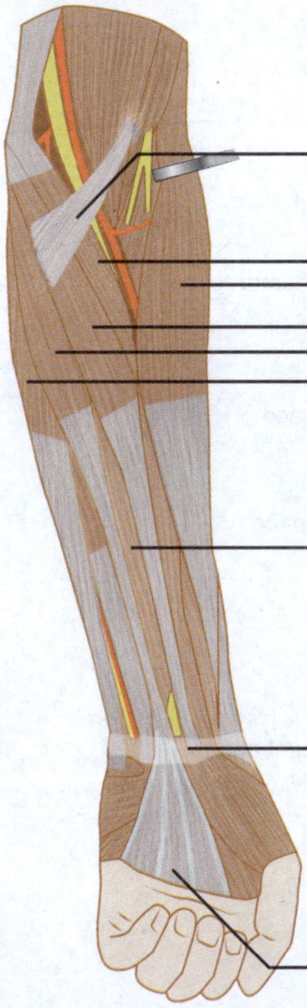

FIG. 26.14 The muscles of the front of the forearm.

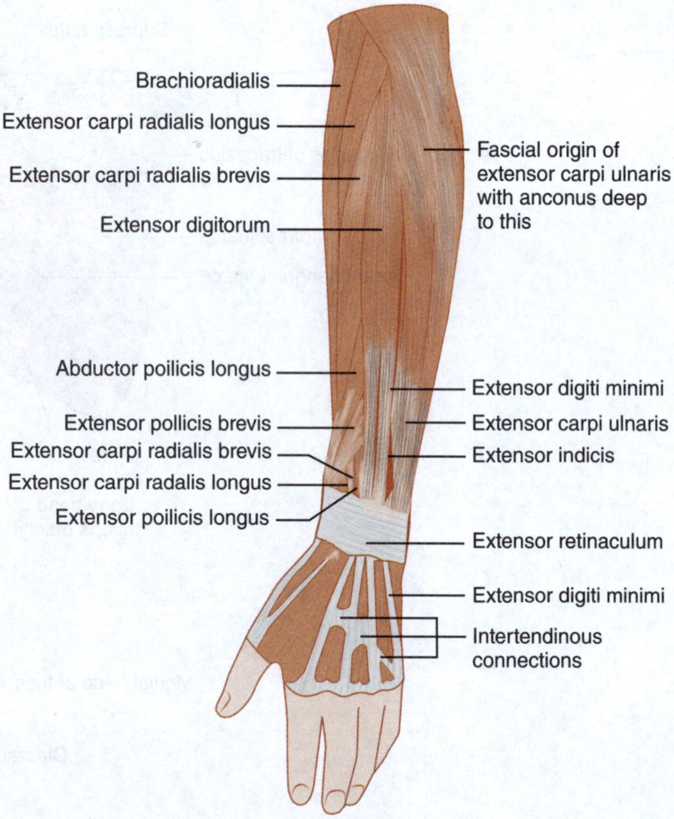

FIG. 26.15 The muscles of the back of the forearm.

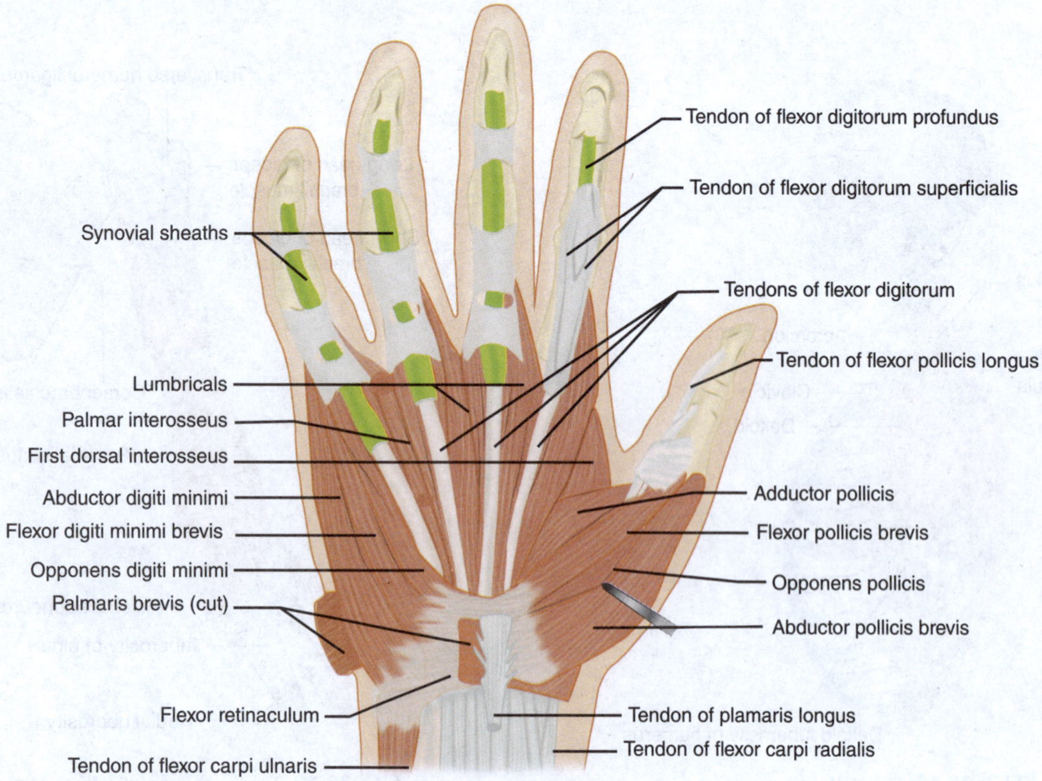

FIG. 26.16 The muscles of the hand (right hand, anterior or palmar view).

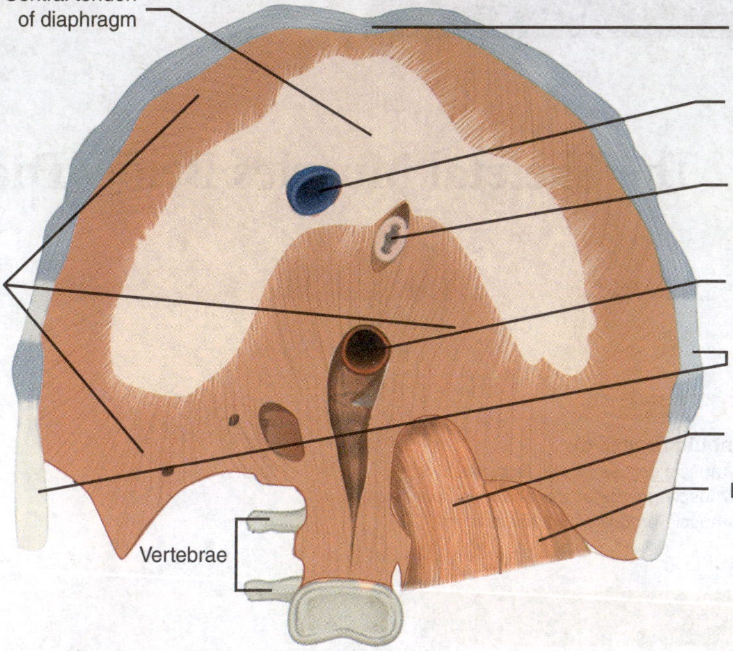

FIG. 26.17 The thoracoabdominal diaphragm (inferior view).

- Weakness or paralysis of the extraocular muscles can cause blurring of vision or **diplopia** and malalignment of axes of the eye or **strabismus**.
- The muscles of larynx can be paralysed as a complication of thyroid surgeries or carcinomas. This causes **hoarseness** of voice.
- One of the commonest sites for administering **intramuscular injections** is the deltoid muscle. Injections are given in the lower half of the muscle to avoid injury to the axillary nerve that supplies it.
- The radial nerve can be injured in the arm, as it is in close contact with the humerus in this location. This causes inability to extend the hand at the wrist joint, due to paralysis of the muscles of the back of the forearm, leading to a clinical condition called '**wrist drop**'.
- The ulnar nerve is more likely to be injured at the level of the medial epicondyle of the humerus, as they are in close contact here. This causes paralysis of the hypothenar muscles and other small muscles of the hand leading to '**clawing**' of the fourth and fifth digits.
- The median nerve can be compressed as it passes from the wrist to the hand. This leads to paralysis of the thenar muscles and is called '**carpal tunnel syndrome**'.
- High **spinal cord injuries** can affect the motor nerve supply to the diaphragm. This can lead to difficulty in breathing and require ventilator support for the patient.

APPLICATIONS IN NURSING

- Nurses will often have to administer **intramuscular injections** into the deltoid muscle in older children and adults. The injection is given into the deltoid muscle about 3–5 cm below the acromion process.

SUMMARY

- The muscles of the head and neck are arranged in the following groups: (1) face and scalp; (2) mastication; (3) tongue; (4) pharynx and soft palate; (5) extraocular; (6) middle ear; (7) larynx; (8) floor of the mouth; and (9) infrahyoid.
- The above-mentioned muscles are supplied by the cranial nerves.
- Their actions include the control of dimensions of orifices, chewing, deglutition, movements of the eyeball and speech.
- The sternocleidomastoid is an important muscle in the neck that divides it into anterior and posterior triangles.
- The external intercostal, internal intercostal and innermost intercostal muscles are seen in the intercostal spaces between adjacent ribs.
- They cause movements of the ribs, thus helping in inspiration and expiration.
- The muscles of the upper limb are arranged in the following groups: (1) pectoral; (2) superficial back; (3) shoulder; (4) front of arm; (5) back of arm; (6) front of forearm; (7) back of forearm; and (8) hand.
- Most of the above-mentioned muscles are supplied by branches from the brachial plexus.
- The muscles cause gross movements at the more proximal joints such as the shoulder and elbow joints, as well as finer movements at the joints of the hand.
- The deltoid is an important muscle of the shoulder region which is often used for administering intramuscular injections.
- The muscle of the thoracoabdominal diaphragm arises from the vertebrae, sternum and ribs and is inserted into the central tendon.
- It is supplied by the phrenic nerve.

CHAPTER 27

The Skeletal Muscles Below Diaphragm

SPECIFIC LEARNING OBJECTIVES

At the end of this chapter, the student should be able to:

- Describe the gross anatomy of the major muscle groups of the abdominal wall.
- Describe the gross anatomy of the major muscle groups of the pelvis and perineum.
- Describe the gross anatomy of the major muscle groups of the lower limb.

GLOSSARY OF TERMS

- **Muscles of the anterior abdominal wall:** muscles that are present on the front and sides of the abdominal wall
- **Rectus sheath:** connective tissue covering of the rectus abdominis muscle formed by the aponeuroses of the other three muscles of the anterior abdominal wall
- **Linea alba:** midline structure formed by the meeting of the aponeuroses of the three muscles of the anterior abdominal wall
- **Muscles of the posterior abdominal wall:** muscles that are present behind the viscera and peritoneal cavity
- **Muscles of the pelvis:** muscles that line the walls of the pelvis and those that separate the pelvic cavity and perineum
- **Pelvic diaphragm:** muscular partition between the pelvis and perineum formed mainly by the levator ani muscle
- **Muscles of the perineum:** muscles below the pelvis in close relation to the urethra, vagina and anal canal
- **Perineal body:** fibromuscular node responsible for maintaining structural stability into which the perineal muscles are attached
- **Gluteal muscles:** muscles located in the region above the back of the thigh
- **Ligamentum patellae:** the tendon of insertion of the quadriceps femoris muscle in which the patella is located
- **Achilles tendon:** the combined tendon of insertion of the gastrocnemius and soleus muscles
- **Gluteus maximus:** a large muscle of the gluteal region into which intramuscular injections are commonly given

INTRODUCTION

This chapter will focus on the muscles of the abdominal wall, pelvis and lower limbs. The main functions of the muscles of the abdominal wall and pelvis are to provide flexible supports to the viscera and control changes in pressure within these cavities. The lower limb muscles are arranged in a similar pattern to the muscles of the upper limb but are considerably modified as they serve the functions of locomotion and maintaining posture.

MUSCLES OF THE ABDOMINAL WALL

Anterior Abdominal Wall (Fig. 27.1)

The muscles of the abdominal wall can be divided into those of the anterior abdominal wall and posterior abdominal wall. The muscles of the anterior abdominal wall are arranged in the form of three layers on each side. From outside to inside, the muscles are the **external oblique, internal oblique** and **transversus abdominis**. These muscles extend from the **ribs** and **hip bone** towards the midline. As they approach the midline, they form aponeuroses which cover another muscle called the **rectus abdominis**. This is called the **rectus sheath**. The aponeuroses from both sides meet in the midline at the **linea alba**.

The rectus abdominis is a vertically placed muscle extending from the **pubis** of the **hip bone** to the **costal cartilages** above. All the muscles are supplied by the **lower intercostal nerves**. These muscles provide a flexible **protective covering** for the abdominal viscera. They also help to **increase** the **intra-abdominal pressure** when the need arises such as during micturition, defecation and parturition. Additionally, they cause **flexion** of the **trunk** when they contract.

Posterior Abdominal Wall (Fig. 27.2)

The muscles of the posterior abdominal wall form the posterior relations of the retroperitoneal contents of the abdomen. The main muscles are the **psoas major**, **quadratus lumborum** and **iliacus**. The **psoas major** arises from the **lumbar vertebrae** and extends to the upper end of the **femur**. It is supplied by branches of the **lumbar plexus**. Along with the iliacus, it causes **flexion** of the **thigh** at the hip joint. The **quadratus lumborum** lies

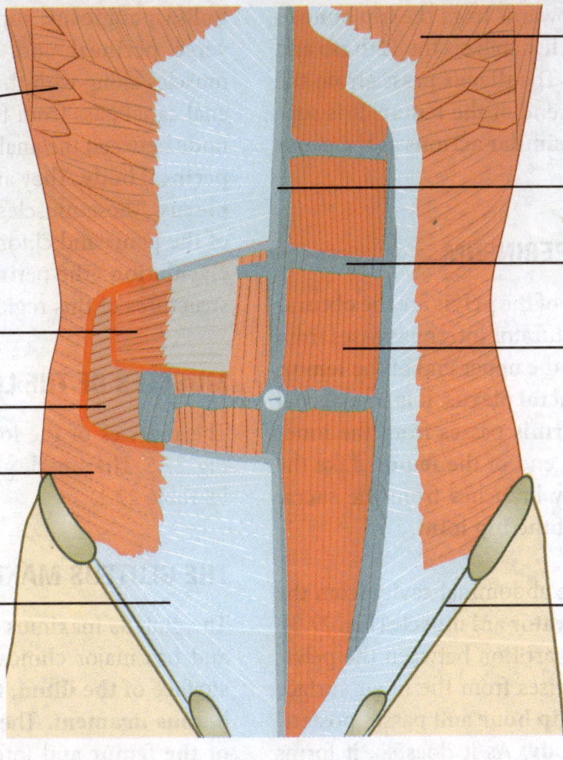

FIG. 27.1 The muscles of the anterior abdominal wall.

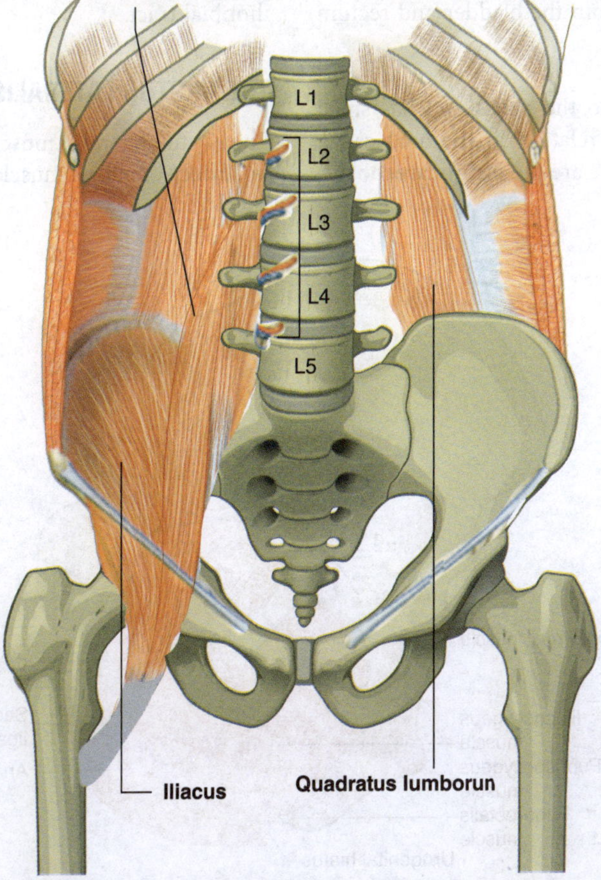

FIG. 27.2 The muscles of the posterior abdominal wall.

lateral to the psoas major passing upwards from the **hip bone** to the **lumbar vertebrae** and **12th rib**. It stabilizes the 12th rib and causes lateral bending of the trunk. The **iliacus** passes from the **ilium** of the **hip bone** to the upper end of the **femur**. It is supplied by the **femoral nerve** and has **similar actions** as the **psoas major**.

MUSCLES OF THE PELVIS AND PERINEUM

The main muscles that line the **walls** of the **pelvis** are the **obturator internus** and **piriformis**. The obturator internus passes from the inner surface of the **hip bone** to the upper end of the **femur**. It is supplied by a branch from the **sacral plexus**. It is an **external rotator** of the hip joint. The **piriformis** passes from the inner surface of the **sacrum** to the upper end of the **femur**. Like the obturator internus, it is supplied by branches from the **sacral plexus** and is an **external rotator** of the **hip joint**.

The **pelvic diaphragm** separates the abdominal cavity from the pelvic cavity and is formed by the **levator ani muscle** (Fig. 27.3). This is a thin, sheet-like muscular partition between the pelvic cavity and perineum. The muscle arises from the inner surface of the **pubic** and **iliac parts** of the **hip bone** and passes posteriorly to the **coccyx** and **perineal body**. As it does so, it forms muscular **slings** around the urethra, vagina and rectum. It is supplied by branches from the **sacral plexus**. The main function of the levator ani is to provide **support** for the **pelvic viscera**, preventing them from prolapsing downwards. Additionally, it controls the **passage** of **contents** from the bladder and rectum via the slings it forms around them.

The **perineum** is located inferior to the pelvis and has small muscles that are situated in close relation to the anal canal, vagina and urethra (Fig. 27.4). These are the **ischiocavernosus, bulbospongiosus, superficial transverse perineal, deep transverse perineal** and **sphincter urethrae muscles**. All these muscles along with the levator ani and external sphincter of the anal canal pass from the **bones** of the **pelvis** to a fibromuscular node between the anal canal and urogenital apparatus called the **perineal body**. They are all supplied by branches from the **sacral plexus**. These muscles surround the urethra and erectile tissue of the penis and clitoris and control **micturition, erection** and **ejaculation**. The perineal body serves to **stabilize** all the other structures of this region.

MUSCLES OF THE LOWER LIMB

The muscles of the lower limb are described as mentioned in Fig. 27.5. The muscle groups mentioned in Fig. 27.5 are described in Table 27.1.

THE GLUTEUS MAXIMUS MUSCLE (Fig. 27.7)

The gluteus maximus is one of the largest muscles in the body and has major clinical importance. It arises from the **gluteal surface of the ilium, the sacrum, the coccyx and the sacrotuberous ligament**. The insertion is onto the **gluteal tuberosity of the femur** and into the deep fascia of the thigh (**iliotibial tract**). It is supplied by the **inferior gluteal nerve**. The muscle is a **powerful extensor** of the thigh at the **hip joint**. Its other actions include lateral rotation of the thigh and maintenance of extension at the knee joint through its insertion into the iliotibial tract.

THE VASTUS LATERALIS MUSCLE (FIG. 27.8)

The vastus lateralis muscle is one of the components of the quadriceps femoris muscle and is situated on the lateral aspect

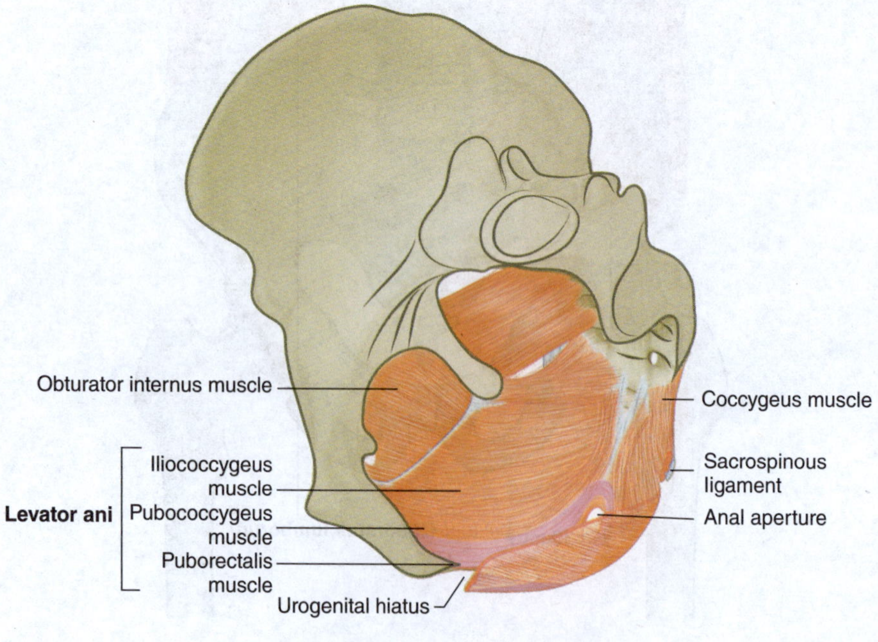

FIG. 27.3 The levator ani muscle.

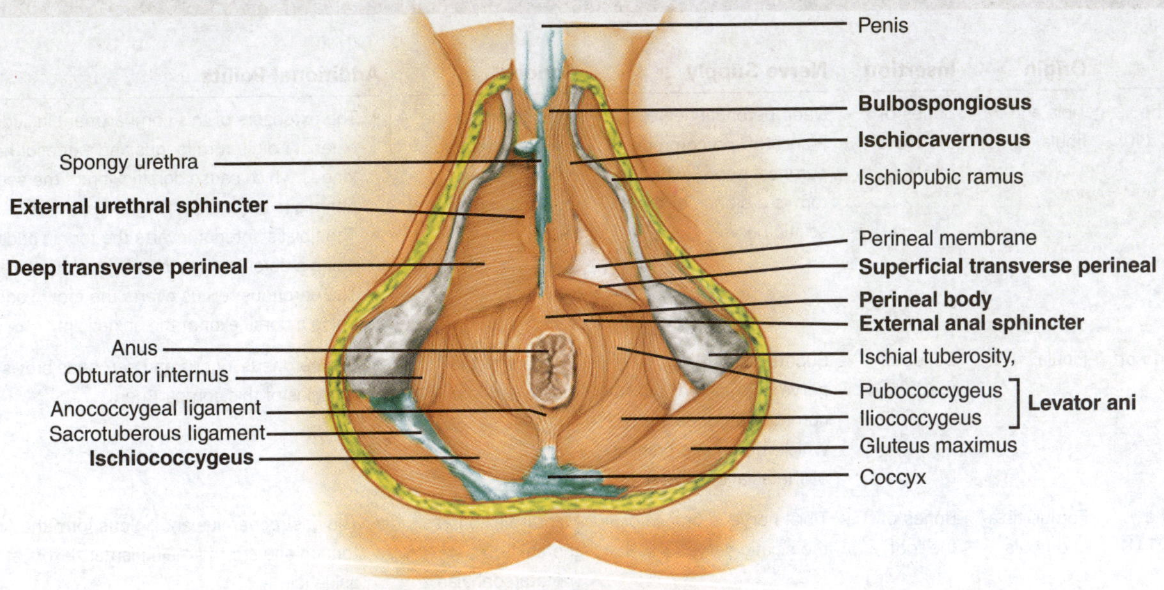

FIG. 27.4 Muscles of the perineum (inferior view).

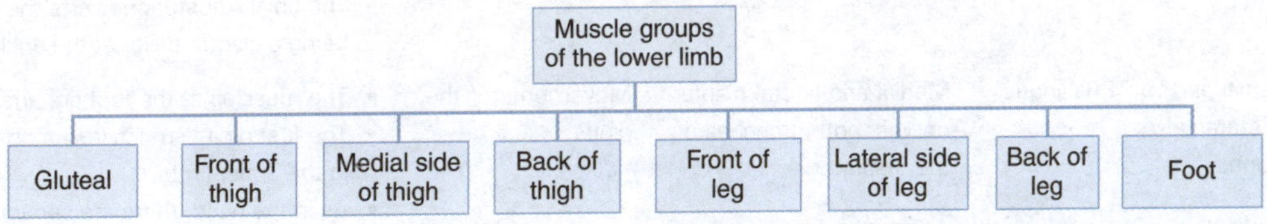

FIG. 27.5 Names of the different muscle groups of the lower limb.

Table 27.1 Essential Features of the Different Muscle Groups of the Lower Limb

Muscle Group	Origin	Insertion	Nerve Supply	Actions	Additional Points
Gluteal (Figs 27.6 and 27.7)	Hip bone	Upper end of femur	Branches from the sacral plexus	Movements at the hip joint	• The gluteus maximus, gluteus medius and gluteus minimus are the large gluteal muscles • The gluteus maximus is described in more detail in this chapter • The gluteus medius and minimus are essential for maintaining a normal gait
Front of the thigh (Fig. 27.8)	Hip bone and femur	Tibia and patella	Branches from the femoral nerve, a branch of the lumbar plexus	Extension at the knee joint	• The quadriceps femoris is the main muscle of this compartment • It is composed of four muscles, vastus lateralis, vastus intermedius, vastus medialis and rectus femoris • The patella is a sesamoid bone located within the tendon of this muscle, called the ligamentum patellae
Medial side of the thigh	Hip bone	Femur	Branches from the obturator nerve, a branch of the lumber plexus	Adduction at the hip joint	• The adductor longus, adductor brevis and adductor magnus are the three large muscles of this compartment
Back of the thigh (Fig. 27.9)	Hip bone	Tibia and fibula	Sciatic nerve, a branch of the sacral plexus	Extension at the hip joint and flexion at the knee joint	• The muscles of this compartment are called the hamstring muscles • The hamstring muscles include the semimembranosus, semitendinosus and biceps femoris

Continued

Table 27.1 Essential Features of the Different Muscle Groups of the Lower Limb—cont'd

Muscle Group	Origin	Insertion	Nerve Supply	Actions	Additional Points
Front of the leg (Fig. 27.10)	Tibia and fibula	Bones of the foot	Deep peroneal nerve, a branch of the common peroneal nerve, which in turn is a branch of the sciatic nerve	Dorsiflexion at the ankle, metatarso-phalangeal and interphalangeal joints	• The extensors of this compartment include the extensor digitorum longus and extensor hallucis longus which cause dorsiflexion of the second to fifth digits and the first digit, respectively • The tibialis anterior inverts the foot in addition to being a dorsiflexor at the ankle joint • The peroneus tertius everts the foot in addition to being a dorsiflexor at the ankle joint
Lateral side of the leg	Fibula	Bones of the foot	Superficial peroneal nerve, a branch of the common peroneal nerve, which in turn is a branch of the sciatic nerve	Evertors of the foot	• The peroneus longus and peroneus brevis are muscles of this compartment
Back of the leg (Fig. 27.11)	Femur, tibia and fibula	Bones of the foot	Tibial nerve, a branch of the sciatic nerve	Plantar flexion at the ankle, metatarsophalangeal and interphalangeal joints	• The gastrocnemius and soleus form the Achilles tendon and are the main plantar flexors at the ankle joint • The flexor digitorum longus and flexor hallucis longus cause plantar flexion of the second to fifth digits and the first digit, respectively • The tibialis posterior inverts the foot in addition to being a plantar flexor at the ankle joint
The foot (Fig. 27.12)	Tarsal and metatarsal bones	Phalanges	Medial and lateral plantar nerves, both branches of the tibial nerve	Movements of the digits	• The muscles of the foot are arranged in four layers • The first digit is much less mobile than the thumb in the upper limb • As in the hand, there are separate muscles for the movements of the first and fifth digits • The lumbricals and interossei are responsible for fine movements of the other digits

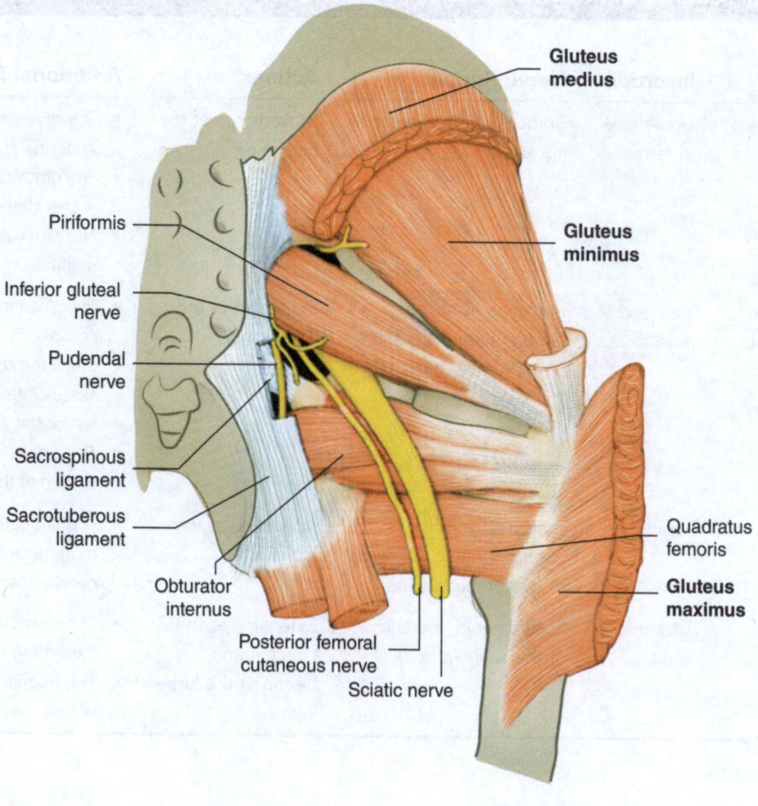

FIG. 27.6 Muscles of the gluteal region.

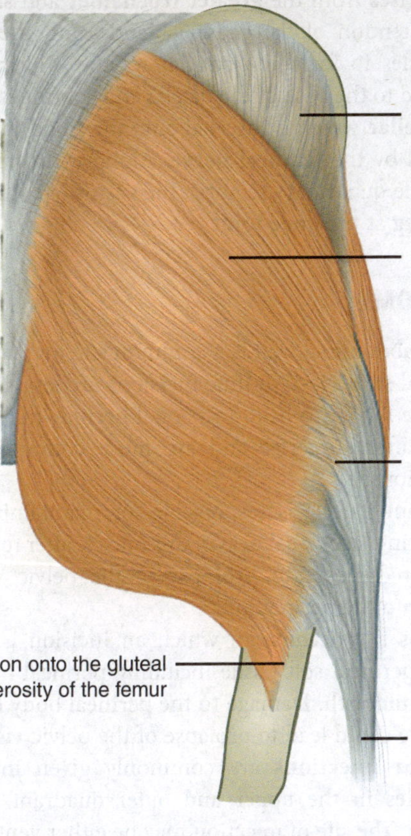

FIG. 27.7 The gluteus maximus muscle.

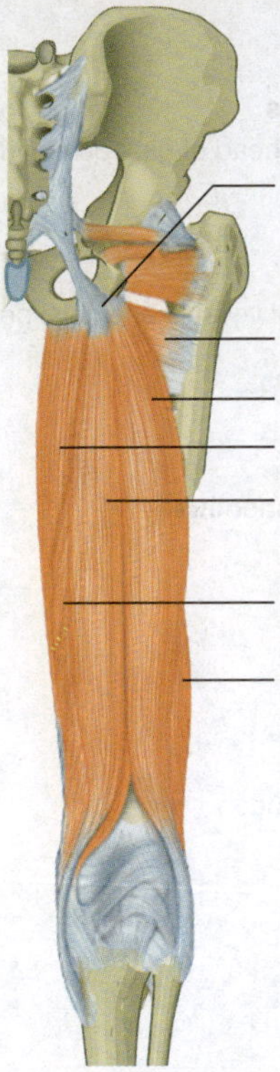

FIG. 27.9 Muscles of the back of the thigh.

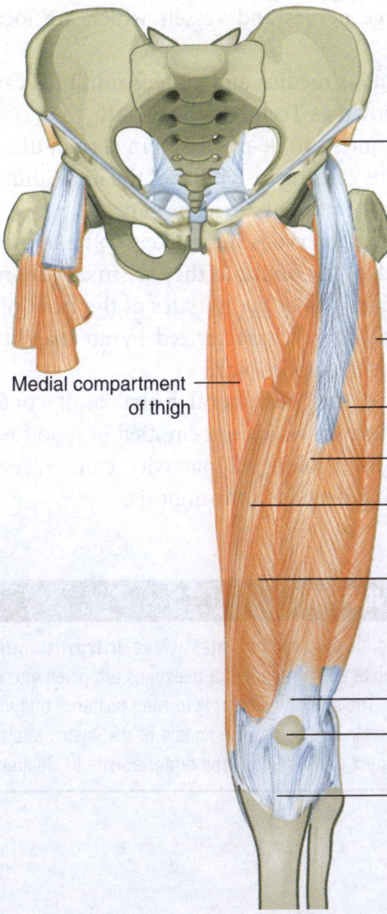

FIG. 27.8 Muscles of the front of the thigh.

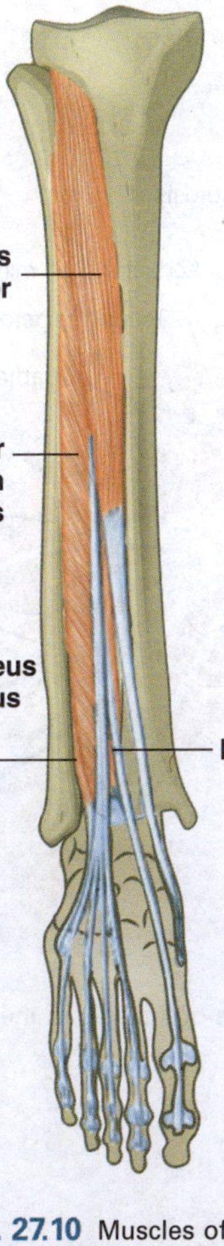

FIG. 27.10 Muscles of the front of the leg.

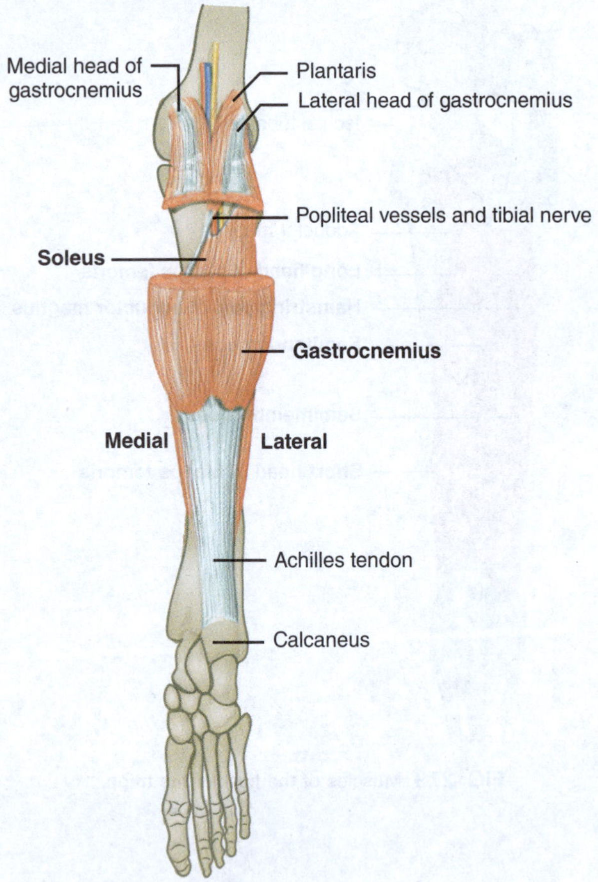

FIG. 27.11 Muscles of the back of the leg.

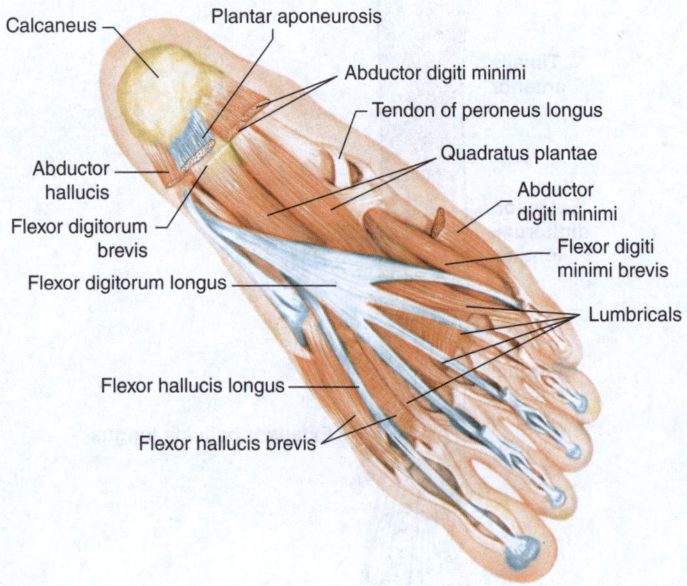

FIG. 27.12 Muscles of the sole of the foot.

of the thigh. It arises from the **greater trochanter** and **shaft** of the **femur**. The tendon of the muscle blends with the other quadriceps muscles to form the patellar tendon. The patellar tendon is attached to the base of the patella and continues as the **ligamentum patellae** which is inserted onto the **tibial tuberosity**. It is supplied by the **femoral nerve**. Along with the other components of the quadriceps femoris, the vastus lateralis is an **extensor** of the leg at the **knee joint**.

APPLIED ANATOMY

- The anterior abdominal wall is a common site for **incisions** for abdominal surgeries. Midline incisions are less likely to bleed but take longer to heal. Incisional hernias can potentially occur after surgeries and are more common after midline incisions.
- The levator ani muscle is responsible for maintaining the pelvic viscera in place. Weakness of this muscle after repeated childbirths predisposes to **prolapse** of the pelvic viscera downwards into the perineum.
- **Episiotomy** is a procedure in which an incision is made through the perineal soft tissue including perineal muscles to facilitate childbirth. Damage to the perineal body during this procedure could lead to prolapse of the pelvic viscera.
- **Intramuscular injections** are commonly given into the gluteal muscles in the upper and outer quadrant of the gluteal region. The site of injection may be either ventrogluteal or dorsogluteal into the gluteus medius and gluteus maximus, respectively. These sites are chosen to avoid damage to the large nerves and vessels which are located more medially.
- Paralysis of the gluteus medius and gluteus minimus causes a waddling gait known as **Trendelenburg gait**.
- The quadriceps femoris can be paralysed in certain diseases such as poliomyelitis causing instability of the knee joint and an abnormal gait called the **quadriceps gait**.
- The common peroneal nerve is more likely to be injured at the level of the neck of the fibula, as they are in close contact here. This causes paralysis of the muscles of the front of the leg leading to '**foot drop**' characterized by an inability to dorsiflex the foot at the ankle joint.
- The soleus is called the '**peripheral heart**' as it contains valveless venous plexuses which are emptied of blood when the soleus contracts. Prolonged inactivity can cause this blood to clot causing deep vein thrombosis.

APPLICATIONS IN NURSING

- The gluteal region and thigh are other sites where **intramuscular injections** are administered. Intramuscular injections are given into the gluteus medius muscle. The site of injection is located posterior and inferior to the anterior superior iliac spine. The middle of the vastus lateralis muscle on the outer aspect of the thigh is the preferred site in children.

SUMMARY

- The muscles of the abdominal wall can be divided into those of the anterior and posterior abdominal wall.
- The muscles of the anterior abdominal wall are the external oblique, internal oblique, transversus abdominis and rectus abdominis.
- Their actions include protection of the viscera, control of the intra-abdominal pressure and flexion of the trunk.
- They are supplied by the lower intercostal nerves.
- The muscles of the posterior abdominal wall are situated retroperitoneally.
- The muscles that line the pelvic walls are the obturator internus and piriformis.
- The levator ani is the major muscle that forms the pelvic diaphragm, separating the pelvic cavity from the perineum.
- The muscles of the perineum are located in relation to the urethra, vagina and anal canal and are attached to the perineal body.
- The muscles of the lower limb are arranged in the following groups: (1) gluteal; (2) front of the thigh; (3) medial side of the thigh; (4) back of the thigh; (5) front of the leg; (6) lateral side of the leg; (7) back of the leg; and (8) foot.
- Most of the above-mentioned muscles are supplied by branches from the sacral plexus.
- The muscles are responsible for locomotion and maintaining posture.
- The gluteus maximus is an important muscle of the gluteal region which is often used for administering intramuscular injections.

8

SECTION

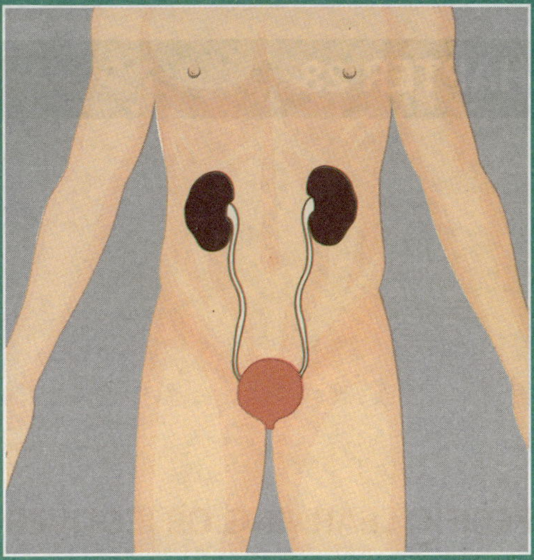

The Excretory System

Section Outline

CHAPTER 28

The Kidneys

SPECIFIC LEARNING OBJECTIVES

At the end of this chapter, the student should be able to:

- Name the structures that constitute the excretory system.
- Describe the functions of each part of the excretory system.
- Describe the gross anatomy, microstructure and applied anatomy of the kidney.

GLOSSARY OF TERMS

- **Hilum:** region of the kidney along its medial border where structures enter or leave the kidney
- **Renal sinus:** cavity within the kidney that communicates with the exterior through the hilum
- **Pyramids:** well-defined areas in the medulla that drain into the renal sinus through the papillae
- **Papillae:** apices of the pyramids where they open into the renal sinus
- **Minor calyces:** relatively small spaces lined by renal fascia into which papillae open
- **Major calyces:** relatively large spaces formed by convergence of the minor calyces
- **Pelvis of ureter:** funnel-shaped, dilated origin of the ureter formed by convergence of the major calyces
- **Cortex:** peripheral darker region of the substance of the kidney
- **Medulla:** central lighter region of the substance of the kidney
- **Cortical arch:** cap of cortex around the base of a pyramid
- **Column:** extension of the cortex between adjacent pyramids
- **Medullary ray:** extension of the medulla into the cortex
- **Uriniferous tubules:** tubules formed by nephrons and collecting ducts
- **Nephron:** structural and functional unit of the kidney consisting of the renal corpuscle and renal tubule
- **Renal corpuscle:** filtration unit of the kidney containing the glomerulus and Bowman's capsule
- **Renal tubule:** tubule responsible for the selective reabsorption and concentration of the urine, consisting of a proximal tubule, loop of Henle and distal tubule
- **Mesangial cells:** connective tissue cells of the kidney
- **Juxtaglomerular apparatus:** a group of structures that is responsible for maintaining blood pressure by regulating blood flow through the glomerulus

INTRODUCTION

The excretory or urinary system consists of the kidneys, ureters, urinary bladder and urethra (Fig. 28.1). Urine is produced in the kidney as an ultrafiltrate of blood. It then passes through the ureters to the urinary bladder, where it is stored till it is ready to be emptied through the urethra. The functions of the kidneys include removal of waste products, regulation of blood pressure and volume, regulation of electrolyte and pH levels, production of hormones such as erythropoietin, renin and prostaglandins and activation of vitamin D3. While the kidneys are the primary excretory organs, other organs such as the liver (excretes bile pigments), sweat glands and lungs also function as excretory organs.

THE KIDNEYS

The kidneys are situated **retroperitoneally**, by the side of the vertebral column and below the diaphragm (Fig. 28.2). They are **bean shaped** with their **hila** directed medially. They **extend** from the 12th thoracic to the 3rd lumbar vertebra. The kidneys **measure** around 11 cm in length, 6 cm in breadth and 3 cm in thickness. They **weigh** about 150–170 g in males and 130–140 g in females. The right kidney is slightly lower than the left because of the presence of the liver on that side. The kidneys move around an inch with respiration due to their subdiaphragmatic location. The **position** of the kidneys is maintained by the pressure exerted by neighbouring viscera, tone of the abdominal muscles, disposition of renal fascia, distribution of renal fat and pedicles of the kidney attached to the hilum containing the renal vessels and pelvis of the ureter.

The kidney has four **coverings**, namely the **fibrous capsule** (true capsule), **perinephric fat**, **renal fascia** (false capsule or fascia of Gerota) and **paranephric fat** (Fig. 28.3). The true capsule is a condensation of fibrous stroma that covers the entire organ. The perinephric fat occupies the interval between the fibrous capsule

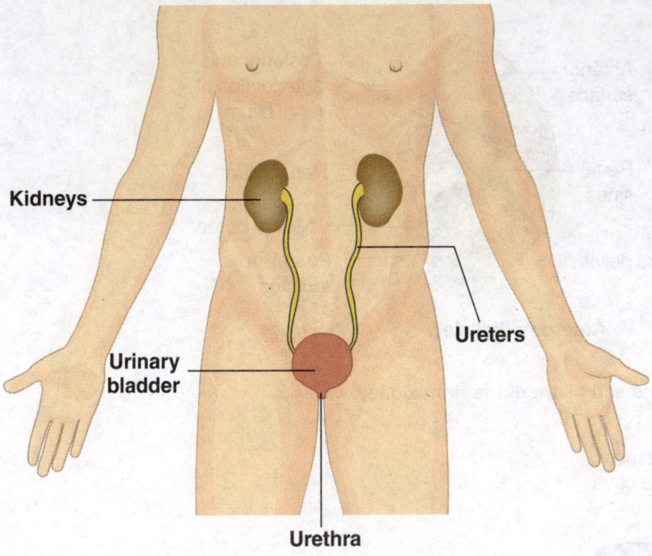

FIG. 28.1 The parts of the excretory system.

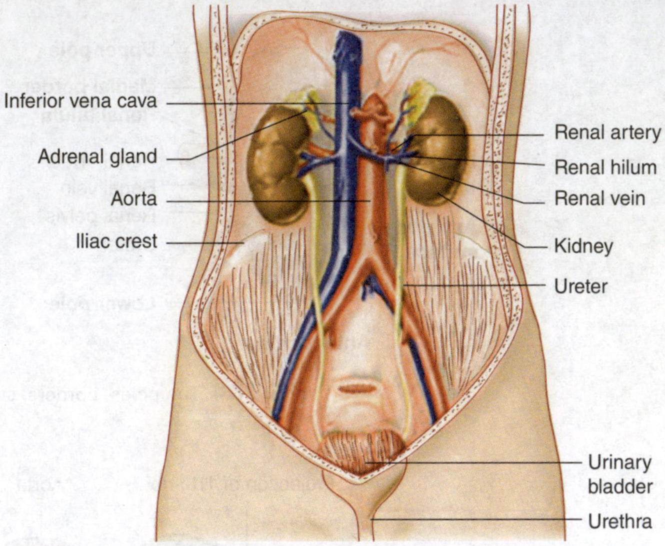

FIG. 28.2 The location and orientation of the kidneys.

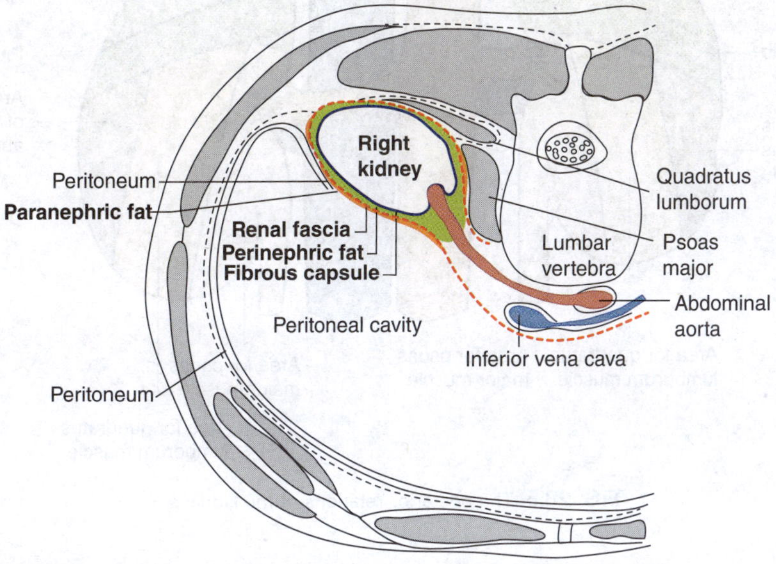

FIG. 28.3 The coverings of the kidney as seen on a horizontal section of the abdomen.

and renal fascia. The renal fascia has both anterior and posterior layers which fuse at the lateral borders of the kidneys. Medially, the renal fascia is continuous with that of the opposite side after passing anterior to the aorta and inferior vena cava. Superiorly it covers the upper pole and splits to enclose the suprarenal gland. Inferiorly the two layers do not fuse and merge with the extraperitoneal tissue of the iliac fossa. The paranephric fat occupies the interval between the renal fascia and surrounding tissues and is abundant on the posterior surface of the lower part of the kidneys.

The kidneys have two ends or **poles**, upper and lower (Fig. 28.4). The position of the kidneys is such that the upper poles are closer to the midline than the lower poles. The convex lateral and concave medial **borders** separate anterior and posterior **surfaces**. Because the posterior surface rests on the firm posterior abdominal wall, it is less convex than the anterior surface. The medial border presents a central concavity known as the **hilum**. The hilum lies at the level of the transpyloric plane which passes through the lower border of L1 vertebra. The structures passing through the hilum from before backwards are the renal vein, renal artery, pelvis of ureter, lymphatics, nerves and perinephric fat.

While the posterior **relations** of the kidneys are similar, the anterior relations differ considerably (Fig. 28.5). **Posteriorly**, the kidneys lie on the diaphragm near their upper poles. As the left kidney is located higher up, it is related to the 11th and 12th ribs, whereas the right kidney is related only to the 12th rib. From medial to lateral, both kidneys are related to the psoas major, quadratus lumborum and transversus abdominis which are muscles of the posterior and lateral abdominal wall. The subcostal nerve and branches of the lumbar plexus that lie on these

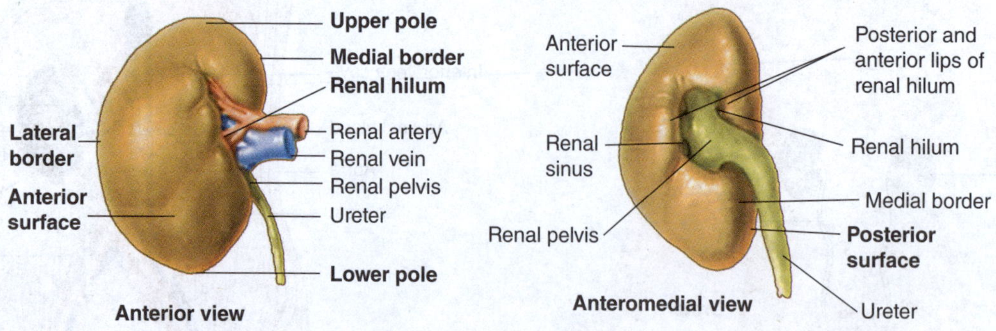

FIG. 28.4 The poles, borders, surfaces and hilum of the right kidney.

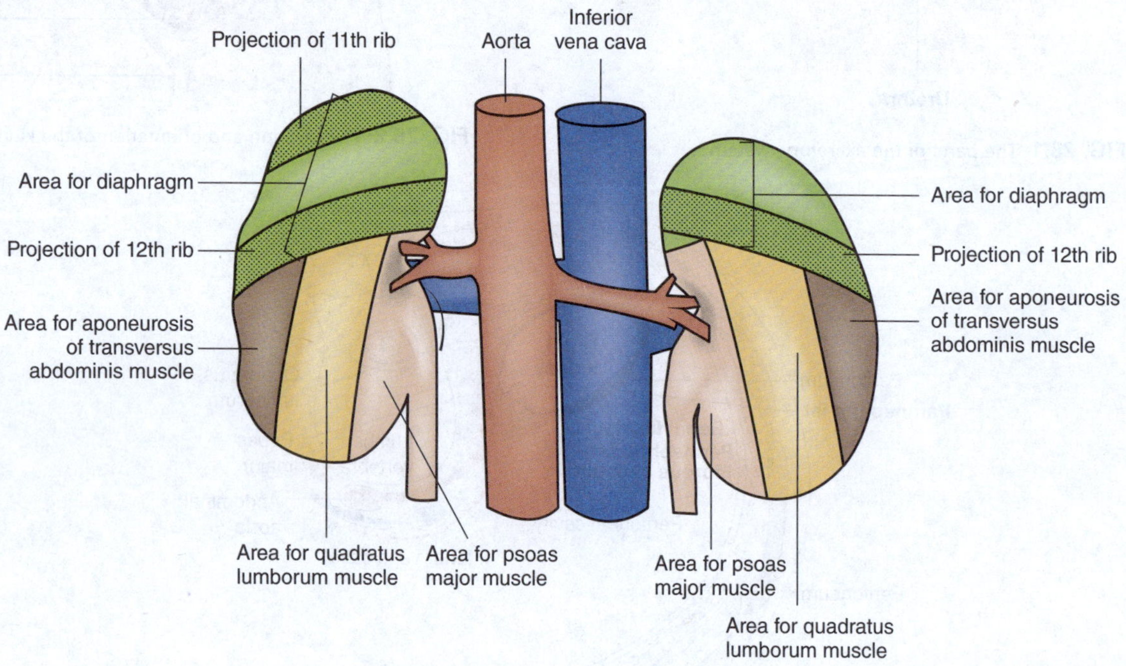

FIG. 28.5 The posterior relations of the kidneys.

muscles also form posterior relations. The suprarenal gland forms the **anterior relation** of both kidneys near their upper poles (Fig. 28.6). The liver, duodenum and hepatic flexure of the colon form the major anterior relations of the right kidney. The remaining area is related to the coils of the small intestine. The left kidney is mainly related to the stomach, spleen, pancreas and upper part of the descending colon. The remaining portion is related to coils of the small intestine.

Macroscopically, a coronal section of the kidneys reveals two parts, an **outer renal substance** and **inner renal sinus** (Fig. 28.7). The **renal sinus** is a cavity within the kidney that communicates with the outside through the hilum. The wall of the sinus is lined by the renal capsule and presents the openings of several renal **papillae**. The renal papillae open into 7–13 **minor calyces**, which in turn open into 2–3 **major calyces**. The major calyces unite to form a funnel-shaped dilatation, the **pelvis** of the **ureter** which passes through the hilum and continues as the ureter at the lower pole of the kidney. The sinus also contains the renal

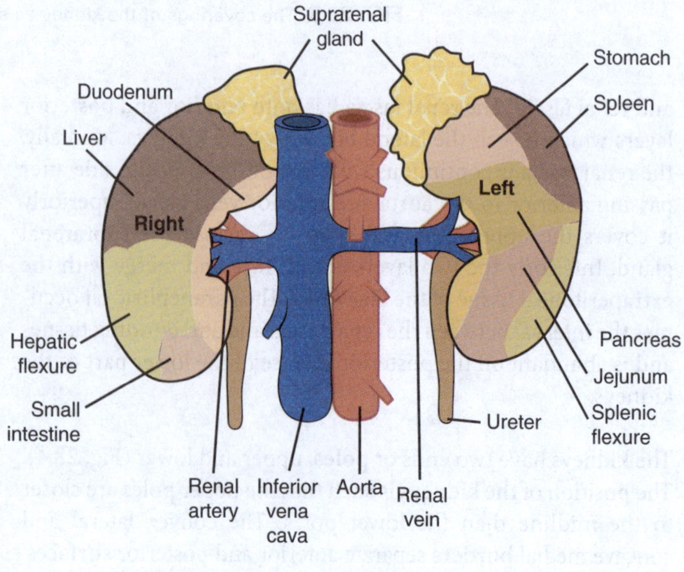

FIG. 28.6 The anterior relations of the kidneys.

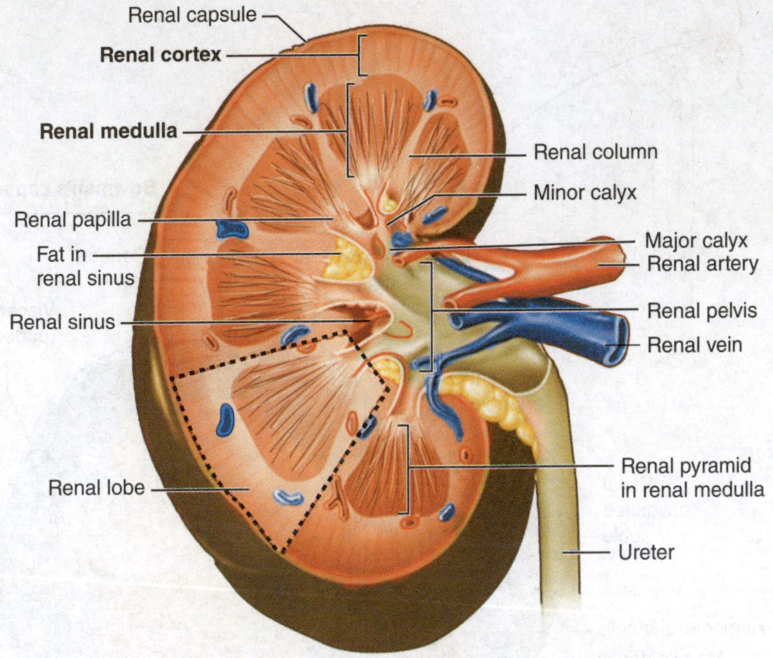

FIG. 28.7 Coronal section of the kidney.

blood vessels, lymph vessels and nerves. The spaces between all these structures in the renal sinus are filled by perinephric fat. The **outer renal substance** can be divided into a dark outer **cortex** and an inner lighter **medulla**. The medulla is seen to consist of **renal pyramids** which open via papillae into the minor calyces. Each pyramid has a base facing the cortex and an apex facing the minor calyces. Parts of the medulla are seen to extend linearly into the cortex as **medullary rays**. The parts of the cortex cupping the bases of the pyramids are known as **cortical arches**. Extensions of the cortex into the medulla on either side of the pyramids are called **renal columns**.

Microscopically, the kidney is composed of **uriniferous tubules**. Uriniferous tubules consist of **nephrons** which produce urine and **collecting ducts** which complete the concentration of urine and through which urine passes out of the kidney. **Nephrons** are the structural and functional units of the kidney (Fig. 28.8). They consist of the **renal corpuscle**, concerned with filtration of the plasma, and the **renal tubule**, concerned with selective reabsorption of the filtrate. **Cortical** and **juxtamedullary nephrons** have been described. Around 85% of nephrons are cortical nephrons which have short tubules and loops of Henle and are mostly retained within the cortex. Juxtaglomerular nephrons constitute the remaining 15% of nephrons and have much longer tubules that extend deep into the medulla. The **connective tissue** of the kidney is called **interstitial tissue** and increases in amount from the cortex to the inner region of the medulla. Two kinds of interstitial cells are found in the cortex, **fibroblasts** and **macrophages.** Fibroblasts secrete collagen and glycosaminoglycans of the extracellular matrix. The principal interstitial cells in the medulla resemble myofibroblasts.

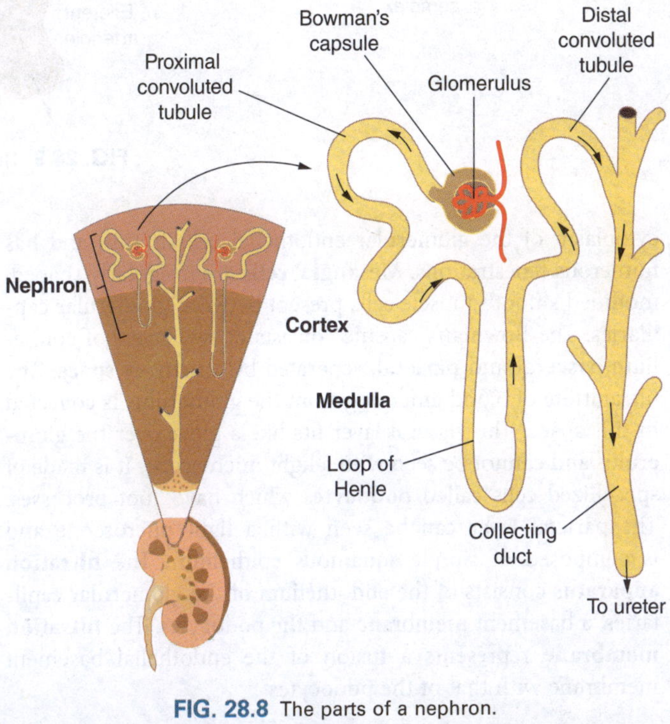

FIG. 28.8 The parts of a nephron.

The **renal corpuscle** is roughly spherical and has **two poles** at opposite ends (Fig. 28.9). The **vascular pole** receives the afferent and efferent arterioles, while the proximal tubule exits at the **urinary pole**. Associated with the vascular pole is the **juxtaglomerular complex**. The renal corpuscle consists of the **glomerulus** and **Bowman's capsule**. The glomerulus is a capillary ball which is supplied with blood by way of the afferent arteriole and from which the blood leaves via the efferent arteriole. The

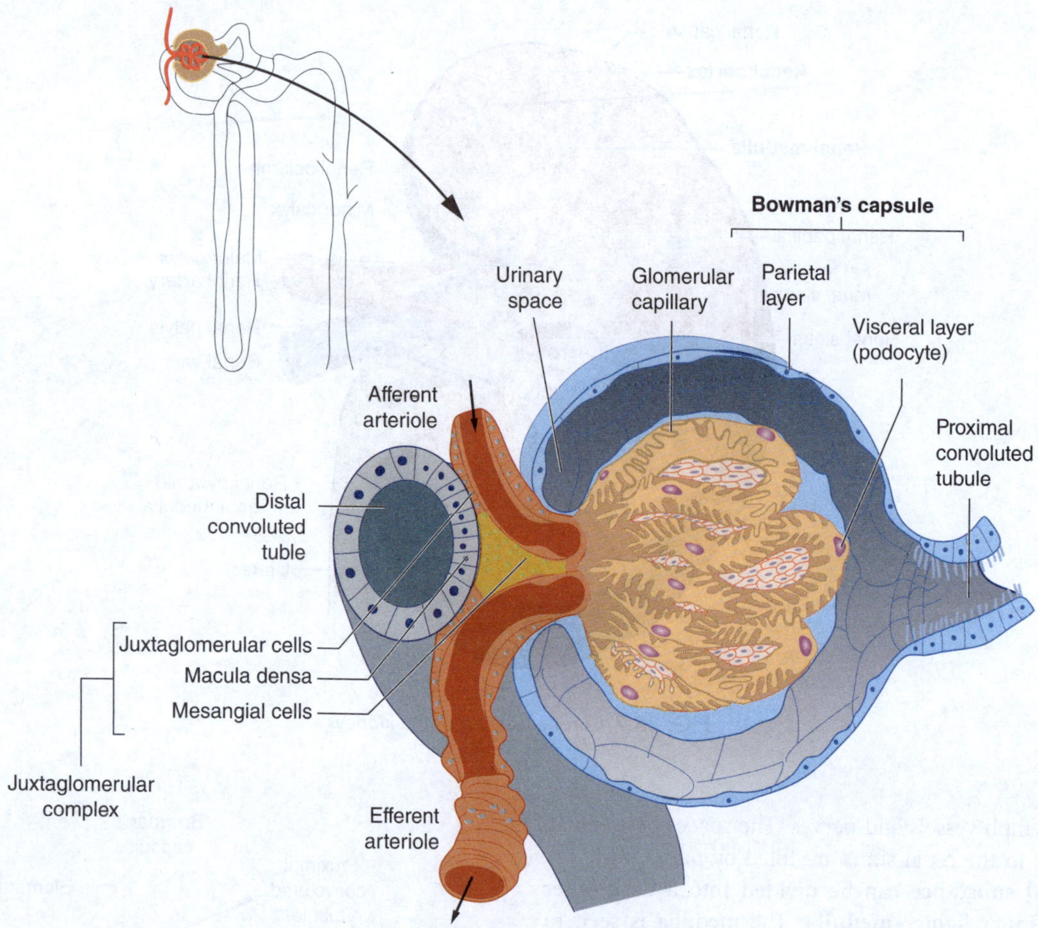

FIG. 28.9 The renal corpuscle.

cytoplasm of the glomerular endothelial cells is thin and has numerous fenestrations. **Mesangial cells** are irregularly shaped, modified smooth muscle cells present between glomerular capillaries. The Bowman's capsule consists of two layers of epithelium, **visceral** and **parietal**, separated by a **urinary space**. The ultrafiltrate of blood emerging from the glomerulus is collected in this space. The visceral layer fits like a glove over the glomerulus and cannot be seen with a light microscope. It is made of specialized cells called **podocytes** which have 'foot processes'. The parietal layer can be seen with a light microscope and is composed of simple squamous epithelium. The **filtration apparatus** consists of the endothelium of the glomerular capillaries, a basement membrane and the podocytes. The **filtration membrane** represents a fusion of the endothelial basement membrane with that of the podocytes.

The **renal tubule** consists of a **proximal** and **distal** tubule (Fig. 28.8). Both tubules consist of **thick** and **thin segments**. The proximal thick segment consists of the **proximal convoluted tubule** (PCT, also known as pars convoluta) and **proximal straight tubule** (pars recta). The distal thick segment also consists of a **distal straight tubule** (pars recta) and **distal convoluted tubule** (DCT or pars convoluta). The **loop of Henle** consists of a descending limb, having an initial short thick segment followed by a long thin segment, and an ascending limb, having a thin segment followed by a thick segment. Each distal tubule is connected to a **collecting duct** through **collecting tubules**. Several collecting ducts merge into a large **papillary duct** (of Bellini) in the medulla. The papillary ducts open at the papilla into the **minor calyces**. The minor calyces drain into the **major calyces** which then open into the **renal pelvis** (Fig. 28.10).

When viewed under the **microscope**, the **cortex** contains **renal corpuscles** with the convoluted and straight parts of both the proximal and distal renal tubules (Fig. 28.8). The microscopic structure of the renal corpuscles has been described earlier. The **PCT** is the longest and widest part of the nephron. It constitutes most tubular sections seen in the cortex and terminates by straightening out and passing into the nearest medullary ray to become the proximal straight tubule. The PCT is lined by **simple cuboidal epithelium** specialized for tubular reabsorption. The **DCT** is one-third the length of the PCT, follows a less tortuous course and ends in an arched collecting tubule. Like the PCT, it is also lined by simple cuboidal epithelium. Collecting tubules and numerous **blood vessels** are also seen.

Microscopically, the renal pyramids in the **medulla** contain **loops of Henle** and the **collecting ducts** (Fig. 28.8). The **loops of Henle** can be recognized by their much lower epithelium which is either **simple squamous** or low cuboidal. The function

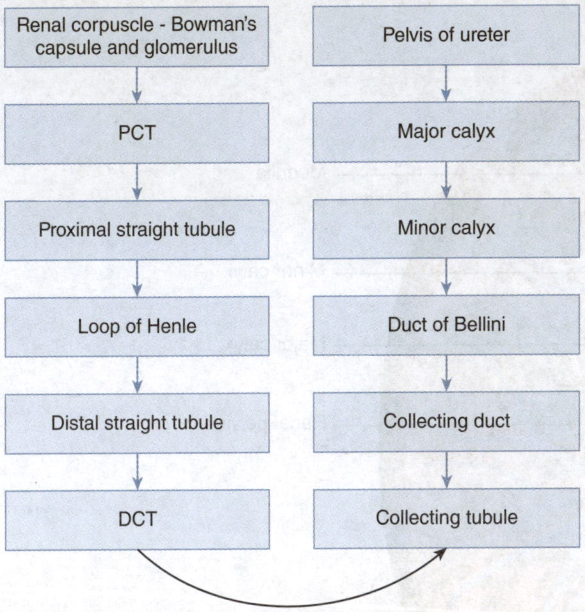

FIG. 28.10 The formation and passage of urine through the kidneys.

of the thin segments of the loop of Henle is to create a countercurrent multiplier mechanism, essential for the formation of urine. The smaller **collecting ducts** can be recognized by their lining of pale-staining, simple cuboidal epithelium. The larger ducts in the deeper parts of the medulla (papillary ducts or ducts of Bellini) have a wide lumen and tall lining cells. The papillary ducts eventually open through the area cribrosa at the apex of each papilla into the minor calyces. The pyramids are accompanied by a capillary network called the **vasa recta**.

The **DCT** comes near the **afferent arteriole** of the glomerulus. This facilitates the formation of a complex of structures associated with the vascular pole of each renal corpuscle called the **juxtaglomerular apparatus (JGA)** (Fig. 28.11). JGA has two principal components: the **macula densa** and **juxtaglomerular cells**. The macula densa is a patch of densely packed epithelial cell nuclei along DCT. The juxtaglomerular cells of the afferent arteriole are specialized smooth muscle cells containing secretory granules of the hormone **renin**. The juxtaglomerular region also includes extraglomerular connective tissue cells called mesangial or **lacis cells.** The JGA participates in the regulation of blood flow through the glomerular capillaries and blood pressure through the downstream effects of renin.

Each kidney is supplied by a **renal artery** arising from the **abdominal aorta** (Fig. 28.12). The artery reaches the hilum between the renal vein anteriorly and pelvis of the ureter posteriorly, after which it divides into anterior and posterior trunks. Further subdivisions course through the medulla and finally terminate as the afferent arterioles which supply the glomeruli. Blood from the glomeruli drains into the efferent arterioles which form peritubular capillaries. The blood from these capillaries is drained through progressively larger veins which form the right and left **renal veins** which finally end in the **inferior vena cava**. The left renal vein is longer than the right and drains blood from the left gonad and left suprarenal gland in addition to the left kidney. **Lymph** from the kidneys drains into the lateral (para-aortic) aortic nodes following the course of the blood vessels. The **nerve supply** of the kidney is via the renal plexus. Sympathetic supply is via T10 to L1 spinal segments, while the parasympathetic supply is via the vagus nerve.

APPLIED ANATOMY

- Kidney stones or **renal calculi** can form within the kidneys when substances like calcium oxalate and uric acid precipitate and accumulate within the kidneys.
- **Renal colic** is a severe colicky pain felt in the loin and radiating to the groin.
- Inflammation of the glomeruli is called **glomerulonephritis**. This is usually due to accumulation of immune complexes in the glomeruli secondary to infections or autoimmune disorders.
- Infection anywhere from the renal tubules to the pelvicalyceal system is called **pyelonephritis.**

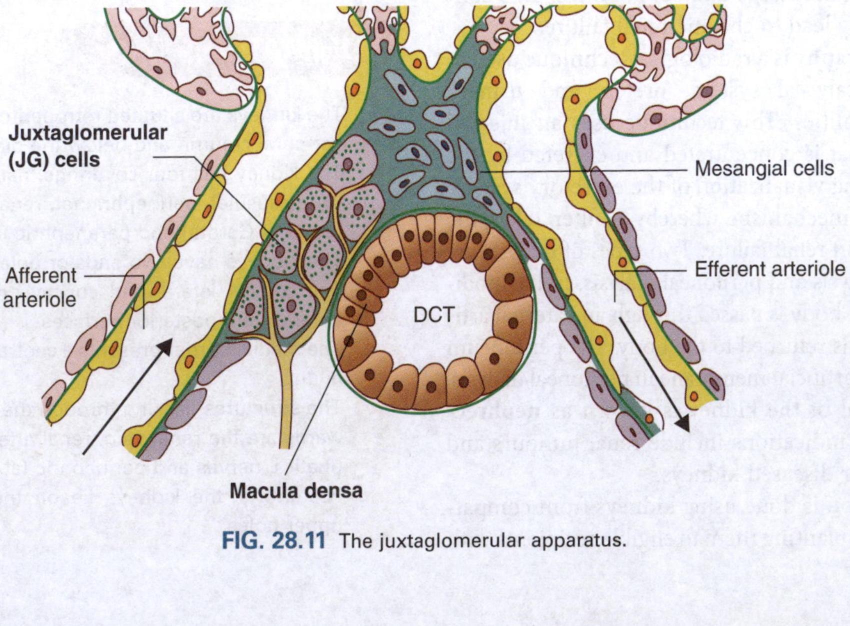

FIG. 28.11 The juxtaglomerular apparatus.

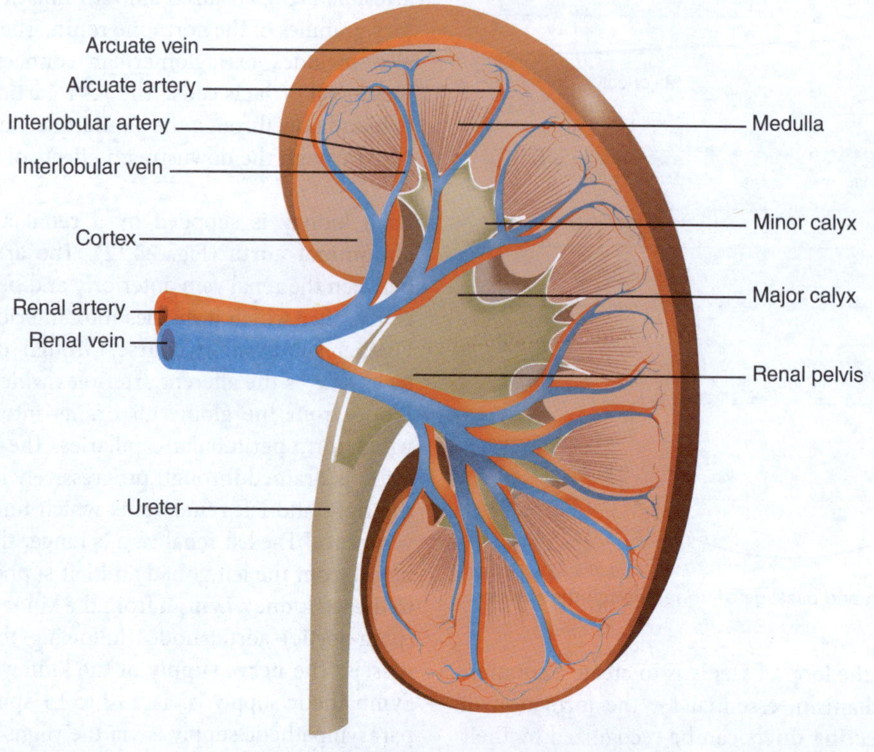

FIG. 28.12 The blood supply of the kidney.

- **Acute renal failure** refers to the sudden cessation of urine production due to causes such as shock and needs emergency management.
- **Chronic renal failure** is an inability of the kidney to perform its function of glomerular filtration and tubular reabsorption leading to the accumulation of usually excreted metabolites in the body. The common causes of chronic renal failure are long-standing diabetes mellitus, hypertension and overuse of nonsteroidal anti-inflammatory drugs.
- Congenital anomalies of the kidney are not uncommon. **Polycystic kidney disease** is a congenital condition in which the kidney tissue contains large numbers of cysts. This condition may eventually lead to chronic renal failure.
- **Intravenous pyelography** is a radiological technique used to visualize the pelvicalyceal system, ureters and urinary bladder for abnormalities. This technique uses an injected radio-opaque dye that is concentrated and excreted by the kidneys, thus enabling visualization of the excretory system.
- **Renal dialysis** is a mechanism whereby a filter takes the place of the kidneys in renal failure. Two types of dialysis are described, haemodialysis and peritoneal dialysis. In haemodialysis, blood from the body is passed through an external artificial membrane and is returned to the body. The peritoneum is used in place of an artificial membrane in peritoneal dialysis.
- The surgical removal of the kidney is known as **nephrectomy.** The common indications include renal tumours and seriously damaged or diseased kidneys.
- **Renal transplantation** is done using kidneys from compatible donors and transplanting them to eligible recipients with end-stage renal disease. The common causes for such end-stage renal disease are diabetes, hypertension, glomerulonephritis and cystic disease.

APPLICATIONS IN NURSING

- **Arteriovenous fistulae** are created for vascular access in patients with renal failure who require haemodialysis. The proper maintenance of these fistulae is essential. Nursing personnel may need to identify any signs of infection or obstruction early so that appropriate measures could be taken.

SUMMARY

- The kidneys are situated retroperitoneally, by the side of the vertebral column and below the diaphragm.
- The kidney has four coverings, namely the fibrous capsule (true capsule), perinephric fat, renal fascia (false capsule or fascia of Gerota) and paranephric fat.
- The kidneys have two ends or poles, upper and lower.
- The convex lateral and concave medial borders separate anterior and posterior surfaces.
- The medial border presents a central concavity known as the hilum.
- The structures passing through the hilum from before backwards are the renal vein, renal artery, pelvis of ureter, lymphatics, nerves and perinephric fat.
- Posteriorly, the kidneys lie on the diaphragm near their upper poles.

- Both kidneys are related to the muscles of the posterior abdominal wall, the subcostal nerve and branches of the lumbar plexus.
- The suprarenal glands form the anterior relation of both kidneys near their upper poles.
- The liver, duodenum, hepatic flexure of the colon and coils of the small intestine form the major anterior relations of the right kidney.
- The left kidney is related to the stomach, spleen, pancreas, upper part of the descending colon and coils of the small intestine anteriorly.
- The renal substance can be divided into a dark outer cortex and an inner lighter medulla.
- The medulla consists of renal pyramids which open via papillae into the minor calyces.
- The parts of the cortex cupping the base of the pyramids are known as cortical arches.
- Extensions of the cortex into the medulla on either side of the pyramids are called renal columns.
- Microscopically, the kidney is composed of uriniferous tubules.
- Uriniferous tubules consist of nephrons which produce urine and collecting ducts which complete the concentration of urine and through which urine passes out of the kidney.
- Nephrons are the structural and functional units of the kidney.
- They consist of the renal corpuscle and renal tubule.
- The connective tissue of the kidney is called interstitial tissue and increases in amount from the cortex to the inner region of the medulla.
- The renal corpuscle consists of the glomerulus and Bowman's capsule.
- The glomerulus is a capillary ball which is supplied with blood by way of the afferent arteriole and from which the blood leaves via the efferent arteriole.
- The Bowman's capsule consists of two layers of epithelium, visceral and parietal, separated by a urinary space.
- The filtration apparatus consists of the endothelium of the glomerular capillaries, a basement membrane and the podocytes.
- The renal tubule consists of a proximal and distal tubule.
- The proximal thick segment consists of PCT, also known as pars convoluta, and the proximal straight tubule (pars recta).
- The distal thick segment consists of a distal straight tubule (pars recta) and a DCT or pars convoluta.
- The loop of Henle consists of a descending limb, having an initial short thick segment followed by a long thin segment, and an ascending limb, having a thin segment followed by a thick segment.
- Each distal tubule is connected to a collecting duct through collecting tubules.
- Several collecting ducts merge into a large papillary duct (of Bellini) in the medulla.
- The papillary ducts open at the papilla into the minor calyces.
- The minor calyces drain into the major calyces which then open into the renal pelvis.
- When viewed under the microscope, the cortex contains renal corpuscles as well as the convoluted and straight parts of both the proximal and distal renal tubules.
- The PCT is lined by simple cuboidal epithelium specialized for tubular reabsorption.
- Like the PCT, the DCT too is lined by simple cuboidal epithelium.
- Microscopically, the renal pyramids in the medulla contain loops of Henle and the collecting ducts.
- The loops of Henle can be recognized by their much lower epithelium which is either simple squamous or low cuboidal.
- The smaller collecting ducts can be recognized by their lining of pale-staining, simple cuboidal epithelium.
- The larger ducts in the deeper parts of the medulla (papillary ducts or ducts of Bellini) have a wide lumen and tall lining cells.
- The pyramids are accompanied by a capillary network called the vasa recta.
- The DCT comes near the afferent arteriole of the glomerulus.
- The JGA has two principal components: the macula densa and juxtaglomerular cells.
- The JGA participates in the regulation of blood flow through the glomerular capillaries and blood pressure through the downstream effects of renin.
- Each kidney is supplied by a renal artery arising from the abdominal aorta.
- The venous blood drains through the right and left renal veins into the inferior vena cava.
- Lymph from the kidneys drains into the lateral (para-aortic) aortic nodes.
- The nerve supply of the kidney is via the renal plexus.
- Sympathetic supply is via T10 to L1 spinal segments, while the parasympathetic supply is via the vagus nerve.

CHAPTER 29

The Ureters, Urinary Bladder and Urethra

SPECIFIC LEARNING OBJECTIVES

At the end of this chapter, the student should be able to:

- Describe the gross, microscopic and applied anatomy of the ureter.
- Describe the gross, microscopic and applied anatomy of the urinary bladder.
- Describe the gross and applied anatomy of the male and female urethra.

GLOSSARY OF TERMS

- **Pelviureteric junction:** junction between the renal pelvis and the beginning of the ureter at the lower pole of the kidney
- **Intravesical part of the ureter:** part of the ureter that courses through the wall of the bladder
- **Trigone:** triangular area in the interior of the urinary bladder that is bounded by the two ureteric orifices and the opening of the urethra
- **Internal urethral sphincter:** smooth muscle surrounding the upper portion of the urethra
- **Detrusor muscle:** smooth muscle of the urinary bladder
- **Urogenital diaphragm:** skeletal muscle covered superiorly and inferiorly by connective tissue through which the urethra passes
- **External urethral sphincter:** skeletal muscle which is part of the urogenital diaphragm which surrounds the membranous urethra

INTRODUCTION

Once urine is produced by the kidneys, it must be stored and voided at an appropriate time. The ureters are tubular structures with muscular walls that transport urine from the kidneys to the urinary bladder. Urine is stored in the urinary bladder till the time it is required to be expelled. The urinary bladder is a bag-like structure with thick muscular walls that can expand to accommodate the urine that collects in it. Subsequently, the muscle in its wall contracts to force urine through the urethra to the exterior. The urethra is a tubular structure which is very different in males and females. Males have a much longer urethra as compared to females and this has important clinical implications.

THE URETERS

The ureters are a pair of narrow thick-walled tubes around 25 cm in length which convey urine from the kidneys to the urinary bladder (Fig. 29.1). Like the kidneys, they are **retroperitoneal** and run inferiorly from the kidneys to the urinary bladder along the posterior abdominal wall. The ureter has **three parts**, namely abdominal, pelvic and intravesical. As the names suggest, the abdominal part is situated within the abdominal cavity, the pelvic part within the pelvic cavity and the intravesical part passes through the wall of the urinary bladder.

The ureter begins within the renal sinus as a funnel-shaped dilatation called the **renal pelvis** which extends to the lower pole of the kidneys. The **renal vessels** are related **anteriorly** to the renal pelvis on both sides. It then passes downwards and slightly medially on the **psoas major muscle** which has the genitofemoral nerve lying on it. The **gonadal vessels** cross the ureter anteriorly on either side along with branches of the superior and inferior mesenteric vessels. The right ureter is crossed by the **root of the mesentery** while the left ureter is related anteriorly to the apex of the **sigmoid mesocolon**.

The ureters then cross the **pelvic brim** to enter the **pelvic cavity**. They initially pass downwards along the anterior margin of the **greater sciatic notch** and reach the level of the **ischial spine**. From the ischial spine, the ureter passes forward and medially through the extraperitoneal tissue above the levator ani muscle and reaches the **superolateral angle** of the base of the **urinary bladder**. In females, the ureters are crossed by the **uterine artery** while in males they are crossed by the **vas deferens**. The ureter then has an oblique course through the bladder wall which represents its **intravesical part**. The intravesical course acts as a valve, preventing reflux of urine into the ureter during bladder contraction. This part is represented by a ureteric fold of mucous membrane that is visible inside the urinary bladder. The ureter is **constricted** at three places along its length, namely the

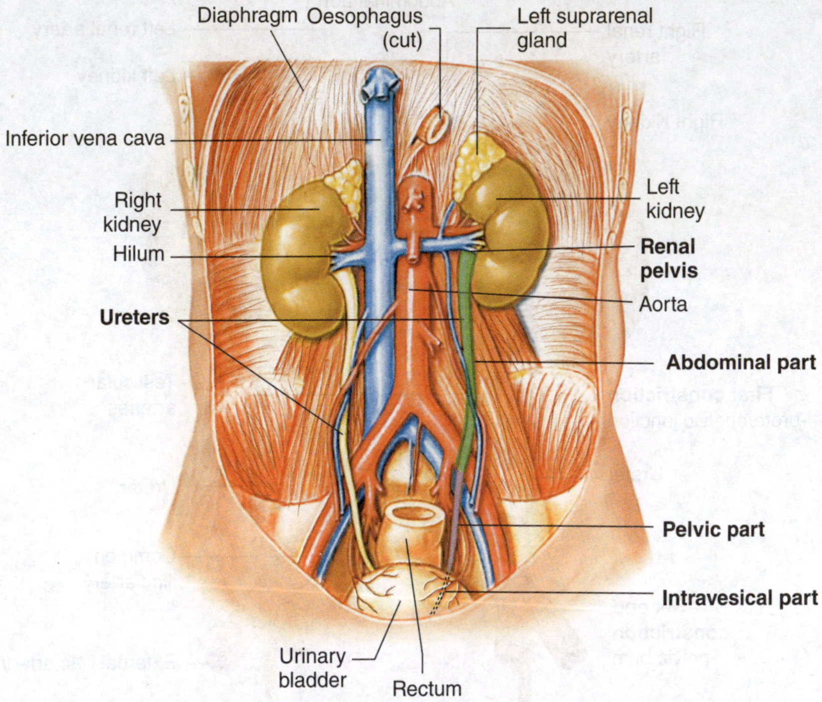

FIG. 29.1 Gross anatomy of the ureters.

pelviureteric junction, the pelvic brim and during its passage through the bladder wall (Fig. 29.2).

Histologically, the ureter consists of the following **three layers**: inner mucosa, middle muscular layer and outer adventitia (Fig. 29.3). The **mucosa** is thrown into longitudinal folds lined by **transitional epithelium** which lies on a thin lamina propria. The **muscular layer** consists of inner longitudinal and outer circular layers of muscle fibres. Blood vessels and nerves course through the **adventitia** which is composed of connective tissue. The transitional epithelium protects the underlying structures from harmful effects of the urine that passes through it. The smooth muscles in the muscular layer contract rhythmically to drive the urine towards the urinary bladder.

The ureter is supplied by branches of several **arteries** as it courses from its origin to termination. These include the renal, gonadal, lumbar, peritoneal, common iliac, internal iliac and inferior vesical arteries. In **females**, the uterine and vaginal arteries contribute to the blood supply of the ureter. The **veins** drain into the corresponding veins accompanying the arteries. The **lymph** from the upper part of the ureter drains into the para-aortic lymph nodes. The common iliac, internal and external iliac nodes drain the lower part of the ureter. **Autonomic nerve supply** is provided to the ureter through the ureteric plexus. This plexus contains sympathetic fibres from T12 to L2 segments and parasympathetic fibres from S2 to S4 segments of the spinal cord.

THE URINARY BLADDER

The **size, shape** and **location** of the urinary bladder are variable and depend on the amount of urine that it contains. The **empty bladder** is an entirely pelvic organ that is **tetrahedral** in shape (Fig. 29.4). However, when the bladder is fully **distended**, it becomes an abdominopelvic organ which is **ovoid** in shape. The empty bladder which is tetrahedral has an **apex** anterosuperiorly and a **base** or posterior surface that faces posteriorly. The **neck** of the bladder is situated inferiorly immediately above the base of the prostate gland in males and urogenital diaphragm in females. It is a part of the bladder whose position remains constant irrespective of the degree of bladder distension. The bladder has a **superior surface** and a pair of **inferolateral surfaces**. The anterior border separates the two inferolateral surfaces, while the lateral borders separate the inferolateral surfaces from the superior surface. The posterior border lies between the superior surface and base.

The **relations** of the urinary bladder differ in **males** and **females** (Fig. 29.5). The **inferolateral surfaces** in both males and females are related to the pelvic diaphragm, which supports it inferiorly. The **superior surface** is related to the uterus in females and coils of the intestine in males. **Posteriorly** are related the seminal vesicles and rectum in males and the cervix of the uterus and vagina in females. As mentioned previously, the neck is related to the prostate gland in males and the urogenital diaphragm in females.

Ligaments hold the bladder in place (Fig. 29.6). They can be classified as **true ligaments** which are condensations of pelvic fascia or developmental in origin, and **false ligaments** which are peritoneal folds. The true ligaments which are formed by condensations of pelvic fascia include the puboprostatic (pubovesical in females), lateral and posterior ligaments. All these ligaments anchor the bladder to the walls of the pelvis. The

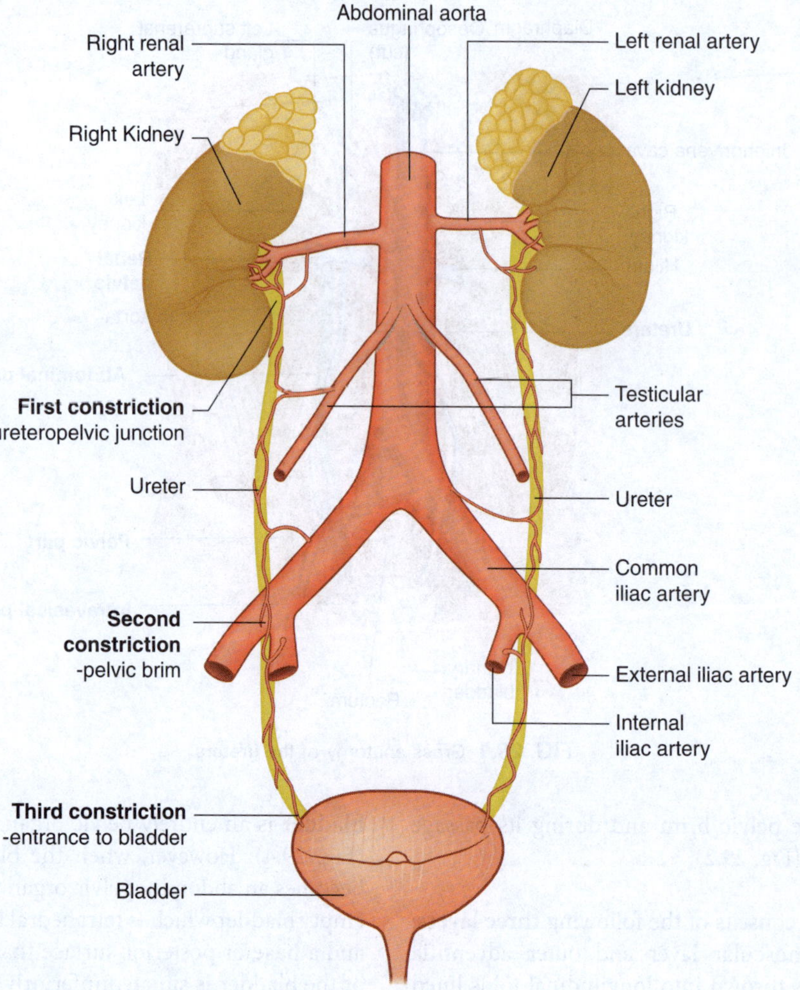

FIG. 29.2 The constrictions of the ureter.

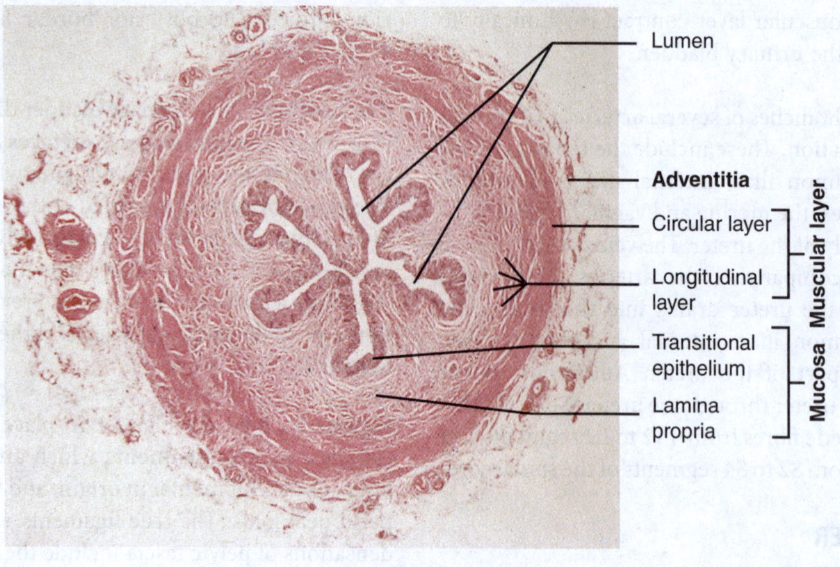

FIG. 29.3 The microscopic anatomy of the ureter.

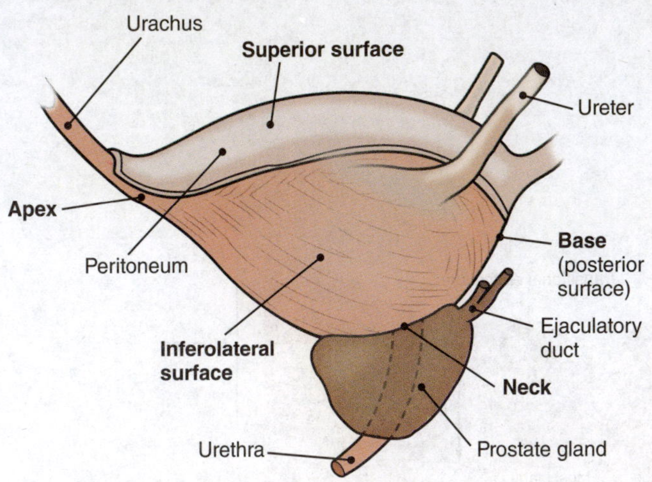

FIG. 29.4 The parts and surfaces of the urinary bladder.

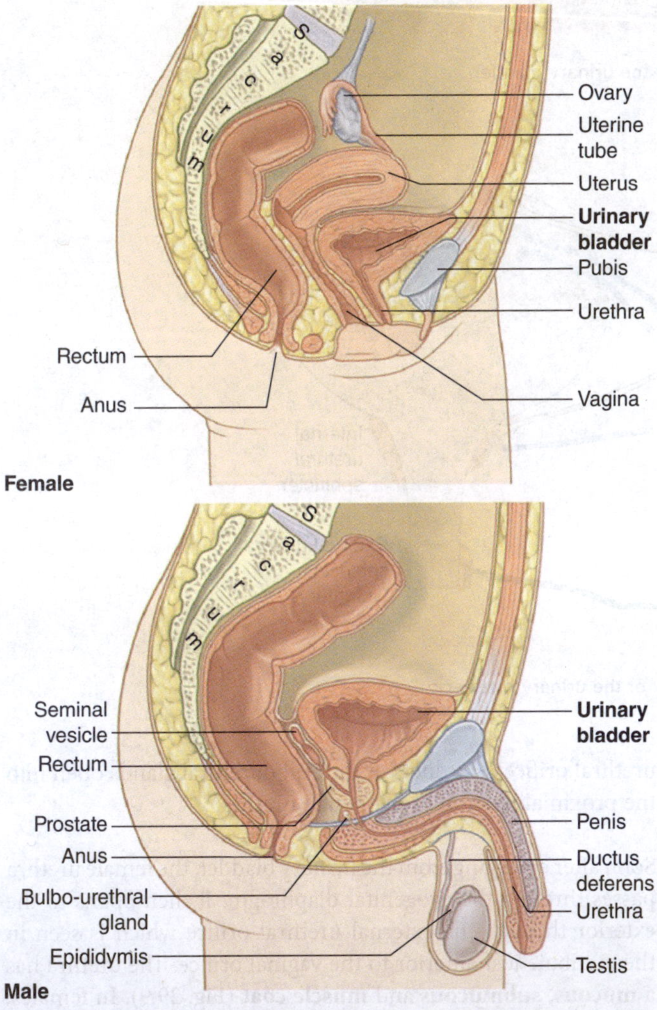

FIG. 29.5 The relations of the urinary bladder.

median and medial umbilical ligaments are developmental in origin and are derived from the urachus and umbilical arteries, respectively. The false ligaments include the lateral, posterior, median and medial umbilical folds.

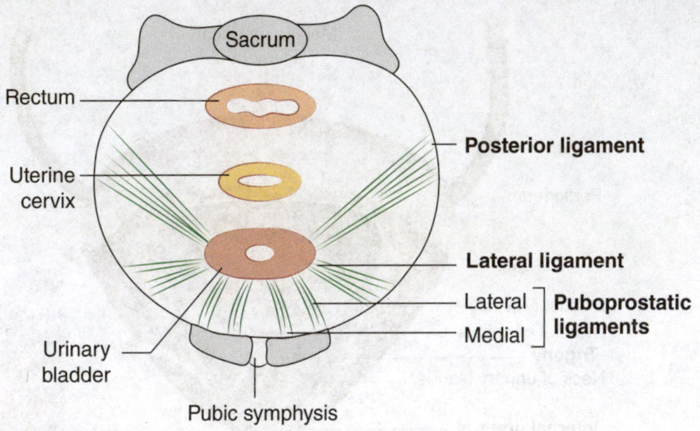

FIG. 29.6 The ligaments of the urinary bladder in a transverse section of the pelvis.

The appearance of the interior of the bladder depends on its state of distension. **Folds**, which are seen when it is empty, disappear when it fills. A smooth, triangular area without folds seen in the interior of the bladder is called the **trigone** (Fig. 29.7). The three vertices of the trigone are the two openings of the ureter superiorly and the urethral opening inferiorly. The upper limit of the trigone is formed by the interureteric ridge, which connects the two ureteric openings. The trigone has a rich nerve and blood supply and is the area from which sensations of distension are conveyed to the central nervous system. The **internal urethral sphincter** surrounds the upper part of the urethra and is situated in close relation to the lowest portions of the neck of the urinary bladder.

Microscopically, the urinary bladder is similar to the ureter and contains the same **three layers** (Fig. 29.7). However, it has a much bigger lumen and thicker muscle wall consisting of inner and outer longitudinal and middle circular layers. The muscles are not arranged in as regular a fashion as in the ureter. This smooth muscle is known as the **detrusor** whose function is to contract and expel urine from the urinary bladder at the time of micturition. The **arterial supply** of the urinary bladder is through the superior and inferior vesical arteries which are branches of the internal iliac artery. **Venous drainage** is into the internal iliac veins. **Lymphatic drainage** is into the external iliac group of lymph nodes. The **autonomic nerve supply** to the urinary bladder is via spinal segments T10 to L2 for the sympathetic component and S2 to S4 for the parasympathetic component (Fig. 29.8). Parasympathetic stimulation is responsible for the emptying of the bladder by contraction of the detrusor muscle and relaxation of the sphincters. Sympathetic stimulation causes contraction of sphincters and relaxation of the detrusor muscle.

THE URETHRA

Unlike the urinary bladder and ureter, the urethra shows significant **gender differences** (Table 29.1). The **male urethra** is much longer (around 20 cm) and has **three parts**: the **prostatic**, **membranous** and **penile** (or spongy) urethra (Fig. 29.9). The

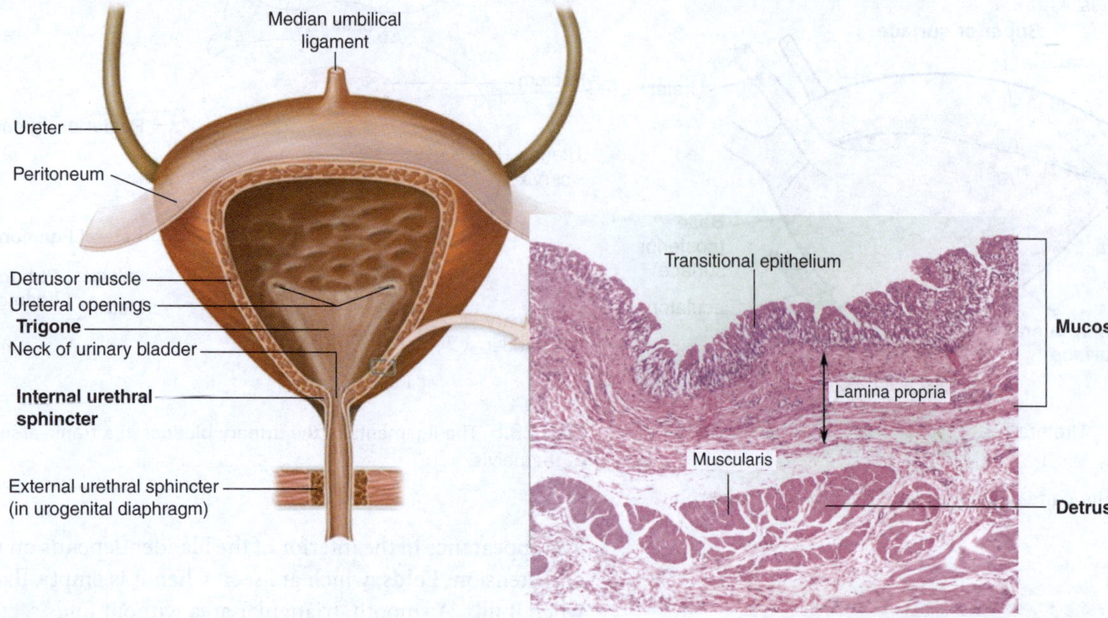

FIG. 29.7 The interior of the urinary bladder.

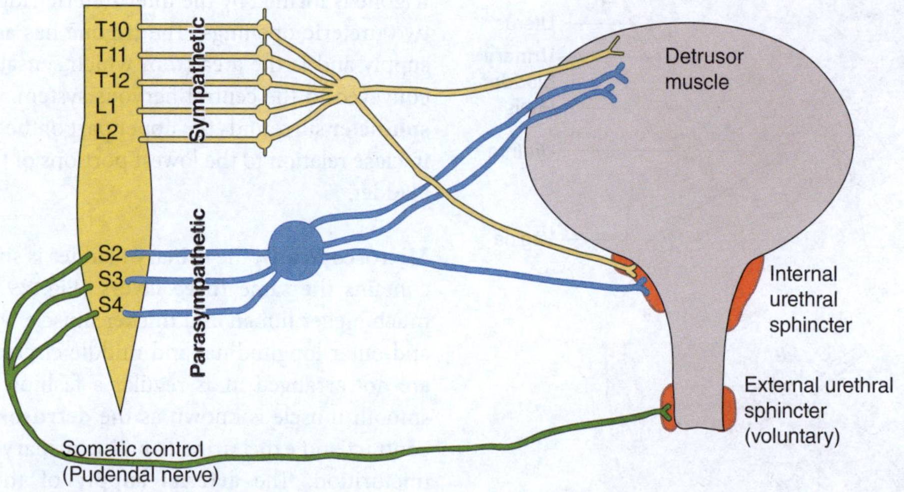

FIG. 29.8 The nerve supply of the urinary bladder.

female urethra (around 5 cm) is equivalent to the proximal part of the male urethra (Fig. 29.9). The prostatic urethra courses through the prostate gland, receiving the openings of the ejaculatory ducts and prostatic glands as it does so. This part of the urethra is surrounded by smooth muscle known as the internal urethral sphincter, just as it emerges from the urinary bladder. On emerging from the prostate, the urethra passes through the urogenital diaphragm, which consists of skeletal muscle covered both superiorly and inferiorly by connective tissue. This is the narrowest portion of the male urethra. It is surrounded by skeletal muscle located within the urogenital diaphragm known as the external urethral sphincter. This sphincter is under voluntary control and needs to be relaxed before voiding of urine. The penile urethra passes through the bulb of the penis and corpus spongiosum before it opens to the exterior at the external urethral orifice. The ducts of the bulbourethral glands open into the proximal portion of the penile urethra.

Soon after emerging from the urinary bladder, the female urethra passes through the urogenital diaphragm. It then opens to the exterior through the external urethral orifice which is seen in the vestibule just anterior to the vaginal orifice. The urethra has a **mucous, submucous** and **muscle coat** (Fig. 29.9). In females, the upper portion is lined by **transitional epithelium** which changes to **stratified squamous nonkeratinized epithelium**, near the external orifice. In males, the prostatic urethra is lined by **transitional epithelium**, the long middle portion nearly till the external urethral orifice by **stratified columnar epithelium** and the terminal portion by **stratified squamous nonkeratinized epithelium**. The **blood supply** is through vessels of the

Table 29.1 The Differences Between the Male and the Female Urethra

S. No.	Characteristic	Male	Female
1.	Length	• Long – 20 cm	• Short – 5 cm
2.	Parts	Three parts: • Prostatic • Membranous • Penile	• Represents the proximal portion of the male urethra
3.	Lining epithelium	• Transitional – most of the prostatic urethra • Stratified columnar – rest of urethra almost till the external orifice • Stratified squamous nonkeratinized epithelium – terminal portion	• Transitional – the upper two-thirds • Stratified squamous nonkeratinized epithelium – lower one-third
4.	Structures opening	• Ejaculatory ducts – into prostatic urethra • Prostatic glands – into prostatic urethra • Bulbourethral glands – into proximal portion of penile urethra	• None

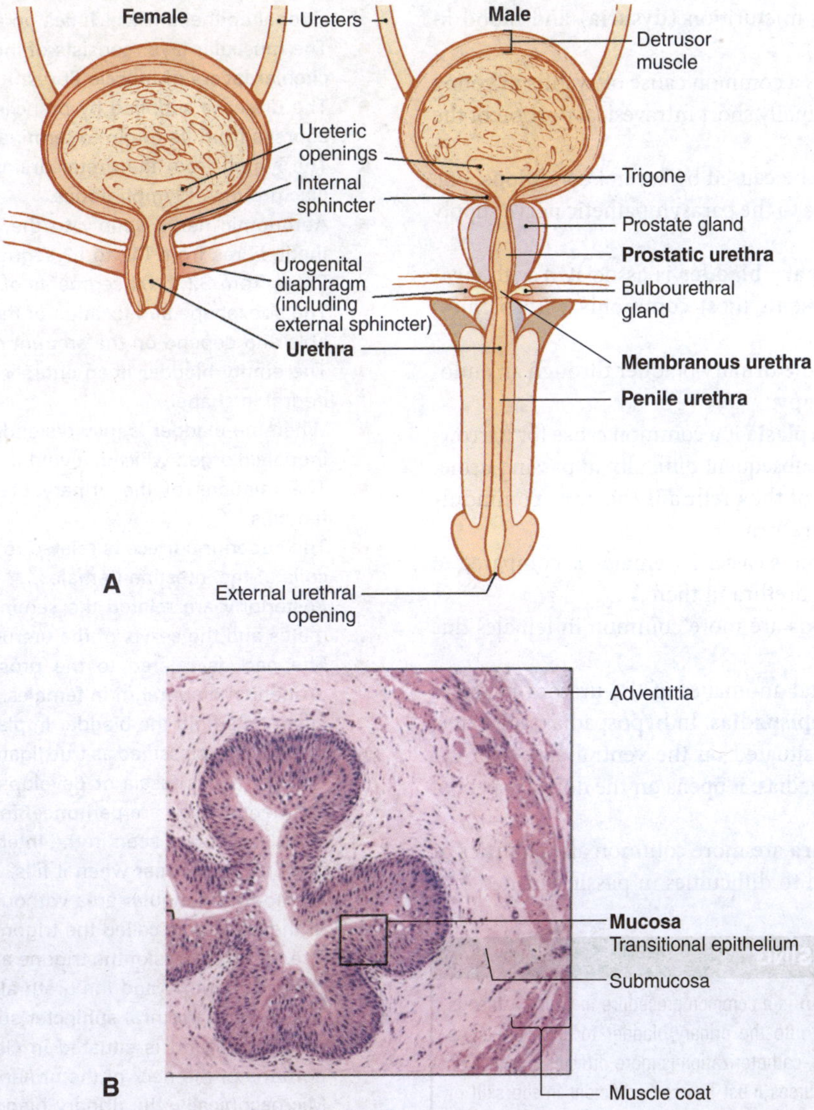

FIG. 29.9 (A) The gross anatomy of the urethra. (B) Microscopic anatomy of the urethra.

bladder, prostate and vagina and from the internal pudendal vessels. **Lymphatic drainage** is into the internal iliac, external iliac and inguinal groups of lymph nodes. **Nerve supply** is from the inferior hypogastric plexus and pudendal nerve.

APPLIED ANATOMY

- **Injury** to the **ureter** is common during **hysterectomy** because of the proximity of the uterine artery to the ureter.
- Any injury to the ureter can lead to **stricture** formation and subsequent damage to the kidney due to retention of urine in the pelvicalyceal system.
- **Ureteric stones** usually get impacted at any of the three sites of constriction of the ureter.
- The bladder can be **catheterized** either through the urethra or via the abdomen when the bladder is distended.
- Inflammation of the bladder is known as **cystitis** and is more common in females.
- Just as in the kidney and ureter, stones can occur in the bladder and are known as **bladder calculi**. This condition can cause pain during micturition (**dysuria**) and blood in the urine (**haematuria**).
- **Vesicoureteric reflux** is a common cause of cystitis in young children with an abnormally short intravesical portion of the ureter.
- **Urinary retention** can be caused by several conditions, one among which is damage to the parasympathetic nerve supply to the urinary bladder.
- **Carcinoma** of the **urinary bladder** is associated with cigarette smoking and presents most commonly with painless haematuria.
- Direct visualization of the urinary bladder through an endoscope is called **cystoscopy**.
- **Benign prostatic hyperplasia** is a common cause for narrowing of the urethra and subsequent difficulty in passing urine.
- The membranous part of the urethra is the most commonly **ruptured** part of the **urethra**.
- **Bladder catheterization** is easier in females as compared to males due to a shorter urethra in them.
- **Urinary tract infections** are more common in females due to their short urethra.
- The common congenital anomalies of the urethra in males are **hypospadias** and **epispadias**. In hypospadias, the external urethral orifice is situated on the ventral aspect of the penis, whereas in epispadias, it opens on the dorsal aspect of the penis.
- **Strictures** of the **urethra** are more common after injuries or infections and can lead to difficulties in passing urine.

APPLICATIONS IN NURSING

- **Urinary catheterization** is a common procedure in which a tube is passed through the urethra into the urinary bladder to drain urine. As males have a longer urethra, catheterization is more difficult in males as compared to females. All nurses must become proficient in the skill of urinary catheterization and assist in the maintenance of an indwelling catheter to prevent infections, leaks and blockages.

SUMMARY

- The ureters are a pair of narrow thick-walled tubes around 25 cm in length which convey urine from the kidneys to the urinary bladder.
- The ureter has three parts, abdominal, pelvic and intravesical.
- The ureter begins within the renal sinus as a funnel-shaped dilatation called the renal pelvis which extends till the lower pole of the kidneys.
- The ureters cross the pelvic brim to enter the pelvic cavity.
- In females, the ureters are crossed by the uterine artery, while in males they are crossed by the vas deferens.
- The ureter has an oblique course through the bladder wall which represents its intravesical part.
- The ureter is constricted at three places along its length, namely the pelviureteric junction, the pelvic brim and during its passage through the bladder wall.
- Histologically, the ureter is seen to consist of the following three layers: inner mucosa, middle muscular layer and outer adventitia.
- The mucosa is thrown into longitudinal folds lined by transitional epithelium which lies on a thin lamina propria.
- The muscular layer consists of inner longitudinal and outer circular layers of muscle fibres.
- The ureter is supplied by branches of several arteries as it courses from its origin to termination.
- The lymph from the ureter drains into the para-aortic and iliac groups of lymph nodes.
- Autonomic nerve supply to the ureter is through sympathetic fibres from T12 to L2 segments and parasympathetic fibres from S2 to S4 segments of the spinal cord.
- The size, shape and location of the urinary bladder are variable and depend on the amount of urine that it contains.
- The empty bladder is an entirely pelvic organ that is tetrahedral in shape.
- When the bladder is fully distended, it becomes an abdominopelvic organ which is ovoid in shape.
- The relations of the urinary bladder differ in males and females.
- The superior surface is related to the uterus in females and coils of the intestine in males.
- Posteriorly are related the seminal vesicles and rectum in males and the cervix of the uterus and vagina in females.
- The neck is related to the prostate gland in males and urogenital diaphragm in females.
- Ligaments hold the bladder in place.
- They can be classified as true ligaments which are condensations of pelvic fascia or developmental in origin, and false ligaments which are peritoneal folds.
- Folds, which are seen in the interior of the bladder when it is empty, disappear when it fills.
- A smooth, triangular area without folds seen in the interior of the bladder is called the trigone.
- The three vertices of the trigone are the two openings of the ureter superiorly and the urethral opening inferiorly.
- The internal urethral sphincter surrounds the upper part of the urethra and is situated in close relation to the lowest portions of the neck of the urinary bladder.
- Microscopically, the urinary bladder is similar to the ureter and contains the same three layers.

- It has a much bigger lumen and a thicker muscle wall consisting of irregularly arranged inner and outer longitudinal and middle circular layers (detrusor muscle).
- The arterial supply of the urinary bladder is through the superior and inferior vesical arteries which are branches of the internal iliac artery.
- Venous drainage is into the internal iliac veins.
- Lymphatic drainage is into the external iliac group of lymph nodes.
- The autonomic nerve supply to the urinary bladder is via spinal segments T10 to L2 for the sympathetic component and S2 to S4 for the parasympathetic component.
- Unlike the urinary bladder and ureter, the urethra shows significant gender differences.
- The male urethra is much longer (around 20 cm) and has three parts: the prostatic, membranous and penile (or spongy) urethra.
- The female urethra (around 5 cm) is equivalent to the proximal part of the male urethra.
- The prostatic urethra courses through the prostate gland, receiving the openings of the ejaculatory ducts and prostatic glands as it does so.
- The membranous urethra passes through the urogenital diaphragm, which consists of skeletal muscle covered both superiorly and inferiorly by connective tissue.
- The external urethral sphincter surrounds the membranous urethra.
- The penile urethra passes through the bulb of the penis and corpus spongiosum before it opens to the exterior at the external urethral orifice.
- The ducts of the bulbourethral glands open into the proximal portion of the penile urethra.
- The female urethra opens to the exterior through the external urethral orifice which is seen in the vestibule just anterior to the vaginal orifice.
- In females, the upper portion of the urethra is lined by transitional epithelium which changes to stratified squamous nonkeratinized epithelium, near the external orifice.
- In males, the prostatic urethra is lined by transitional epithelium, the long middle portion nearly till the external urethral orifice by stratified columnar epithelium and the terminal portion by stratified squamous nonkeratinized epithelium.

9
SECTION

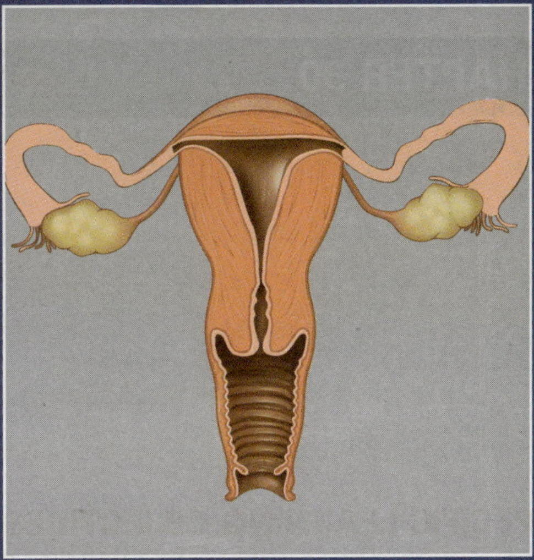

The Reproductive System

Section Outline

CHAPTER 30

The Female Reproductive System

SPECIFIC LEARNING OBJECTIVES

At the end of this chapter, the student should be able to:

- Name the parts of the female reproductive system.
- Describe the gross, microscopic and applied anatomy of the ovary.
- Describe the gross, microscopic and applied anatomy of the Fallopian tube.
- Describe the gross, microscopic and applied anatomy of the uterus.
- Describe the gross, microscopic and applied anatomy of the mammary gland.
- Describe the gross anatomy of the female external genitalia.

GLOSSARY OF TERMS

- **Follicle:** oocyte surrounded by follicular cells
- **Zone pellucida:** glycoprotein layer surrounding the oocyte
- **Theca folliculi:** connective tissue surrounding the developing follicle
- **Cumulus oophorus:** granulosa cells surrounding the oocyte
- **Corona radiata:** granulosa cells immediately surrounding the oocyte
- **Ampulla:** part of the Fallopian tube where fertilization takes place
- **Mesosalpinx:** part of the broad ligament enclosing the Fallopian tube
- **Fundus:** uppermost part of the uterus
- **Cervix:** lower part of the uterus
- **Internal os:** opening between the body of the uterus and cervix
- **External os:** opening between the cervix and vagina
- **Isthmus:** upper part of the cervix
- **Broad ligament:** curtain-like peritoneal fold on either side of the uterus
- **Stratum basalis:** deeper part of the endometrium that is retained during menstruation
- **Stratum functionalis:** superficial part of the endometrium that is shed during menstruation
- **Fornix:** upper part of the vagina surrounding the lower part of the cervix
- **Axillary tail of Spence:** extension of breast tissue into the axilla
- **Ligaments of Cooper:** connective tissue framework of the breast

INTRODUCTION

The female reproductive system is specialized to produce the female gamete, transport the zygote, nourish it for around 9 months, enable its birth and provide its nutrition in the initial months following birth. This system consists of the internal organs, namely the ovaries, oviducts, uterus and vagina (Fig. 30.1). The external genitalia include the vestibule, clitoris, labia majora and labia minora (Fig. 30.2). The mammary gland is considered an accessory reproductive gland. In addition, special structures like the placenta and umbilical cord develop during pregnancy (Fig. 30.3). All functions of the female reproductive system are facilitated by a complex interplay of hormones secreted by the pituitary gland, ovaries and placenta.

THE OVARIES

The ovaries are small, oval, paired organs in the **pelvic cavity** (Fig. 30.4). They have an irregular surface due to projections caused by developing follicles and the scars of previous ovulatory cycles. The functions of the ovaries are the production of female **gametes** and manufacture and secretion of **sex hormones**. They are homologous in embryological development to the testes. They lie in a fossa in the lateral wall of the pelvic cavity called the **ovarian fossa**. Each ovary has upper and lower **poles**, anterior and posterior **borders** and medial and lateral **surfaces**. The anterior border and medial surface are closely related to the infundibulum of the Fallopian tube. The ovary is the only truly **intraperitoneal** organ and is held in place by **ligaments** (Fig. 30.4). It is related anteriorly to a part of the broad ligament called the **mesovarium**. The **ovarian ligament** connects the lower pole of the ovary with the uterus, and the infundibulopelvic or **suspensory ligament** connects the upper pole of the ovary to the lateral pelvic wall.

The surface of the ovary is covered by simple cuboidal epithelium, called **germinal epithelium**, which is continuous with the

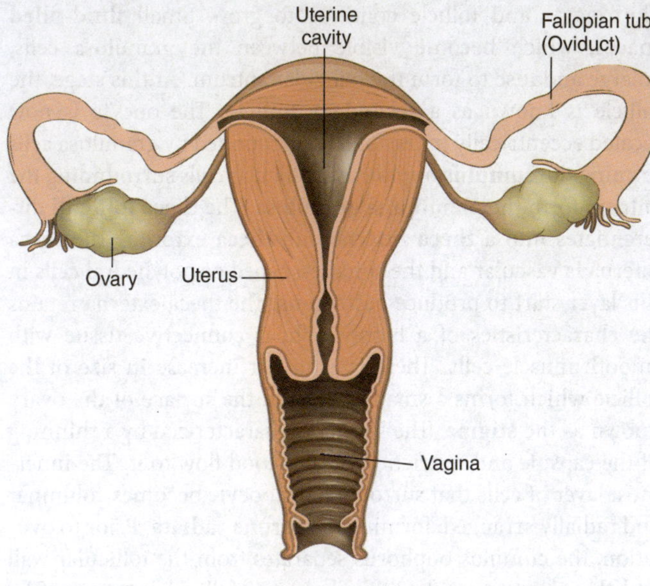

FIG. 30.1 The parts of the female reproductive system.

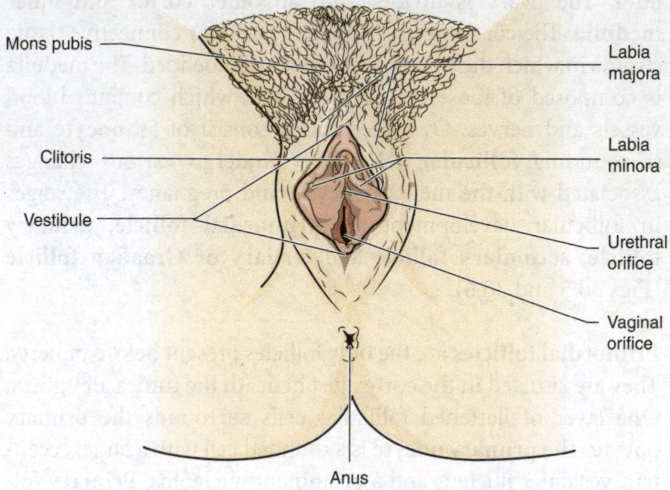

FIG. 30.2 The female external genitalia.

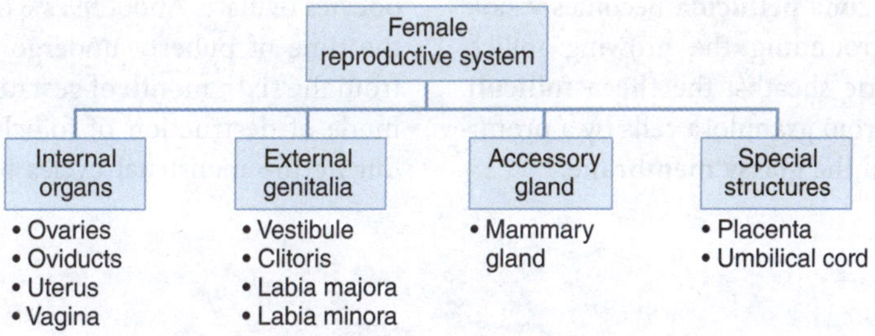

FIG. 30.3 The parts of the female reproductive system.

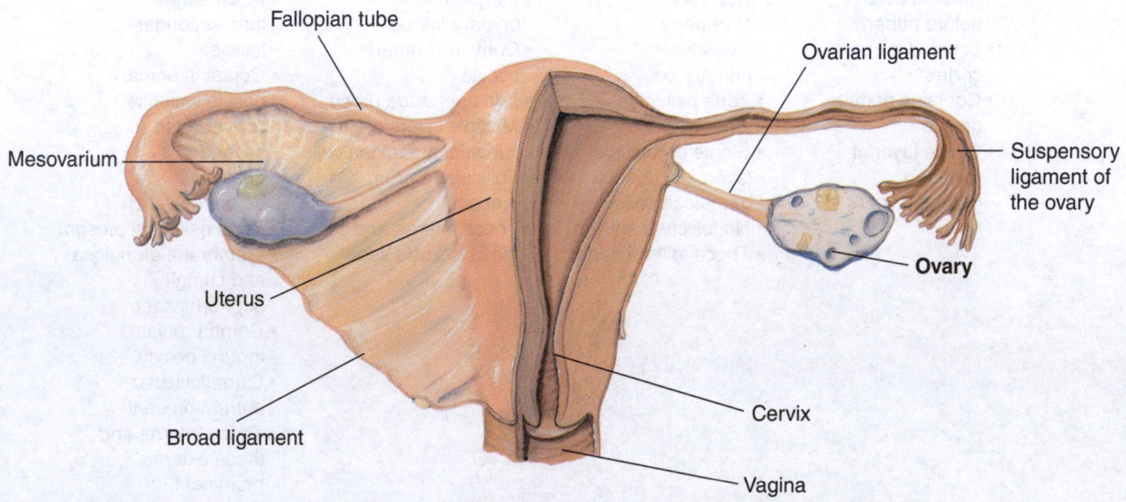

FIG. 30.4 The gross anatomy of the ovary.

peritoneal mesothelium. Fibrous connective tissue forms a thin capsule, the **tunica albuginea**, immediately beneath the epithelium. The ovary is divided into an outer **cortex** and inner **medulla**. The cortex consists of a very cellular connective tissue stroma in which the **ovarian follicles** are embedded. The medulla is composed of loose connective tissue, which contains blood vessels and nerves. Ovarian follicles consist of an **oocyte** and surrounding **follicular cells**. They undergo various changes associated with the menstrual cycle and pregnancy. The stages in follicular development are **primordial follicle, primary follicle, secondary follicle** and **tertiary or Graafian follicle** (Figs 30.5 and 30.6).

Primordial follicles are the only follicles present before puberty. They are situated in the cortex just beneath the tunica albuginea. One layer of flattened follicular cells surrounds the primary oocyte. The **primary oocyte** is a rounded cell with a large, eccentric, vesicular nucleus and a prominent nucleolus. **Primary follicles** are the first morphological stage that marks the onset of follicular maturation. Previously flattened cells surrounding the oocyte now form a cuboidal epithelium surrounding the oocyte. Their cytoplasm may have a granular appearance, and therefore they are also called **granulosa cells**. The follicle is initially surrounded by a single layer of cuboidal cells and subsequently more cell layers are added. The **zona pellucida** becomes visible at this stage. The stroma surrounding the growing follicle becomes organized in concentric sheaths, the **theca folliculi**. The theca folliculi is separated from granulosa cells by a prominent basement membrane called the **glassy membrane**.

The oocyte and follicle continue to grow. Small **fluid-filled spaces**, which become visible between the granulosa cells, enlarge and fuse to form the follicular antrum. At this stage, the follicle is known as a **secondary follicle**. The oocyte is now located eccentrically in the follicle surrounded by granulosa cells forming the **cumulus oophorus**. Follicular cells surrounding the antrum form the **membrana granulosa**. The **theca folliculi** differentiates into a **theca interna** and **theca externa**. The theca interna is vascular and the spindle-shaped or polyhedral cells in this layer start to produce oestrogens. The theca externa retains the characteristics of a highly cellular connective tissue with smooth muscle cells. There is a further increase in size of the follicle which forms a small 'bump' on the surface of the ovary known as the **stigma**. The stigma is characterized by a thinning of the capsule and restriction of the blood flow to it. The innermost layer of cells that surrounds the oocyte becomes columnar and radially arranged, forming the **corona radiata**. Prior to ovulation, the cumulus oophorus separates from the follicular wall and the oocyte now floats freely in the follicular antrum. The follicle finally ruptures at the stigma and the oocyte is released from the ovary surrounded by the cells of the corona radiata.

Atresia is the degenerative process by which oocytes and follicles die without having been expelled by ovulation. Only about 400 oocytes ovulate. About 99.9% of the oocytes that were present at the time of puberty undergo atresia. Follicular atresia occurs from the sixth month of gestation until menopause. It is also the mode of destruction of follicles whose maturation is initiated during the menstrual cycles but which do not ovulate. In the

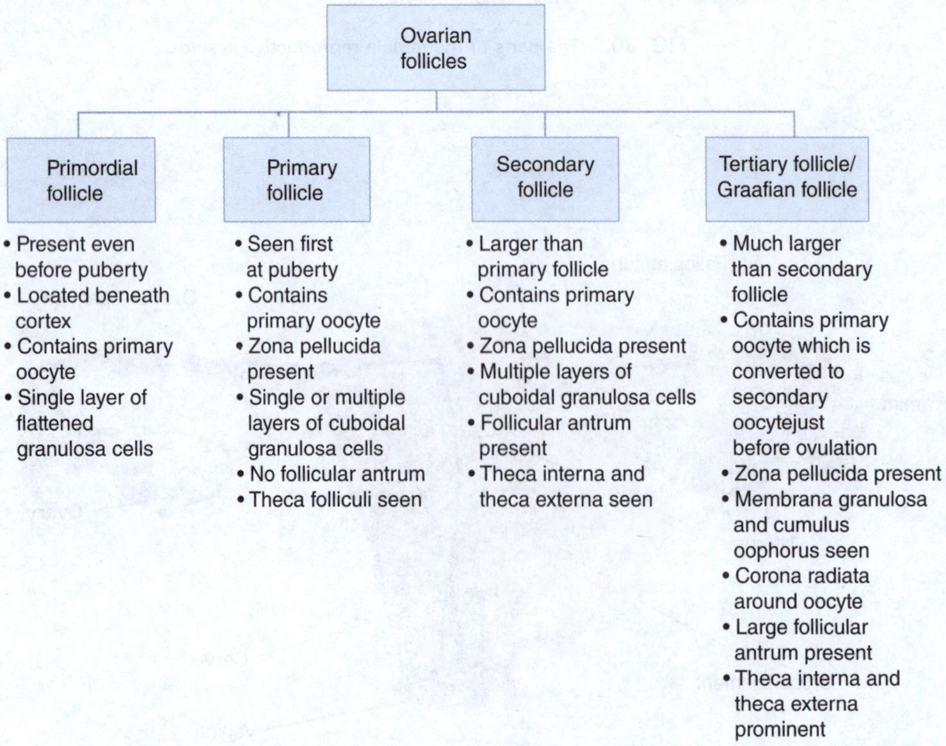

FIG. 30.5 Salient features of the different types of follicles in the ovary.

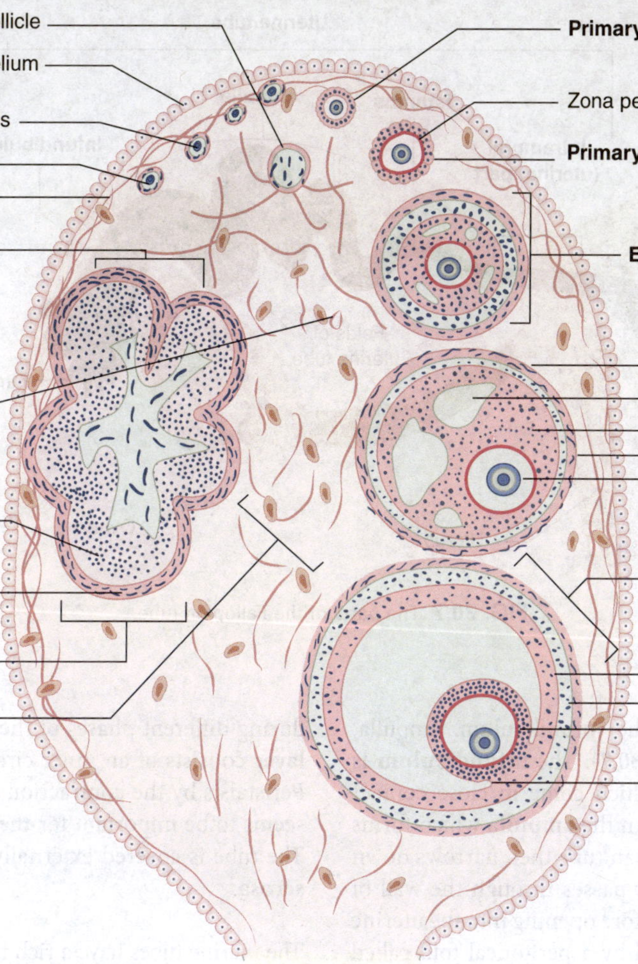

FIG. 30.6 The internal structure of the ovary.

early stages, there is disorganization of the follicular cells and degeneration of the oocyte. It is characterized in the later stages by the presence of fibroblasts in the follicle and a degenerated oocyte.

Following ovulation, the ruptured follicle reorganizes into a specialized endocrine structure called the **corpus luteum**. The walls of the remaining granulosa and theca interna cells are thrown into deep folds and a temporary **corpus haemorrhagicum** with a central blood clot is formed. Rich vascular networks arise from vessels of the theca interna and grow into the developing corpus luteum. Granulosa and theca interna cells increase in size and become filled with lipid droplets and are now, respectively, called granulosa **lutein cells** and theca lutein cells. The main function of the corpus luteum is to produce progesterone and oestrogens to sustain pregnancy till such time as the placenta can take over its functions. After the first trimester of pregnancy, or if pregnancy does not ensue, the corpus luteum degenerates into a fibrous scar called **corpus albicans**.

The bulk of the ovary, both cortex and medulla, consists of **stroma**. It consists of spindle-shaped stromal cells like fibroblasts and arranged in characteristic spirals. Unlike ordinary connective tissue, ovarian stroma is highly cellular while supporting fibres are inconspicuous. Stromal cells associated with maturing follicles acquire endocrine function and secrete oestrogens. The entire ovarian stroma is highly vascular. The **arterial supply** of the ovary is through the ovarian artery, which is a branch of the abdominal aorta. The **ovarian veins** drain into the inferior vena cava on the right side and left renal vein on the left. The **lymphatic drainage** is into the para-aortic group of lymph nodes.

Parasympathetic **nerve supply** is via the vagus while sympathetic nerve supply is from the T10 segment of the spinal cord.

THE FALLOPIAN TUBES

The Fallopian tubes, otherwise known as the **uterine tubes** or **oviducts**, function as a passage for the oocyte and are the sites of fertilization. Each tube extends from the lateral aspect of the upper part of the uterus to the ovary, which lies on the lateral pelvic wall. The lateral part of the tube is curved to come in close relation with the ovary. The **four subdivisions** of the Fallopian

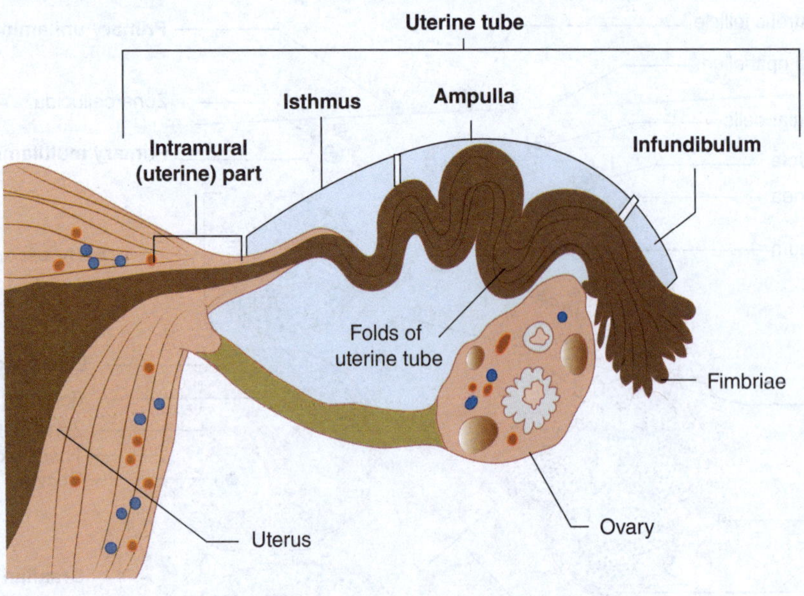

FIG. 30.7 The parts of the Fallopian tube.

tube from lateral to medial are the infundibulum, ampulla, isthmus and intramural part (Fig. 30.7). The **infundibulum** is funnel shaped and has fimbriae which come in close contact with the ovary. Fertilization occurs in the **ampulla** which forms a major part of the tube. The Fallopian tube then narrows down to form the **isthmus**, after which it passes through the wall of the uterus as the **intramural** part before opening into the uterine cavity. The uterine tube is enclosed by a peritoneal fold called the **mesosalpinx** which is the upper portion of the broad ligament of the uterus.

The wall of the uterine tube has three **layers**, namely the mucosa, muscularis and serosa (Fig. 30.8). The size of the lumen, shape of the mucosa and thickness of the muscularis vary along the length of the tube. The distinguishing feature of the **mucosa** is its many tall and branching longitudinal folds. The mucosa is formed by **simple columnar epithelium** resting on a very cellular lamina propria. Two types of cells, **ciliated cells** and nonciliated secretory cells called **peg cells**, can be distinguished in the epithelium. The activity of ciliated and secretory cells varies

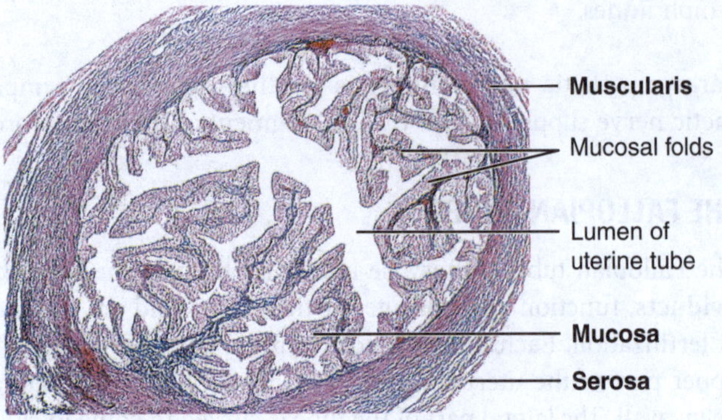

FIG. 30.8 The microstructure of the Fallopian tube.

during different phases of the menstrual cycle. The **muscularis layer** consists of an inner circular and outer longitudinal layer. Peristalsis by the contraction of smooth muscles of the oviduct seems to be important for the transport of sperms and oocytes. The tube is covered externally by peritoneum which forms the **serosa**.

The uterine tubes have a rich blood supply. The **arterial supply** is via the uterine and ovarian arteries which anastomose in the upper portion of the broad ligament. **Venous blood** accompanies the arteries to the inferior vena cava and internal iliac veins. **Lymphatic drainage** of the uterine tubes is to the iliac and para-aortic nodes. Sympathetic and parasympathetic **nerve supply** is from T11 to L1 and S2–S4 segments of the spinal cord, respectively.

THE UTERUS

In the nongravid state, the uterus lies within the **true pelvis**. However, major changes occur in pregnancy when the uterus reaches the level of the xiphisternum. The description that follows relates to a nongravid uterus. It resembles a **flattened pear** in shape and is about the size of a **clenched fist**. From superior to inferior, it has **three parts**, namely the fundus, body and cervix. It is both **anteflexed** and **anteverted**. Anteflexion refers to a forward bending of the body of the uterus on the cervix. Anteversion is a forward bending of the cervix on the vagina.

The part of the uterus above the entrance of uterine tubes is known as the **fundus** (Fig. 30.9). It is convex on all sides, directed forwards and covered by peritoneum. The cavity of the uterus does not extend into the fundus. The **body** of the uterus extends from the fundus to the isthmus. It is flattened anteroposteriorly and has two **surfaces**, two **borders** and a **uterine cavity**. The surfaces are the anterior or vesical surface and the posterior or

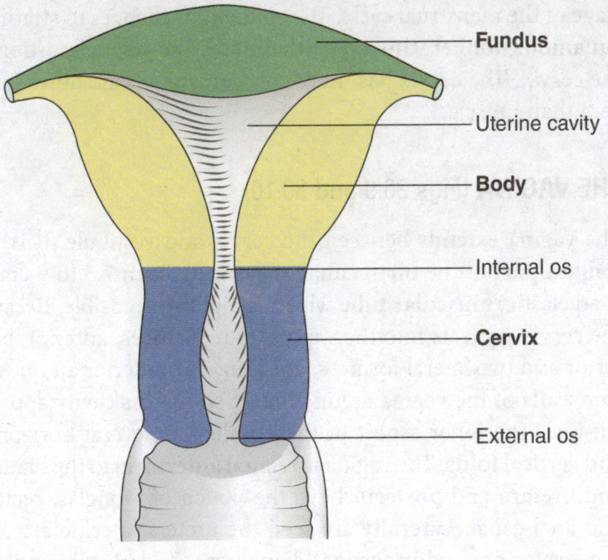

FIG. 30.9 The parts of the uterus.

intestinal surface. Separating the two surfaces are the lateral borders on either side. The **lateral angles** of the body are known as **cornua** which provide attachment to the uterine tube, round ligament and ovarian ligament. On taking a cross-section, the **uterine cavity** appears as a transverse slit, while in sagittal section, it appears as a vertical slit. It appears triangular with the base at the fundus and apex at the internal os in the coronal section. The **cervix** extends from the **internal os** to the **external os** and is around 1 inch long. Its upper portion is called the **isthmus.** The cavity of the cervix is the **cervical canal**. Palm-shaped folds from the walls of the cervix called arbor vitae uteri project into the cervical canal. It is divided into two parts, the **supravaginal** and **vaginal**, which lie above and within the vagina, respectively.

The **anterior surface** of the **body** of the **uterus** is **related** to the urinary bladder and vesicouterine pouch (Fig. 30.10). The relations of the **posterior surface** are the rectouterine pouch (of Douglas) along with the sigmoid colon and small intestine. The **broad ligament** and its contents are related to the lateral border. An important content of the broad ligament is the uterine artery. The **cervix** is related **anteriorly** to the upper part of the base of the bladder and **posteriorly** to the rectum. The **peritoneal folds** related to the uterus are the uterovesical folds, rectouterine folds and the broad ligament. The **uterovesical** and **rectouterine** folds pass anteriorly and posteriorly from the uterus to the urinary bladder and rectum, respectively. Hanging like curtains on either side of the uterus are the **broad ligaments** which have a quadrilateral outline (Fig. 30.8). The important contents of the broad ligaments are the uterine vessels and uterine tubes. The **mesovarium** and **mesosalpinx** are parts of the broad ligament that are related to the ovary and uterine tube, respectively. The remaining part of the broad ligament is called the **mesometrium.**

The uterus has several **supports** that prevent it from sinking from its position in the pelvis (Fig. 30.11). From below, the major

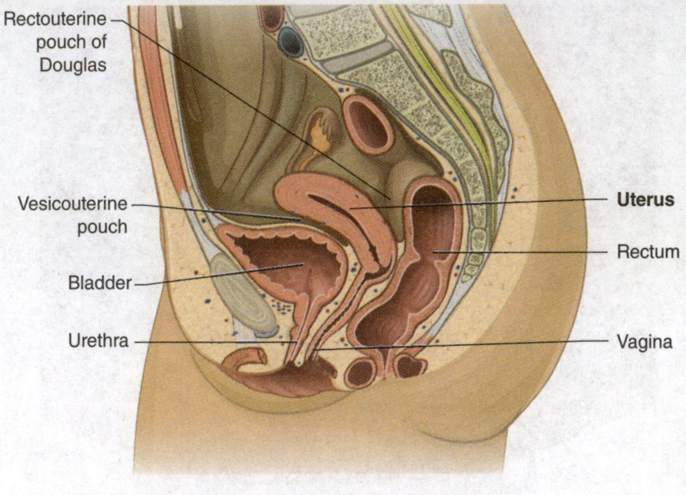

FIG. 30.10 The relations of the uterus.

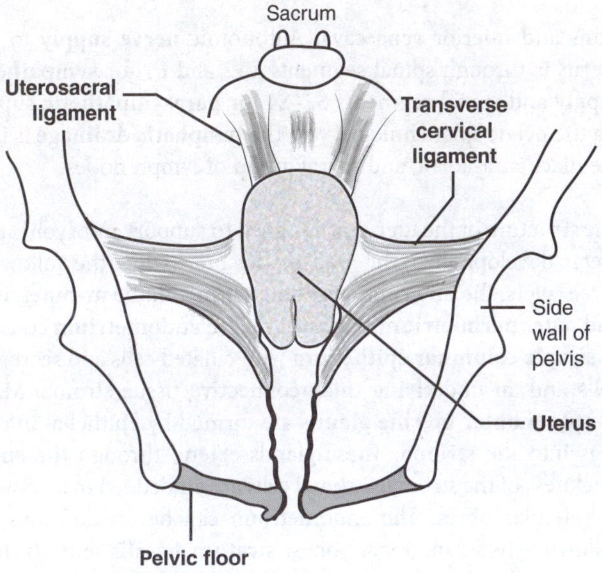

FIG. 30.11 The supports of the uterus.

supports provided to the uterus are **muscular.** These include the **pelvic diaphragm** which is constituted mainly by the levator ani muscle, the urogenital diaphragm and the perineal body. The **endopelvic fascial ligaments** provide the major anchors which pass from the cervix to the walls of the pelvis. These include the **transverse cervical**, pubocervical and uterosacral ligaments. Of these, the transverse cervical ligament is the most important of the fascial supports. Other factors that help to maintain the position of the uterus include peritoneal folds, the angles of anteversion and anteflexion and pressure from the surrounding viscera.

The **blood supply** of the uterus is mainly from the uterine and partly from the ovarian vessels. The **uterine** and **ovarian arteries** are branches of the internal iliac artery and abdominal aorta, respectively. The corresponding veins drain into the internal iliac

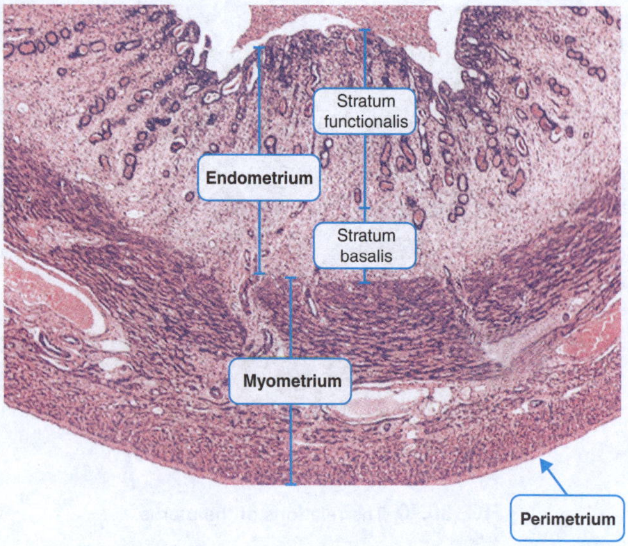

FIG. 30.12 The histology of the uterus.

veins and inferior vena cava. Autonomic **nerve supply** to the uterus is through spinal segments T12 and L1 for **sympathetic** supply and spinal segments S2–S4 for **parasympathetic** supply via the pelvic splanchnic nerves. The **lymphatic drainage** is into the iliac, para-aortic and sacral group of lymph nodes.

The structure of the uterus is designed to support embryonic and foetal development. The wall of the uterus has the following three layers: the innermost **endometrium**, middle **myometrium** and outer **perimetrium** (Fig. 30.12). The **endometrium** consists of **simple columnar epithelium** with ciliated cells and secretory cells and an underlying thick connective tissue stroma. Many **simple tubular uterine glands** are formed by epithelial infoldings into the **stroma**. These glands extend through the entire thickness of the stroma. Stromal cells are embedded in a network of reticular fibres. The endometrium can be divided into the following two functional zones: **stratum basalis** and **stratum functionalis**. The stratum basalis is not shed during menstruation but functions as a regenerative zone for the stratum functionalis after its shedding. In contrast, the stratum functionalis is shed during menstruation as it is the site of cyclic changes in the endometrium. The endometrium is highly **vascular** and has **basal arteries** in the stratum basalis which are permanent and **spiral arteries** in the stratum functionalis which are shed with the rest of the layer during menstruation. The **myometrium** is thick and consists of three poorly defined inner and outer longitudinal and middle circular smooth muscle layers. It undergoes both hyperplasia and hypertrophy in response to the hormonal changes of pregnancy. The **perimetrium** is mostly covered by serosa and partly by adventitia.

The **endometrium** of the **cervix** differs from the rest of the uterus. It has numerous branching, mucus-secreting glands called **cervical glands**. No spiral arteries are seen, and it does not change in thickness or become sloughed off during the menstrual cycle. The quantity and nature of mucus change with the stage of the menstrual cycle. The epithelium changes to stratified **squamous nonkeratinized epithelium** at the vaginal portion of the cervix. The cervix has more collagen and elastic fibres in its wall than muscle.

THE VAGINA (Figs 30.9 and 30.10)

The vagina **extends** between the cervix and vestibule. It is the **longest part** of the **birth canal**, measuring from 7.5 to 9 cm. It is an elastic, **muscular tube** which is highly distensible. Because the cervix projects into the vagina, four **fornices**, anterior, posterior and two lateral fornices, are seen. The anterior and posterior **walls** of the vagina are in contact so that its cavity appears slit-like. The inner aspect of these walls has several horizontal and vertical **folds**. The vagina is **related anteriorly** to the bladder and urethra and **posteriorly** to the pouch of Douglas, rectum and anal canal. **Laterally** are seen the ureters, uterine arteries, the levator ani and urogenital diaphragm. The **blood supply** is mainly via the vaginal vessels and partly via the uterine vessels, as well as the internal pudendal and middle rectal vessels. The **autonomic nerve supply** is via the spinal segments L1 and L2 for the sympathetic component and pelvic splanchnic nerves from the S2–S4 segments for the parasympathetic component. **Lymphatic drainage** from the upper portion of the vagina is into the external and internal iliac nodes, the lower portion draining into the superficial inguinal lymph nodes.

Histologically, the vagina is a fibromuscular tube with a wall consisting of **three layers**, namely the mucosa, muscularis and adventitia. The **mucosa** is lined by stratified squamous nonkeratinized epithelium resting on a very cellular lamina propria. Vascular cavernous spaces may be seen in the deeper mucosa. The **muscularis** consists of inner circular and outer longitudinal layers of smooth muscle. Inferiorly, the bulbospongiosus muscle forms a sphincter around the vagina. The **adventitia** contains many elastic fibres with a prominent venous plexus.

THE BREAST (Fig. 30.13)

The breast is an accessory gland of the female reproductive system. It is bilaterally situated in the **pectoral region** of both sexes. Developmentally, it is derived from ectoderm and is a **modified sweat gland**. It is rudimentary in males and prepubertal females. However, it undergoes several **changes** during puberty, pregnancy and lactation. Its **vertical extent** is from the third to the sixth rib and **horizontal extent** from the sternum to the axilla. It is surrounded by superficial fascia and rests on the deep fascia beneath which is the pectoralis major muscle. A **retromammary space** separates the breast tissue from the underlying deep fascia enabling it to move freely over the deep structures. The **nipple** is a darkly pigmented elevation on the breast where its ducts open. A darkly pigmented area surrounding the nipple is the **areola** which contains small elevations called Montgomery's tubercles. These are modified sebaceous glands which help to prevent drying of the area. An extension of breast tissue into the axilla is called the **axillary tail of Spence**. **Suspensory ligaments of Cooper** extend from the deep fascia

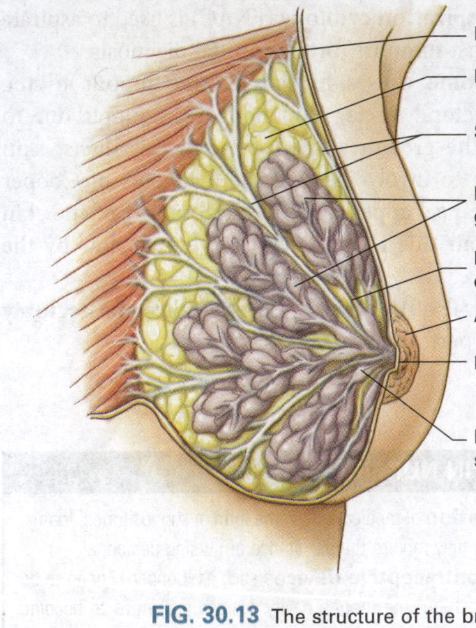

FIG. 30.13 The structure of the breast.

to the skin, helping to maintain the structural integrity of the breast. The areas between the ligaments are filled with fat and breast tissue.

The **arterial supply** of the breast is mainly through branches of the first and second parts of the axillary artery and internal thoracic artery (Fig. 30.14). **Venous drainage** is into the corresponding veins. The **nerve supply** is through the fourth to sixth intercostal nerves. **Lymphatic drainage** of the breast is mainly into the axillary and internal mammary lymph nodes. Among the axillary groups, most of the lymph drains into the anterior group of lymph nodes. From here, the lymph eventually reaches the right lymphatic and thoracic ducts through the apical group of axillary lymph nodes. Some of the lymphatics cross the midline to drain into nodes on the opposite side. The posterior intercostal lymph nodes drain a small portion of lymph from the breast.

Histologically, the breast is a compound **tubuloalveolar** gland. Like other exocrine glands, it consists of both parenchyma and stroma (Fig. 30.13). The **parenchyma** is arranged in the form of lobes containing glandular tissue separated by dense interlobar connective tissue and fat which form the **stroma.** The glandular tissue contains secretory units called alveoli, which are lined by cuboidal or columnar epithelium. The excretory duct of each lobule, called the **lactiferous duct**, has its own opening on the nipple. Each lactiferous duct has a dilatation called the **lactiferous sinus** before it opens at the nipple. Myoepithelial cells surround the secretory elements to enable expulsion of secretions from the alveoli. Widespread changes occur to the histology of the breast during **pregnancy** and **lactation**, with the parenchyma expanding greatly relative to the stroma to fulfil its function of lactation.

THE EXTERNAL GENITALIA (Fig. 30.2)

The external genitalia are located in a region called the **vulva** and consist of the mons pubis, labia majora, labia minora and

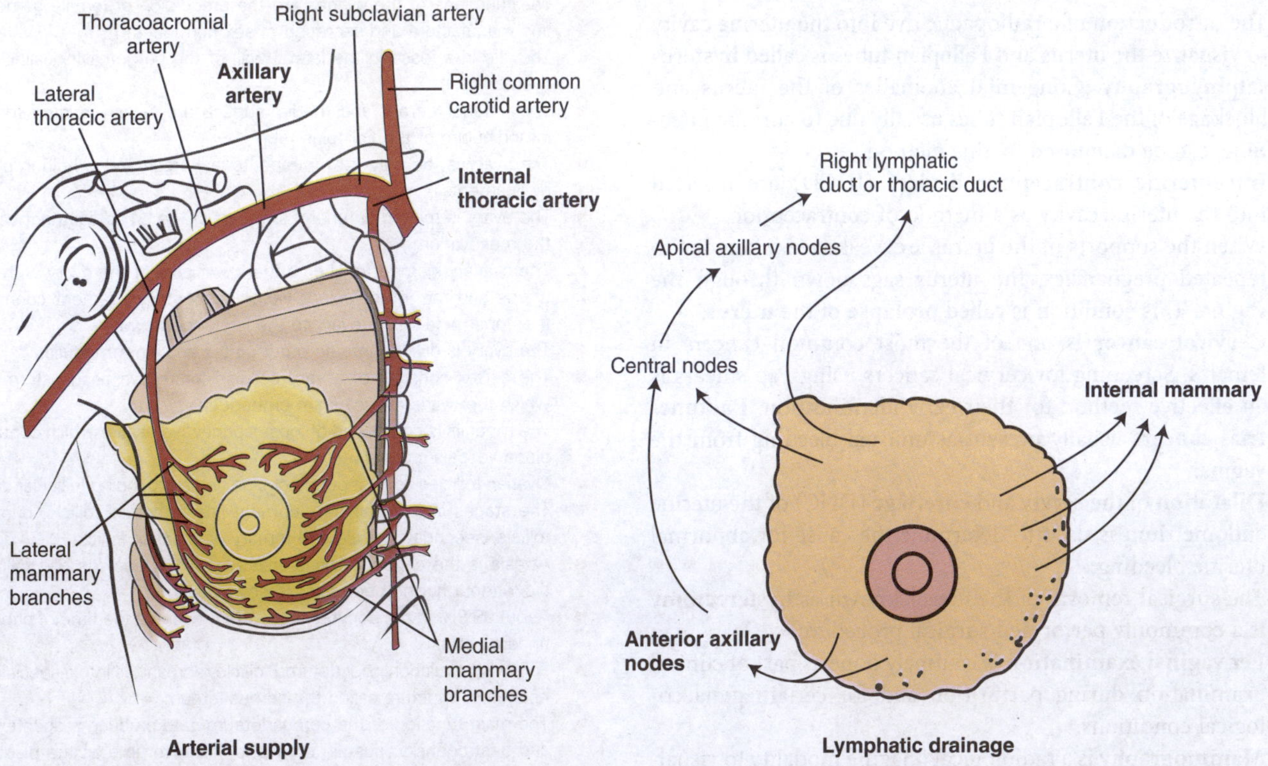

FIG. 30.14 The blood supply and lymphatic drainage of the breast.

vestibule. The **mons pubis** is the area that lies just superior to the vestibule and contains pubic hair. The **labia majora** and **minora** are folds that are lined by skin resting on a loose, fatty, vascular lamina propria. From anterior to posterior, the **vestibule** contains the clitoris, urethral orifice and vaginal orifice. The **clitoris** contains erectile tissue like the penis. **Bartholin's glands** are mucus-secreting, compound, tubuloalveolar glands homologous to Cowper's glands in males, which open into the vestibule and whose secretions are released during sexual stimulation. The **hymen** is a connective tissue fold that partially covers the vaginal orifice in virgin females.

APPLIED ANATOMY

- **Ovarian cysts** are most commonly remnants of previous ovarian cycles or rarely an indication of an underlying carcinoma. Polycystic ovarian syndrome is associated with multiple ovarian cysts and sex hormonal imbalances. It is one of the more common causes of female infertility.
- Surgical removal of the ovaries is known as **oophorectomy**.
- In **assisted reproductive techniques**, the ovaries are artificially stimulated to produce oocytes which are then fertilized by spermatozoa, either in vitro or in vivo.
- The **uterus** undergoes tremendous changes in size, shape and structure during **pregnancy**. The muscle cells in the myometrium undergo great hypertrophy and hyperplasia such that the uterus reaches the xiphisternum at full term.
- **Caesarean section** refers to delivery of the newborn through an incision made through the anterior abdominal and uterine walls. It is one of the most commonly performed operations.
- The introduction of a radiopaque dye into the uterine cavity to visualize the uterus and Fallopian tubes is called **hysterosalpingography**. Congenital anomalies of the uterus and blockage of the Fallopian tubes usually due to chronic infections can be diagnosed by this method.
- **Intrauterine contraceptive devices** (IUCD) are inserted into the uterine cavity as a method of contraception.
- When the supports of the uterus are weakened, often due to repeated pregnancies, the uterus sags down through the vagina. This condition is called **prolapse** of the **uterus**.
- **Cervical cancer** is one of the most common cancers in females. Screening for cervical cancers using Pap smears is an effective method for their early identification. **Endometrial cancers** usually present as unusual bleeding from the vagina.
- **Dilatation** of the cervix and **curettage** (DNC) of the uterine endometrium is used to determine the cause for abnormal uterine bleeding.
- The surgical removal of the uterus known as **hysterectomy** is a commonly performed surgical procedure.
- **Per vaginal examination** is routinely done as part of clinical examination during parturition and for certain gynaecological conditions.
- **Mammography** is a radiological imaging modality to visualize breast tissue and screen for breast cancer.
- **Fine-needle aspiration cytology** (FNAC) is used to aspirate cells from breast tumours for their initial diagnosis.
- **Breast carcinoma** causes fixation of the tumour to the underlying pectoral fascia, retraction of the nipple due to extension of the growth along the lactiferous ducts, skin retraction due to involvement of the ligaments of Cooper and an orange peel appearance (peau d'orange) of the skin over the tumour due to obstruction of lymph flow by the malignant cells.
- Surgical removal of the breast tissue is called **mastectomy** and is usually performed for breast cancers.

APPLICATIONS IN NURSING

- **Vaginal instillation** of medications in the form of suppositories, foams, jellies and creams may require the assistance of nursing personnel.
- **Intrauterine contraceptive devices** such as 'Copper-T' need to be inserted or removed into the uterine cavity. Nurses may have to become familiar with this procedure.

SUMMARY

- The female reproductive system consists of the internal organs, namely the ovaries, oviducts, uterus and vagina.
- The external genitalia include the vestibule, clitoris, labia majora and labia minora.
- The mammary gland is an accessory reproductive gland.
- In addition, special structures like the placenta and umbilical cord develop during pregnancy.
- The ovaries are small, oval, paired organs in the pelvic cavity.
- The functions of the ovaries are the production of female gametes and manufacture and secretion of sex hormones.
- They lie in a fossa in the lateral wall of the pelvic cavity called the ovarian fossa.
- The anterior border and medial surface are closely related to the infundibulum of the Fallopian tube.
- The ovary is the only truly intraperitoneal organ and is held in place by ligaments.
- The ovary is related anteriorly to a part of the broad ligament called the mesovarium.
- The ovarian ligament connects the lower pole of the ovary with the uterus and the infundibulopelvic or suspensory ligament connects the upper pole of the ovary to the lateral pelvic wall.
- The ovary is divided into an outer cortex and inner medulla.
- The cortex consists of a very cellular connective tissue stroma in which the ovarian follicles are embedded.
- The medulla is composed of loose connective tissue, which contains blood vessels and nerves.
- Ovarian follicles consist of one oocyte and surrounding follicular cells.
- The stages in follicular development are primordial follicle, primary follicle, secondary follicle and tertiary or Graafian follicle.
- Atresia is the degenerative process by which oocytes and follicles die without having been expelled by ovulation.
- About 99.9% of the oocytes that were present at the time of puberty undergo atresia.
- Following ovulation, the ruptured follicle reorganizes into a specialized endocrine structure called the corpus luteum.
- The main function of the corpus luteum is to produce progesterone and oestrogens to sustain pregnancy till such time as the placenta can take over its functions.

- After the first trimester of pregnancy, or if pregnancy does not ensue, the corpus luteum degenerates into a fibrous scar called corpus albicans.
- The bulk of the ovary, both cortex and medulla, consists of a vascular stroma.
- The arterial supply of the ovary is through the ovarian artery, which is a branch of the abdominal aorta.
- The ovarian veins drain into the inferior vena cava on the right side and left renal vein on the left.
- The lymphatic drainage is into the para-aortic group of lymph nodes.
- Parasympathetic nerve supply is via the vagus while sympathetic nerve supply is from the T10 segment of the spinal cord.
- The Fallopian tubes, otherwise known as the uterine tubes or oviducts, function as a passage for the oocyte and are the sites of fertilization.
- Each tube extends from the lateral aspect of the upper part of the uterus to the ovary.
- The four subdivisions of the Fallopian tube from lateral to medial are the infundibulum, ampulla, isthmus and intramural part.
- Fertilization occurs in the ampulla which forms a major part of the tube.
- The uterine tube is enclosed by a peritoneal fold called the mesosalpinx which is the upper portion of the broad ligament of the uterus.
- The wall of the uterine tube has three layers, the mucosa, muscularis and serosa.
- The characteristic feature of the mucosa is its many tall and branching longitudinal folds.
- The mucosa is formed by simple columnar epithelium resting on a very cellular lamina propria.
- The arterial supply is via the uterine and ovarian arteries which anastomose in the upper portion of the broad ligament.
- Venous blood accompanies the arteries to the inferior vena cava and internal iliac veins.
- Lymphatic drainage of the uterine tubes is to the iliac and para-aortic nodes.
- Sympathetic and parasympathetic nerve supply is from T11 to L1 and S2 to S4 segments of the spinal cord, respectively.
- In the nongravid state, the uterus lies within the true pelvis.
- It resembles a flattened pear in shape and is about the size of a clenched fist.
- From above downwards, it has three parts, the fundus, body and cervix.
- It is both anteflexed and anteverted.
- It is flattened anteroposteriorly and has two surfaces, two borders and a uterine cavity.
- The surfaces are the anterior or vesical surface and the posterior or intestinal surface.
- Separating the two surfaces are the lateral borders on either side.
- The cervix extends from the internal os to the external os and is around 1 inch long.
- The anterior surface of the body of the uterus is related to the urinary bladder and vesicouterine pouch.
- The relations of the posterior surface are the rectouterine pouch (of Douglas) along with the sigmoid colon and small intestine.
- The broad ligament and its contents are related to the lateral border.
- The peritoneal folds related to the uterus are the uterovesical folds, rectouterine folds and the broad ligament.
- Hanging like curtains on either side of the uterus are the broad ligaments.
- The important contents of the broad ligaments are the uterine vessels and uterine tubes.
- The mesovarium and mesosalpinx are parts of the broad ligament that are related to the ovary and uterine tube, respectively.
- The remaining part of the broad ligament is called the mesometrium.
- The uterus has several supports that prevent it from sinking from its position in the pelvis.
- From below, the major supports provided to the uterus are muscular.
- These include the pelvic diaphragm which is constituted mainly by the levator ani muscle, the urogenital diaphragm and the perineal body.
- The endopelvic fascial ligaments provide the major anchors which pass from the cervix to the walls of the pelvis.
- These include the transverse cervical, pubocervical and uterosacral ligaments.
- The blood supply of the uterus is mainly from the uterine and partly from the ovarian vessels.
- Autonomic nerve supply to the uterus is through spinal segments T12 and L1 for sympathetic supply and spinal segments S2–S4 for parasympathetic supply via the pelvic splanchnic nerves.
- The lymphatic drainage is into the iliac, para-aortic and sacral group of lymph nodes.
- The wall of the uterus has the following three layers: the innermost endometrium, middle myometrium and outer perimetrium.
- The endometrium can be divided into the following two functional zones: stratum basalis and stratum functionalis.
- The stratum basalis is not sloughed off during menstruation but functions as a regenerative zone for the stratum functionalis after its shedding.
- In contrast, the stratum functionalis is sloughed off during every menstruation as it is the site of cyclic changes in the endometrium.
- The myometrium is thick and consists of three poorly defined inner and outer longitudinal and middle circular smooth muscle layers.
- The perimetrium is mostly covered by serosa and partly by adventitia.
- The vagina extends between the cervix and vestibule.
- It is an elastic, muscular tube which is highly distensible.
- Because the cervix projects into the vagina, four fornices, anterior, posterior and two lateral fornices, are seen.
- The blood supply is mainly via the vaginal vessels and partly via the uterine vessels, as well as the internal pudendal and middle rectal vessels.
- The autonomic nerve supply is via the spinal segments L1 and L2 for the sympathetic component and pelvic splanchnic nerves arising from the S2 to S4 segments for the parasympathetic component.
- Lymphatic drainage from the upper portion of the vagina is into the external and internal iliac nodes, the lower portion draining into the superficial inguinal lymph nodes.
- The breast is an accessory gland of the female reproductive system.
- Developmentally, it is derived from ectoderm and is a modified sweat gland.
- The nipple is a darkly pigmented elevation on the breast where its ducts open.
- A darkly pigmented area surrounding the nipple is the areola which contains small elevations called Montgomery's tubercles.
- An extension of breast tissue into the axilla is called the axillary tail of Spence.
- Suspensory ligaments of Cooper extend from the deep fascia to the skin, helping to maintain the structural integrity of the breast.
- The areas between the ligaments are filled by fat and breast tissue.
- The arterial supply of the breast is mainly through branches of the first and second parts of the axillary artery and internal thoracic artery.
- The nerve supply is through the fourth to sixth intercostal nerves.
- Lymphatic drainage of the breast is mainly into the axillary and internal mammary lymph nodes.
- Histologically, the breast is a compound tubuloalveolar gland.
- The excretory duct of each lobule, called the lactiferous duct, has its own opening on the nipple.
- Widespread changes occur to the histology of the breast during pregnancy and lactation, with the parenchyma expanding greatly relative to the stroma to fulfil its function of lactation.
- The external genitalia are located in a region called the vulva and consist of the mons pubis, labia majora, labia minora and vestibule.
- Bartholin's glands are mucus-secreting, compound, tubuloalveolar glands homologous to Cowper's glands in males.
- The hymen is a connective tissue fold that partially covers the vaginal orifice in virgin females.

CHAPTER 31

The Male Reproductive System

SPECIFIC LEARNING OBJECTIVES

At the end of this chapter, the student should be able to:

- Describe the parts and functions of the male reproductive system.
- Describe the gross anatomy, histology and applied anatomy of the testis.
- Describe the gross anatomy, histology and applied anatomy of the ducts of the male reproductive system.
- Describe the gross anatomy, histology and applied anatomy of the accessory glands of the male reproductive system.

GLOSSARY OF TERMS

- **Tunica vaginalis:** mesothelial covering of the testes
- **Tunica albuginea:** connective tissue covering of the testes
- **Tunica vasculosa:** innermost vascular covering of the testes
- **Seminiferous tubules:** tubules within the testes lined by spermatogenic and supporting cells
- **Spermatogenic cells:** cells which divide to form spermatozoa
- **Sertoli cells:** supporting cells seen within seminiferous tubules
- **Interstitial cells of Leydig:** cells seen between seminiferous tubules that secrete testosterone
- **Pampiniform plexus of veins:** plexus of veins draining the testes
- **Corpora amylacea:** calcified secretions located within prostatic acini
- **Glans penis:** the expanded distal end of the body of the penis
- **Prepuce:** fold of skin covering the glans penis
- **Bulb of the penis:** erectile tissue located in the middle of the root of the penis
- **Crura:** erectile tissue situated on either side of the bulb
- **Corpora cavernosa:** erectile tissue situated dorsolaterally within the body of the penis
- **Corpus spongiosum:** erectile tissue situated ventrally within the body of the penis
- **Buck's fascia:** fascia surrounding the circumference of the penis
- **Tunica albuginea:** connective tissue covering of the corpora cavernosa
- **Dartos:** smooth muscle of the scrotum

INTRODUCTION

The male reproductive system is specialized to produce, transport and release the male gamete. Like the female reproductive system, it can be divided into the internal and external genitalia (Fig. 31.1). The internal genitalia include the testis, epididymis, vas deferens, ejaculatory ducts, seminal vesicles, prostate gland and bulbourethral glands. The external genitalia include the scrotum, penis and male urethra (Fig. 31.2). The male reproductive system can also be functionally divided into the gonad (organ of gamete production), the duct system (to transport the gamete), accessory glands (to add to the bulk of the semen and aid in the transport of the gamete) and the organ of copulation. The functions of the male reproductive system are controlled by hormones secreted by the pituitary gland and testis.

THE TESTES (Fig. 31.3)

The testes are the **male gonads** that are homologous to the ovaries. They are **ovoid** in shape, weigh between 10 and 15 g and measure around 5 cm in length, 3 cm in breadth and 2.5 cm in thickness. Each testis has upper and lower **poles**, anterior and posterior **borders** and medial and lateral **surfaces**. From outside to inside, the testes are covered by the tunica vaginalis, tunica albuginea and tunica vasculosa. The **tunica vaginalis** is a smooth, mesothelial covering of the testes derived from the peritoneum. The **tunica albuginea** consists of closely packed collagen and elastic fibres. Loose areolar, vascular tissue underlies the tunica albuginea, forming the **tunica vasculosa**. Multiple septa extend from the **mediastinum testis**, a thickened area of the tunica albuginea, into the substance of the testis, dividing it into 200–300 **lobules**. Each lobule contains highly coiled **seminiferous tubules** which are lined by cells producing spermatozoa. Between the seminiferous tubules are seen clusters of **interstitial cells of Leydig** which secrete testosterone. The seminiferous tubules continue as **straight tubules**, which form **efferent ductules**, which in turn join to form a single tube called the **epididymis**.

The **arterial supply** of the testes is via the testicular artery which is a branch of the abdominal aorta. **Venous blood** from the testes

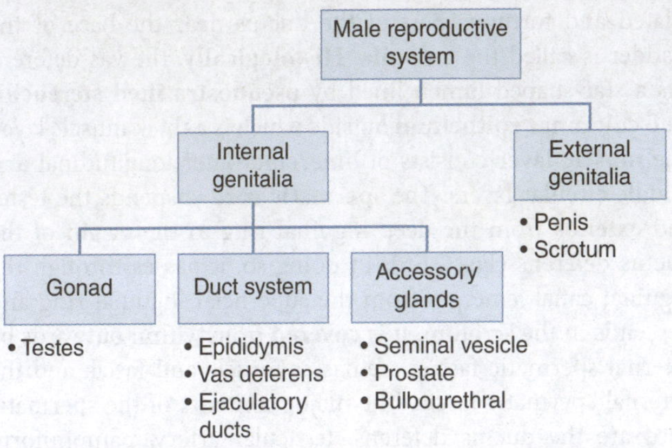

FIG. 31.1 The parts of the male reproductive system.

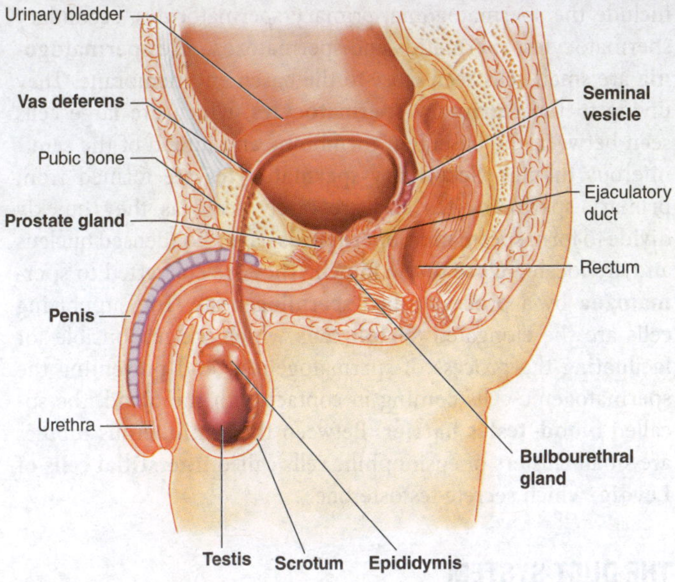

FIG. 31.2 Parts of the male reproductive system.

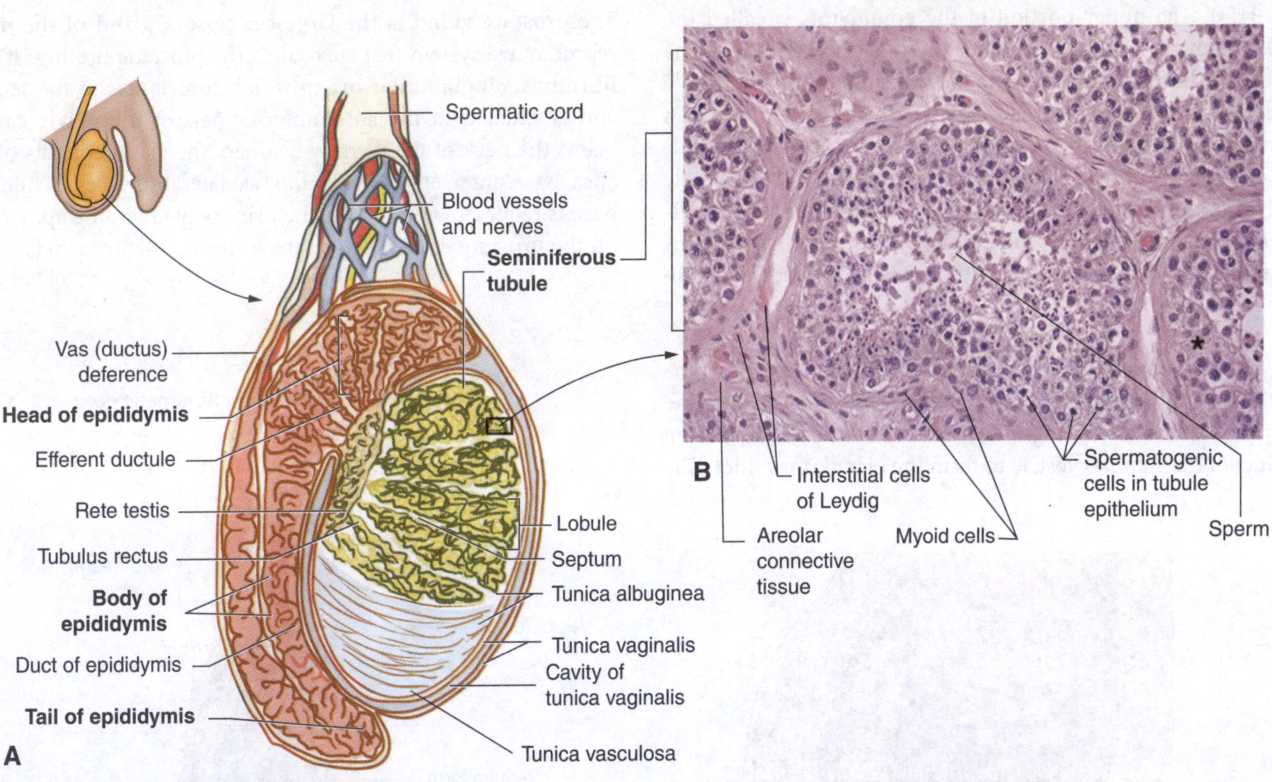

FIG. 31.3 The gross anatomy **(A)** and microscopic anatomy **(B)** of the testis.

drains into the pampiniform plexus of veins which continues as the testicular vein on each side. On the right side, the testicular vein drains into the inferior vena cava, whereas it drains into the left renal vein on the left side. The **lymphatic drainage** of the testes is into the para-aortic group of lymph nodes. **Sympathetic nerve supply** arises from the T10 segment of the spinal cord. The testes develop in the lumbar region and subsequently **descend** through the inguinal canal in the seventh month of foetal life, reaching the scrotal sac by the ninth month. As the testes descend, they carry their blood supply with them, explaining the origin of the testicular arteries from the abdominal aorta.

Histologically, each **seminiferous tubule** is enclosed by a basement membrane and myoid cells, which resemble smooth muscle cells. The seminiferous tubules are lined by **spermatogenic** and **supporting cells** (Fig. 31.3). The spermatogenic cells include the spermatogonia, primary spermatocytes, secondary spermatocytes, spermatids and spermatozoa. The **spermatogonia** are small cells seen close to the basement membrane. They divide to form **primary spermatocytes**, which are large cells seen between the basement membrane and lumen of the seminiferous tubules. **Secondary spermatocytes** are formed from primary spermatocytes and are rarely seen, as they quickly divide to form spermatids. **Spermatids** have a condensed nucleus and are located close to the lumen. They are converted to **spermatozoa** by a process called spermiogenesis. The supporting cells are the elongated **Sertoli cells** which are responsible for facilitating the process of spermatogenesis and preventing the spermatogenic cells coming in contact with the blood, the so-called **blood–testes barrier**. Between the seminiferous tubules are small clusters of eosinophilic cells called **interstitial cells of Leydig**, which secrete testosterone.

THE DUCT SYSTEM

The **epididymis** is a highly **coiled tube** that is formed by fusion of the efferent ductules near the upper pole of the testis (Fig. 31.3). The upper portion of the epididymis is called the **head**, which then continues along the posterior border of the testis as the **body**, finally forming the **tail** close to the lower pole of the testis. It then continues as the ductus deferens. On a **microscopic section**, the epididymis is seen to consist of multiple rounded outlines. This is because, although it is a single tube, it is highly coiled. The lining is **pseudostratified stereociliated columnar epithelium** surrounding a lumen which contains numerous spermatozoa. Each outline is surrounded by a thin layer of smooth muscle.

The **vas deferens** or ductus deferens is a thick muscular tube which is a continuation of the duct of the epididymis near the lower pole of the testes (Fig. 31.4). Each ductus ends by joining the duct of the seminal vesicle to form the **ejaculatory duct**. The dilated and tortuous part of the ductus near the base of the bladder is called the **ampulla**. **Histologically**, the vas deferens has a star-shaped lumen lined by **pseudostratified stereociliated columnar epithelium** outside which is a thick muscle layer. The **muscle layer** consists of inner and outer longitudinal and middle circular layers. The **spermatic cord** suspends the testes and **extends** from the deep inguinal ring to the origin of the ductus deferens (Fig. 31.5). In doing so, it passes through the inguinal canal, emerges from the superficial inguinal ring and descends in the scrotum. It is **covered** from within outwards by internal spermatic fascia, cremaster muscle and fascia and the external spermatic fascia. The major **contents** of the spermatic cord are the ductus deferens, testicular artery, pampiniform plexus of veins, lymph vessels from the testes and autonomic nerves supplying the testes. The **ejaculatory ducts** are formed by fusion of the vas deferens and duct of the seminal vesicle. They are about 2.5 cm long and open into the **prostatic urethra** on each side (Fig. 31.6).

THE ACCESSORY GLANDS (Fig. 31.6)

The **prostate gland** is the largest accessory gland of the male reproductive system that surrounds the prostatic urethra. It is a **fibromusculoglandular organ** which contributes to the semen and is situated in the anteroinferior part of the **pelvic cavity** below the neck of the urinary bladder. The gland consists of an apex, base, anterior, posterior and two lateral surfaces. While the **base** is related to the neck of the urinary bladder, the **apex** rests on the urogenital diaphragm. The **anterior surface** is related to

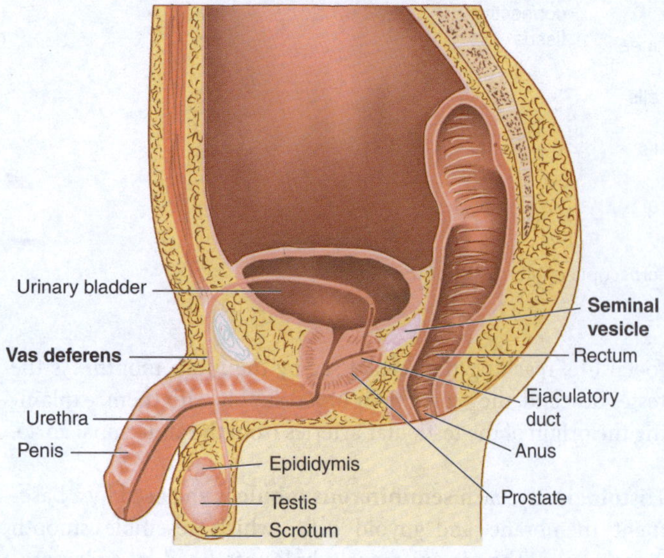

FIG. 31.4 The anatomy of the vas deferens.

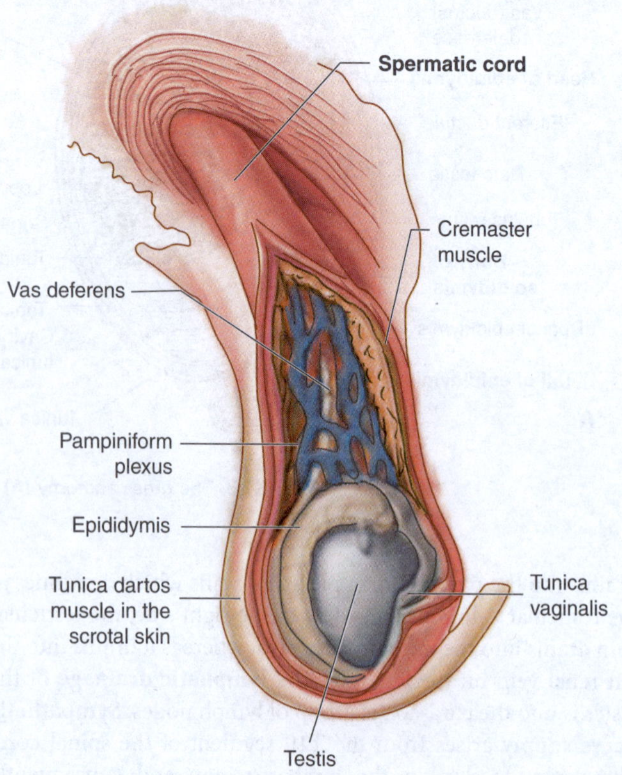

FIG. 31.5 The anatomy of the spermatic cord.

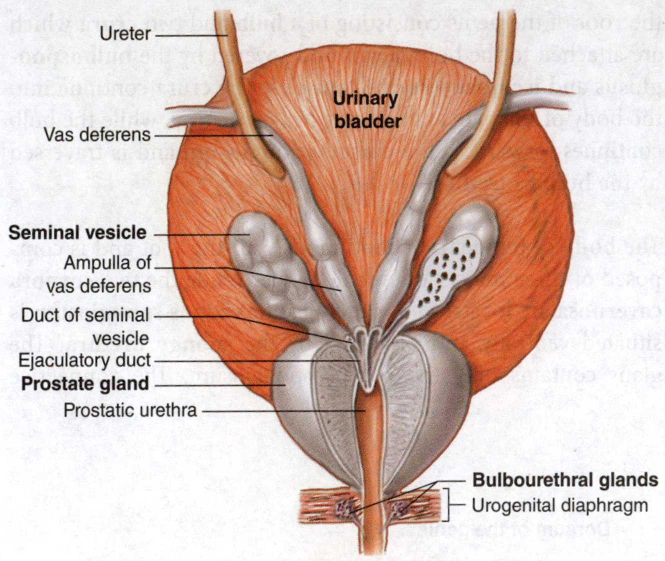

FIG. 31.6 The anatomy of the accessory glands.

the posterior surface of the body of the pubis, whereas the **posterior surface** is related to the rectum. Two **capsules**, an outer false and inner true capsule, surround the prostate gland. The prostatic **venous plexus** is seen between the two capsules. The **prostatic urethra** traverses the gland from the base to the apex and receives the openings of the **ejaculatory ducts** near its middle. **Histologically**, the prostate has numerous **acini**, the ducts of which open into the prostatic urethra (Fig. 31.7). Calcified prostatic secretions called prostatic concretions or **corpora amylacea** can often be seen in the lumen of the acini. The **stroma** consists of fibrous tissue and smooth muscle. The glandular tissue is divided into **three concentric zones** (Fig. 31.8). The zone that immediately surrounds the urethra is the transition zone. The central zone lies between the transition zone on the inside and peripheral zone on the outside. The prostate gland is supplied by the inferior vesical artery, a branch of the internal iliac artery. Venous drainage is via the prostatic venous plexus which drains into the internal iliac vein.

The **seminal vesicles** are thin-walled structures situated between the base of the bladder and the rectum (Fig. 31.6). They secrete a **thick alkaline fluid** which contributes to most of the volume of semen. The ducts of the seminal vesicles join the ductus deferens on each side to form the ejaculatory ducts. The seminal vesicle consists of a single tube which is highly coiled. **Histologically**, the gland is seen to consist of multiple rounded profiles lined by a pale-staining pseudostratified columnar epithelium. The **bulbourethral glands** contribute a mucus secretion to the semen and are situated on either side of the membranous urethra (Fig. 31.6). Their ducts open into the penile urethra. **Histologically**, they are seen to consist of typical mucous acini.

THE PENIS

It is the male organ of **copulation** and consists of a **root** and **body**. The root is the proximal part that is attached to the bony pelvis, whereas the body is the free distal portion. The distal end of the penis is enlarged to from the **glans penis** and contains the **external urethral orifice** (Fig. 31.9). The skin and fascia over the body are prolonged over the glans as a free fold known as the **prepuce**. The prepuce is connected to the undersurface of the glans by an elastic fold called the **frenulum**. A sulcus called the **corona** separates the glans from the rest of the body. The **skin** over the penis is freely movable due to the loose nature of the underlying connective tissue.

Much of the penis is occupied by masses of **erectile tissue** (Fig. 31.10). Erectile tissue consists of spaces located within fibrous connective tissue and lined by endothelium. This tissue gets engorged with blood during the process of erection. The erectile tissue is organized into a proximal portion located within

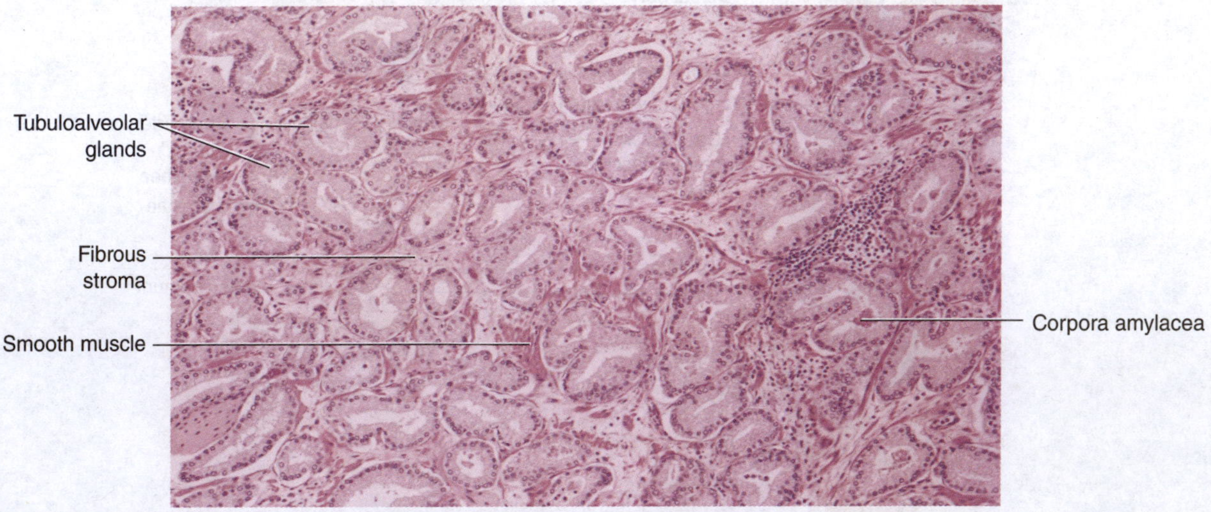

FIG. 31.7 The microstructure of the prostate gland.

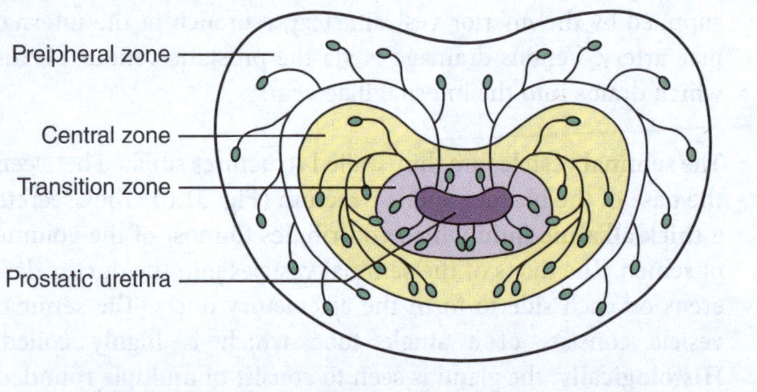

FIG. 31.8 The zonal anatomy of the prostate gland.

the **root** of the penis consisting of a **bulb** and two **crura** which are attached to the bony pelvis and covered by the **bulbospongiosus** and **ischiocavernosus** muscles. The crura continue into the body of the penis as the **corpora cavernosa**, while the bulb continues forward as the **corpus spongiosum** and is traversed by the **bulbar urethra**.

The **body** of the penis is continuous with the root and is composed of three masses of erectile tissue. While the two **corpora cavernosa** are located dorsolaterally, the **corpus spongiosum** is situated ventrally and traversed by the **spongy urethra**. The glans contains only the corpus spongiosum. The connective

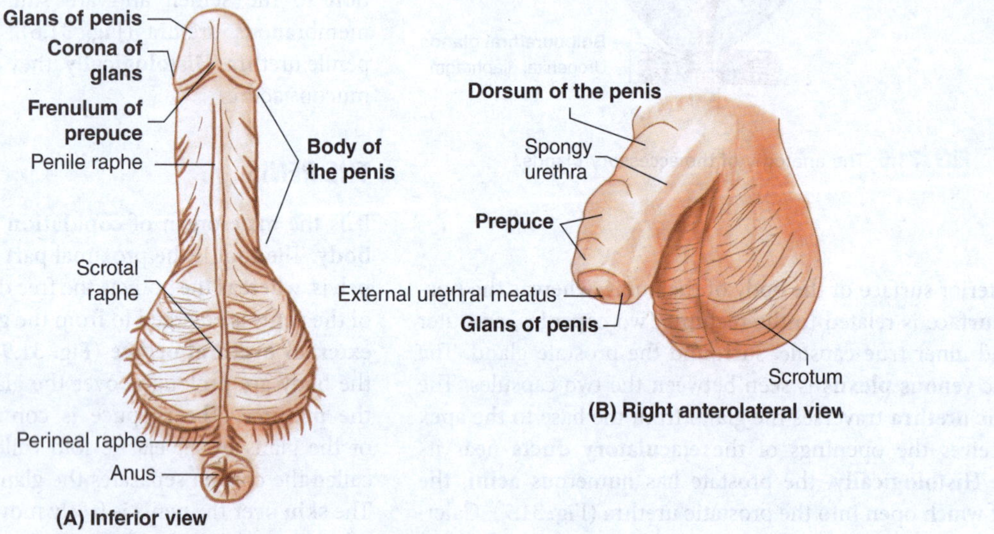

FIG. 31.9 The external anatomy of the penis.

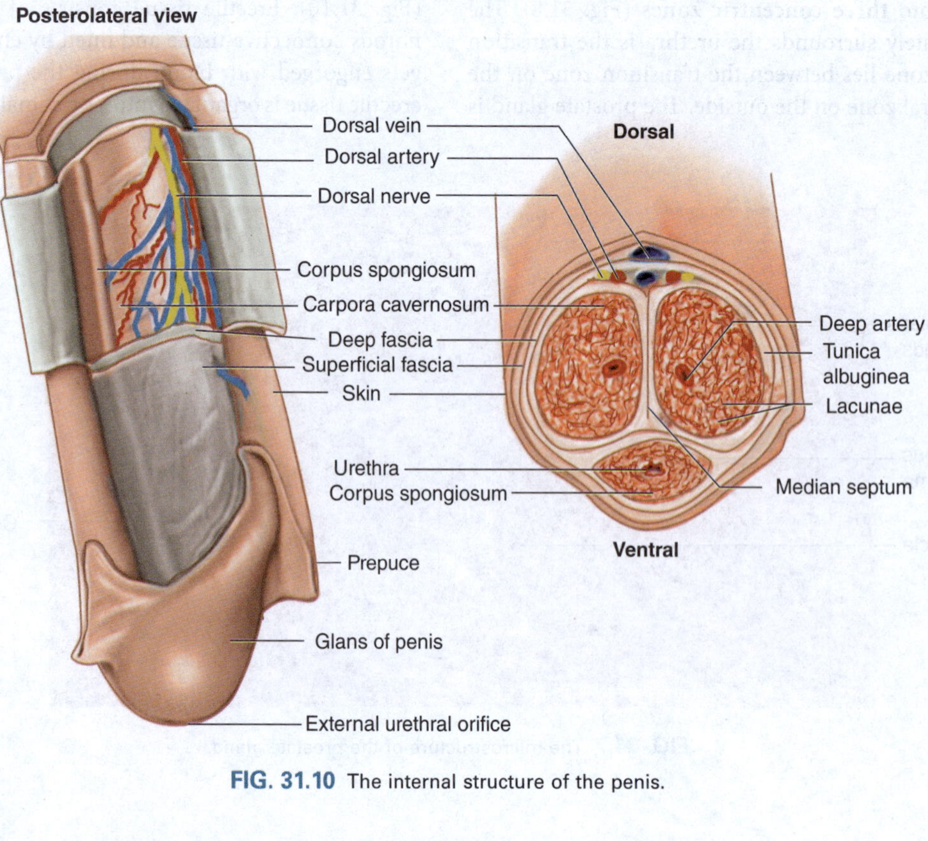

FIG. 31.10 The internal structure of the penis.

tissue of the penis is organized in the form of a tough deep fascial covering called **Buck's fascia**, which encloses the entire circumference of the penis, and the **tunica albuginea** which covers the two corpora cavernosa. The penis is also supported by two **ligaments** called the fundiform ligament and suspensory ligament.

The **arterial supply** of the penis is via branches of the internal pudendal artery which separately supply the corpora cavernosa, corpus spongiosum and the rest of the penis. The veins accompany the arteries and drain into the internal pudendal vein and ultimately into the internal iliac vein. Both sensory and motor **nerve supply** are through branches of the pudendal nerve. Autonomic nerve supply is through the pelvic splanchnic nerves. The glans drains into the deep **inguinal group** of lymph nodes, whereas the rest of the penis drains into the superficial inguinal nodes.

THE SCROTUM (Fig. 31.11)

The scrotum is a loose, cutaneous, **fibromuscular sac**. It is covered by **five layers** of tissue. From outside to inside, they are the skin, dartos muscle, external spermatic fascia, cremasteric fascia and internal spermatic fascia. The layers represent an extension of the layers of the anterior abdominal wall. The scrotum **contains** the testes, epididymis and lower part of the spermatic cord. The contraction and relaxation of the dartos muscle help to maintain the optimum **temperature** for spermatogenesis. The **arterial supply** of the scrotum is from branches of the femoral, internal pudendal and inferior epigastric arteries. The veins follow the corresponding arteries. The **nerve supply** of the scrotum is via cutaneous branches of the lumbar and sacral plexuses. **Lymph** from the scrotum drains into the superficial inguinal lymph nodes.

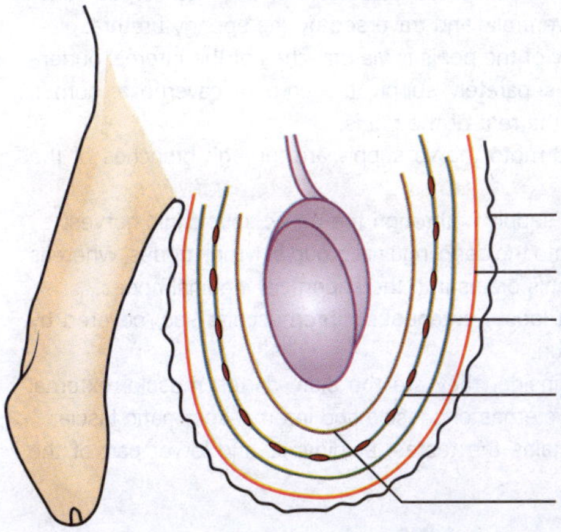

FIG. 31.11 The layers of the scrotum.

APPLIED ANATOMY

- **Cryptorchidism** is a term used for undescended testes. It is the most common congenital anomaly of the male genitalia. In this condition, the testes may be located anywhere in the pathway of descent from the lumbar region to the upper portion of the scrotum. Undescended testes are a definite risk factor for infertility and the development of testicular cancers.
- The surgical procedure to place the undescended testes in the scrotum is called **orchidopexy**.
- Inflammation of testicular tissue is called **orchitis**. A relatively common cause of orchitis is mumps which is a viral infection.
- **Testicular tumours** are one of the most common tumours in males between 20 and 40 years of age. They have a relatively good prognosis.
- **Varicocoele** is a dilatation of the pampiniform plexus of veins and one of the common causes of reduced fertility in males.
- **Vasectomy** is a permanent method of contraception in males in which the vas deferens is ligated, preventing the passage of spermatozoa into the ejaculate.
- **Benign prostatic hyperplasia** is a common condition occurring in older males, in which the prostatic tissue surrounding the urethra undergoes hypertrophy and hyperplasia. This leads to difficulties in urination and its related problems. It can be corrected either by sympathetic blocking drugs or in more advanced cases by surgery. The most common surgery performed for this condition is known as transurethral resection of the prostate (TURP).
- **Prostate cancer** is a relatively common cancer in males that usually occurs in the peripheral portion of the gland. Increased blood levels of prostate-specific antigen are indicative of prostate cancer. Prostate tumours are usually slow growing and often found incidentally. Prostate cancers can be felt on per rectal examinations, as they involve the peripheral portion of the gland.

APPLICATIONS IN NURSING

- **Condom catheters** are rubber sheaths placed over the shaft of the penis which are connected to a urinary bag for the collection of urine. They provide a convenient and noninvasive method of collecting urine.

SUMMARY

- The male reproductive system is specialized to produce, transport and release the male gamete.
- The internal genitalia include the testis, epididymis, vas deferens, ejaculatory ducts, seminal vesicles, prostate gland and bulbourethral glands.
- The external genitalia include the scrotum, penis and male urethra.
- The testes are the male gonads that are homologous to the ovaries.
- They are ovoid in shape and have upper and lower poles, anterior and posterior borders and medial and lateral surfaces.
- From outside to inside, the testes are covered by the tunica vaginalis, tunica albuginea and tunica vasculosa.
- Multiple septa extend from the mediastinum testis, a thickened area of the tunica albuginea, into the substance of the testis dividing it into 200–300 lobules.
- Each lobule contains highly coiled seminiferous tubules which are lined by cells producing spermatozoa.
- Between the seminiferous tubules are seen clusters of interstitial cells of Leydig which secrete testosterone.
- The arterial supply of the testes is via the testicular artery which is a branch of the abdominal aorta.
- Venous blood from the testes drains into the pampiniform plexus of veins which continues as the testicular vein on each side.
- The lymphatic drainage of the testes is into the para-aortic group of lymph nodes.
- Sympathetic nerve supply arises from the T10 segment of the spinal cord.
- The testes develop in the lumbar region and subsequently descend through the inguinal canal in the seventh month of foetal life, reaching the scrotal sac by the ninth month.
- Histologically, seminiferous tubules are lined by spermatogenic and supporting cells.
- The spermatogenic cells include the spermatogonia, primary spermatocytes, secondary spermatocytes, spermatids and spermatozoa.
- The supporting cells are the elongated Sertoli cells.
- The epididymis is a highly coiled tube that is formed by fusion of the efferent ductules near the upper pole of the testis.
- The upper portion of the epididymis is called the head, which then continues along the posterior border of the testis as the body, finally forming the tail close to the lower pole of the testis.
- The lining is pseudostratified stereociliated columnar epithelium surrounding a lumen which contains numerous spermatozoa.
- The vas deferens or ductus deferens is a thick muscular tube which is a continuation of the duct of the epididymis near the lower pole of the testes.
- Each ductus ends by joining the duct of the seminal vesicle to form the ejaculatory duct. The dilated and tortuous part of the ductus near the base of the bladder is called the ampulla.
- Histologically, the vas deferens has a star-shaped lumen lined by pseudostratified stereociliated columnar epithelium outside which is a thick muscle layer.
- The spermatic cord suspends the testes and extends from the deep inguinal ring to the origin of the ductus deferens.
- It is covered from within outwards by internal spermatic fascia, cremaster muscle and fascia and external spermatic fascia.
- The major contents of the spermatic cord are the ductus deferens, testicular artery, pampiniform plexus of veins, lymph vessels from the testes and autonomic nerves supplying the testes.
- The ejaculatory ducts are formed by fusion of the vas deferens and duct of the seminal vesicle and open into the prostatic urethra on each side.
- The prostate gland is the largest accessory gland of the male reproductive system that surrounds the prostatic urethra.
- It is a fibromusculoglandular organ which contributes to the semen and is situated in the anteroinferior part of the pelvic cavity below the neck of the urinary bladder and anterior to the rectum.
- The prostatic urethra traverses the gland from the base to apex and receives the openings of the ejaculatory ducts near its middle.
- Histologically, the prostate has numerous acini, the ducts of which open into the prostatic urethra.
- The stroma consists of fibrous tissue and smooth muscle.
- The seminal vesicles are thin-walled structures situated between the base of the bladder and rectum.
- The ducts of the seminal vesicles join the ductus deferens on each side to form the ejaculatory ducts.
- The bulbourethral glands contribute a mucus secretion to the semen and are situated on either side of the membranous urethra.
- Their ducts open into the penile urethra.
- The penis is the male organ of copulation and consists of a root and body.
- The root is the proximal part that is attached to the bony pelvis, whereas the body is the free distal portion.
- The distal end of the penis is enlarged to from the glans penis and contains the external urethral orifice.
- Much of the penis is composed of masses of erectile tissue.
- The erectile tissue within the root of the penis consists of a bulb and two crura.
- The crura continue into the body of the penis as the corpora cavernosa, while the bulb continues forward as the corpus spongiosum and is traversed by the bulbar urethra.
- The body of the penis is composed of three masses of erectile tissue, two corpora cavernosa located dorsolaterally and the corpus spongiosum situated ventrally and traversed by the spongy urethra.
- The arterial supply of the penis is via branches of the internal pudendal artery which separately supply the corpora cavernosa, corpus spongiosum and the rest of the penis.
- Both sensory and motor nerve supply are through branches of the pudendal nerve.
- Autonomic nerve supply is through the pelvic splanchnic nerves.
- The glans drains into the deep inguinal group of lymph nodes, whereas the rest of the penis drains into the superficial inguinal nodes.
- The scrotum is a loose, cutaneous, fibromuscular sac, covered by five layers of tissue.
- From outside to inside, they are the skin, dartos muscle, external spermatic fascia, cremasteric fascia and internal spermatic fascia.
- The scrotum contains the testes, epididymis and lower part of the spermatic cord.

10
SECTION

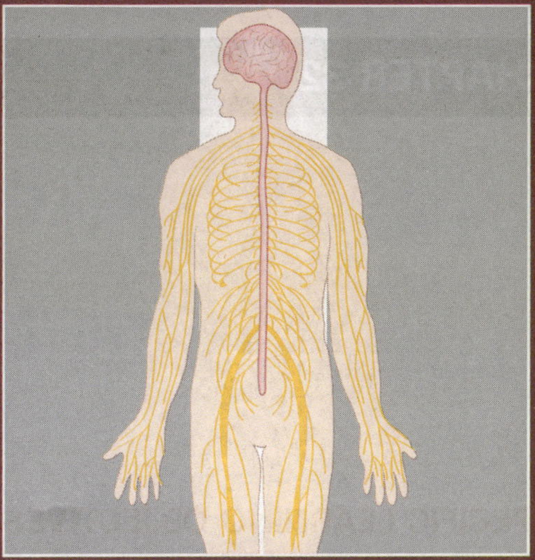

The Nervous System

Section Outline

CHAPTER 32

Introduction to the Nervous System

SPECIFIC LEARNING OBJECTIVES

At the end of this chapter, the student should be able to:

- Classify the nervous system.
- Name the individual parts of the nervous system.
- Classify neurons.
- Describe the structure of a typical neuron.
- Describe the structure and functions of the supporting cells of the nervous system.
- Describe the layers and structure of the meninges.
- Describe the gross anatomy of the dural venous sinuses.
- Describe the formation, flow and absorption of cerebrospinal fluid.
- Describe the salient features of the autonomic nervous system.

GLOSSARY OF TERMS

- **Grey matter:** outer layer of the cerebrum and cerebellum and inner part of the spinal cord containing neuronal cell bodies and unmyelinated neuronal processes
- **White matter:** inner layer of the cerebrum and cerebellum and outer part of the spinal cord containing myelinated neuronal processes
- **Nuclei:** collections of neuronal cell bodies within the central nervous system (CNS)
- **Ganglia:** collections of neuronal cell bodies outside the CNS
- **Tract:** collection of neuronal processes in the CNS
- **Nerve:** collection of neuronal processes outside the CNS
- **Perikaryon:** cell body of neuron
- **Nissl substance:** prominent rough endoplasmic reticulum of a neuron
- **Dendrite:** neuronal cell process carrying impulses towards the cell body
- **Axon:** neuronal cell process carrying impulses away from the cell body
- **Telodendria:** axon terminals
- **Myelin:** whitish phospholipid covering of neuronal cell processes
- **Nodes of Ranvier:** periodic gaps in the myelin sheath
- **Synapse:** site of functional contact between excitable cells
- **Dural folds:** projections of the meningeal layer of dura into the cranial cavity
- **Dural venous sinuses:** endothelial lined spaces between dural folds carrying venous blood
- **Subarachnoid space:** space between arachnoid mater and pia mater containing cerebrospinal fluid (CSF)
- **Cistern:** local expansion of the subarachnoid space
- **Arachnoid villi:** minute projections of the arachnoid mater into the dural venous sinuses

INTRODUCTION

The nervous system is complex and enables the body to respond and adapt to the environment. To do this, it possesses sensory, integrative and motor functions. It also coordinates all the body functions to maintain homeostasis. It can be classified structurally into a **central** nervous system (CNS) and **peripheral** nervous system (PNS) (Fig. 32.1). The CNS consists of the **brain** and **spinal cord**. The PNS consists of the **cranial** and **spinal nerves** and their associated sensory **ganglia**. Functionally, it can be classified into the somatic nervous system and autonomic nervous system (ANS). The **somatic nervous system** is under voluntary control, whereas the **ANS** is involuntary and has sympathetic and parasympathetic components (Fig. 32.2). The brain can further be classified into the **forebrain, midbrain** and **hindbrain**, each with its own components (Figs 32.3 and 32.4). The **brainstem** includes the midbrain, pons and medulla oblongata.

NERVOUS TISSUE

The two principal cell types of the nervous system are **neurons** and their **supporting cells**. Neurons are the excitable cells that carry impulses. Supporting cells are cells that surround and support neurons. The neuron is the structural and functional unit of the nervous system. It is specialized to receive stimuli and conduct impulses. More than 10 billion neurons are arranged as an integrated communications network within the nervous

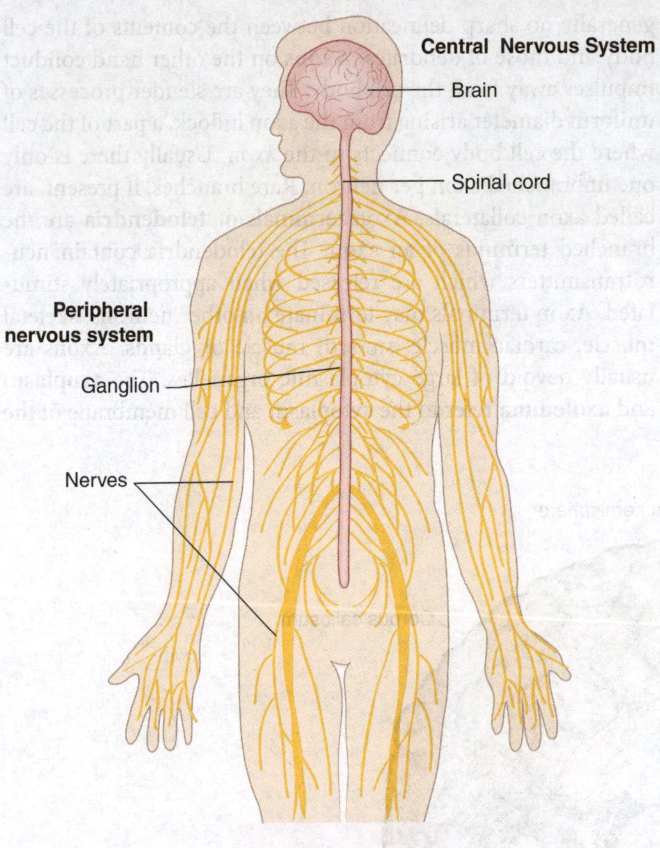

FIG. 32.1 The parts of the nervous system.

system. Neurons show the greatest variety of sizes and shapes of any group of cells in the body. Each neuron consists of a cell body or **perikaryon** containing a nucleus with nucleolus and cytoplasm with cell organelles. The unique feature of neurons is the presence of cell processes called **dendrites** and **axons**. Mammalian neurons have a limited ability to regenerate. In the PNS, damage to myelinated axons and dendrites may be repaired if the Schwann cells are intact. In the CNS, little or no repair occurs as growth and propagation is inhibited by glial cells. Neuronal plasticity refers to the ability of neurons to alter their structure to adapt to changing conditions.

Neurons may be **classified** according to their structure or function (Fig. 32.5). **Structurally** they may be pseudounipolar, bipolar or multipolar (Fig. 32.6). **Pseudounipolar** neurons have a single process which soon divides into a central and peripheral process. These neurons are somatic sensory neurons and reside in the dorsal root ganglia and sensory ganglia of cranial nerves. The peripheral process functions as the dendrite, carrying impulses towards the cell body. The central process serves as the axon carrying impulses away from the cell body. **Bipolar** neurons have two processes that arise from two ends of the cell. They are special sensory neurons seen in the inner ear, olfactory epithelium and retina. Nearly all the other neurons in the CNS and PNS are **multipolar**. These neurons have many dendrites and one axon. Functionally, neurons may be sensory, motor or interneurons. **Sensory** neurons carry impulses from the periphery to the CNS. They are seen in the dorsal root ganglia and sensory ganglia of the cranial nerves. **Motor** neurons are seen in the ventral horn of the spinal cord, motor nuclei of the cranial nerves and autonomic ganglia and supply skeletal muscles, cardiac muscle, smooth muscle and glands. Nearly all the other neurons of CNS are **interneurons**.

Microscopically, neurons show all the characteristics of protein-secreting cells (Fig. 32.7). They have a large, euchromatic nucleus with a prominent nucleolus. There is abundant rough endoplasmic reticulum which is prominently stained in histological preparations and is called **Nissl substance**. A large perinuclear Golgi apparatus is visible with numerous mitochondria. Microtubules and neurofilaments are also abundant and are responsible for intracellular transport and for maintaining the structural integrity of the cell, respectively. Like other cells, lysosomes, vesicles and inclusion bodies are seen. **Dendrites** are the receptive or input regions of the neuron. They are short, tapering and diffusely branched processes forming dendritic trees. They have a greater diameter than axons and are unmyelinated. There is

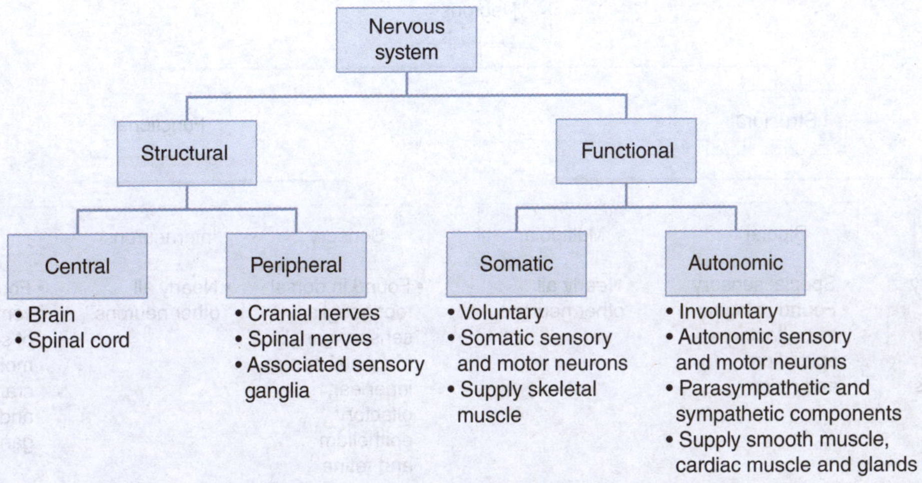

FIG. 32.2 The classification of the nervous system.

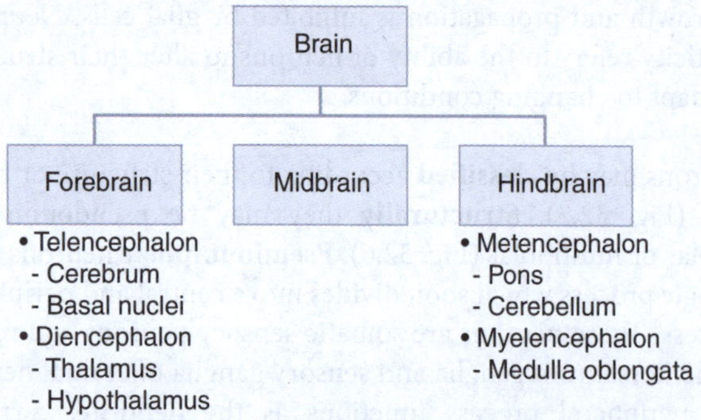

FIG. 32.3 The classification of the brain.

generally no sharp delineation between the contents of the cell body and those of dendrites. **Axons** on the other hand conduct impulses away from the cell body. They are slender processes of uniform diameter arising from the axon hillock, a part of the cell where the cell body connects to the axon. Usually there is only one unbranched axon per neuron. Rare branches, if present, are called axon collaterals. Axon terminals or **telodendria** are the branched terminus of an axon. The telodendria contain neurotransmitters which are released when appropriately stimulated. Axon terminals may terminate on other neurons, skeletal muscle, cardiac muscle, smooth muscle or glands. Axons are usually devoid of large cytoplasmic organelles. The **axoplasm** and **axolemma** refer to the cytoplasm and cell membrane of the

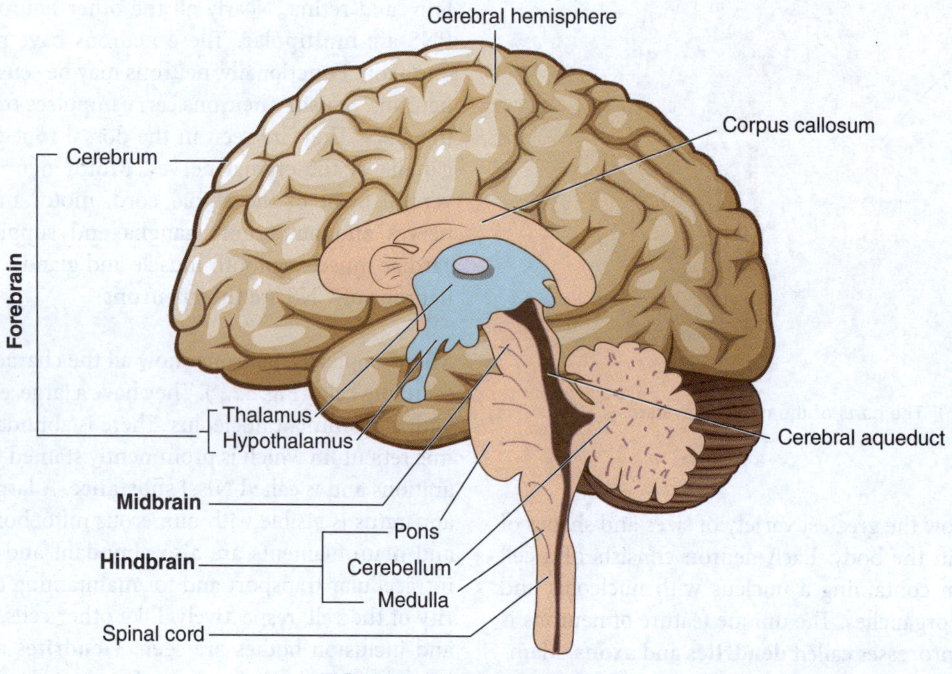

FIG. 32.4 The parts of the brain.

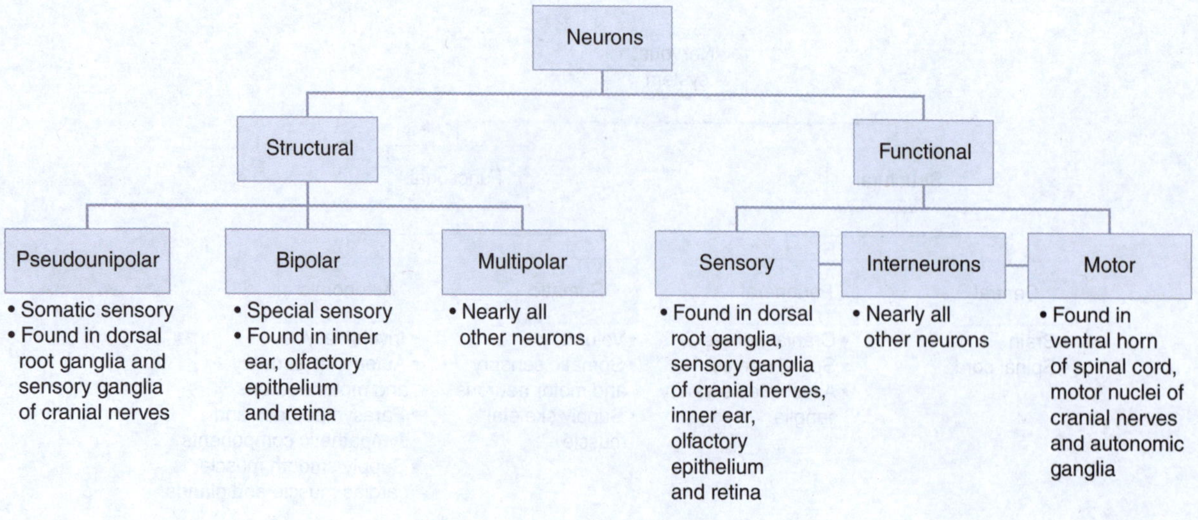

FIG. 32.5 The classification of neurons.

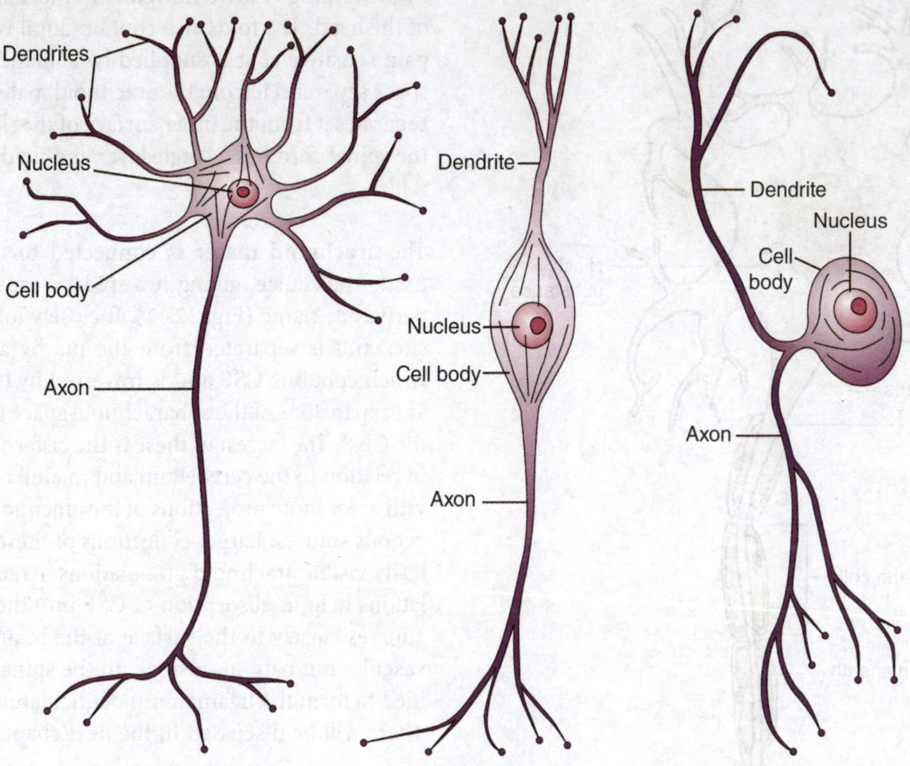

FIG. 32.6 The structural classification of neurons.

axon, respectively. The movement of substances along axons occurs in two ways. Anterograde movement occurs towards the axonal terminal, while retrograde movement occurs away from the axon terminal.

Supporting cells are nonconducting cells in intimate physical contact with neurons (Fig. 32.8). Approximately, 90% of cells in the CNS and 50% by volume are supporting cells. Supporting cells in the CNS are called neuroglia or glia and include astrocytes, oligodendrocytes, microglia and ependymal cells. In the PNS, they include Schwann cells and satellite cells. **Astrocytes** provide a supportive framework for neurons, guide young neurons to the proper connections, provide metabolic exchange pathways, help in the formation of the blood–brain barrier and aid in the response of neurons to injury. **Oligodendrocytes** form the myelin sheaths of neuronal cell processes within the CNS. **Microglia** perform the function of macrophages. **Ependymal cells** line the ventricles of the brain and help in the formation of cerebrospinal fluid (CSF).

Schwann cells surround all axons in the PNS. They are responsible for the **myelination** of peripheral axons and participate in the repair process after injury. Myelin is the whitish, fatty, segmented sheath around larger axons. It is present in the white matter of the CNS as well as around larger axons in the PNS and is composed primarily of phospholipids. It is produced by oligodendrocytes in the CNS and Schwann cells in the PNS. It functions to protect the axon, electrically insulate fibres from one another and increase the speed of nerve impulse transmission. A Schwann cell envelopes an axon in a trough and encloses the axon with its plasma membrane. It produces myelin sheaths in a jelly-roll-like fashion by wrapping the axon in many layers of membrane. The neurilemma is the peripheral cytoplasmic layer of the Schwann cell enclosing the myelin sheath. The myelin sheath has **nodes of Ranvier**, which are periodic gaps in the myelin sheath and **internodes** where myelin is present. **Satellite cells** are flat, epithelioid cells that surround neuronal cell bodies in ganglia. They regulate the entry of nutrients and protect neurons.

Synapses are sites of functional contact between two excitable cells. They may be electrical or chemical. Chemical synapses produce only a one-way information transfer from a presynaptic neuron to a postsynaptic neuron. Axon terminals contain synaptic vesicles filled with **neurotransmitter** molecules which are released when an impulse reaches them. Both **excitatory** and **inhibitory** neurotransmitters are present in the CNS and PNS. An excitatory neurotransmitter depolarizes and an inhibitory neurotransmitter hyperpolarizes the postsynaptic neuron. A neurotransmitter may be excitatory in some locations and inhibitory in others. Broadly, there are two classes of neurotransmitters, namely small-molecule (acetylcholine, amino acids, biogenic amines, adenosine triphosphate, purines and gases) and neuropeptides (chains of 3–40 amino acids).

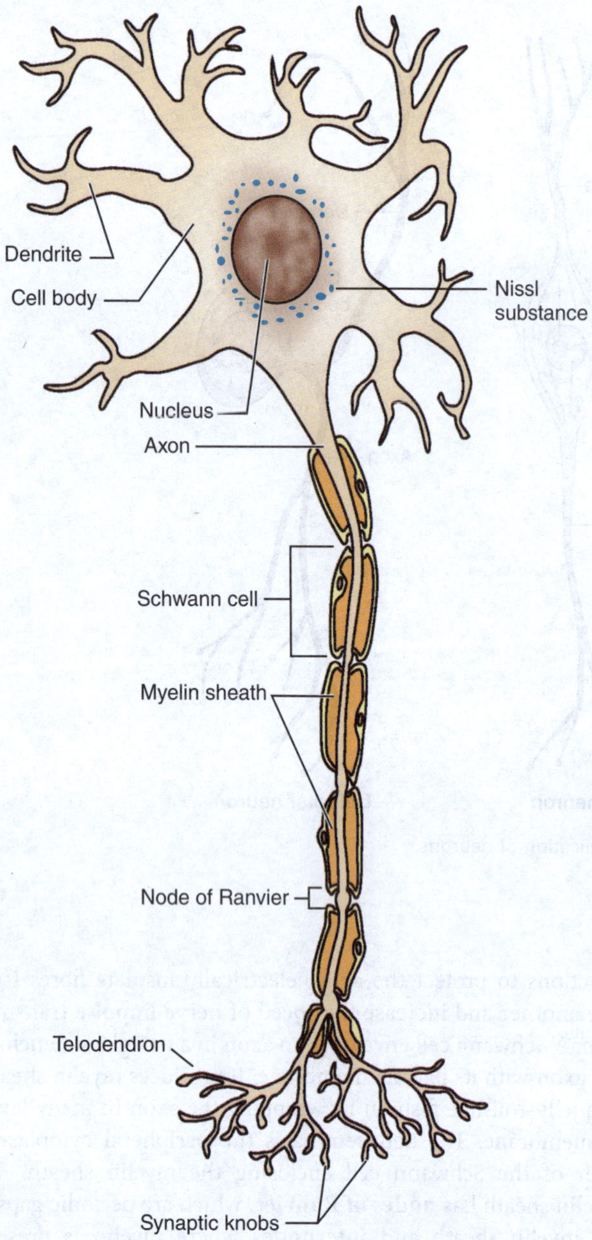

FIG. 32.7 The structure of a typical neuron.

THE MENINGES (Fig. 32.9)

The meninges are three membranes that cover the brain and spinal cord. Their main functions are protection and nutrition of the CNS. From superficial to deep, the three layers are dura mater, arachnoid mater and pia mater. The **dura mater** is a thick, inelastic membrane that has two layers, endosteal and meningeal. Two special features of the dura are dural venous sinuses and dural folds. **Dural venous sinuses** are blood-filled spaces between the two layers of dura that are lined by endothelium. They function as veins that drain blood from the brain. **Dural folds** are inward extensions of the meningeal layer of dura into the cranial cavity (Fig. 32.10). The four dural folds are the falx cerebri, tentorium cerebelli, falx cerebelli and diaphragma sellae. These folds help to stabilize the brain within the cranial cavity by preventing relative movement of its parts during movements of the head. The folds also contain dural venous sinuses. Dura is pain sensitive as it is supplied by somatic nerves. The subdural space separates it from the arachnoid mater and extradural space separates it from the inner surface of the skull. The dura covering the spinal cord has a single layer and no dural venous sinuses or folds.

The **arachnoid mater** is connected to the pia by connective tissue trabeculae, giving it a spidery appearance from which it derives its name (Fig. 32.11). It closely follows the dura at most sites and is separated from the pia by a **subarachnoid space** which contains **CSF** and is traversed by blood vessels. **Cisterns** are expansions of the subarachnoid space in certain areas around the CNS. The largest of these is the cisterna magna which is seen in relation to the cerebellum and medulla oblongata. **Arachnoid villi** are minute projections of the arachnoid mater into the dural venous sinuses. Larger collections of these form the macroscopically visible arachnoid granulations. Arachnoid villi and granulations help in absorption of CSF into the veins. The **pia mater** adheres closely to the surface of the brain and spinal cord. It is vascular but pain insensitive. In the spinal cord, the pia is modified to form the ligamentum denticulatum and filum terminale. These will be discussed in the next chapter.

THE DURAL VENOUS SINUSES (Fig. 32.12)

The dural venous sinuses are found in relation to the dural folds. Nearly all the sinuses are found between the endosteal and meningeal layers of dura. They are lined by **endothelium**, but unlike typical veins, they **lack** both **valves** and **smooth muscle** in their walls. **Emissary veins** are valveless veins that connect the dural venous sinuses to extracranial veins. Dural venous sinuses drain blood from the brain, meninges, diploe, internal ear and orbit. In addition to providing a mechanism for the venous drainage of the brain, dural venous sinuses also help in the absorption of CSF. Dural venous sinuses are classified as either **paired** or **unpaired** (Table 32.1). The salient features of the major dural venous sinuses are described in Table 32.2. Eventually all blood from the dural venous sinuses drains into the internal jugular vein on each side through the sigmoid sinus. The flow of blood in the dural venous sinuses is shown in Fig. 32.13.

THE CEREBROSPINAL FLUID

The CSF is a clear colourless liquid that bathes the brain and spinal cord. It acts as a transport medium for nutrients and waste products and provides a protective fluid cushion for the CNS. The CSF also provides a route for chemical messengers that are widely distributed through the CNS. It is produced by the **choroid plexuses** within the lateral, third and fourth **ventricles** and circulates throughout the CNS. The ventricles are a complex series of spaces within the brain which produce and contain CSF (Fig. 32.14). There are four ventricles within the brain. A pair of **lateral ventricles** is contained within the cerebral hemispheres. The **third ventricle** is a small cleft-like space in the midline between the thalamus and hypothalamus on each side. It is

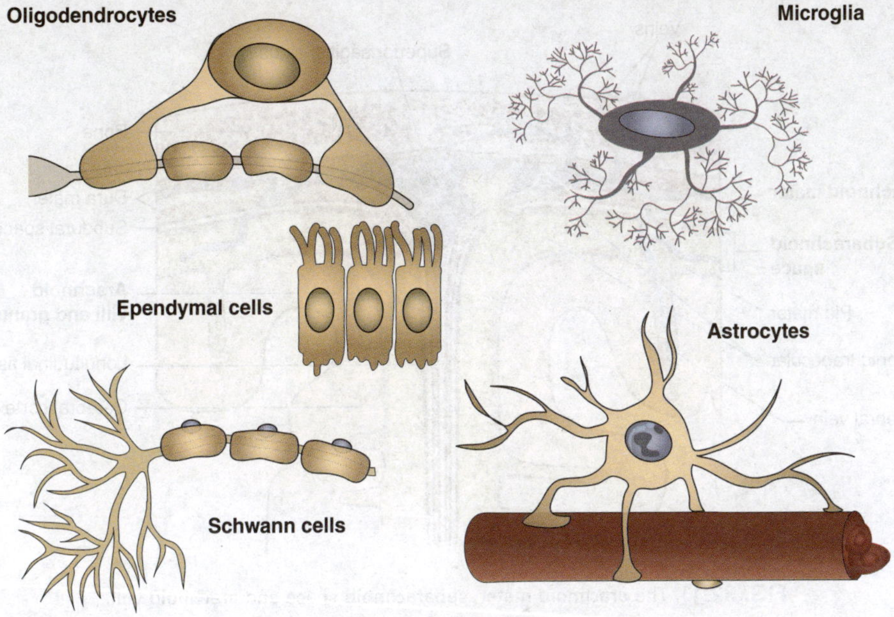

FIG. 32.8 The supporting cells of the nervous system.

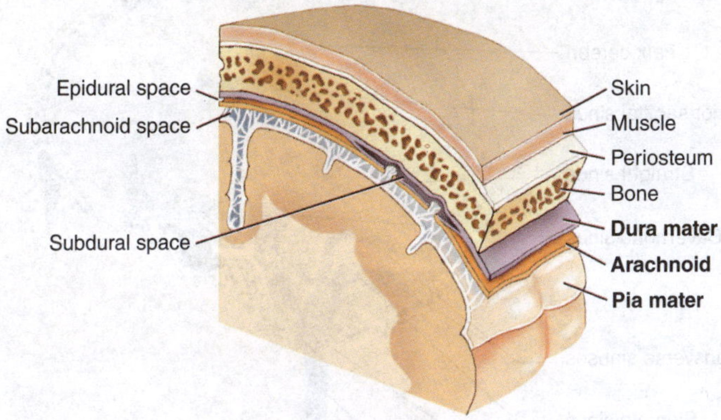

FIG. 32.9 The meninges of the brain.

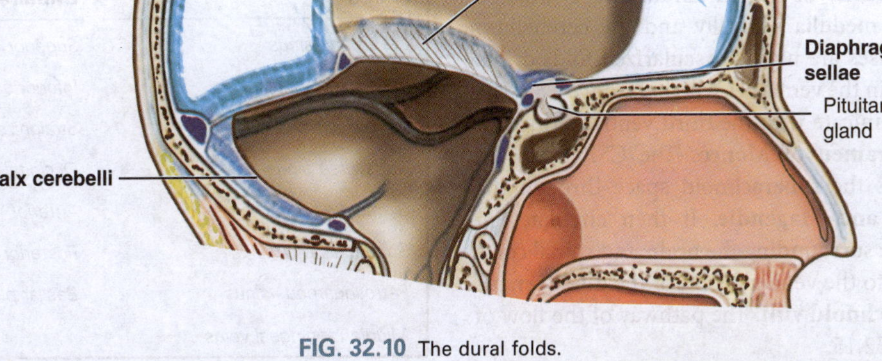

FIG. 32.10 The dural folds.

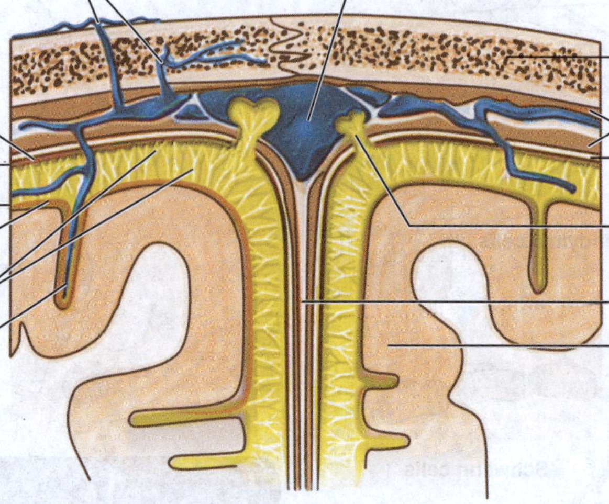

FIG. 32.11 The arachnoid mater, subarachnoid space and arachnoid villi.

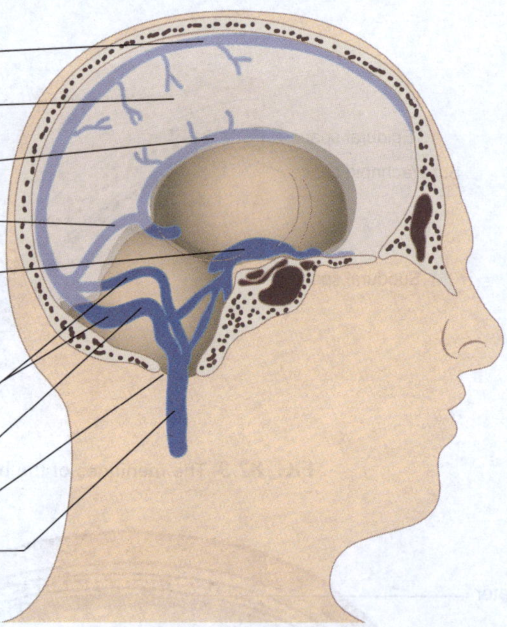

FIG. 32.12 The major dural venous sinuses.

connected to the **fourth ventricle** by the **aqueduct** of Sylvius which is a narrow canal running though the midbrain. The fourth ventricle is the cavity of the hindbrain and is situated between the pons and medulla ventrally and the cerebellum dorsally. **Choroid plexuses** are highly vascularized folds of pia lined by ependyma within the ventricles which produce CSF. The lateral ventricles communicate with the third ventricle through the interventricular **foramen of Monro**. The CSF from the fourth ventricle reaches the subarachnoid space through the **foramina of Luschka and Magendie**. It then circulates in the **subarachnoid space** surrounding the brain and spinal cord. Finally, it is absorbed into the venous blood of the dural venous sinuses through the **arachnoid villi**. The pathway of the flow of CSF is depicted in Fig. 32.15.

Table 32.1 The Paired and Unpaired Dural Venous Sinuses

Paired	Unpaired
Cavernous sinus	*Superior sagittal sinus*
Superior petrosal sinus	*Inferior sagittal sinus*
Inferior petrosal sinus	*Straight sinus*
Transverse sinus	*Occipital sinus*
Sigmoid sinus	*Anterior intercavernous sinus*
Sphenoparietal sinus	*Posterior intercavernous sinus*
Petrosquamous sinus	*Basilar plexus of veins*
Middle meningeal veins	

Table 32.2 The Salient Features of the Major Dural Venous Sinuses

Sinus	Location	Formation	Termination
• Superior sagittal sinus	• Attached margin of the falx cerebri	• Just posterior to the foramen caecum	• Confluence of sinuses
• Inferior sagittal sinus	• Free margin of the falx cerebri	• Junction of the anterior one-third and posterior two-thirds of the free margin of the falx cerebri	• Straight sinus
• Straight sinus	• Junction of falx cerebri and tentorium cerebelli	• Continuation of inferior sagittal sinus	• Transverse sinus
• Transverse sinus	• Attached margin of the tentorium cerebelli	• Fusion of the superior sagittal and straight sinus	• Sigmoid sinus
• Sigmoid sinus	• Along the sigmoid sulcus	• Continuation of transverse sinus	• Internal jugular vein
• Cavernous sinus	• Lateral surface of sella turcica from apex of petrous temporal bone to superior orbital fissure • Laterally related to the following nerves: oculomotor, trochlear, ophthalmic division and maxillary division of the trigeminal nerve • The internal carotid artery and abducent nerve are related inferomedially	• Separation of endosteal and meningeal layers of dura in the location mentioned • Has numerous tributaries and connections including with the facial vein and the pterygoid plexus of veins	• Superior and inferior petrosal sinuses

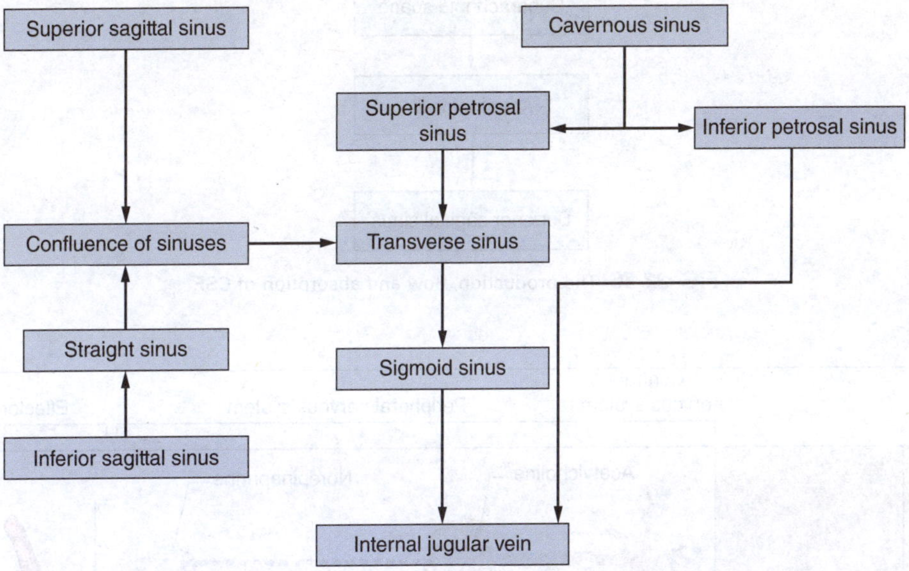

FIG. 32.13 The direction of blood flow in the dural venous sinuses.

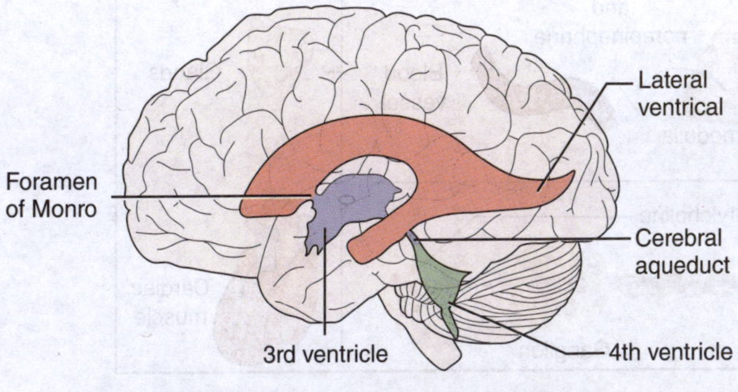

FIG. 32.14 The ventricles of the brain.

THE AUTONOMIC NERVOUS SYSTEM (Fig. 32.16)

The ANS controls involuntary effectors such as the cardiac muscle, smooth muscle and various glands. It has two divisions, **sympathetic** and **parasympathetic**. It consists of **central components** like the hypothalamus, brainstem and spinal cord. The **peripheral components** are composed of the sympathetic and parasympathetic nerves with their associated ganglia. The ganglia are situated in relation to the autonomic nerves and contain multipolar neurons. The axons of the preganglionic neurons synapse in the ganglia. The similarities and differences between the sympathetic and

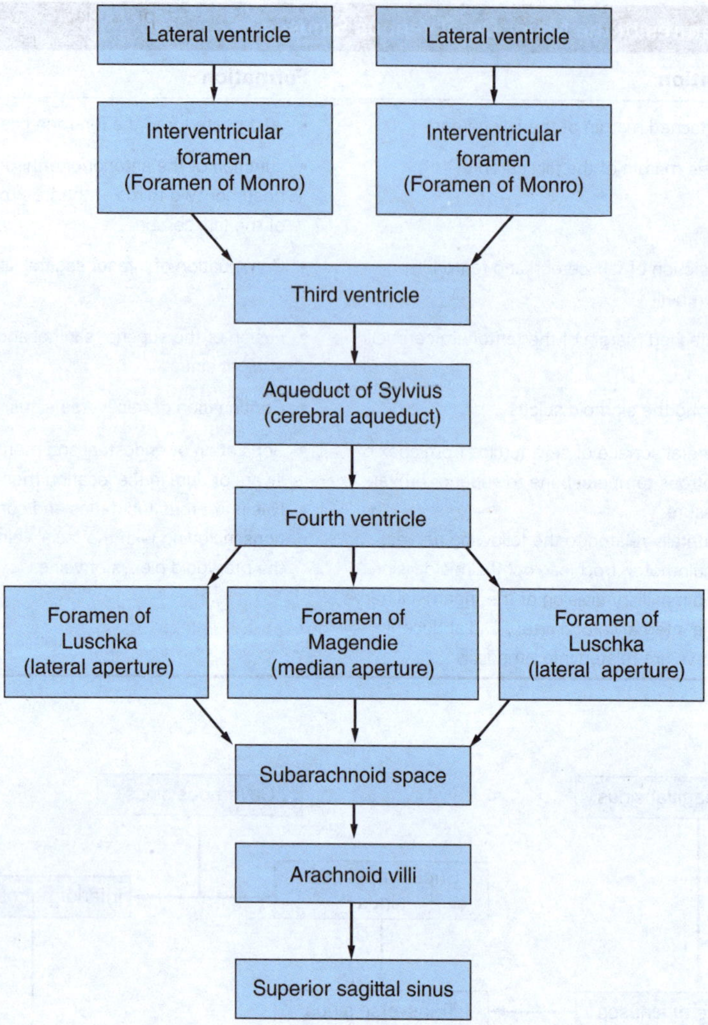

FIG. 32.15 The production, flow and absorption of CSF.

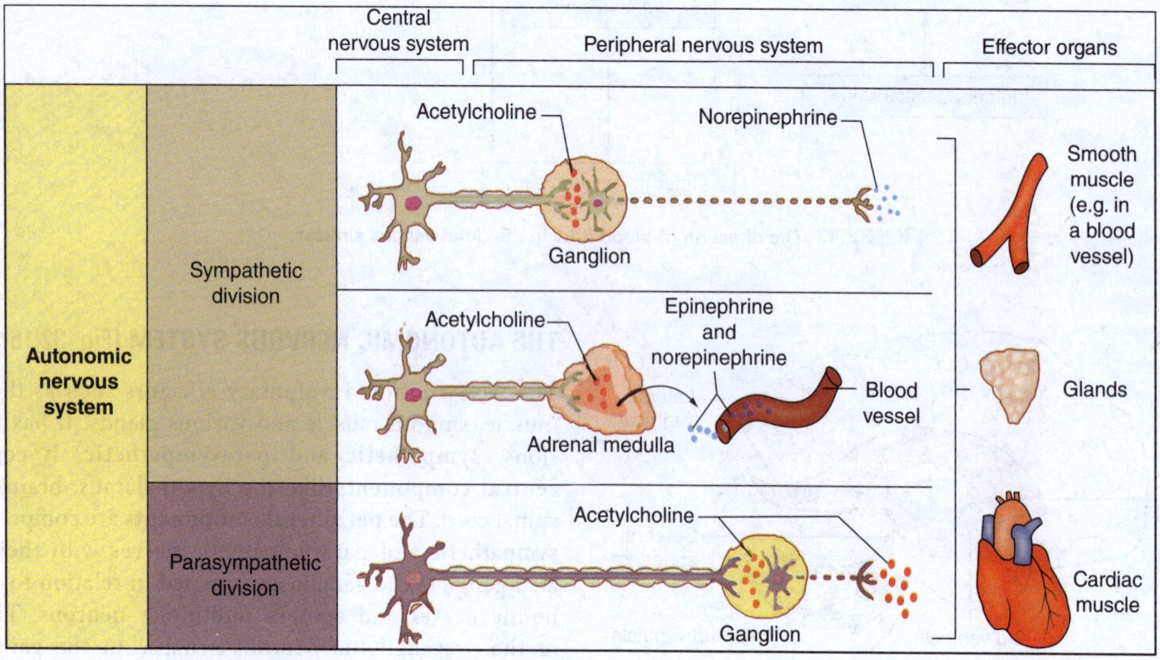

FIG. 32.16 The salient features of the autonomic nervous system.

Table 32.3 The Similarities Between the Sympathetic and Parasympathetic Nervous System

Similarities
• Are controlled by the hypothalamus
• Have a peripheral ganglion
• Have preganglionic and postganglionic nerves
• Preganglionic nerves arise from CNS
• Postganglionic fibres arise from peripheral ganglia
• Use acetylcholine as the preganglionic neurotransmitter
• Carry afferent (sensory) and efferent (motor) signals
• Innervate major organs

CNS, Central nervous system. See Fig. 32.16.

Table 32.4 The Differences Between the Sympathetic and Parasympathetic Nervous System

Sympathetic	Parasympathetic
• Fight or flight	• Rest and digest
• Thoracolumbar (preganglionic neurons)	• Craniosacral (preganglionic neurons)
• Short preganglionic nerves going to sympathetic chain	• Long preganglionic nerves going to organ-associated ganglia
• Long postganglionic nerves going to organs	• Short postganglionic nerves going to organs
• Postganglionic nerves release norepinephrine	• Postganglionic nerves release acetylcholine

See Fig. 32.16.

parasympathetic components of the ANS are summarized in Tables 32.3 and 32.4.

APPLIED ANATOMY

- **Astrocytomas** are tumours arising from astrocytes and cause symptoms by compression and invasion of the brain parenchyma.
- Demyelinating disorders such as **multiple sclerosis** cause symptoms due to the abnormal conduction of impulses in the myelinated nerve fibres.
- Inflammation of the meninges is known as **meningitis**. It can occur due to viral or bacterial infections and causes headaches, neck rigidity and vomiting. It can be fatal if untreated.
- **Haemorrhage** can occur in the extradural, subdural or subarachnoid spaces. The accumulated blood can cause symptoms when it presses upon the brain.
- **Analgesic agents** can be introduced into the extradural space surrounding the spinal cord for pain relief.
- **Cavernous sinus thrombosis** is a serious condition that occurs due to the spread of infection to the cavernous sinus through one of its numerous connections such as the facial vein. It is a potentially fatal condition due to the important structures surrounding it.
- **Emissary veins** can carry infections from the scalp to the dural venous sinuses.
- Excessive accumulation of CSF within the ventricles is known as **hydrocephalus.**
- **Lumbar puncture** refers to the insertion of a needle into the spinal subarachnoid space usually at a level between L3–L4 and L4–L5 vertebra for diagnostic purposes or to introduce anaesthetic agents for spinal anaesthesia.
- **Autonomic neuropathy** is the malfunctioning of ANS. A common cause is long-standing diabetes mellitus.
- **Phaeochromocytoma** is a tumour of the adrenal medulla, resulting in the excessive secretion of catecholamines into the circulation and overstimulation of the sympathetic nervous system.
- **Vasovagal attacks** occur due to the excessive stimulation of the parasympathetic system by unpleasant external stimuli. This often leads to fainting or syncope due to the rapid drop of the heart rate and blood pressure.

APPLICATIONS IN NURSING

- **Epidural analgesia** is the administration of analgesics into the spinal epidural space and is used for the management of acute pain such as in labour. Nurses need to be familiar with the maintenance of the epidural catheter and appropriately monitor patients for complications such as respiratory depression.

SUMMARY

- The nervous system can be classified structurally into the CNS and PNS.
- The CNS consists of the brain and spinal cord.
- The PNS consists of the cranial and spinal nerves and their associated sensory ganglia.
- Functionally, the nervous system can be classified into the somatic nervous system and ANS.
- The somatic nervous system is under voluntary control, whereas the ANS is involuntary and has sympathetic and parasympathetic components.
- The brain can further be classified into the forebrain, midbrain and hindbrain, each with its own components.
- The brainstem includes the midbrain, pons and medulla oblongata.
- The two principal cell types of the nervous system are neurons and their supporting cells.
- Neurons are the excitable cells that carry impulses.
- Supporting cells are cells that surround and support neurons.
- The neuron is the structural and functional unit of the nervous system.
- Each neuron consists of a cell body or perikaryon containing a nucleus with nucleolus and cytoplasm with cell organelles.
- The unique feature of neurons is the presence of cell processes called dendrites and axons.
- Neurons may be classified structurally into pseudounipolar, bipolar or multipolar.
- Functionally, neurons may be sensory, motor or interneurons.

- Microscopically, neurons show all the characteristics of a protein-secreting cell.
- There is abundant rough endoplasmic reticulum which is prominently stained in histological preparations and is called Nissl substance.
- Dendrites are the receptive or input regions of the neuron.
- Axons conduct impulses away from the cell body.
- Axon terminals or telodendria are the branched terminus of an axon.
- Axon terminals may terminate on other neurons, skeletal muscle, cardiac muscle, smooth muscle or glands.
- Supporting cells are nonconducting cells in intimate physical contact with neurons.
- Supporting cells in the CNS are called neuroglia or glia and include astrocytes, oligodendrocytes, microglia and ependymal cells.
- In the PNS, they include Schwann cells and satellite cells.
- Schwann cells surround all axons in PNS.
- They are responsible for the myelination of peripheral axons and participate in the repair process after injury.
- The myelin sheath has nodes of Ranvier, which are periodic gaps in the myelin sheath and internodes where myelin is present.
- Satellite cells are flat, epithelioid cells that surround neuronal cell bodies in ganglia.
- Synapses are sites of functional contact between two excitable cells.
- Axon terminals contain synaptic vesicles filled with neurotransmitter molecules which are released when an impulse reaches them.
- Both excitatory and inhibitory neurotransmitters are present in the CNS and PNS.
- The meninges are three membranes that cover the brain and spinal cord.
- From superficial to deep, the three layers are dura mater, arachnoid mater and pia mater.
- Dural venous sinuses are blood-filled spaces between the two layers of dura that are lined by endothelium.
- Dural folds are inward extensions of the meningeal layer of dura into the cranial cavity.
- The four dural folds are the falx cerebri, tentorium cerebelli, falx cerebelli and diaphragma sellae.
- The arachnoid mater closely follows the dura at most sites and is separated from the pia by a subarachnoid space which contains CSF and is traversed by blood vessels.
- Arachnoid villi are minute projections of the arachnoid mater into the dural venous sinuses.
- Arachnoid villi help in absorption of CSF into the veins.
- The pia mater adheres closely to the surface of the brain and spinal cord.
- The dural venous sinuses are found in relation to the dural folds.
- They are lined by endothelium, but unlike typical veins, they lack both smooth muscle in their walls and valves.
- Emissary veins are valveless veins that connect the dural venous sinuses to extracranial veins.
- Dural venous sinuses drain blood from the brain, meninges, diploe, internal ear and orbit.
- Dural venous sinuses are classified as either paired or unpaired.
- Eventually all the blood from the dural venous sinuses drains into the internal jugular vein on each side through the sigmoid sinus.
- The CSF is a clear colourless liquid that bathes the brain and spinal cord.
- It is produced by the choroid plexuses within the lateral, third and fourth ventricles and circulates throughout CNS.
- The ventricles are a complex series of spaces within the brain which produce and contain CSF.
- There are four ventricles, a pair of lateral ventricles, the third ventricle and the fourth ventricle within the brain.
- Choroid plexuses are highly vascularized folds of pia lined by ependyma within the ventricles which produce CSF.
- The CSF circulates in the subarachnoid space surrounding the brain and spinal cord.
- It is finally absorbed into the venous blood of the dural venous sinuses through the arachnoid villi.
- The ANS controls involuntary effectors such as cardiac muscle, smooth muscle and various glands.
- It has two divisions, sympathetic and parasympathetic.
- It consists of central components like the hypothalamus, brainstem and spinal cord.
- The peripheral components are composed of the sympathetic and parasympathetic nerves with their associated ganglia.
- The sympathetic nervous system is responsible for fight-or-flight responses.
- The parasympathetic nervous system is active during rest and digestion.

CHAPTER 33

The Spinal Cord and Spinal Nerves

SPECIFIC LEARNING OBJECTIVES

At the end of this chapter, the student should be able to:

- Describe the gross and cross-sectional anatomy of the spinal cord.
- Describe the structure of a typical spinal nerve.
- Describe the formation, important branches and distribution of the cervical, brachial, lumbar and sacral plexuses.

GLOSSARY OF TERMS

- **Conus medullaris:** tapered tip of the lower end of the spinal cord
- **Cauda equina:** the lower spinal nerves that emerge from the spinal cord and resemble a horse's tail
- **Denticulate ligaments:** lateral triangular projections of the pia towards the dura that keep the spinal cord in place
- **Filum terminale:** thin strand of pia extending from the lower end of the spinal cord to the coccyx
- **Grey horns:** projections of the central grey matter of the spinal cord
- **White columns or funiculi:** subdivisions of the white matter containing tracts
- **Tract or fasciculus:** nerve fibres with a similar origin, termination and function
- **Decussation:** crossing of nerve fibres from one side to the other
- **Contralateral:** the origin and destination of pathways are on opposite sides
- **Ipsilateral:** the origin and destination of pathways are on the same side
- **Dermatome:** an area of skin supplied by a single spinal segment
- **Myotome:** all skeletal muscle fibres supplied by a single spinal segment
- **Nerve plexus:** ventral rami of spinal nerves that become interconnected to form a network and supply a particular region of the body

INTRODUCTION

The spinal cord is a cylinder of nerve tissue situated within the vertebral canal. It transmits information between the brain and body. Its functions include the conduction of impulses, control of locomotion and mediation of reflexes. Thirty-one pairs of spinal nerves emerge from the spinal cord to provide sensory, motor and autonomic nerve supply to the entire body except for the head and some regions of the neck. Sensations from the body are transmitted through the spinal cord to the brain via ascending sensory tracts. Motor signals from the brain to the spinal cord are transmitted through descending motor tracts. Large numbers of interneurons help to integrate the sensory and motor impulses.

THE SPINAL CORD

The spinal cord is located within the **vertebral canal** (Fig. 33.1). It extends from the foramen magnum to L1 vertebra in adults. It shows five **regions**, namely cervical, thoracic, lumbar, sacral and coccygeal. Each region has several segments. There are a total of 31 **segments** (8 cervical, 12 thoracic, 5 lumbar, 5 sacral and 1 coccygeal). Each segment gives attachment to a pair of **spinal nerves**. Two **enlargements** are seen along the length of the spinal cord. These are the cervical and lumbar enlargements. These enlargements occur due to the increased number of neurons that need to be accommodated in these regions to supply the upper and lower limbs. The tapered tip of the cord is called the **conus medullaris**. From the lower end of the spinal cord are seen to emerge a large number of nerve fibres that resemble a horse's tail. This structure is known as the **cauda equina**. The pia mater, arachnoid mater and dura mater cover the spinal cord from inside to outside. The pia mater of the spinal cord is modified to form the **ligamentum denticulatum** or **denticulate ligament** and **filum terminale**. The denticulate ligaments are triangular lateral projections of the pia that are attached to the dura and stabilize the spinal cord within the vertebral canal. The filum terminale is a thin, shiny strand that passes from the conus medullaris to the coccyx. It represents the continuation of the pia mater beyond the termination of the spinal cord.

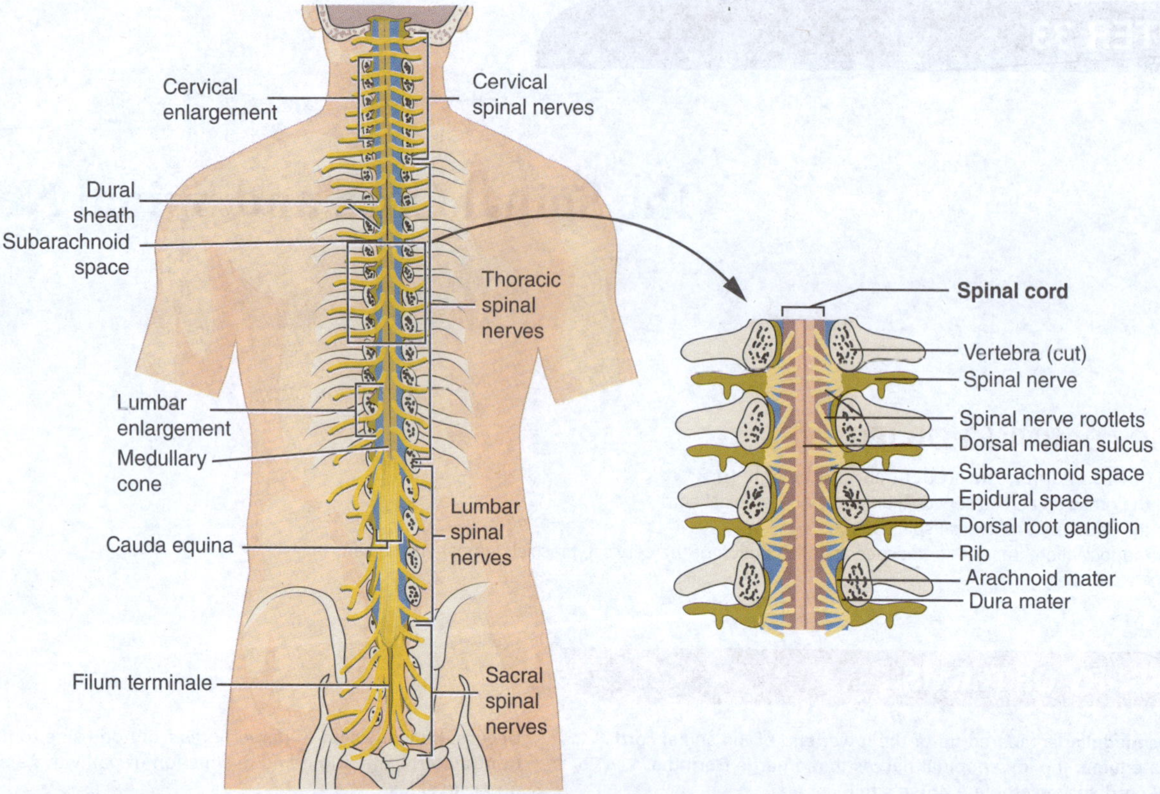

FIG. 33.1 The gross anatomy of the spinal cord.

In cross-section, the spinal cord is seen to consist of a central area of grey matter shaped like a butterfly and peripheral white matter (Fig. 33.2). The **grey matter** surrounds the central canal of the spinal cord. It contains neuronal cell bodies, neuroglia and unmyelinated axons. Three projections known as the anterior, lateral and posterior **grey horns** arise from the grey matter. The anterior horn contains motor neurons, the axons of which supply the skeletal muscles of the body. Sympathetic fibres arise from the lateral horn in the thoracic and upper lumbar segments of the spinal cord. The neurons of the posterior horn are involved in the sensory pathways. A large proportion of neurons in the grey matter are interneurons which serve an integrative function. The **white matter** contains myelinated and unmyelinated neuronal cell processes. Three pairs of **columns** or **funiculi**, dorsal, lateral and anterior, can be seen peripherally. Each column is occupied by named tracts or fasciculi. **Tracts** are nerve fibres with a similar origin, destination and function. They may be ascending or descending. Ascending tracts are sensory and carry information to the brain, whereas descending tracts carry motor commands to the spinal cord.

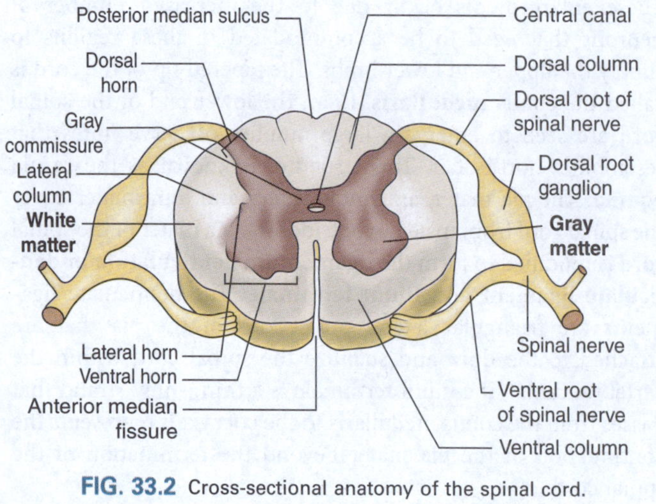

FIG. 33.2 Cross-sectional anatomy of the spinal cord.

The **sensory pathways** usually have three neurons that are involved, known as first-, second- and third-order neurons. The cell bodies of all **first-order neurons** lie in the dorsal root ganglia. The **second-order neurons** lie in either the spinal cord or the brainstem, whereas the third-order neurons are situated in the thalamus. The axons of the second-order neurons decussate before they terminate in the thalamus. From the thalamus, the axons of the **third-order neurons** reach the primary sensory area of the cerebral cortex. **Motor pathways** have two neurons, the **upper** and **lower motor neurons**, in the pathway. The cell bodies of the upper and lower motor neurons are located in the brain and spinal cord, respectively. The major sensory and motor tracts are summarized in Table 33.1.

The **arterial supply** of the spinal cord is through the anterior and posterior spinal arteries which are branches of the vertebral artery. The anterior two-thirds and posterior one-third of the spinal cord are supplied by the anterior and posterior spinal arteries, respectively. These arteries are supplemented by

Table 33.1 The Salient Features of the Major Sensory and Motor Tracts (Fig. 33.3)

Tract	Type	Pathway	Function
• Dorsal column	• Sensory	• Fasciculus gracilis and cuneatus carry signals from the lower and upper limbs • Decussation of second-order neurons in the medulla • Third-order neurons in the thalamus carry signals to the cerebral cortex	• Carry vibration and proprioception
• Spinothalamic	• Sensory	• Decussation of the second-order neurons in the spinal cord • Third-order neurons arise in the thalamus and continue to the cerebral cortex	• Carry touch, pain, temperature and pressure
• Spinocerebellar	• Sensory	• Second-order neurons in the spinal cord ascend in the ipsilateral lateral column • End in the cerebellar cortex	• Carry proprioceptive signals from the limbs and trunk
• Corticospinal	• Motor	• Upper motor neuron in the primary motor cortex • Decussation in the medulla • Lower motor neuron in the anterior horn of the spinal cord	• For precise, coordinated limb movements
• Tectospinal	• Motor	• Upper motor neuron in the tectum of the brain • Lower motor neuron in the anterior horn of the spinal cord	• Reflex turning of the head in response to sights and sounds
• Vestibulospinal	• Motor	• Upper motor neuron in the vestibular nuclei of the brainstem • Lower motor neuron in the anterior horn of the spinal cord	• Postural muscle activity in response to inner ear signals
• Reticulospinal	• Motor	• Upper motor neuron in the reticular formation of the pons and medulla • Lower motor neuron in the anterior horn of the spinal cord	• Controls limb movements that are important in maintaining posture and balance

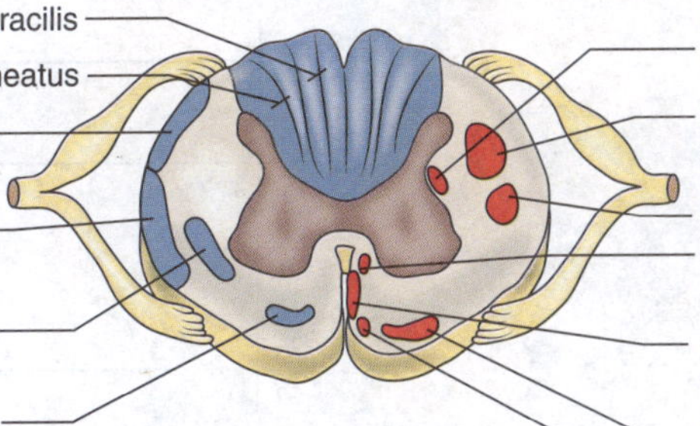

FIG. 33.3 The important ascending and descending tracts in the spinal cord. Red colour marks descending tracts while blue colour marks ascending tracts.

radicular arteries which arise from segmental arteries at each level. The radicular arteries in the lower thoracic level are particularly large and important for the arterial supply of the spinal cord. The **venous drainage** is into the internal vertebral venous plexus which is situated within the vertebral canal. From here, the venous blood drains into the external vertebral venous plexus and then into the segmental veins.

THE SPINAL NERVES (Fig. 33.4)

There are **31 pairs** of spinal nerves, 8 cervical, 12 thoracic, 5 lumbar, 5 sacral and 1 coccygeal. Each spinal nerve is a **mixed nerve** that exits at the intervertebral foramen and receives sensory information and sends motor signals to muscles and glands. Spinal nerves are formed by the joining of ventral and dorsal **roots** (Fig. 33.5). These roots are seen within the vertebral canal. The **dorsal root** with a ganglion carries sensory information to the spinal cord, whereas the **ventral root** carries motor signals to muscles and glands. The **dorsal root ganglia** or sensory ganglia are situated in relation to the dorsal spinal roots and some cranial nerves. Located within the ganglia are pseudounipolar neurons having a peripheral process (functionally dendrite) and a central process (functionally axon). No synapses occur within the sensory ganglia. The mixed spinal nerve so formed divides to form a **ventral** and **dorsal ramus**. Both the dorsal and ventral rami carry sensory and motor fibres. The dorsal ramus supplies the skin and muscles of the back, whereas the ventral ramus supplies the ventrolateral body surfaces and

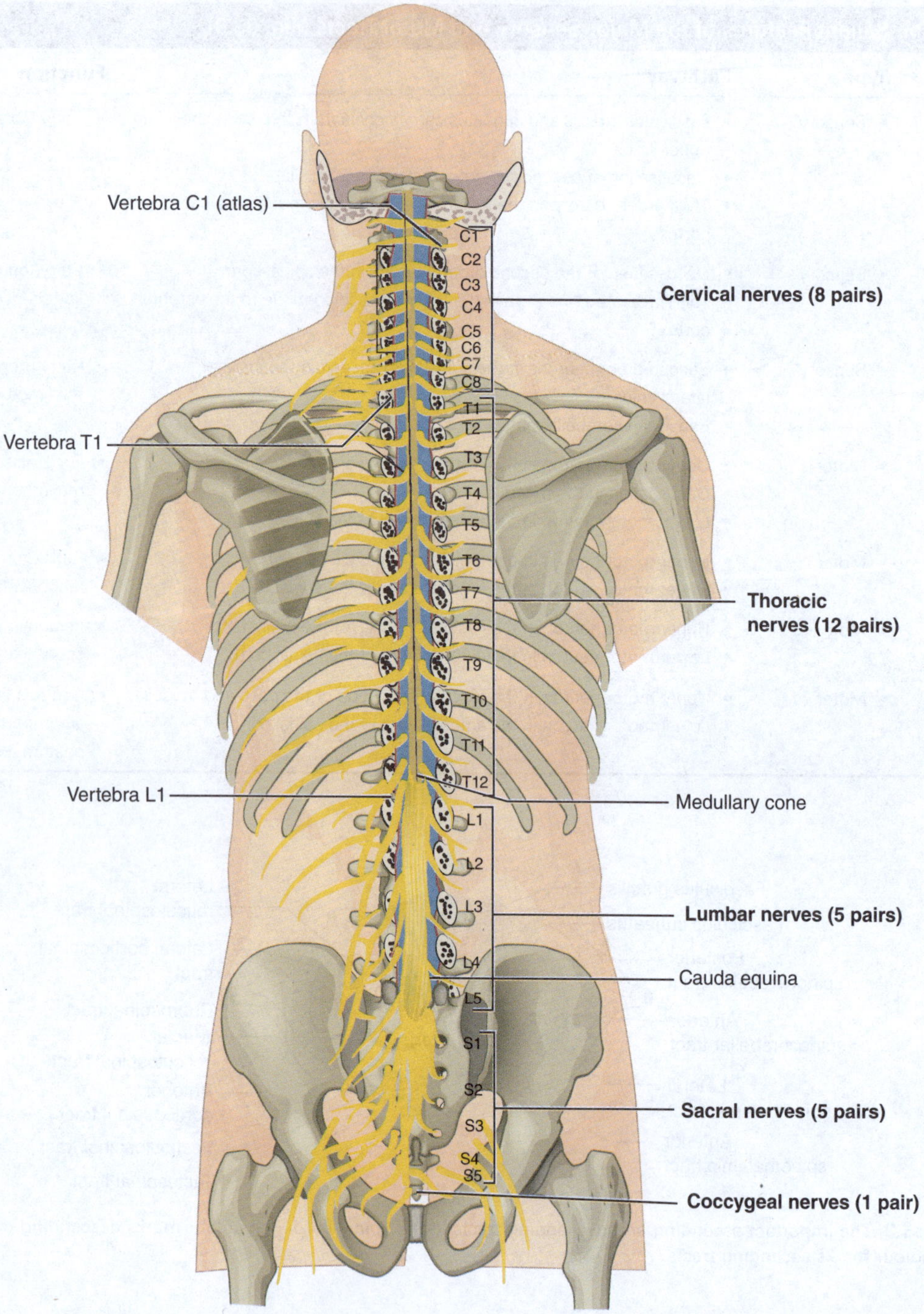

FIG. 33.4 The spinal nerves.

limbs. A **dermatome** is an area of skin supplied by a single spinal segment, whereas a **myotome** consists of all skeletal muscle fibres supplied by a single spinal segment.

Histologically, a nerve is composed of numerous neuronal processes or **nerve fibres** which have a characteristic wavy appearance. The nerve fibres are grouped into bundles called **fasciculi** (Fig. 33.6). Three connective tissue sheaths, the epineurium, perineurium and endoneurium, are associated with each nerve. The **epineurium** encloses the entire nerve, the **perineurium** surrounds a fascicle and the **endoneurium** separates individual nerve fibres. Each nerve fibre consists of an eosinophilic, centrally placed, relatively darkly staining **axon**. Surrounding the axon is a lightly stained **myelin sheath**. **Schwann cell** nuclei are observed at the periphery of the myelin sheath. The myelin sheath is enclosed by the neurilemma with the endoneurium.

The blended fibres of ventral rami of adjacent spinal nerves form a complex, interwoven network of nerve fibres called **nerve plexuses**. These nerve plexuses control skeletal muscles of the neck and limbs and supply the skin of the above-mentioned regions.

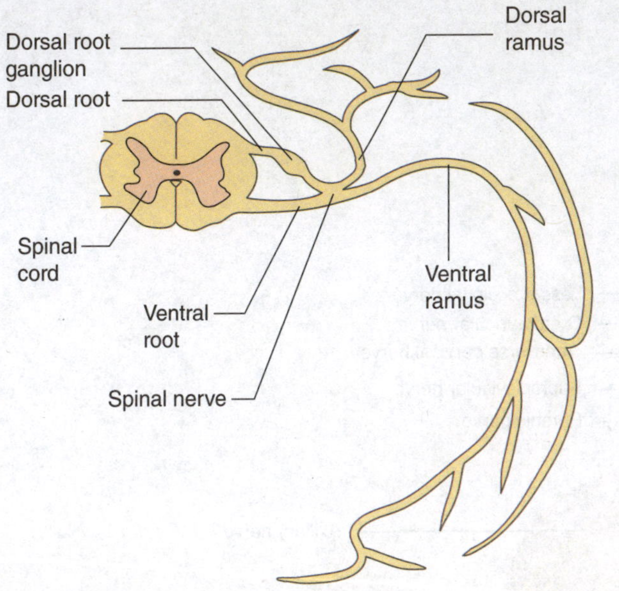

FIG. 33.5 The formation and branching of a typical spinal nerve.

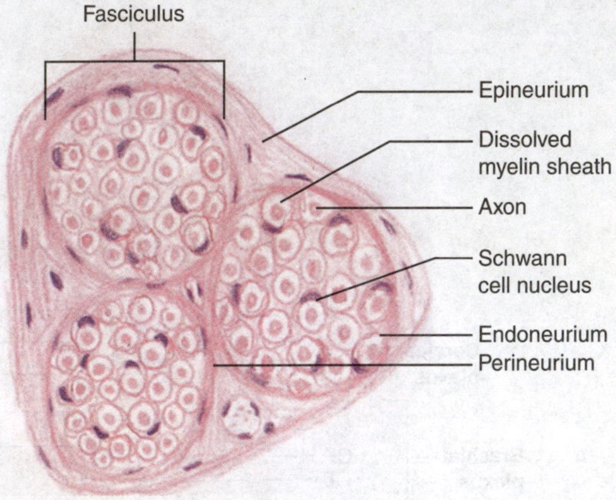

FIG. 33.6 The microstructure of the cross-section of a nerve.

The formation of a plexus permits individual nerve fibres to pass from one peripheral nerve to another allowing redistribution of nerves. The nerve plexuses are the cervical, brachial, lumbar, sacral and coccygeal. The coccygeal plexus is small and supplies the skin in the coccygeal region. The other plexuses are described in Table 33.2.

Table 33.2 The Salient Features of the Nerve Plexuses (Fig. 33.7)

Plexus	Location	Formation	Major Branches	Distribution
• Cervical	• Posterior triangle of the neck	• Ventral rami of C1–C4	• Phrenic nerve • Cutaneous nerves to the neck • Muscular branches to the trapezius and sternocleido-mastoid	• Supplies neck and diaphragm

• Brachial	• Root of the neck and axilla
	• Cords of brachial plexus surround the axillary artery
		• Roots formed by the ventral rami of C5–T1
		• Trunks formed by union of roots: upper (C5, C6), middle (C7), lower (C8, T1)
		• Anterior and posterior divisions are formed from each trunk
		• Cords are formed from divisions as follows:
		  • The lateral cord is formed by the anterior divisions of the upper and middle trunks
		  • The medial cord is formed by the anterior division of the lower trunk
		  • The posterior cord is formed by the posterior divisions of the upper, middle and lower trunks
		  • Branches arise from the cords
			• Musculocutaneous nerve (lateral cord)
			• Median nerve (lateral and medial cords)
			• Ulnar nerve (medial cord)
			• Axillary nerve (posterior cord)
			• Radial nerve (posterior cord)
				• Innervates the pectoral girdle and upper limbs

• Lumbar	• Posterior abdominal wall	• Ventral rami of L1–L4	• Femoral nerve • Obturator nerve • Cutaneous branches to the anterior abdominal wall, anterior thigh and genitalia	• Supplies the abdominal wall, anterior thigh and genitalia
• Sacral	• Posterior pelvic wall	• Ventral rami of L4–S3	• Sciatic nerve • Superior and inferior gluteal nerves • Pudendal nerve	• Supplies the gluteal region, the remainder of the lower limb, the pelvic muscles and perineum

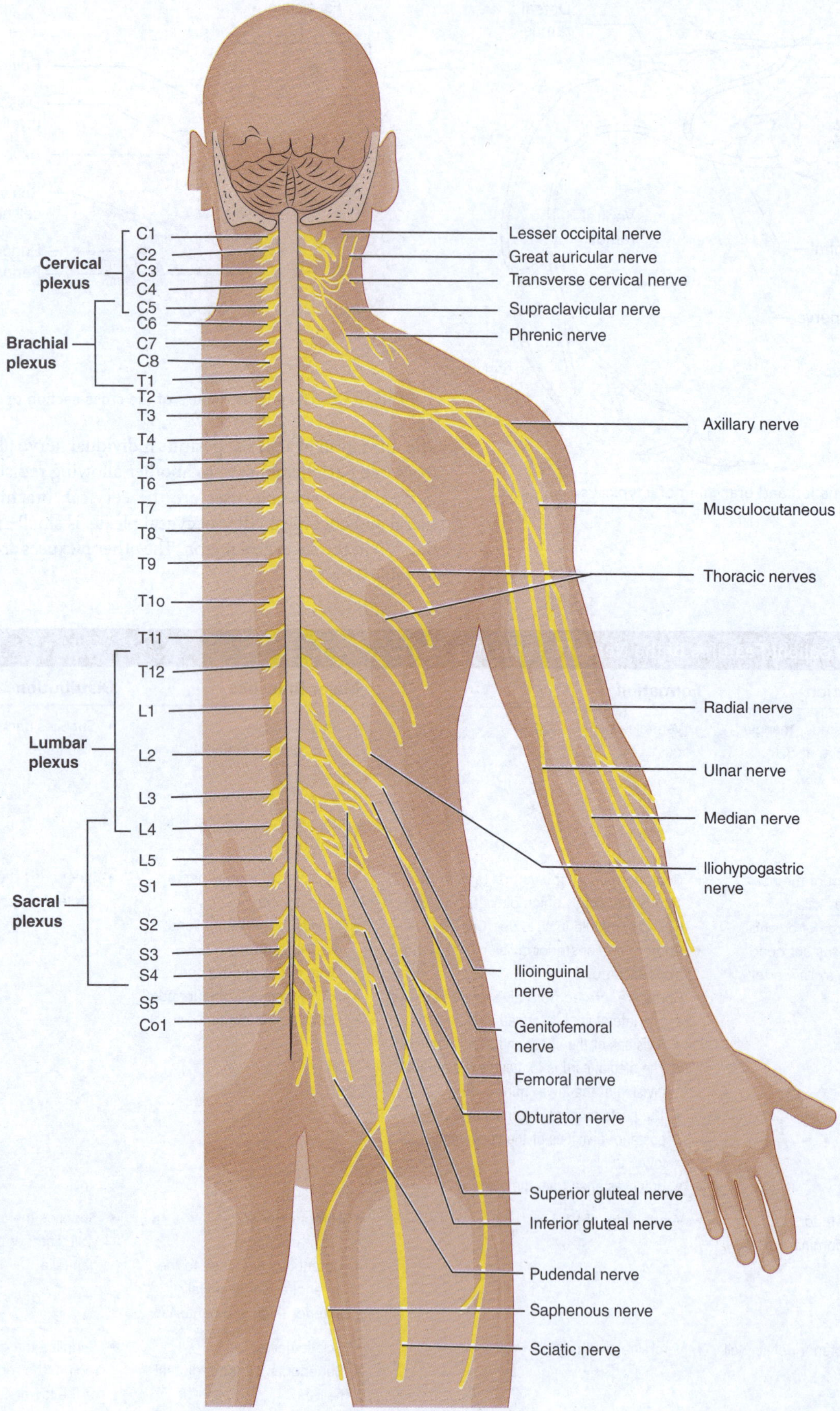

FIG. 33.7 The major nerve plexuses of the body and their branches.

APPLIED ANATOMY

- Injuries to the cervical region of the spinal cord can cause paralysis of all the four limbs, a condition called **quadriplegia**. Paralysis of the lower limbs, known as **paraplegia**, can occur due to injuries to the lower part of the spinal cord.
- **Spina bifida** is a congenital disorder, usually seen in the lumbar region, in which there is a defect in the vertebrae leading to varying degrees of exposure of the meninges and spinal cord. This can in certain instances lead to neurological problems.
- **Poliomyelitis** is a viral infection that causes death of the anterior horn cells of the spinal cord and results in atrophy of the muscles supplied by them.
- **Amyotrophic lateral sclerosis** is a progressive disorder of unknown aetiology that causes death of motor neurons.
- Traumatic injuries can cause hemisection of the spinal cord resulting in **Brown-Sequard syndrome**. The motor and sensory deficits in this condition can be explained by the course and level of decussation of the affected tracts.
- **Herpes zoster** or shingles is a viral infection of the sensory ganglia that causes painful vesicles along the course of a sensory nerve.
- **Deep tendon reflexes** are exaggerated in upper motor neuron lesions and lost in lower motor neuron lesions.
- **Babinski's sign** is dorsiflexion of the big toe and fanning of the other toes when the lateral part of the sole is stroked. It is seen characteristically in upper motor neuron lesions.
- A knowledge of **dermatomes** and **myotomes** is important in localizing the site of lesions in the spinal cord.
- **Erb paralysis** occurs due to injuries to the upper trunk of the brachial plexus. The affected limb is held in a characteristic 'waiter's tip' position.
- **Klumpke paralysis** occurs due to injuries to the lower trunk of the brachial plexus. In this condition, there is a complete claw hand deformity.

APPLICATIONS IN NURSING

- Patients with spinal cord injuries may have sensory and motor loss which prevents them from feeling discomfort at pressure points and makes them unable to independently change position. This predisposes them to developing **pressure ulcers**. Nurses need to ensure proper positioning of such patients and regular monitoring to prevent the development of pressure ulcers.

SUMMARY

- The spinal cord is located within the vertebral canal.
- It extends from the foramen magnum to L1 vertebra.
- It shows five regions, namely cervical, thoracic, lumbar, sacral and coccygeal.
- There are a total of 31 segments (8 cervical, 12 thoracic, 5 lumbar, 5 sacral and 1 coccygeal).
- Two enlargements, the cervical and lumbar, are seen along the length of the spinal cord.
- The tapered tip of the cord is called the conus medullaris.
- From the lower end of the spinal cord are seen to emerge many nerve fibres that resemble a horse's tail, known as the cauda equina.
- The pia mater of the spinal cord is modified to form the ligamentum denticulatum or denticulate ligament and filum terminale.
- In cross-section, the spinal cord is seen to consist of a central area of grey matter shaped like a butterfly and peripheral white matter.
- Three projections, known as the anterior, lateral and posterior grey horns, arise from the grey matter.
- The anterior horn contains motor neurons, the axons of which supply the skeletal muscles of the body.
- Sympathetic fibres arise from the lateral horn in the thoracic and upper lumbar segments of the spinal cord.
- The neurons of the posterior horn are involved in the sensory pathways.
- The white matter contains three pairs of columns or funiculi, dorsal, lateral and anterior.
- Tracts are nerve fibres with a similar origin, destination and function.
- Ascending tracts are sensory and carry information to the brain, whereas descending tracts carry motor commands to the spinal cord.
- The sensory pathways usually have three neurons that are involved, known as first-, second- and third-order neurons.
- Motor pathways have two neurons, the upper and lower motor neurons, in the pathway.
- The large sensory tracts are the dorsal column, spinothalamic and spinocerebellar tracts.
- The large motor tracts are the corticospinal, tectospinal, reticulospinal and vestibulospinal tracts.
- The arterial supply of the spinal cord is through the anterior and posterior spinal arteries and the radicular arteries.
- The venous drainage is into the internal vertebral venous plexus which is situated within the vertebral canal.
- There are 31 pairs of spinal nerves, namely 8 cervical, 12 thoracic, 5 lumbar, 5 sacral and 1 coccygeal.
- Each spinal nerve is a mixed nerve that exits at the intervertebral foramen and receives sensory information and issues motor signals to muscles and glands.
- Spinal nerves are formed by the joining of ventral and dorsal roots.
- The dorsal root with a ganglion carries sensory information to the spinal cord, whereas the ventral root carries motor signals to muscles and glands.
- The mixed spinal nerve so formed divides to form a ventral and dorsal ramus.
- The dorsal ramus supplies the skin and muscles of the back, whereas the ventral ramus supplies the ventrolateral body surfaces and limbs.
- A dermatome is an area of skin supplied by a single spinal segment.
- A myotome consists of all skeletal muscle fibres supplied by a single spinal segment.
- Histologically, a nerve is composed of nerve fibres which are grouped into bundles called fasciculi.
- Three connective tissue sheaths, namely the epineurium, perineurium and endoneurium, are associated with each nerve.
- Each nerve fibre consists of an eosinophilic, centrally placed, relatively darkly staining axon.
- Surrounding the axon is a lightly stained myelin sheath.
- Schwann cell nuclei are observed at the periphery of the myelin sheath.
- The myelin sheath is enclosed by the neurilemma with the endoneurium.
- The blended fibres of ventral rami of adjacent spinal nerves form a complex, interwoven network of nerve fibres called nerve plexuses.
- These nerve plexuses control skeletal muscles of the neck and limbs and supply the skin of the above-mentioned regions.
- The nerve plexuses are the cervical, brachial, lumbar, sacral and coccygeal.
- The cervical plexus is formed by spinal nerves C1–C4 and supplies the neck and diaphragm.
- The brachial plexus is formed by spinal nerves C5–T1 and supplies the pectoral girdle and upper limbs.
- The lumbar plexus is formed by spinal nerves L1–L4 and supplies the abdominal wall, anterior thigh and genitalia.
- The sacral plexus is formed by spinal nerves L4–S3 and supplies the gluteal region, the remainder of the lower limb, the pelvic muscles and perineum.

CHAPTER 34

The Brainstem, Cranial Nerves, Cerebellum and Fourth Ventricle

SPECIFIC LEARNING OBJECTIVES

At the end of this chapter, the student should be able to:

- Name the parts of the brainstem.
- Describe the basic structure of the medulla, pons and midbrain.
- Describe the formation, course and distribution of the cranial nerves.
- Describe the gross anatomy of the cerebellum.
- Describe the gross anatomy of the fourth ventricle.

GLOSSARY OF TERMS

- **Pyramid:** an elongated projection on the ventral aspect of the medulla caused by the underlying corticospinal fibres
- **Olive:** a rounded projection on the ventral aspect of the medulla caused by the underlying inferior olivary nucleus
- **Cerebellar peduncle:** connection between the brainstem and cerebellum
- **Reticular formation:** collection of neurons and nerve fibres found interspersed between the nuclei and white matter
- **Crus cerebri:** prominent ventral aspect of the midbrain caused by descending fibres from the cerebral cortex
- **Substantia nigra:** pigmented part of the midbrain containing dopaminergic neurons
- **Tegmentum:** anterior part of the midbrain
- **Tectum:** posterior part of the midbrain
- **Colliculi:** rounded projections forming part of the tectum of the midbrain
- **Vermis:** midline portion of the cerebellum connecting the two hemispheres
- **Folia:** elevated areas of the cerebellar cortex
- **Fissures:** depressed areas of the cerebellar cortex
- **Foramina of Luschka:** foramina at the lateral angles of the fourth ventricle
- **Foramen of Magendie:** median foramen at the inferior angle of the fourth ventricle

INTRODUCTION

The brainstem consists of the midbrain, pons and medulla oblongata. It is like the spinal cord but contains embedded nuclei. The brainstem controls automatic behaviours necessary for survival, provides pathways for tracts between higher and lower brain centres and is associated with 10 of the 12 pairs of cranial nerves. Twelve pairs of cranial nerves connect the brain to parts of the head, neck and trunk. Most cranial nerves are mixed, but some are sensory and others motor. The names of the cranial nerves indicate their primary functions or the general distribution of their fibres. They are also identified by numbers indicating their order. The cerebellum makes up around 10% of the brain's mass. Cerebellar activity occurs subconsciously. Its functions include maintenance of equilibrium, tone and posture and coordination of movements.

THE BRAINSTEM (Fig. 34.1)

The **medulla oblongata** is the most inferior part of the brainstem (Fig. 34.2). It is continuous above with the pons and below with the spinal cord. Along with the pons, it forms the **floor** or ventral wall of the **fourth ventricle**. The **pyramids** and **olives** are two prominent projections on the ventral aspect of the medulla. It is connected with the cerebellum through the **inferior cerebellar peduncle**. **Cranial nerve nuclei** VIII, IX, X, XI and XII are associated with the medulla. The **nucleus cuneatus** and **gracilis**, which receive fibres of the dorsal column, are seen in the medulla. The olives are formed by the underlying **inferior olivary nuclei** which relay sensory information. The pyramids are formed by the underlying **corticospinal tracts**, while the dorsal columns continue upward as the **fasciculus gracilis** and **cuneatus** from the spinal cord to relay in the nucleus gracilis and cuneatus, respectively. Interspersed with the nuclei and white matter is the **reticular formation** which contains cardiovascular and respiratory control centres. The major **functions** of the medulla include the maintenance of cardiovascular and respiratory functions; regulation of reflexes like coughing, gagging, swallowing and vomiting; and control of the cranial nerves VIII, IX, X, XI and XII.

The **pons** forms a bridge between the two cerebellar hemispheres and is continuous above with the midbrain and below with the

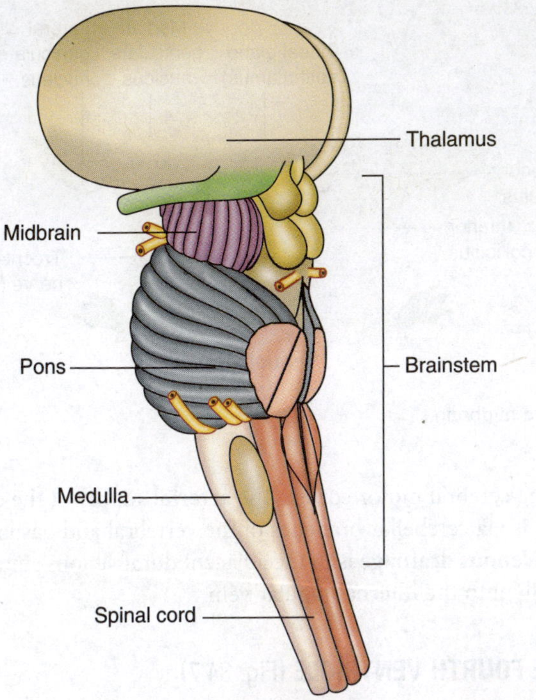

FIG. 34.1 The parts of the brainstem.

medulla (Fig. 34.3). Along with the medulla, it forms the **floor** or ventral wall of the **fourth ventricle**. The ventral or **basilar part** of the pons is prominent. It is connected to the cerebellum by the thick **middle cerebellar peduncles. Cranial nerve nuclei** V, VI, VII and VIII are associated with the pons. The **pontine nuclei** are present in the basilar part and form part of the corticopontocerebellar pathway. Like the medulla, the pons contains the **reticular formation** interspersed between the nuclei and white matter. The fibres of the pons in the basilar part connect higher brain centres and the spinal cord and relay impulses between the motor cortex and cerebellum. The reticular formation controls various autonomic and visceral responses, while the nuclei associated with cranial nerves V, VI, VII and VIII are responsible for the functioning of these nerves.

The **midbrain** is continuous above with the diencephalon and below with the pons (Fig. 34.4). It encloses the **aqueduct of Sylvius**. The **crura cerebri** are prominently seen on the ventral aspect. On the dorsal aspect are seen a pair each of rounded prominences called superior and inferior **colliculi**. The **superior cerebellar peduncle** connects the midbrain with the cerebellum. The midbrain is divided into a dorsal **tectum** and ventral **cerebral peduncle**. The cerebral peduncle is further divided into the crus

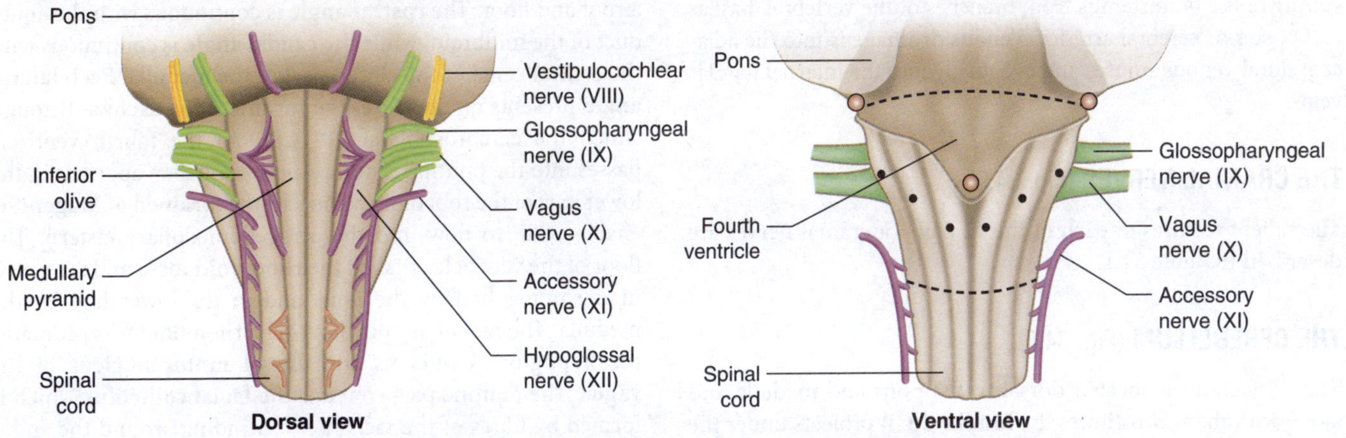

FIG. 34.2 The anatomy of the medulla oblongata.

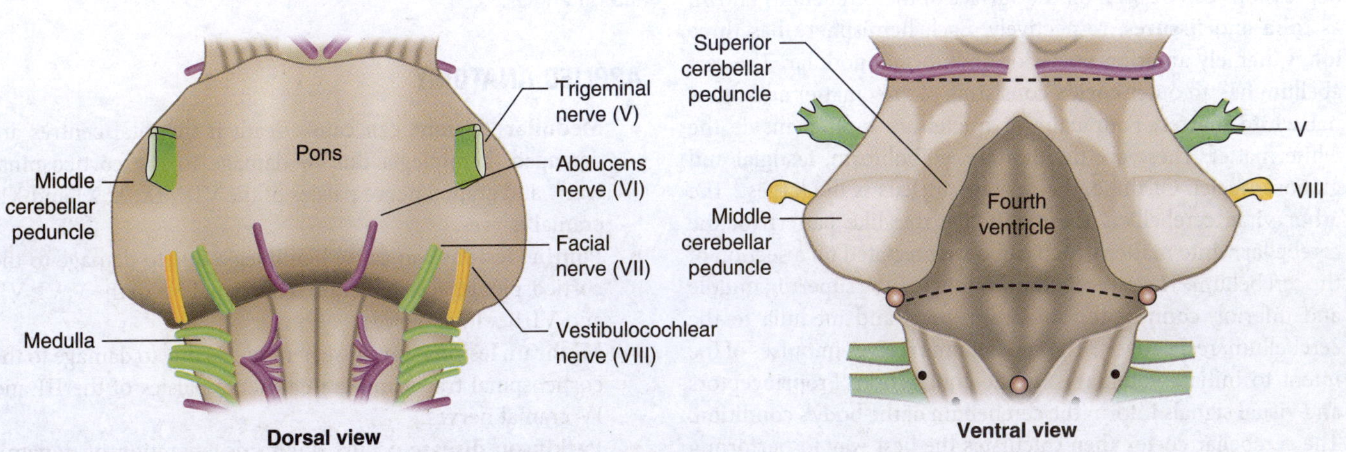

FIG. 34.3 The anatomy of the pons.

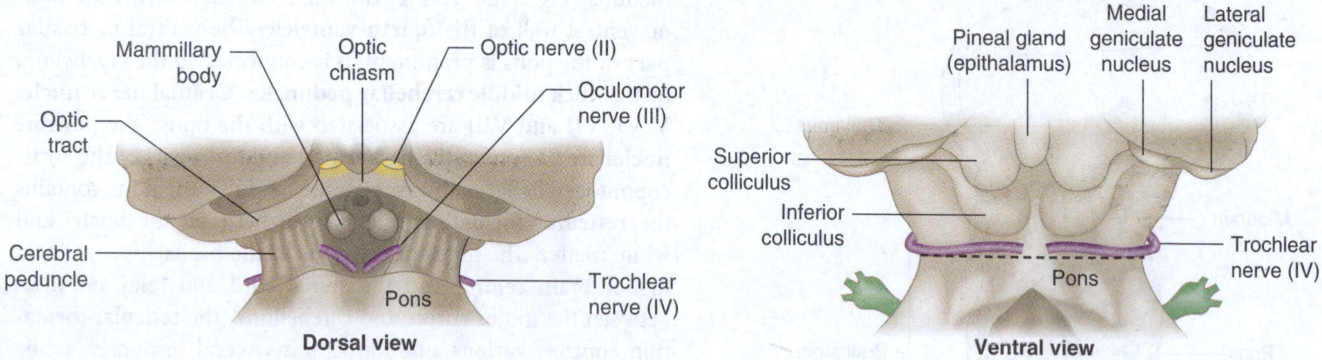

FIG. 34.4 anatomy of the midbrain.

cerebri, **substantia nigra** and tegmentum. Cranial nerve nuclei III and IV are associated with the **tegmentum**. Located in the tegmentum is a prominent nucleus called the **red nucleus** which is a relay nucleus for some descending motor pathways. The **tectum** consists of the superior and inferior colliculi. The crus cerebri contains descending fibres from the cerebral cortex, while the red nucleus and substantia nigra are concerned with motor control. Visual and auditory reflexes are mediated by the superior and inferior colliculi. The nuclei associated with cranial nerves III and IV are responsible for functioning of these nerves. The **arterial supply** of the brainstem is from branches of the vertebral, basilar and posterior cerebral arteries. **Venous drainage** is into the adjacent dural venous sinuses and eventually into the internal jugular veins.

THE CRANIAL NERVES (Fig. 34.5)

The salient features of each of the 12 pairs of cranial nerves are described in Table 34.1.

THE CEREBELLUM (Fig. 34.6)

The cerebellum is located dorsal to the pons and medulla and along with them constitutes the **hindbrain**. It projects under the occipital lobes of the cerebrum and has two bilaterally symmetrical **hemispheres** connected by the **vermis**. Elevations and depressions can be seen on the surface of the cerebellum known as **folia** and **fissures**, respectively. Each hemisphere has three **lobes**, namely anterior, posterior and flocculonodular. The cerebellum has an outer **cortex** consisting of grey matter and internal **white matter**. Four pairs of **nuclei** are located inside the white matter. These are the **dentate**, emboliform, fastigial and globose nuclei. Of these, the dentate nucleus is the largest. The arbor vitae cerebelli is the distinctive tree-like pattern of the cerebellar white matter which can be appreciated on a section of the cerebellum. Three **cerebellar peduncles**, the superior, middle and inferior, connect the midbrain, pons and medulla to the cerebellum, respectively. The cerebellum receives impulses of the intent to initiate voluntary muscle contraction. Proprioceptors and visual signals inform the cerebellum of the body's condition. The cerebellar cortex then calculates the best way to perform a movement and a blueprint of the **coordinated movement** is sent to the cerebral motor cortex. The **arterial supply** of the cerebellum is via cerebellar branches of the vertebral and basilar arteries. **Venous drainage** is to the adjacent dural venous sinuses and finally into the internal jugular vein.

THE FOURTH VENTRICLE (Fig. 34.7)

The fourth ventricle is the **cavity** of the **hindbrain**. It intervenes between the cerebellum **dorsally** and the pons and medulla **ventrally**. It is roughly **diamond shaped** and has four angles, a roof and floor. The **rostral angle** is continuous with the aqueduct of the midbrain, while the **caudal angle** is continuous with the central canal of the closed part of the medulla. Each **lateral angle** presents an aperture, the **foramen of Luschka**, through which the cerebrospinal fluid (CSF) of the fourth ventricle passes into the pontine cistern. Another median aperture in the lower part of the roof of the ventricle, the **foramen of Magendie**, enables CSF to flow into the cerebellomedullary cistern. The floor of the ventricle is called the **rhomboid fossa** and is formed in the upper half by the pons and in the lower half by the medulla. The medullary portion of the rhomboid fossa contains the **hypoglossal nucleus** and **dorsal motor nucleus** of the **vagus**. The pontine part contains the **facial colliculus** which is formed by fibres of the facial nerve winding around the abducent nucleus. The **vestibular nuclei** are seen in relation to both the medullary and pontine parts of the rhomboid fossa near the lateral angles.

APPLIED ANATOMY

- **Medullary lesions** can cause death if the vital centres are damaged, hemiplegia due to damage to the corticospinal tracts and cranial nerve palsies of the VIII, IX, X, XI and XII cranial nerves.
- **Pontine lesions** can cause hemiplegia due to damage to the corticospinal tracts and cranial nerve palsies of the V, VI, VII and VIII cranial nerves.
- **Midbrain lesions** can cause hemiplegia due to damage to the corticospinal tracts and cranial nerve palsies of the III and IV cranial nerves.
- **Parkinson disease** occurs due to degeneration of dopaminergic neurons in the substantia nigra of the midbrain. This

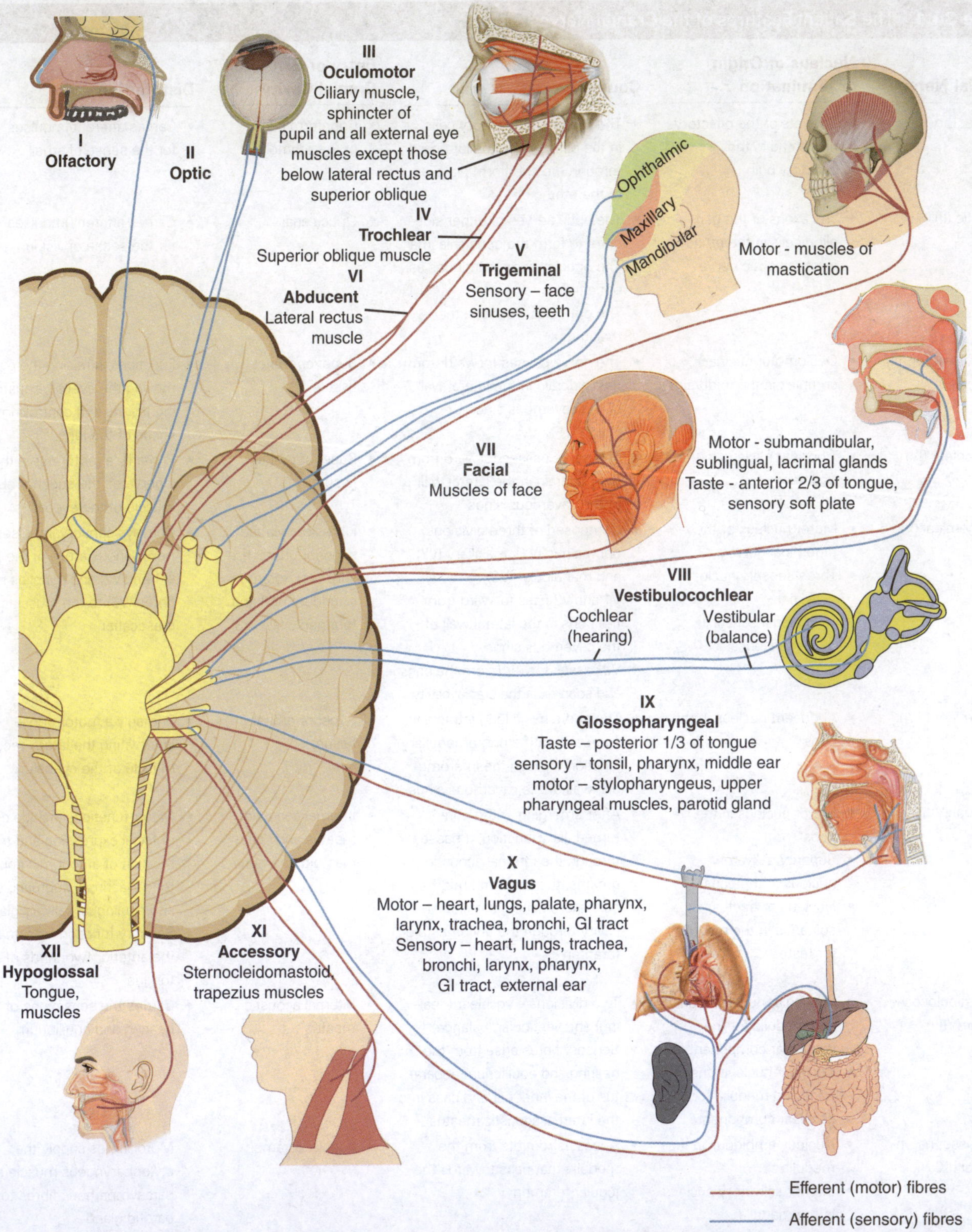

FIG. 34.5 The anatomy of the cranial nerves.

causes the characteristic symptoms of rigidity, tremors and akinesia (difficulty in initiating movements).

- **Tumours** at the **cerebellopontine angle** can cause symptoms related to cranial nerves V, VII and VIII. One of the more common tumours at this site is an acoustic neuroma arising from the Schwann cells of the VIII cranial nerve.
- **Cerebellar lesions** cause a decrease in the tone of skeletal muscles, poor balance and lack of coordination of movements known as hypotonia, ataxia and dyssynergia, respectively.
- **Hydrocephalus** can occur if there is blockage of the foramina of Luschka or Magendie due to either congenital or acquired causes.

Table 34.1 The Salient Features of the Cranial Nerves

Cranial Nerve	Nucleus of Origin or Termination	Course	Entry or Exit From Cranial Cavity	Distribution
• Olfactory (I)	• Rootlets of the olfactory nerve end in the olfactory bulb	• The rootlets of olfactory cells in the olfactory epithelium pass through the cribriform plate of the ethmoid	• Cribriform plate of the ethmoid	• Carries afferent impulses for the sense of smell
• Optic (II)	• The axons of the ganglion cells in the retina form the optic nerve	• The optic nerves of either side unite to form the optic chiasma • The optic chiasma continues as optic tract • The optic tract relays in the thalamus	• Optic canal	• Carries afferent impulses for the sense of vision
• Oculomotor (III)	• Oculomotor nuclear complex in the midbrain	• The nerve passes forward from the midbrain in the lateral wall of the cavernous sinus	• Superior orbital fissure	• Functions in raising the eyelid, moving the eyeball, constricting the iris and controlling the shape of the lens
• Trochlear (IV)	• Trochlear nucleus in the midbrain	• The nerve passes forward from the midbrain in the lateral wall of the cavernous sinus	• Superior orbital fissure	• Primarily a motor nerve that innervates the superior oblique muscle of the eyeball
• Trigeminal (V)	• Motor nucleus of the trigeminal nerve • Three sensory nuclei: - Spinal - Principal sensory - Mesencephalic	• Composed of three divisions: ophthalmic (V1), maxillary (V2) and mandibular (V3) • V1 and V2 pass forward from the pons in the lateral wall of the cavernous sinus • V3 passes forward from the pons and soon exits the cranial cavity	• Fibres run via the superior orbital fissure (V1), foramen rotundum (V2) and foramen ovale (V3)	• Conveys sensory impulses from various areas of the face (V1 and V2) and supplies motor fibres (V3) to the muscles of mastication
• Abducent (VI)	• Abducent nucleus in the pons	• The nerve has a long intracranial course from the pontomedullary junction through the inferomedial wall of the cavernous sinus	• Superior orbital fissure	• Primarily a motor nerve innervating the lateral rectus muscle of the eyeball
• Facial (VII)	• Motor nucleus in the pons • Superior salivatory nucleus in the pons • Nucleus of tractus solitarius in the medulla for taste	• After emerging at the pontomedullary junction, it passes through the internal acoustic meatus, the inner and middle ear before exiting the cranial cavity through the stylomastoid foramen	• Internal acoustic meatus and stylomastoid foramen	• Motor functions include control of facial expression and transmission of autonomic impulses to the lacrimal, submandibular and sublingual salivary glands • Sensory function is taste from the anterior two-thirds of the tongue
• Vestibulocochlear (VIII)	• Vestibular nuclei in pons and medulla for the vestibular component • Cochlear nuclei in the pons and medulla for the cochlear component	• Two divisions – cochlear (hearing) and vestibular (balance) • Sensory fibres arise from the hearing and equilibrium apparatus of the inner ear and pass into the internal acoustic meatus	• Internal acoustic meatus	• Carries the sensations of hearing and equilibrium
• Glossopharyngeal (IX)	• Nucleus ambiguus in the medulla • Inferior salivatory nucleus in the medulla • Nucleus of the tractus solitarius in the medulla for taste	• Arises as rootlets from the medulla that pass towards the jugular foramen	• Jugular foramen	• Motor fibres supply the stylopharyngeus muscle and parasympathetic fibres to the parotid gland • Sensory fibres conduct taste and general sensory impulses from the tongue and pharynx
• Vagus (X)	• Nucleus ambiguus in the medulla • Dorsal motor nucleus in the medulla • Nucleus of the tractus solitarius in the medulla for taste	• The only cranial nerve that extends beyond the head and neck • Arises as rootlets from the medulla that pass towards the jugular foramen	• Jugular foramen	• Most motor fibres are parasympathetic fibres to the heart, lungs and abdominal viscera • It carries taste sensations from the posterior-most part of the tongue

Table 34.1 The Salient Features of the Cranial Nerves—cont'd

Cranial Nerve	Nucleus of Origin or Termination	Course	Entry or Exit From Cranial Cavity	Distribution
• Accessory (XI)	• Nucleus ambiguus in the medulla for the cranial component • Upper six cervical segments of the spinal cord for the spinal component	• The cranial part arises as rootlets from the medulla that pass towards the jugular foramen and join the vagus nerve • The spinal part passes through the foramen magnum, joins the cranial part and then passes towards the jugular foramen	• Jugular foramen	• Cranial part supplies muscles of the larynx, pharynx and soft palate • Spinal part innervates the trapezius and sternocleidomastoid, which move the head and neck
• Hypoglossal (XII)	• Hypoglossal nucleus in the medulla	• Arises as rootlets from the medulla that pass towards the hypoglossal canal	• Hypoglossal canal	• Innervates the muscles of the tongue

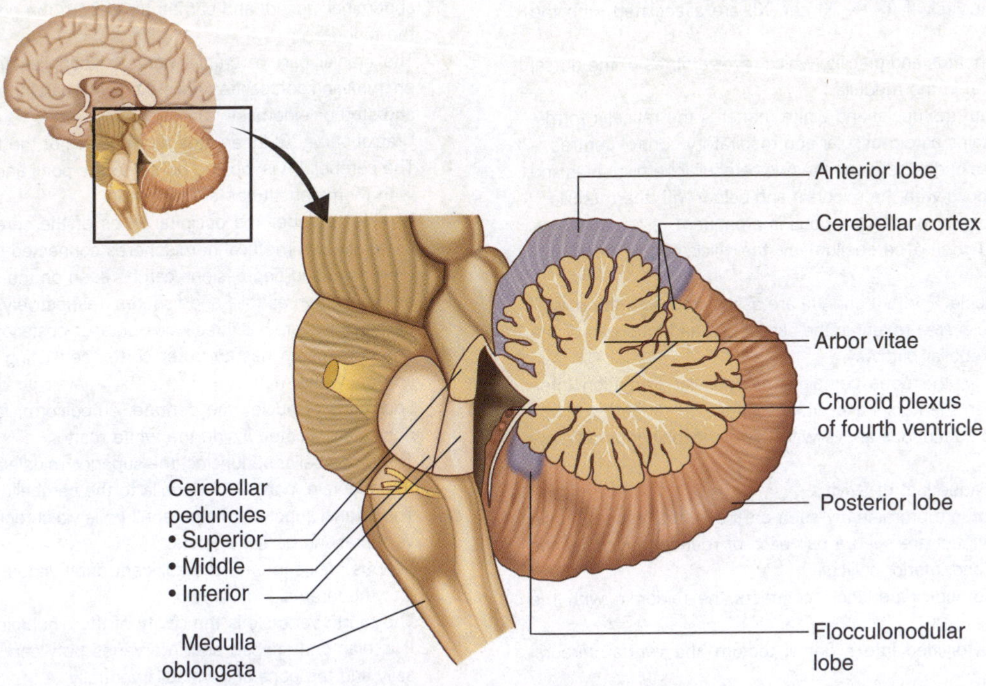

FIG. 34.6 The anatomy of the cerebellum.

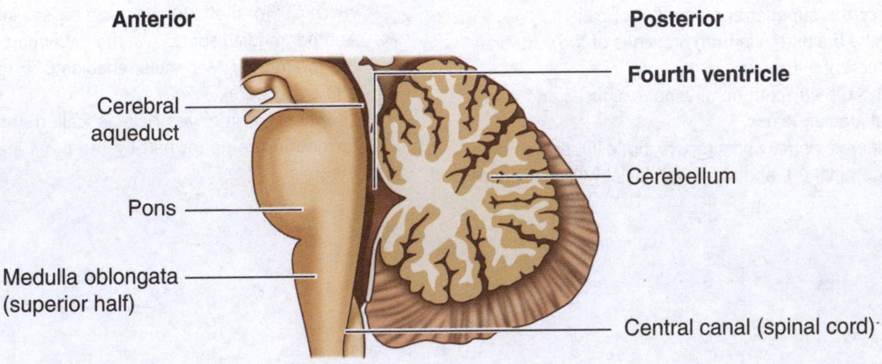

FIG. 34.7 The anatomy of the fourth ventricle – sagittal section of the fourth ventricle.

APPLICATIONS IN NURSING

- Brainstem lesions can cause **coma**. Such patients will usually require admission to an intensive care unit. Nursing personnel will have to ensure that these patients are positioned appropriately to avoid bed sores, take the necessary precautions to avoid aspiration pneumonia and use soft cloth restraints if required to ensure that patients do not pull out tubes or dressings.

SUMMARY

- The medulla oblongata is the most inferior part of the brainstem.
- It is continuous above with the pons and below with the spinal cord.
- Along with the pons, it forms the floor or ventral wall of the fourth ventricle.
- The pyramids and olives are two prominent projections on the ventral aspect of the medulla.
- It is connected to the cerebellum through the inferior cerebellar peduncle.
- Cranial nerve nuclei VIII, IX, X, XI and XII are associated with the medulla.
- The nucleus cuneatus and gracilis, which receive fibres of the dorsal column, are seen in the medulla.
- Interspersed with the nuclei and white matter is the reticular formation which contains cardiovascular and respiratory control centres.
- The pons forms a bridge between the two cerebellar hemispheres and is continuous above with the midbrain and below with the medulla.
- The ventral or basilar part of the pons is prominent.
- It is connected to the cerebellum by the thick middle cerebellar peduncles.
- Cranial nerve nuclei V, VI, VII and VIII are associated with the pons.
- The pontine nuclei are present in the basilar part and form part of the corticopontocerebellar pathway.
- Like the medulla, the pons contains the reticular formation interspersed between the nuclei and white matter.
- The midbrain is continuous above with the diencephalon and below with the pons.
- It encloses the aqueduct of Sylvius.
- The crura cerebri are prominently seen on the ventral aspect, while on the dorsal aspect are seen a pair each of rounded prominences called superior and inferior colliculi.
- The superior cerebellar peduncle connects the midbrain with the cerebellum.
- The midbrain is divided into a dorsal tectum and ventral cerebral peduncle.
- The cerebral peduncle is further divided into the crus cerebri, substantia nigra and tegmentum.
- Cranial nerve nuclei III and IV are associated with the tegmentum.
- Located in the tegmentum is a prominent nucleus called the red nucleus.
- The tectum consists of the superior and inferior colliculi.
- The arterial supply of the brainstem is from branches of the vertebral, basilar and posterior cerebral arteries.
- Venous drainage is into the adjacent dural venous sinuses and eventually into the internal jugular veins.
- There are 12 cranial nerves, namely olfactory (I), optic (II), oculomotor (III), trochlear (IV), trigeminal (V), abducent (VI), facial (VII), vestibulocochlear (VIII), glossopharyngeal (IX), vagus (X), accessory (XI) and hypoglossal (XII).
- Cranial nerve I carries afferent impulses for the sense of smell.
- Cranial nerve II carries afferent impulses for vision.
- Cranial nerve III functions in raising the eyelid, moving the eyeball, constricting the iris and controlling the lens shape.
- Cranial nerve IV is primarily a motor nerve that innervates the superior oblique muscle of the eyeball.
- Cranial nerve V conveys sensory impulses from various areas of the face (V1 and V2) and supplies motor fibres (V3) for the muscles of mastication.
- Cranial nerve VI is primarily a motor nerve that innervates the lateral rectus muscle of the eyeball.
- Cranial nerve VII controls facial expression and transmission of autonomic impulses to the lacrimal, submandibular and sublingual salivary glands and carries taste from the anterior two-thirds of the tongue.
- Cranial nerve VIII carries the sensations of hearing and equilibrium.
- Cranial nerve IX conducts taste and general sensory impulses from the tongue and pharynx and provides motor fibres to the parotid salivary gland.
- Cranial nerve X carries parasympathetic fibres to the heart, lungs and abdominal viscera and carries taste from the posterior-most part of the tongue.
- The cranial part of cranial nerve XI supplies fibres to the larynx, pharynx and soft palate, while the spinal part innervates the trapezius and sternocleidomastoid.
- Cranial nerve XII innervates the muscles of the tongue.
- The cerebellum is located dorsal to the pons and medulla and along with them constitutes the hindbrain.
- It projects under the occipital lobes of the cerebrum and has two bilaterally symmetrical hemispheres connected by the vermis.
- Elevations and depressions can be seen on the surface of the cerebellum known as folia and fissures, respectively.
- Each hemisphere has three lobes, anterior, posterior and flocculonodular.
- The cerebellum has an outer cortex consisting of grey matter and internal white matter.
- Four pairs of nuclei, the dentate, emboliform, fastigial and globose nuclei, are located inside the white matter.
- Three cerebellar peduncles, the superior, middle and inferior, connect the midbrain, pons and medulla to the cerebellum, respectively.
- The arterial supply of the cerebellum is via cerebellar branches of the vertebral and basilar arteries.
- Venous drainage is to the adjacent dural venous sinuses and finally into the internal jugular vein.
- The fourth ventricle is the cavity of the hindbrain.
- It is diamond shaped and intervenes between the cerebellum dorsally and the pons and medulla ventrally.
- It has four angles, a roof and floor.
- The rostral angle is continuous with the aqueduct of the midbrain, while the caudal angle is continuous with the central canal of the closed part of the medulla.
- Each lateral angle presents an aperture, the foramen of Luschka, through which CSF of the fourth ventricle passes into the pontine cistern.
- Another median aperture in the lower part of the roof of the ventricle, the foramen of Magendie, enables CSF to flow into the cerebellomedullary cistern.
- The floor of the ventricle is called the rhomboid fossa and is formed in the upper half by the pons and in the lower half by the medulla.

CHAPTER 35

The Forebrain

SPECIFIC LEARNING OBJECTIVES

At the end of this chapter, the student should be able to:

- Name the parts of the forebrain.
- Describe the structure and functions of the thalamus.
- Describe the structure and functions of the hypothalamus.
- Describe the structure and functions of the basal nuclei.
- Describe the gross anatomy of the cerebrum.
- Describe the gross anatomy of the lateral and third ventricles.

GLOSSARY OF TERMS

- **Pulvinar:** broad, posterior end of the thalamus
- **Internal medullary lamina:** Y-shaped band of white matter within the thalamus
- **Thalamic radiation:** connection between the thalamus and cerebral cortex
- **Infundibulum:** the pituitary stalk connecting the pituitary gland to the hypothalamus
- **Median eminence:** elevation of the hypothalamus around the pituitary stalk
- **Fornix:** fibres arising from the hippocampus
- **Hypothalamo-hypophyseal portal system:** portal system connecting the capillaries around the median eminence and pituitary gland
- **Hypothalamo-hypophyseal tract:** nerve fibres extending from the hypothalamus to the posterior pituitary
- **Corpus striatum:** major component of the basal nuclei having a striated appearance
- **Caudate nucleus:** C-shaped nucleus which forms the medial component of the corpus striatum
- **Lentiform nucleus:** lens-shaped lateral component of the corpus striatum
- **Putamen:** lateral component of the lentiform nucleus
- **Globus pallidus:** medial component of the lentiform nucleus
- **Gyri:** elevations of the cerebral cortex
- **Sulci:** depressions on the cerebral cortex
- **Brodmann areas:** functional areas of the cerebral cortex
- **Homunculus:** representation of the body in the primary motor and somatosensory cortex
- **Limbic system:** forebrain structures that control visceral activity, olfaction, emotion and memory
- **Commissural fibres:** fibres that connect corresponding areas of the cerebrum
- **Association fibres:** fibres connecting areas within a hemisphere
- **Projection fibres:** fibres connecting the cerebrum with lower brain centres and the spinal cord
- **Circle of Willis:** arterial circle formed at the base of the brain by branches of the internal carotid and basilar arteries
- **Horns of the lateral ventricle:** extensions of the lateral ventricle into the frontal, occipital and temporal lobes
- **Foramen of Monro:** communications between the lateral and third ventricle on each side

INTRODUCTION

The forebrain consists of the diencephalon, basal nuclei and cerebrum (Fig. 35.1). The diencephalon is the central core of the forebrain that is continuous inferiorly with the midbrain. It consists of three paired structures, the thalamus, hypothalamus and epithalamus, which enclose the third ventricle. Afferent impulses from all senses converge and synapse in the thalamus. The impulses of similar function are sorted out, edited and relayed as a group to the cerebral cortex. Thus, the thalamus plays a key role in mediating sensation, motor activities, cortical arousal, learning and memory. The hypothalamus regulates many visceral activities. It is involved with the perception of pleasure, fear and rage. It is involved in the regulation of body temperature, feelings of hunger and satiety, the sleep cycle and endocrine functions of the pituitary gland. The basal nuclei regulate the performance of learned movements, motor intentions and the emotional aspects of movements. The cerebrum is responsible for the perception of all general and special senses and the initiation of voluntary movements. Cognitive functions such as memory, judgement, the use of language and problem solving are performed by the cerebrum. Certain parts of the cerebrum are involved in the regulation of emotions. The forebrain contains a pair of lateral ventricles and the third ventricle.

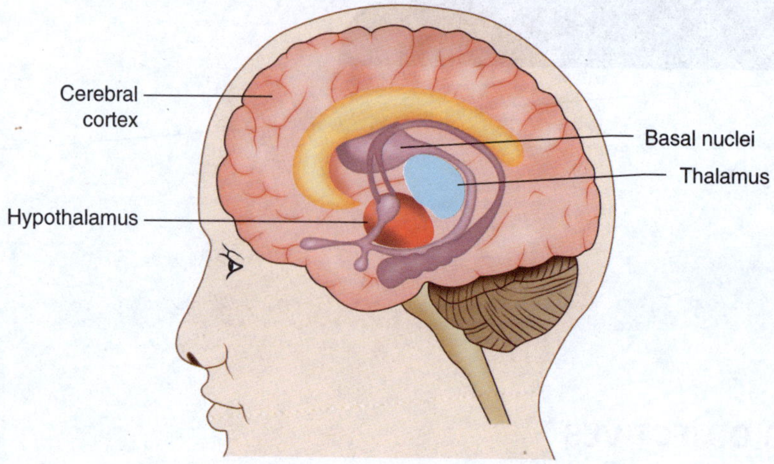

FIG. 35.1 The parts of the forebrain.

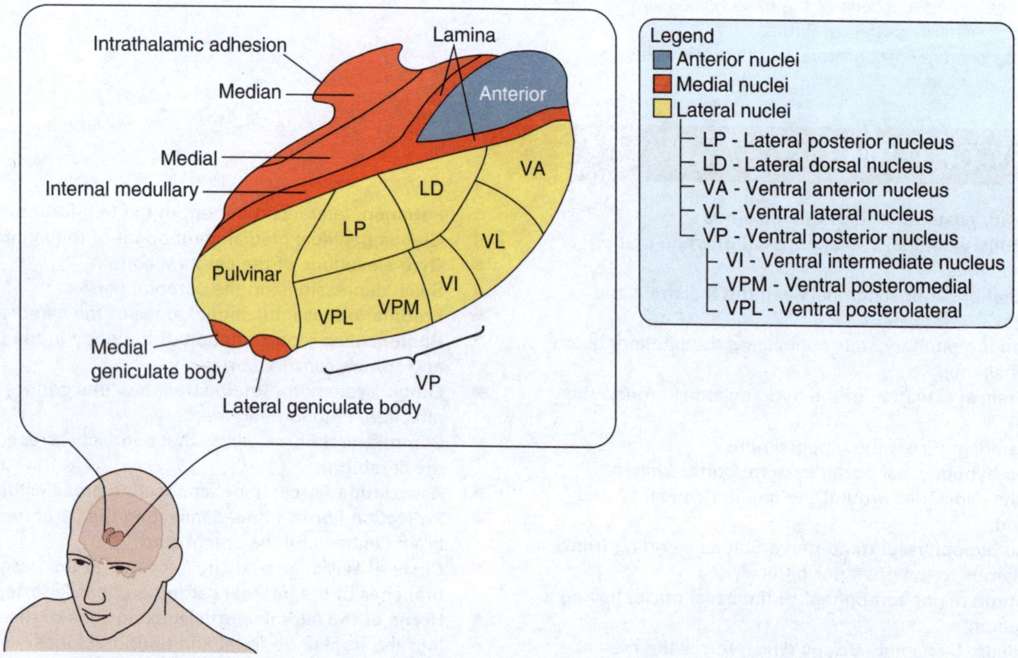

FIG. 35.2 The anatomy of the thalamus.

THE THALAMUS (Fig. 35.2)

The thalami are **paired, egg-shaped** masses that form the superolateral walls of the third ventricle. Each thalamus presents anterior and posterior **ends** and four **surfaces**, upper, lower, medial and lateral. The narrow **anterior end** forms the posterior boundary of interventricular foramen, while the **posterior end** or pulvinar is broad and is related to the lateral geniculate and medial geniculate body. The **medial surface** forms the major portion of the lateral wall of the third ventricle, while the **lateral surface** of the thalamus is related to the internal capsule. The thalamus contains three large groups of nuclei, anterior, medial and lateral, and some smaller groups as well. Separating the nuclei is a Y-shaped lamina of white matter called the internal medullary lamina. The nuclei project to and receive fibres from the cerebral cortex. The **anterior nuclear group** has connections with the limbic system. The **lateral group** of nuclei receive fibres carrying general somatic sensations, vision, hearing and proprioception. They also receive input from the cerebellum, red nucleus and association areas of the cerebrum. The **medial nuclear group** has extensive connections with the prefrontal cortex.

Reciprocal connections between the cerebral cortex and thalamus form a fan-shaped **thalamic radiation**. These fibres pass through different parts of the internal capsule. The thalamic radiation is subdivided into four peduncles: anterior, superior, posterior and inferior. The **anterior peduncle** passes through the anterior limb of the internal capsule and connects the frontal lobe with the dorsomedial nucleus and anterior nucleus of the thalamus. The **superior peduncle** passes through the posterior limb of the internal capsule and connects the ventral nuclei of

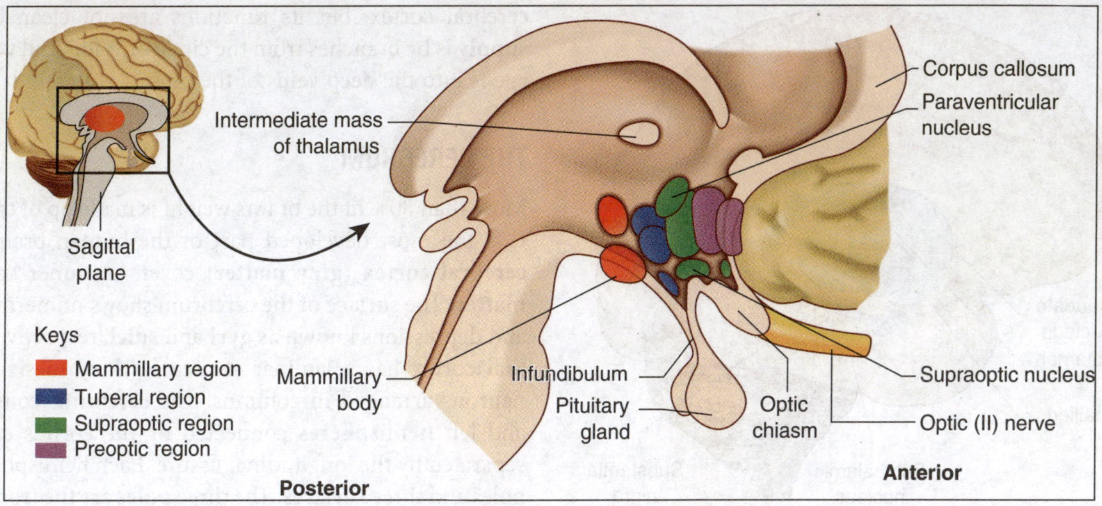

FIG. 35.3 The anatomy of the hypothalamus.

the thalamus with the precentral and postcentral gyri. The **posterior** and **inferior peduncles** pass through the retrolentiform and sublentiform parts of the internal capsule and contain the optic and auditory radiation, respectively. The **arterial supply** to the thalamus is by branches from the circle of Willis and venous drainage is into the deep veins of the brain.

THE HYPOTHALAMUS AND EPITHALAMUS (Fig. 35.3)

The hypothalamus is located below the thalamus and caps the brainstem. It is a very **small** structure that comprises less than 1% of the brain volume and consists of a collection of nerve cells in a matrix of neuroglial tissue, nerve fibres and intricate plexuses of blood capillaries. It forms the inferolateral wall of the third ventricle. The **infundibulum** is the stalk of the hypothalamus which connects it to the pituitary gland. It arises from the **median eminence** which is an elevation around the base of the stalk. There are many nuclear groups contained within the hypothalamus. The **columns of the fornix** subdivide the hypothalamus into medial and lateral subdivisions. Anteroposteriorly, preoptic, supraoptic, tuberal and mammillary regions can be discerned. Each of these regions contains several nuclei. The **supraoptic** and **paraventricular nuclei** produce antidiuretic hormone (ADH) and oxytocin, respectively.

The **connections** of the hypothalamus are widespread and complex, but they fall into three general categories. The hypothalamus has interconnections with various components of the limbic system, outputs which influence the pituitary gland and interconnections with various visceral and somatic nuclei. The **arterial supply** to the hypothalamus is by branches from the circle of Willis and venous drainage is into the deep veins of the brain. The median eminence is supplied by capillaries derived from the superior hypophyseal arteries which are connected to the capillaries around the pituitary gland through the **hypothalamo-hypophyseal portal system**. Releasing factors secreted by the hypothalamus into the capillaries around the median eminence pass through the portal system to regulate the secretions of the pituitary gland. On the other hand, the posterior pituitary is formed by axons from the supraoptic and paraventricular nuclei forming the **hypothalamo-hypophyseal tract**. The axon terminals in the posterior pituitary secrete ADH and oxytocin. The **epithalamus** forms the most dorsal portion of the diencephalon. It forms the roof of the third ventricle and is closely related to the choroid plexus of the third ventricle. The major component of the epithalamus is the **pineal gland** which extends from its posterior aspect and secretes melatonin. **Melatonin** is a hormone involved with sleep regulation, sleep–wake cycles and mood regulation.

THE BASAL NUCLEI (Figs 35.4 and 35.5)

The basal nuclei are masses of grey matter found deep within the cortical white matter. The fibres of the **internal capsule** run through the basal nuclei dividing it into its various components. They are closely related to the **lateral ventricle** and **thalamus**. **Anatomically**, they consist of the caudate nucleus, lentiform nucleus, amygdaloid body and claustrum. **Physiologically**, they

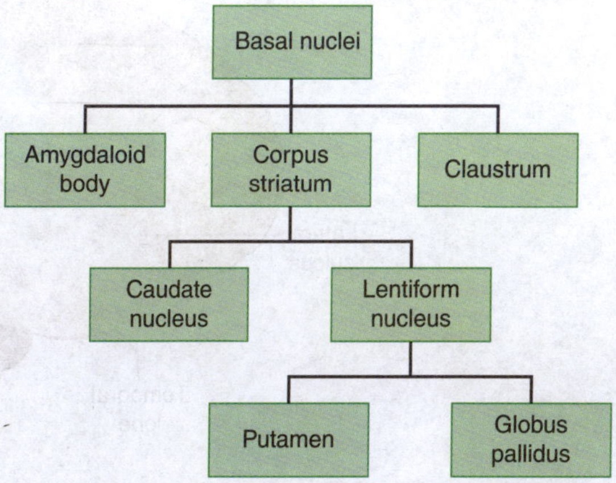

FIG. 35.4 The classification of the basal nuclei.

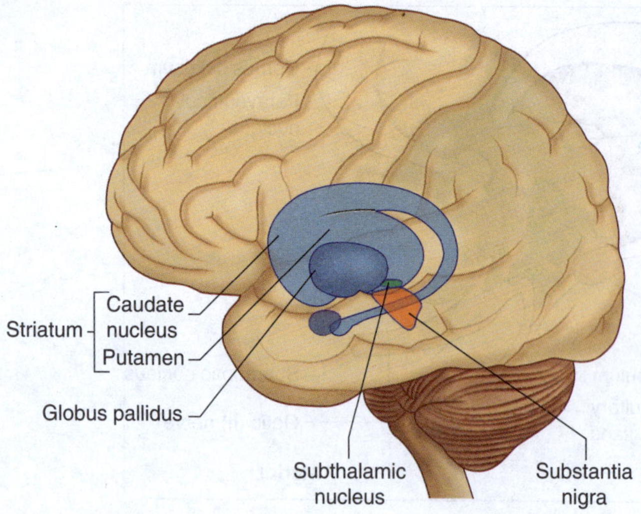

FIG. 35.5 The anatomy of the basal nuclei.

form part of the extrapyramidal motor system along with the red nucleus, subthalamic nucleus, substantia nigra and reticular formation. The **corpus striatum**, called so as it presents a striated appearance, is composed of the caudate and lentiform nuclei. The **caudate nucleus** is C-shaped, with a head, body and tail. The concavity of the C passes along the inner aspect of the cavity of the lateral ventricle. The caudate nucleus is separated from the lentiform nucleus by the internal capsule. The **lentiform nucleus** is lens shaped and composed of the lateral **putamen** and medial **globus pallidus** separated by a thin lamina of white matter. The basal nuclei receive widespread input from the **cerebral cortex**. Fibres then pass to the thalamus and from there to the **premotor area** of the cerebral cortex. Additionally, there are reciprocal connections with the **substantia nigra** and **subthalamic nucleus**. Although anatomically included with the basal nuclei, the amygdaloid body and claustrum are functionally independent. The **amygdaloid body** is part of the limbic system, while the **claustrum** has reciprocal connections with widespread areas of the cerebral cortex, but its functions are not clear. The **arterial supply** is by branches from the circle of Willis and venous drainage is into the deep veins of the brain.

THE CEREBRUM

More than 80% of the brain's weight is made up of the cerebrum. It is the most developed part of the human brain. The outer **cerebral cortex (grey matter)** covers an inner core of **white matter**. The surface of the cerebrum shows numerous elevations and depressions known as **gyri** and **sulci**, respectively. The cerebral cortex has a laminar structure (three to six layers) with neurons arranged in columns. The cerebrum consists of right and left **hemispheres** connected by the corpus callosum and separated by the longitudinal fissure. Each hemisphere has three poles and three surfaces. The three **poles** are the frontal, occipital and temporal, while the **surfaces** are the superolateral, medial and inferior. Four major **lobes**, the frontal, parietal, occipital and temporal, can be identified on each hemisphere (Fig. 35.6). The **sulci** that are important in demarcating the lobes are the central sulcus, lateral sulcus and parieto-occipital sulcus. The **central sulcus** separates the frontal and parietal lobes, while the **lateral sulcus** separates the temporal from the frontal and parietal lobes. The **parieto-occipital sulcus**, seen prominently on the medial surface, is used to demarcate the occipital lobe from the parietal lobe. Another prominent sulcus is the **calcarine sulcus** which is seen on the medial surface inferior to the parieto-occipital sulcus.

The **frontal lobe** has precentral and superior, middle and inferior frontal gyri. Superior, middle and inferior gyri are seen in the **temporal lobe**. The **parietal lobe** has the postcentral gyrus and superior and inferior parietal lobules, while the **occipital lobe** has superior and inferior gyri (Fig. 35.7). **Brodmann** divided each cerebral hemisphere into 52 functional areas. The important Brodmann areas are shown in Table 35.1 (Fig. 35.8).

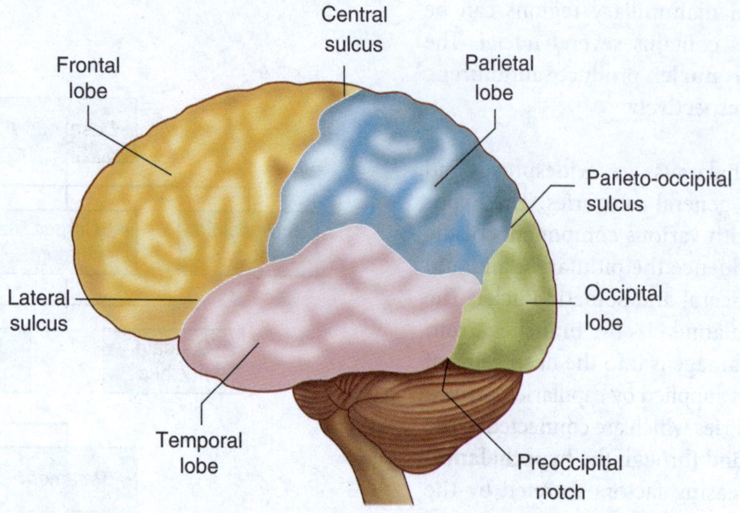

FIG. 35.6 The lobes of the cerebrum.

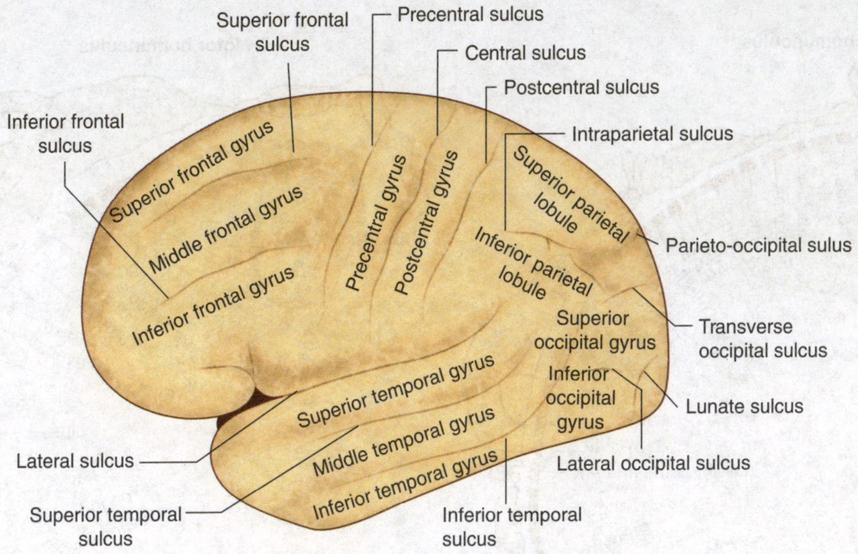

FIG. 35.7 The important gyri and sulci of the cerebrum.

Table 35.1 The Important Brodmann Areas of the Cerebrum

Brodmann Area	Name	Lobe	Gyrus	Function
• 3, 2, 1	• Somatosensory cortex	• Parietal	• Postcentral	• Somaesthetic sensation and proprioception
• 4	• Primary motor cortex	• Frontal	• Precentral	• Voluntary movement
• 6	• Premotor cortex	• Frontal	• Posterior parts of superior and middle frontal gyri	• Coordination of complex movements
• 17	• Primary visual cortex	• Occipital	• Around the occipital pole	• Sensation of vision
• 41, 42	• Primary auditory cortex	• Temporal	• Superior temporal	• Sensation of hearing
• 44, 45	• Broca's area	• Frontal	• Posterior part of the inferior frontal gyrus	• Motor speech area

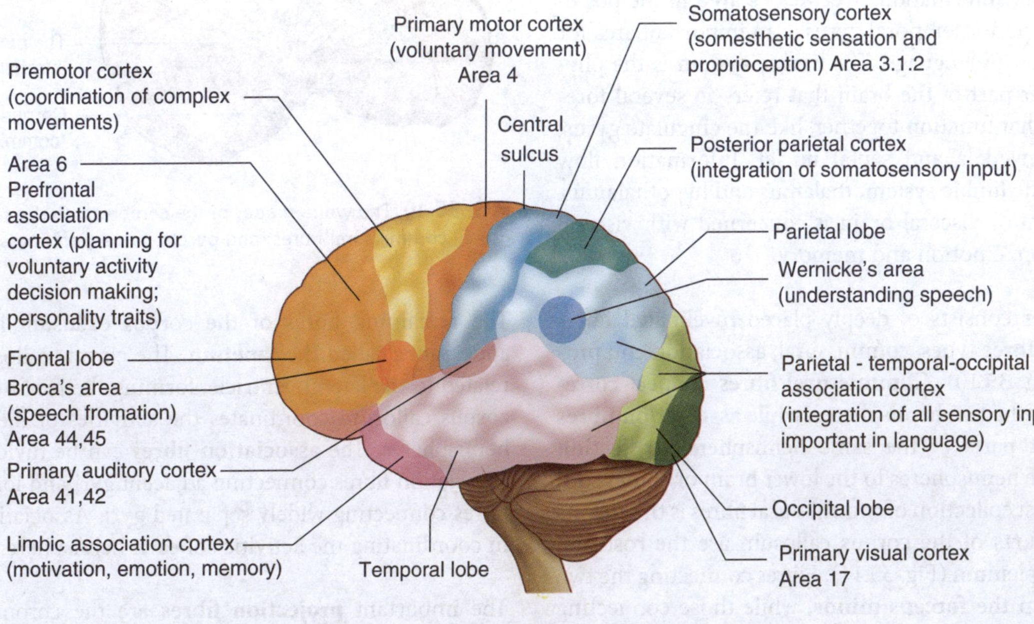

FIG. 35.8 The important Brodmann areas of the cerebrum.

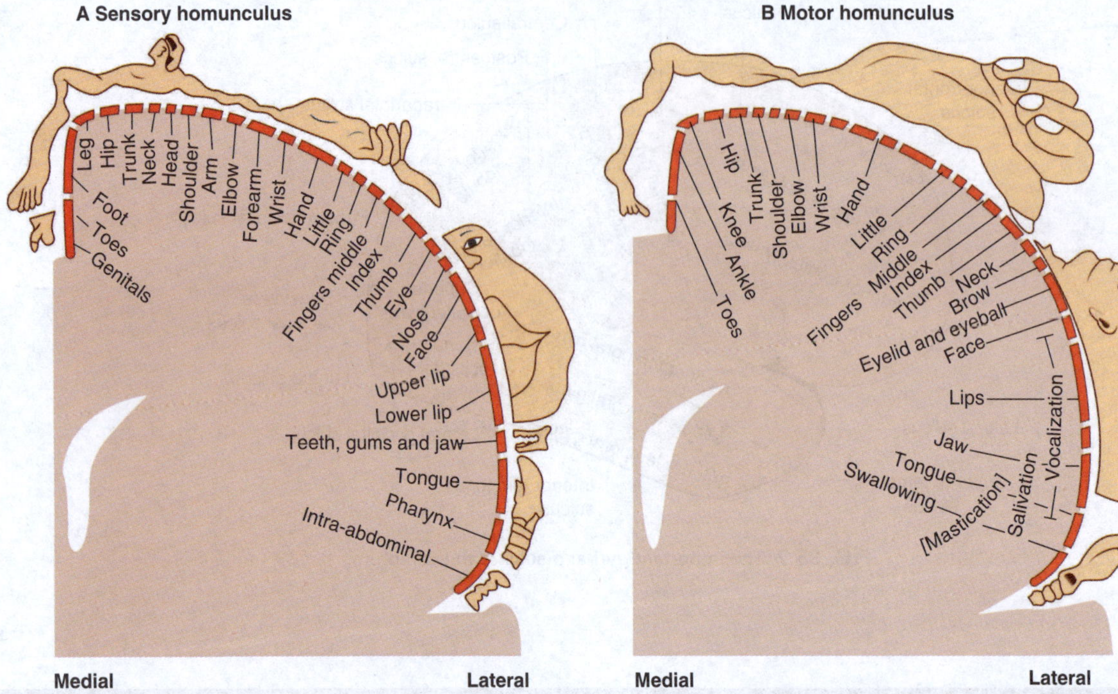

FIG. 35.9 The sensory and motor homunculus.

The representation of the body in the motor and sensory cortex is called the **homunculus** (Fig. 35.9). In these areas, the body is represented in an inverted manner with relatively large areas devoted to the face and hands. In addition to the abovementioned areas, the **prefrontal cortex**, which is used to plan voluntary activities, in decision making and in determining personality traits, forms a large part of the frontal lobe in each cerebral hemisphere. Associated with each of the primary sensory areas are the **sensory association areas** which further process the sensory information. **Wernicke's area** in the posterior part of the superior temporal gyrus is an important area for the comprehension of language. The **limbic system** is the phylogenetically older part of the brain that refers to several forebrain structures that function together, like the cingulate gyrus, hippocampus, amygdala and septal nuclei. Information flow occurs between the limbic system, thalamus and hypothalamus. The limbic system or visceral brain is concerned with visceral activities, olfaction, emotion and memory.

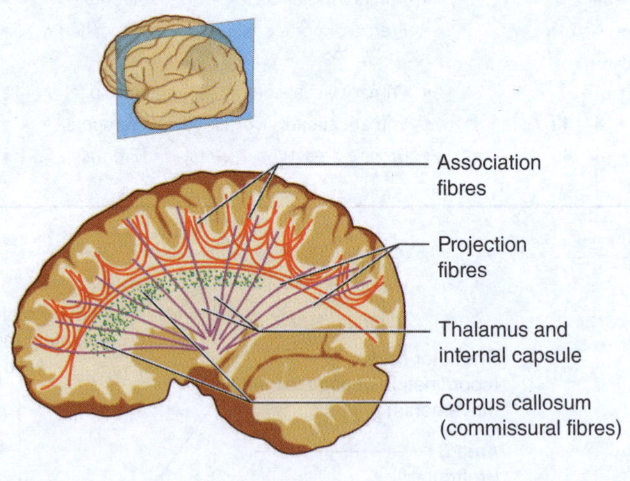

FIG. 35.10 The white matter of the cerebrum. Red, association fibres; green, commissural fibres; and purple, projection fibres.

The **white matter** consists of deeply placed myelinated fibres which may be of three types, commissural, association and projection fibres (Fig. 35.10). **Commissural fibres** connect corresponding areas of the two hemispheres, while **association fibres** connect different parts of the same hemisphere. **Projection fibres** connect the hemispheres to the lower brain or spinal cord centres. The largest collection of commissural fibres is the **corpus callosum**. The **parts** of the corpus callosum are the rostrum, genu, body and splenium (Fig. 35.11). Fibres connecting the two frontal lobes form the **forceps minor**, while those connecting the posterior parts of the occipital lobes form the **forceps major**. The remaining fibres of the corpus callosum have a tented appearance called the **tapetum**. The corpus callosum is closely related to the lateral ventricle, forming the roof of its body. The corpus callosum coordinates the activities of the two cerebral hemispheres. The **association fibres** can be divided into short association fibres connecting adjacent gyri and long association fibres connecting widely separated gyri. Association fibres help in coordinating the activities of each hemisphere.

The important **projection fibres** are the corona radiata and internal capsule. The **corona radiata** is a group of fibres that

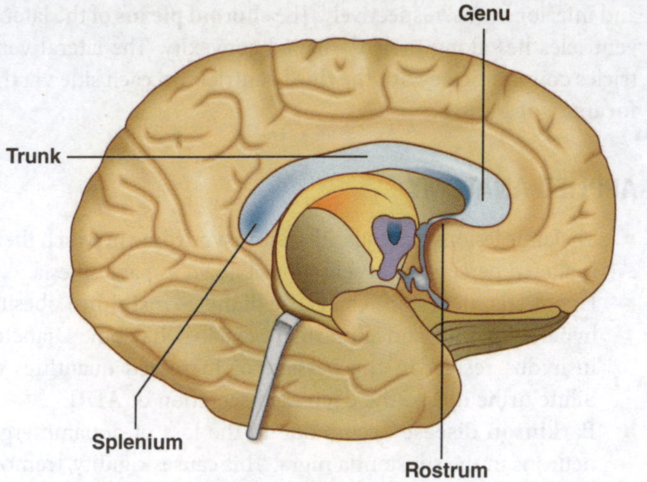

FIG. 35.11 The parts of the corpus callosum seen in a midsagittal section of the cerebrum.

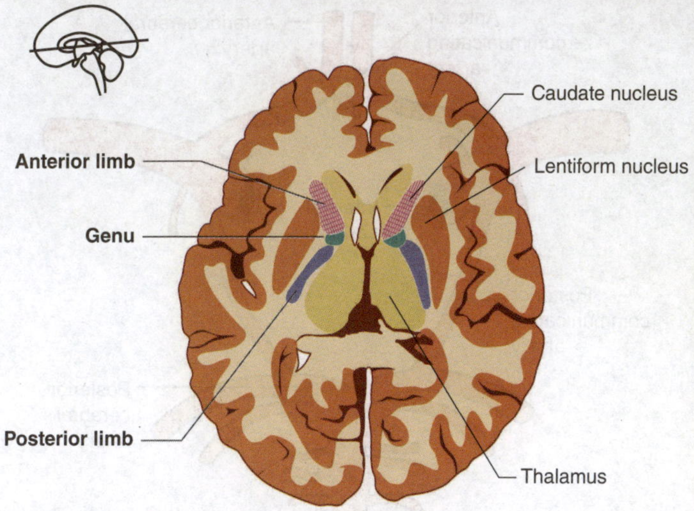

FIG. 35.12 The parts of the internal capsule seen on a horizontal section of the cerebrum.

connect large parts of the cerebral hemispheres to lower centres. The fibres of the corona radiata converge to the **internal capsule** which passes through the corpus striatum. Numerous ascending fibres from the thalamus and descending fibres to lower centres are contained within the internal capsule. The **parts** of the internal capsule are the anterior limb, genu, posterior limb, retrolentiform part and sublentiform part (Fig. 35.12). Lateral to the internal capsule is the lentiform nucleus, while the head of the caudate nucleus and thalamus are located medially. The **posterior limb** contains corticospinal fibres and somatosensory fibres from the lateral nucleus of the thalamus. The **retrolentiform** and **sublentiform** parts contain visual and auditory fibres, respectively. They are supplied by branches from the circle of Willis, especially important of which are the **striate branches** of the **middle cerebral artery**.

The cerebral cortex is supplied by branches from the anterior, middle and posterior cerebral arteries (Fig. 35.13). The **anterior cerebral artery** supplies most of the medial surface, frontal pole, parasagittal portion of the superolateral surface and medial portion of the inferior surface. The **middle cerebral artery** supplies most of the superolateral surface, temporal pole and lateral portion of the inferior surface. The **posterior cerebral artery** supplies most of the inferior surface and occipital lobe including the pole. The **circle of Willis** is an anastomotic circle at the base of the brain formed by branches from the **internal carotid artery** and **basilar artery** (Fig. 35.14). **Anteriorly**, the anterior communicating artery connects the two anterior cerebral arteries which are located **anterolaterally**. **Laterally** are seen the posterior communicating arteries which connect the internal carotid arteries and posterior cerebral arteries. The two posterior cerebral arteries are observed **posterolaterally**. The branches of the circle of Willis are the anterolateral, anteromedial, posterolateral and posteromedial branches. These branches penetrate the surface to supply the deeper structures such as the thalamus, hypothalamus, basal nuclei and internal capsule. The **venous drainage** of the cerebrum is into superficial and deep veins which drain into the dural venous sinuses and finally into the internal jugular vein.

THE THIRD AND LATERAL VENTRICLES (Fig. 35.15)

The **third ventricle** is an interthalamic space that is lined by ependyma. It represents the cavity of the diencephalon and

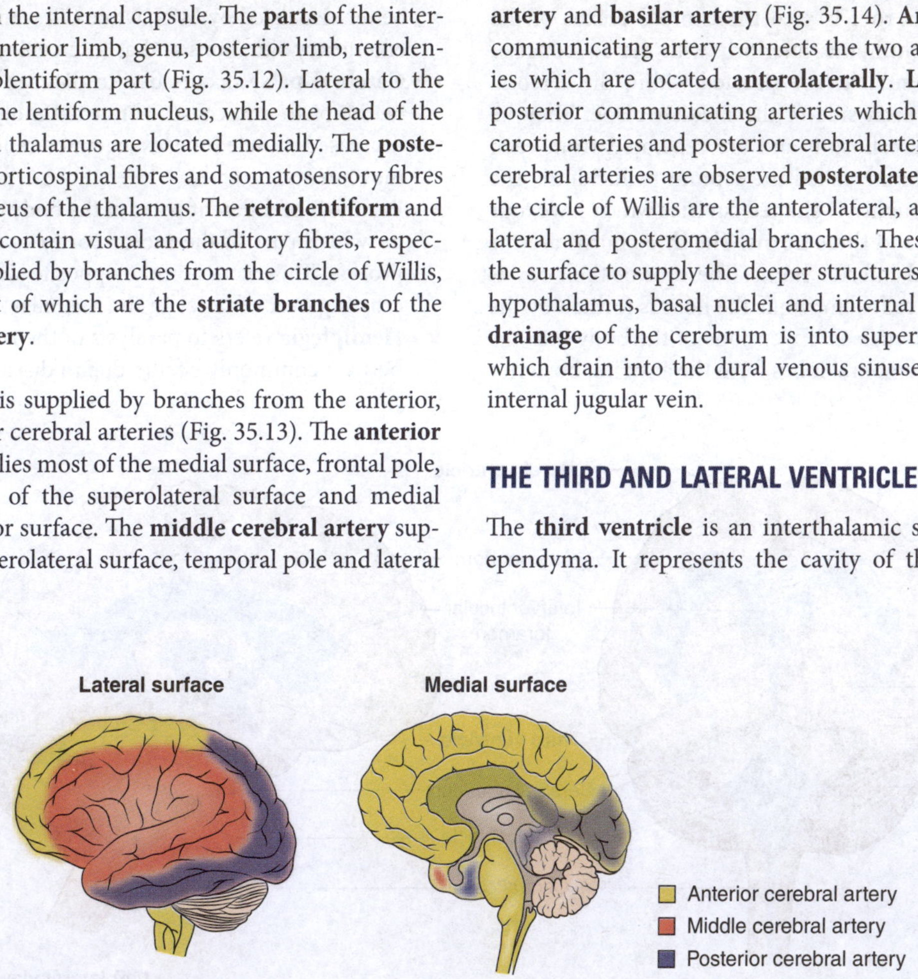

FIG. 35.13 The arterial supply of the cerebral cortex. Yellow, anterior cerebral artery; red, middle cerebral artery; and blue, posterior cerebral artery.

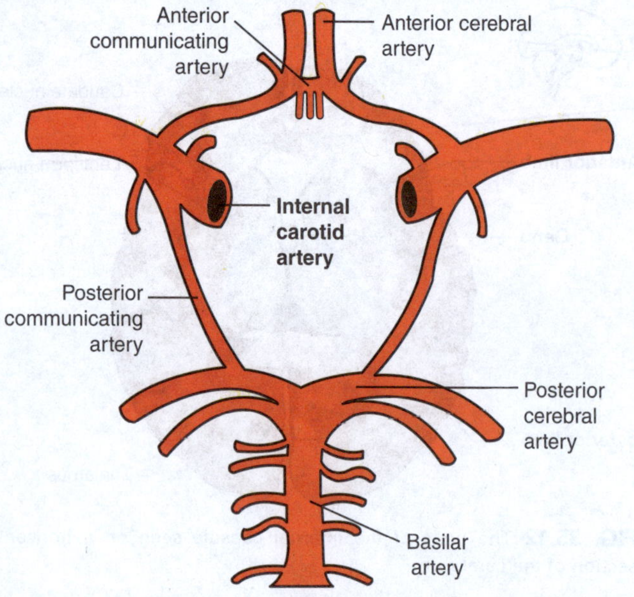

FIG. 35.14 The formation of the circle of Willis.

possesses a roof, floor, and anterior, posterior and two lateral walls. The two lateral walls are formed by the thalamus and hypothalamus. In their roof is seen the choroid plexus of the third ventricle. It is continuous inferiorly with the aqueduct of Sylvius. The **lateral ventricles** are situated within the cerebral hemispheres, one on each side of the median plane. They lie inferior to the corpus callosum and are separated from each other by a thin membrane called the septum pellucidum. The lateral ventricles are roughly **C-shaped cavities** which have four parts, namely a **body** and three **horns**. The three horns are the anterior, posterior and inferior horns. The roof of the body is formed by the corpus callosum, while the floor is formed by the thalamus and caudate nucleus. Extensions of the body into the frontal, occipital and temporal lobes form the anterior, posterior and inferior horns, respectively. The **choroid plexus** of the lateral ventricles lies along their C-shaped convexity. The lateral ventricles communicate with the third ventricle on each side via the **foramen of Monro**.

APPLIED ANATOMY

- Thalamic lesions can cause **thalamic syndrome** in which there is altered perception of sensations known as paraesthesia.
- Hypothalamic lesions can cause **diabetes insipidus**, obesity, hyperglycaemia and abnormal sexual behaviour. Diabetes insipidus results in the passage of increased quantities of dilute urine due to the decreased secretion of ADH.
- **Parkinson disease** occurs due to the loss of dopaminergic neurons in the substantia nigra. This causes rigidity, tremors and difficulty in initiating voluntary movements (akinesia).
- **Chorea** and **athetosis** are involuntary movements caused due to lesions of the basal nuclei. In chorea, rapid, jerky, uncontrolled movements of the feet or hands occur. Athetosis refers to slow, writhing movements of the hands or feet.
- **Hemiballismus** refers to flailing movements of the limbs which occur due to lesions of the subthalamic nucleus.
- Recent **imaging modalities** can be used to accurately visualize the brain. These include CT and MRI. Soft tissues are better visualized by MRI, while CT scans are usually used in emergency situations and as a screening tool.
- **Cerebral palsy** occurs due to damage to the brain usually before birth and causes abnormal motor functions such as decreased muscle tone, exaggerated reflexes and involuntary movements.
- **Paralysis** of different parts of the body can occur depending on which part of the motor cortex is affected by a disease process. This occurs on the opposite side of the body due to crossing over of fibres in the medulla.
- **Hemiplegia** refers to paralysis of the right or left half of the body. It commonly occurs due to disrupted blood supply to

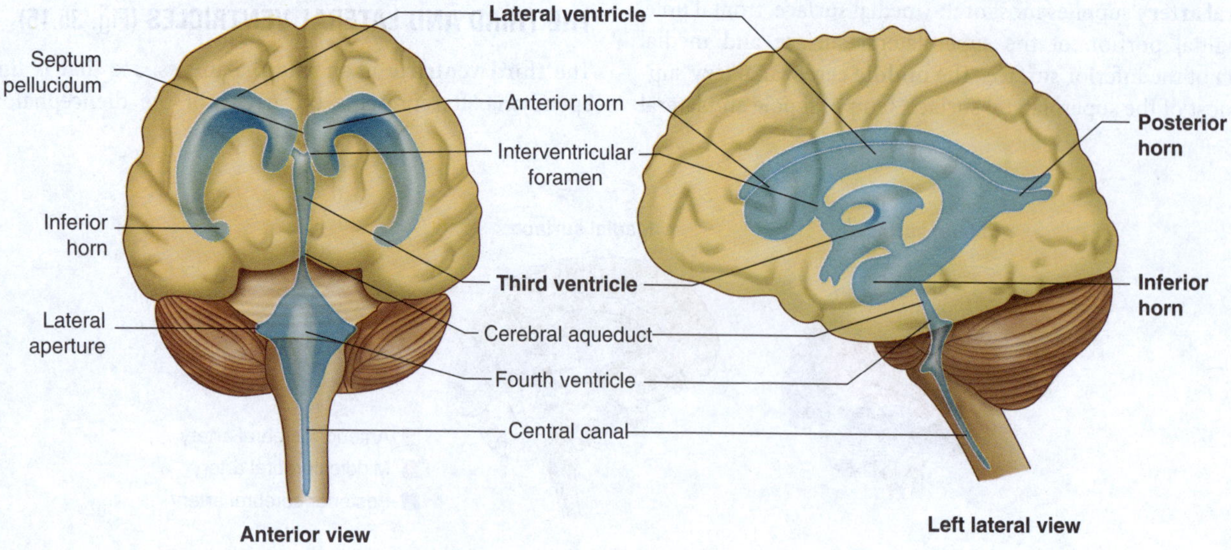

FIG. 35.15 The third and lateral ventricles.

the internal capsule causing degeneration of the corticospinal fibres in the posterior limb of the internal capsule. The striate branches of the middle cerebral artery (Charcot's artery) are most often involved. The resultant hemiplegia occurs on the opposite side of the lesion (contralateral).

- Inflammation of the cerebrum (**encephalitis**) can occur due to several causes. Viral and bacterial infections are among the more common causes. This condition is potentially fatal and presents with headache, vomiting and unconsciousness.
- **Epilepsy** occurs due to excessive uncoordinated neuronal activity in particular areas of the cerebral cortex. When the entire cortex is involved, the seizures become generalized. Tumours, tuberculosis, parasitic cysts, electrolyte disturbances and vascular lesions can cause epilepsy. Often, however, the cause is not known.
- More complex defects can occur due to lesions of specific areas of the cerebral cortex. **Aphasias** refer to a group of disorders with abnormal language function. **Apraxias** are a group of disorders that occur due to abnormalities in motor planning and execution. The disorders that result in the inability to process sensory information are referred to as **agnosias.** Lesions in the prefrontal cortex can result in personality changes and emotional fluctuations.
- **Hydrocephalus** refers to excessive accumulation of cerebrospinal fluid (CSF) within the ventricles due to blockages in the flow, or excessive production or decreased absorption of CSF.

APPLICATIONS IN NURSING

- **Seizures** occur due to uncontrolled activity of a part or the entire brain. The role of the nurse will be to protect patients with seizures from harm. Traumatic injuries and choking are the common dangers that patients need to be protected against during an episode of seizures.

SUMMARY

- The thalami are paired, egg-shaped masses that form the superolateral walls of the third ventricle.
- Each thalamus presents anterior and posterior ends and four surfaces, upper, lower, medial and lateral.
- It contains three large groups of nuclei, anterior, medial and lateral and some smaller groups as well.
- The nuclei project to and receive fibres from the cerebral cortex.
- Reciprocal connections between the cerebral cortex and thalamus form a fan-shaped thalamic radiation.
- These fibres pass through different parts of the internal capsule.
- The thalamic radiation is subdivided into four peduncles: anterior, superior, posterior and inferior.
- Arterial supply to the thalamus is by branches from the circle of Willis.
- The hypothalamus is located below the thalamus and caps the brainstem.
- It forms the inferolateral wall of the third ventricle.
- The infundibulum is the stalk of the hypothalamus which connects it to the pituitary gland.
- There are many nuclear groups contained within the hypothalamus.
- The supraoptic and paraventricular nuclei produce ADH and oxytocin, respectively.
- The hypothalamus has interconnections with various components of the limbic system, outputs which influence the pituitary gland and interconnections with various visceral and somatic nuclei.
- Arterial supply to the hypothalamus is by branches from the circle of Willis and venous drainage is into the deep veins of the brain.
- The median eminence is supplied by capillaries derived from the superior hypophyseal arteries which are connected to the capillaries around the pituitary gland through the hypothalamo-hypophyseal portal system.
- The posterior pituitary is formed by axons from the supraoptic and paraventricular nuclei forming the hypothalamo-hypophyseal tract.
- The epithalamus forms the most dorsal portion of the diencephalon.
- The major component of the epithalamus is the pineal gland which secretes melatonin.
- The basal nuclei are masses of grey matter found deep within the cortical white matter.
- The fibres of the internal capsule run through the basal nuclei dividing it into its various components.
- Anatomically, they consist of the caudate nucleus, lentiform nucleus, amygdaloid body and claustrum.
- Physiologically, they form part of the extrapyramidal motor system.
- The corpus striatum, called so as it presents a striated appearance, is composed of the caudate and lentiform nuclei.
- The caudate nucleus is C-shaped, with a head, body and tail.
- The lentiform nucleus is lens shaped and composed of the lateral putamen and medial globus pallidus.
- The basal nuclei receive widespread input from the cerebral cortex.
- Fibres from here pass to the premotor area of the cerebral cortex via the thalamus.
- Additionally, there are reciprocal connections with the substantia nigra and subthalamic nucleus.
- Arterial supply is by branches from the circle of Willis and venous drainage is into the deep veins of the brain.
- The third ventricle is an interthalamic space that is lined by ependyma.
- It represents the cavity of the diencephalon.
- It is continuous inferiorly with the aqueduct of Sylvius.
- The lateral ventricles are situated within the cerebral hemispheres, one on each side of the median plane.
- The lateral ventricles are roughly C-shaped cavities which have four parts, a body and three horns.
- Extensions of the body into the frontal, occipital and temporal lobes form the anterior, posterior and inferior horns, respectively.
- The lateral ventricles communicate with the third ventricle on each side via the foramen of Monro.
- The cerebrum is the most developed part of the human brain.
- The outer cerebral cortex (grey matter) covers an inner core of white matter.
- The surface of the cerebrum shows numerous elevations and depressions known as gyri and sulci, respectively.
- The cerebrum consists of right and left hemispheres connected by the corpus callosum and separated by the longitudinal fissure.
- Each hemisphere has three poles and three surfaces.
- The three poles are the frontal, occipital and temporal, while the surfaces are the superolateral, medial and inferior.
- Four major lobes, the frontal, parietal, occipital and temporal, can be identified on each hemisphere.
- The sulci that are important in demarcating the lobes are the central sulcus, lateral sulcus and parieto-occipital sulcus.
- Another prominent sulcus is the calcarine sulcus which is seen on the medial surface inferior to the parieto-occipital sulcus.
- The frontal lobe has precentral and superior, middle and inferior frontal gyri.
- Superior, middle and inferior gyri are seen in the temporal lobe.
- The parietal lobe has the postcentral gyrus and superior and inferior parietal lobules, while the occipital lobe has superior and inferior gyri.
- Brodmann divided each cerebral hemisphere into 52 functional areas.
- Areas 3, 2 and 1 form the somatosensory cortex.
- Area 4 is the primary motor cortex.
- Area 6 is the premotor cortex.
- Area 17 is the primary visual cortex.

- Areas 41 and 42 form the primary auditory cortex.
- Areas 44 and 45 form Broca's area.
- The representation of the body in the motor and sensory cortex is called the homunculus.
- The prefrontal cortex is used to plan voluntary activities, in decision making and in determining personality traits.
- The sensory association areas further process the sensory information.
- Wernicke's area in the posterior part of the superior temporal gyrus is an important area for the comprehension of language.
- The limbic system or visceral brain is concerned with visceral activities, olfaction, emotion and memory.
- The white matter consists of deeply placed myelinated fibres which may be of three types, commissural, association and projection fibres.
- Commissural fibres connect corresponding grey areas of the two hemispheres, while association fibres connect different parts of the same hemisphere.
- Projection fibres connect the hemispheres to the lower brain or spinal cord centres.
- The largest collection of commissural fibres is the corpus callosum.
- The parts of the corpus callosum are the rostrum, genu, body and splenium.
- The corpus callosum coordinates the activities of the two cerebral hemispheres.
- The association fibres can be divided into the short association fibres connecting adjacent gyri and long association fibres connecting widely separated gyri.
- The important projection fibres are the corona radiata and internal capsule.
- The corona radiata is a group of fibres that connect large parts of the cerebral hemispheres to lower centres.
- The fibres of the corona radiata converge to the internal capsule which passes through the corpus striatum.
- Numerous ascending fibres from the thalamus and descending fibres to lower centres are contained within the internal capsule.
- The parts of the internal capsule are the anterior limb, genu, posterior limb, retrolentiform part and sublentiform part.
- They are supplied by branches from the circle of Willis, especially important of which are the striate branches of the middle cerebral artery.
- The cerebral cortex is supplied by branches from the anterior, middle and posterior cerebral arteries.
- The anterior cerebral artery supplies most of the medial surface.
- The middle cerebral artery supplies most of the superolateral surface.
- The posterior cerebral artery supplies most of the inferior surface.
- The circle of Willis is an anastomotic circle at the base of the brain formed by branches from the internal carotid artery and basilar artery.
- The branches of the circle of Willis are the anterolateral, anteromedial, posterolateral and posteromedial branches.
- These branches penetrate the surface to supply the deeper structures such as the thalamus, hypothalamus, basal nuclei and internal capsule.
- The venous drainage is into superficial and deep veins which drain into the dural venous sinuses and finally into the internal jugular vein.

SECTION 1

Workbook: Introduction to Anatomical Terms and Organization of the Human Body

SPECIFIC LEARNING OBJECTIVES

At the end of this chapter, the student should be able to:

Chapter 1

- Explain the importance of anatomy in health sciences.
- Describe in brief the history of anatomy.
- Name the major subdivisions of anatomy.
- Describe the scope of each these subdivisions.

Chapter 2

- Define the anatomical position of the body.
- Describe the planes of the body.
- Use the common accepted terms of reference to correctly describe structures of the human body and their movements.
- Describe the major surface and bony landmarks of the body.

Chapter 3

- Describe the structural organization of the human body from cells to organ systems.
- Draw a neat, labelled diagram of the ultrastructure of an animal cell.
- Correlate the structure and function of the cell organelles.
- Compare and contrast mitosis and meiosis.

Chapter 4

- Describe the characteristics of epithelial tissue.
- Correlate the structure and function of epithelial tissue.
- Classify epithelial tissue with suitable examples.
- Describe the mechanisms by which epithelial cells adhere to one another.

Chapter 5

- Define glands.
- Classify glands based on their structure and function.
- Describe the general features of exocrine glands.

Chapter 6

- Describe the general features of connective tissue.
- Classify connective tissue based on its characteristics.

Chapter 7

- Describe the general features of cartilage.
- Classify cartilage based on its characteristics.
- Compare and contrast the different types of cartilage.

Chapter 8

- Classify muscles based on their structure and function.
- Compare and contrast the light microscopic features of skeletal, cardiac and smooth muscles.
- Describe the general gross anatomical features of skeletal muscles.

GLOSSARY OF TERMS

Chapter 1

- **Anatomy:** a study of the structural organization of the human body at different levels
- **Gross anatomy:** a study of the structures of the human body visible to the naked eye
- **Histology:** a study of the microscopic structure of the human body
- **Embryology:** a study of the developing human from the time of conception till birth
- **Surface anatomy:** a study of the surface projections of the various structures of the human body
- **Radiologic anatomy:** a study of bodily structures using radiographic techniques

Chapter 2

- **Anatomical position:** the position of the body which is used as a reference position for describing various structures
- **Planes of the body:** the body viewed from different aspects like sagittal, coronal and transverse
- **Terms of reference:** anatomical terms used to describe the position of various structures in relation to one another

Chapter 3

- **Cell:** the structural and functional unit of the body
- **Tissues:** groups of cells that are structurally and functionally similar
- **Organs:** a collection of tissues that have a specific function
- **Organ systems:** a collection of organs that work together and control major body functions
- **Cell organelles:** cellular components that are responsible for regulating cellular functions

Chapter 4

- **Epithelial tissue:** one of the four basic types of tissues that consist of cells that line body surfaces
- **Basement membrane:** connective tissue layer on which the epithelial cells rest
- **Microvilli:** cell surface projections that help to increase the surface area for absorption
- **Stereocilia:** long microvilli that resemble cilia but are nonmotile
- **Cilia:** whip-like, motile cell surface modifications
- **Junctional complexes:** mechanism by which adherence of epithelial cells to one another is regulated

Chapter 5

- **Gland:** epithelial cells specialized to synthesize and secrete a specific product
- **Endocrine glands:** ductless glands pouring their secretions directly into the blood
- **Exocrine glands:** glands with ducts that carry the secretions onto the surface
- **Capsule:** connective tissue covering of a gland
- **Septa:** inward prolongations of the capsule into the substance of the gland
- **Parenchyma:** the secretory portion of a gland
- **Stroma:** the supporting connective tissue of a gland
- **Lobule:** a unit of a glandular tissue delimited by septa
- **Myoepithelial cells:** contractile cells associated with glands and ducts that help to expel glandular secretions

Chapter 6

- **Connective tissue:** a type of tissue in which cells are widely separated by a matrix which is highly variable in its structure
- **Matrix:** the intervening material between the cells
- **Fibres:** elongated proteins which are part of the matrix and may be collagen, elastic or reticular in nature
- **Ground substance:** part of the matrix seen between the fibres, which is amorphous and composed of glycoproteins
- **Embryonic connective tissue:** type of connective tissue seen in the developing foetus
- **Connective tissue proper:** type of connective tissue that is seen in most parts of the body, serving the role of a dynamic filler material between other tissue components
- **Specialized connective tissue:** connective tissue with special properties and functions such as cartilage, bone and blood

Chapter 7

- **Cartilage:** specialized type of connective tissue which is firm yet flexible
- **Perichondrium:** dense, irregular connective tissue covering of cartilage
- **Chondrocytes:** connective tissue cells seen within cartilage
- **Chondroblasts:** immature chondrocytes
- **Lacunae:** spaces within the matrix that contain chondrocytes
- **Hyaline cartilage:** type of cartilage that contains a glassy homogeneous matrix
- **Elastic cartilage:** type of cartilage that contains numerous elastic fibres
- **Fibrous cartilage:** type of cartilage that contains numerous collagen bundles

Chapter 8

- **Muscle:** one of the four basic types of tissues of the body which are specialized to contract
- **Sarcolemma:** plasma membrane of muscle cells
- **Sarcoplasm:** cytoplasm of muscle cells
- **Sarcoplasmic reticulum:** smooth endoplasmic reticulum of muscle cells
- **Skeletal muscle:** voluntary, striated muscle supplied by the somatic nervous system
- **Cardiac muscle:** involuntary, striated muscle supplied by the autonomic nervous system
- **Smooth muscle:** involuntary, nonstriated muscle supplied by the autonomic nervous system
- **Fascicle:** collection of muscle fibres within a muscle
- **Epimysium:** connective tissue covering of the entire muscle
- **Perimysium:** connective tissue covering of fascicles
- **Endomysium:** connective tissue covering of individual muscle fibres
- **Cross-striations:** alternate dark (A band) and light (I band) bands seen in skeletal and cardiac muscles under the microscope
- **T tubule:** inward extension of the plasma membrane into the cytoplasm of muscle cells
- **Terminal cisternae:** expansions of the sarcoplasmic reticulum adjacent to the T tubule
- **Triad:** one central T tubule flanked by two terminal cisternae
- **Sarcomere:** the contractile unit of a muscle that extends between two Z lines
- **Intercalated disc:** specialized cell junctions between cardiac muscle fibres
- **Tendon:** connective tissue attaching muscles to bones
- **Origin:** the proximal, relatively fixed end of a muscle
- **Insertion:** the distal, relatively mobile end of a muscle
- **Neuromuscular junction:** the junction between the nerve terminals of a motor neuron and muscle fibres
- **Motor unit:** all skeletal muscle fibres supplied a single motor neuron
- **Red fibres:** skeletal muscle fibres with a high content of myoglobin
- **White fibres:** skeletal muscle fibres with a low content of myoglobin
- **Parallel arrangement:** skeletal muscle fibres arranged in a parallel manner
- **Pennate arrangement:** oblique arrangement of skeletal muscle fibres
- **Spiral arrangement:** twisted arrangement of skeletal muscle fibres
- **Cruciate arrangement:** crossed arrangement of skeletal muscle fibres

REVIEW QUESTIONS

1. Describe the various subdivisions of anatomy.
2. Fill in the blanks:

(a) The pioneer of plastic surgery in ancient India was ________________.

(b) The first person to observe cells under the microscope was________________.

(c) Circulation of blood in the body was discovered by ________________.

(d) The father of embalming is considered to be ________________.

(e) Plastination was invented by________________.

3. Define the anatomical position.

4. Label the three planes shown by the letters a, b and c in the figure.

(a)

(b)

(c)

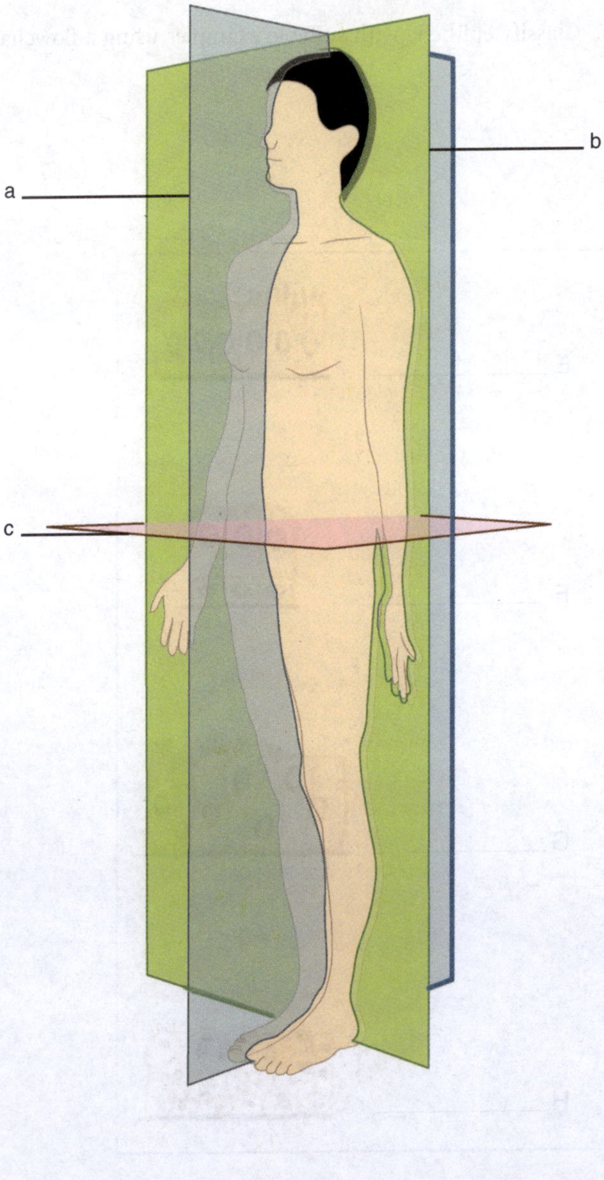

5. Fill in the blanks by using appropriate terms of reference:

(a) The shoulder is located ________________ to the elbow.

(b) The foot is situated ________________ to the hip.

(c) The nose is located ________________ to the eyes.

(d) The thumb is situated ________________ to the index finger.

(e) The heel is located ________________ to the toes.

(f) The premolars are situated ________________ to the molars.

6. Label the movements depicted in the following figures:

(a) i ________________

ii ________________

(b) i ________________

ii ________________

iii ________________

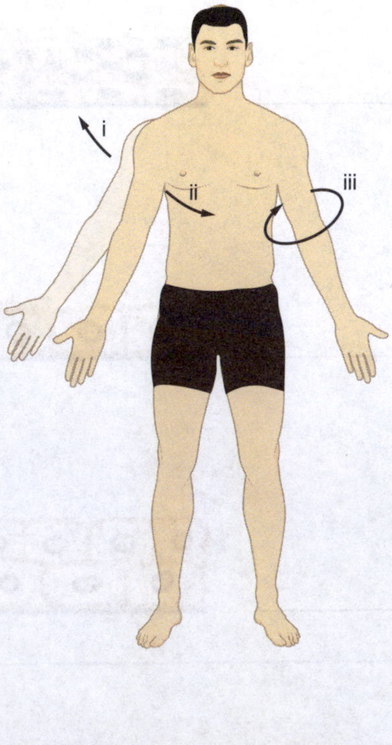

(c) i ____________

ii ____________

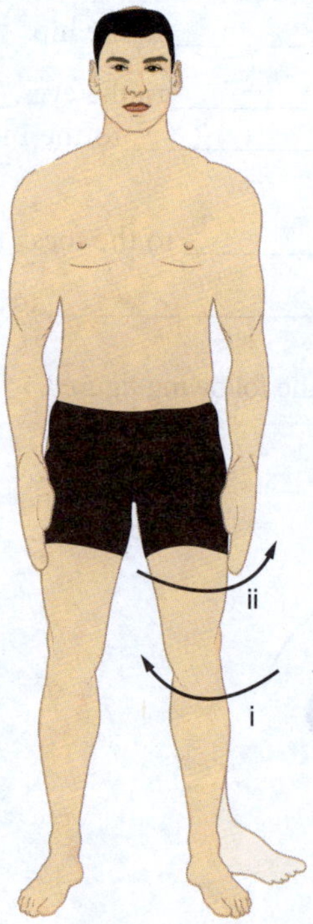

7. Draw a neat, labelled diagram of the ultrastructure of an animal cell.

8. Compare and contrast mitosis and meiosis.

9. Match the following:

Match the cell organelle with the function that it performs.

1. Cell membrane	a. Protein synthesis
2. Cytoplasm	b. Energy production
3. Nucleus	c. Destruction of old cell organelles
4. Nucleolus	d. Lipid synthesis
5. Mitochondria	e. Protection of the cell
6. Golgi apparatus	f. Control of cell functions
7. Rough endoplasmic reticulum	g. Contains all the cell organelles
8. Smooth endoplasmic reticulum	h. Ribosome production
9. Lysosome	i. Production of microtubules
10. Centrosome	j. Modification of proteins

10. Classify epithelia with suitable examples using a flowchart.

11. Identify the type of epithelia shown in the figure.

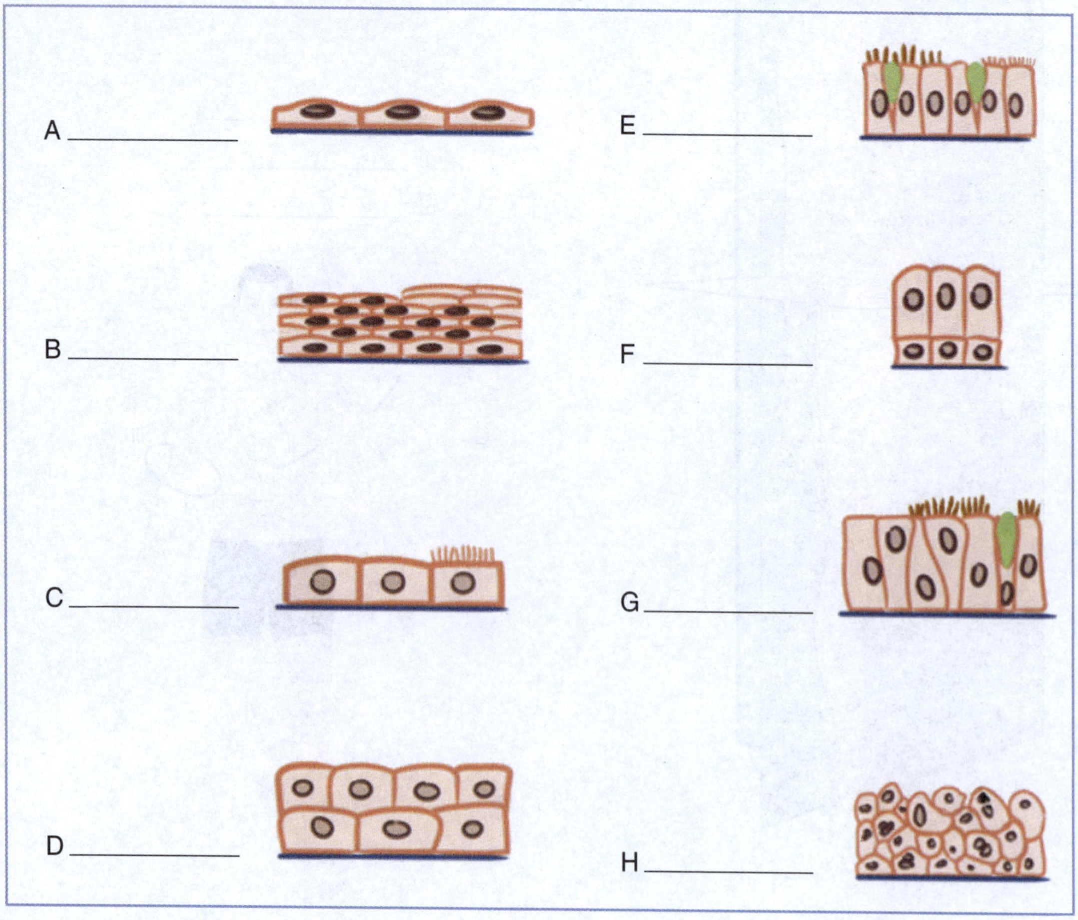

12. Match the following:
Match the type of epithelium to the site where it is found.

1. Simple squamous	a. Small intestine
2. Simple cuboidal	b. Alveoli
3. Simple columnar	c. Urinary bladder
4. Pseudostratified ciliated columnar	d. Oesophagus
5. Stratified squamous nonkeratinized	e. Trachea
6. Stratified squamous keratinized	f. Tubules of the kidney
7. Transitional	g. Skin

13. Classify exocrine glands with suitable examples.
14. Fill in the blanks:
(a) Glands that pour their secretions directly into the blood are called ______________ glands.
(b) The secretions of exocrine glands are carried by ______________.
(c) The connective tissue covering of an exocrine gland is called the ______________.
(d) Septa divide exocrine glands into ______________.
(e) The secretory portion of a gland is called the ______________.
(f) The connective tissue framework of a gland is called the ______________.
15. Classify connective tissue with suitable examples.
16. Fill in the blanks:
(a) The two constituents of connective tissue are the ______________ and ______________.
(b) The two constituents of matrix are ______________ and ______________.
(c) The three types of fibres seen in connective tissue are ______________, ______________ and ______________.
(d) The predominant cell type seen in connective tissue proper is the ______________.
17. Compare and contrast the features of the different types of cartilage.
18. Draw a neat, labelled diagram of the microstructure of hyaline cartilage.
19. Draw a neat, labelled diagram of the microstructure of elastic cartilage.
20. Draw a neat, labelled diagram of the microstructure of fibrous cartilage.
21. Match the following:
Match the type of cartilage to the site where it is found. The options on the left may be matched with more than one option on the right in the instructions

1. Hyaline	a. Pubic symphysis
2. Elastic	b. Septal cartilage in nose
3. White fibrous	c. Epiglottis
	d. Articular cartilage
	e. Intervertebral disc
	f. Pinna
	g. Eustachian tube
	h. Costal cartilage
	i. Menisci of knee joint

22. The three types of muscle are ______________, ______________ and ______________.
23. Label the levels of organization of skeletal muscle in the figure below.
24. Intercalated discs are seen in ______________ muscle.
25. The type of muscle seen in the wall of the intestine is ______________ muscle.
26. Describe the differences in the microstructure of skeletal, cardiac and smooth muscle.
27. Classify skeletal muscles with suitable examples.
28. The three types of muscle are ______________, ______________ and ______________.

29. Label the levels of organization of skeletal muscle in the figure below (a to c).

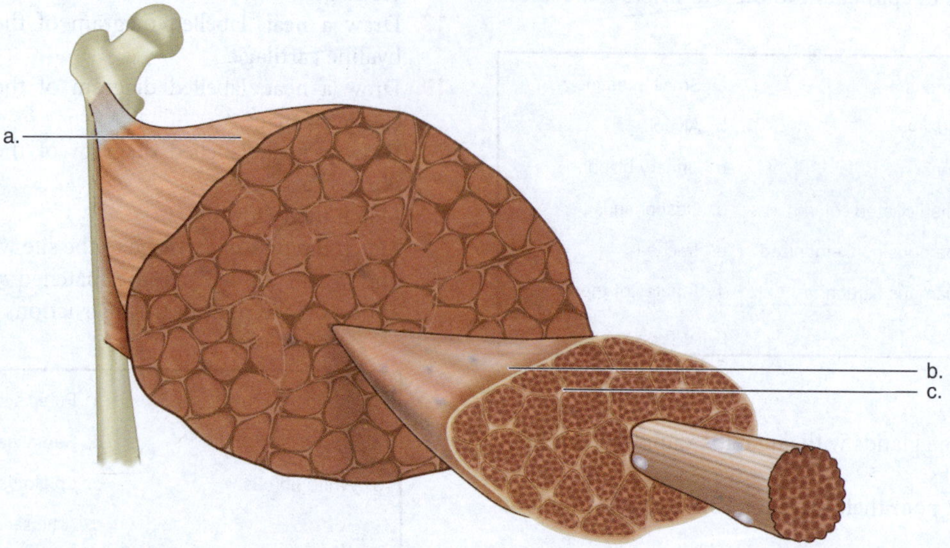

30. Intercalated discs are seen in ______________ muscle.
31. The type of muscle seen in the wall of the intestine is ______________ muscle.
32. Describe the differences in the microstructure of skeletal, cardiac and smooth muscle.
33. Classify skeletal muscles with suitable examples.

SECTION 1: WORKBOOK ANSWER KEY

Introduction to Anatomical Terms and Organization of the Human Body

2. (a) Sushrutha, (b) Robert Hooke, (c) William Harvey, (d) Thomas Holmes, (e) Gunther von Hagens
4. a. Sagittal, b. coronal and c. transverse
5. (a) superior, (b) inferior, (c) medial, (d) lateral, (e) posterior, (f) anterior
6. (a) i) Flexion, Extension; (b) i) Adduction, ii) Abduction and iii) Circumduction; (c) i) Medial rotation, ii) lateral rotation
9. 1, e; 2, g; 3, f; 4, h; 5, b; 6, j; 7, a; 8, d; 9, c; 10, i
11. A – Simple squamous epithelium; B – Stratified squamous epithelium; C – Simple cuboidal epithelium; D – Stratified cuboidal epithelium; E – Simple columnar epithelium; F – Stratified columnar epithelium; G – Pseudostratified columnar epithelium; H – Transitional epithelium
12. 1, b; 2, f; 3, a; 4, e; 5, d; 6, g; 7, c
14. (a) endocrine, (b) ducts, (c) capsule, (d) lobules, (e) parenchyma, (f) stroma
16. (a) cells and matrix; (b) ground substance and fibres; (c) collagen, elastic and reticular; (d) fibroblast
21. 1 – b, d, h; 2 – c, f, g; 3 – a, e, i
22. skeletal, cardiac, smooth
24. cardiac
25. smooth
28. skeletal, cardiac, smooth
29. (a) Epimysium (covering entire muscle); (b) Perimysium (covering individual fascicles); (c) Endomysium (covering individual muscle fibres)
30. cardiac
31. smooth

SECTION 2

Workbook: The Respiratory System

SPECIFIC LEARNING OBJECTIVES

At the end of this chapter, the student should be able to:

Chapter 9

- Name the structures that constitute the respiratory system.
- Describe the functions of each part.
- Describe the gross anatomy of the nasal cavity.
- Describe the location and openings of the paranasal air sinuses.
- Describe the parts and structure of the pharynx.
- Describe the gross anatomy of the larynx.

Chapter 10

- Describe the gross and microscopic anatomy of the trachea.
- Describe the subdivisions, boundaries, contents and applied importance of the mediastinum.
- Describe the gross and microscopic anatomy and applied importance of the lungs.
- Describe the subdivisions and microscopic anatomy of the bronchial tree.
- Describe the anatomical features of the pleura.
- Describe the muscles of respiration.

GLOSSARY OF TERMS

Chapter 9

- **External nose:** bony and cartilaginous framework of the nose that is visible externally
- **Nasal cavity:** part of the nose extending from the nostrils to the choanae
- **Choanae:** posterior apertures of the nasal cavity
- **Nasal septum:** partition between the nasal cavities
- **Conchae:** bony projections from the lateral wall of the nose
- **Turbinates:** conchae covered by the mucous membrane
- **Meatuses:** spaces under the turbinates which receive the openings of the paranasal air sinuses
- **Paranasal air sinuses:** air-filled spaces in the skull opening into the nasal cavity
- **Pharynx:** muscular tube extending from the base of the skull to the oesophagus
- **Nasopharynx:** part of the pharynx posterior to the nasal cavity
- **Oropharynx:** part of the pharynx posterior to the oral cavity
- **Laryngopharynx:** part of the pharynx posterior to the larynx
- **Piriform fossa:** space in the laryngopharynx on either side of the larynx
- **Larynx:** the 'voice box' responsible for speech production and made up of cartilages, membranes and muscles
- **Vestibule:** interior of the larynx superior to the false cords
- **Ventricle or glottis:** interior of the larynx between the true and false cords
- **Infraglottic part:** interior of the larynx below the true vocal cords
- **Extrinsic muscles:** have attachments outside the larynx
- **Intrinsic muscles:** have attachments entirely within the larynx

Chapter 10

- **Trachea:** the windpipe, which extends from the larynx to the primary bronchi
- **Carina:** the ridge formed by the last tracheal ring
- **Mediastinum:** space between the two pleural cavities containing important structures including the heart
- **Hilum:** region on the medial surface of the lung where structures either enter or leave the lung
- **Bronchi:** air-conducting tubes formed as divisions from the trachea containing cartilage and smooth muscles in their walls
- **Bronchopulmonary segment:** volume of lung tissue supplied by a segmental or tertiary bronchus
- **Bronchioles:** smaller subdivisions in the bronchial tree which have only smooth muscle, but no cartilage in their wall
- **Alveolus:** final subdivision of the bronchial tree lined by simple squamous epithelium
- **Pleura:** double-layered covering of the lungs enclosing a pleural cavity
- **Pleural recess:** unusually wide area of the pleural cavity meant to accommodate the lung during deep inspiration

REVIEW QUESTIONS

1. Label the parts of the respiratory system in the figure (a-h).

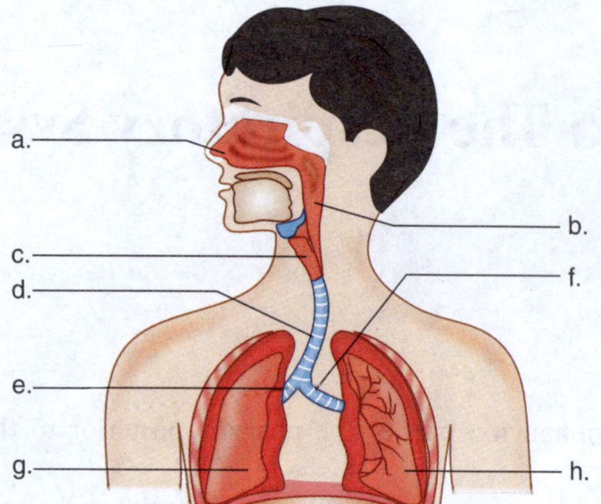

2. Label the parts of the nasal septum in the figure (a-d).

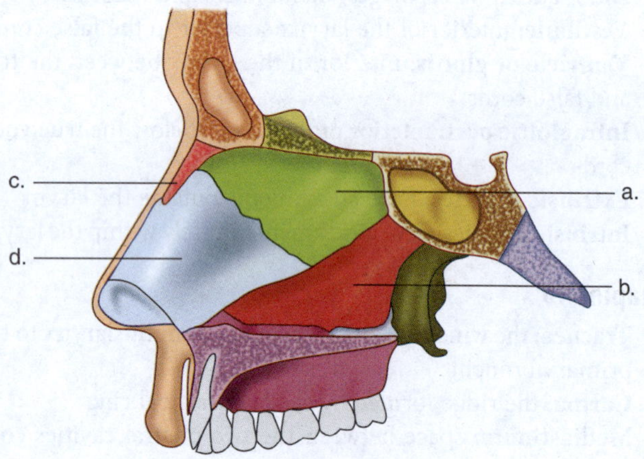

3. Describe the gross anatomy of the lateral wall of the nasal cavity.
4. Describe the gross anatomy of the paranasal air sinuses.
5. Name the parts of the pharynx. Explain the anatomical features of each part.
6. Describe the gross anatomy of the larynx.
7. Fill in the blanks:
   - **(a)** The conducting zone of the respiratory system extends from the ______________ to the ______________.
   - **(b)** The three regions of the nasal cavity are the ______________, ______________ and ______________.
   - **(c)** The nasolacrimal duct opens into the ______________ meatus.
   - **(d)** The largest artery supplying the nose is the ______________ artery.
   - **(e)** The most fractured bone in the skull is the ______________ bone.
   - **(f)** The pharynx extends from the ______________ to the ______________.
   - **(g)** The pharyngeal opening of the auditory tube is seen in the ______________.
   - **(h)** The only muscle of the larynx that causes abduction of the vocal cords is the ______________.
   - **(i)** The vocal cords are lined by ______________ epithelium.
   - **(j)** All the intrinsic muscles of the larynx except the cricothyroid are supplied by the ______________.
8. Describe the microscopic anatomy of the trachea.
9. Label the boundaries of the mediastinum and their subdivisions in the figure (a-h).

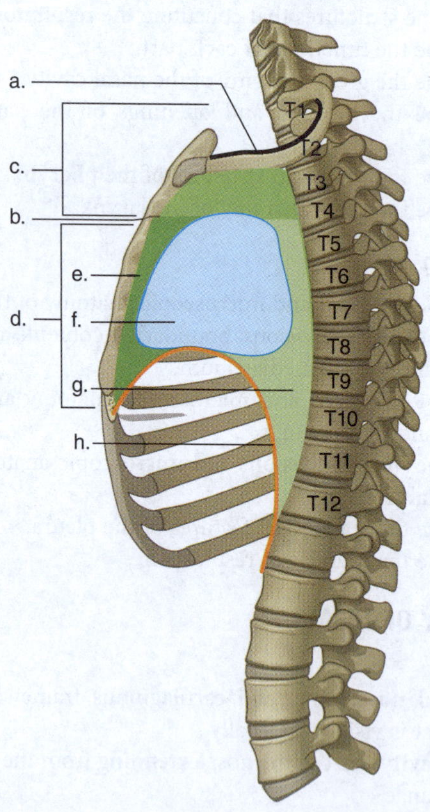

10. Compare and contrast the gross anatomy of the right and left lungs in a tabular form.
11. Define bronchopulmonary segments. What are their characteristic features? Describe in brief their clinical importance.

12. Label the various subdivisions of the bronchial tree in the figure (a-k).

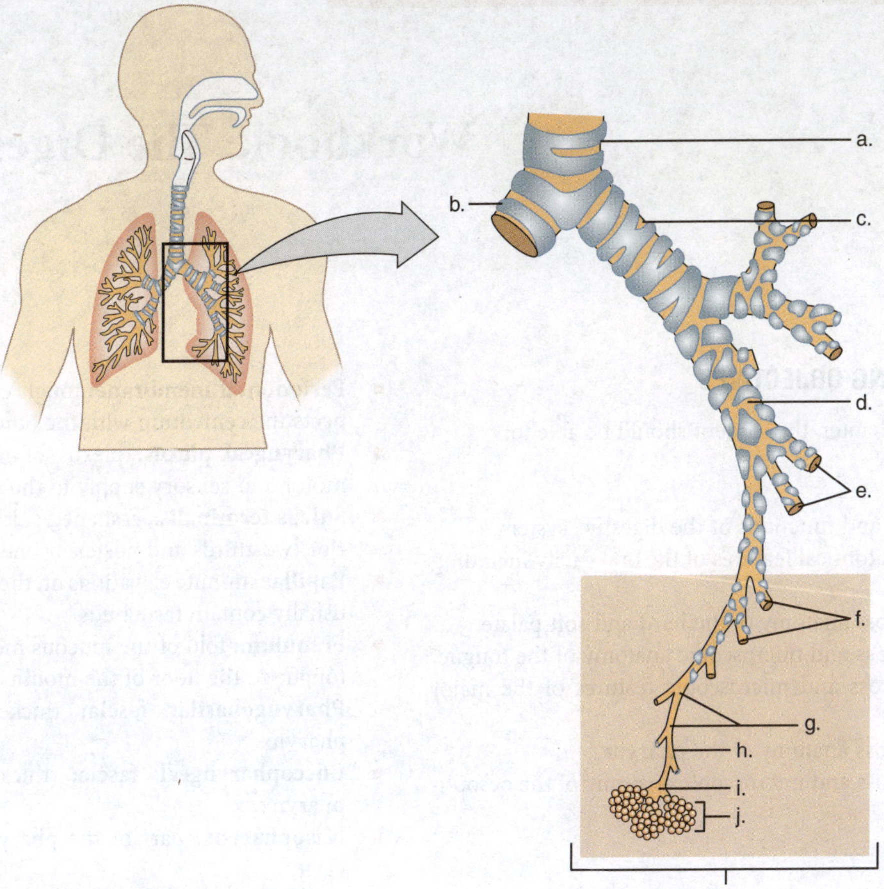

13. Describe the microscopic anatomy of the lung.
14. Describe the gross anatomy and clinical importance of the pleura.

SECTION 2: WORKBOOK ANSWER KEY

The Respiratory System

1. (a) Nasal cavity; (b) Pharynx; (c) Larynx; (d) Trachea; (e) Right main bronchus; (f) Left main bronchus; (g) Right lung; (h) Left lung
2. (a) Ethmoid; (b) Vomer; (c) Nasal bone; (d) Septal cartilage
7. (a) nose, terminal bronchioles; (b) vestibule, respiratory region, olfactory region; (c) inferior; (d) sphenopalatine; (e) nasal; (f) base of the skull, lower border of the cricoid cartilage; (g) nasopharynx; (h) posterior cricoarytenoid; (i) stratified squamous nonkeratinized; (j) recurrent laryngeal nerve
9. (a) Superior thoracic inlet; (b) Sternal angle; (c) Superior mediastinum; (d) Inferior mediastinum; (e) Anterior mediastinum; (f) Middle mediastinum; (g) Posterior mediastinum; (h) Diaphragm
12. (a) Trachea; (b) Right primary bronchus; (c) Left primary bronchus; (d) Secondary bronchus; (e) Teritiary bronchi; (f) Smaller bronchi; (g) Bronchioles; (h) Terminal bronchiole; (i) Respiratory bronchiole; (j) Alveoli; (k) Bronchopulmonary segment

SECTION 3

Workbook: The Digestive System

SPECIFIC LEARNING OBJECTIVES

At the end of this chapter, the student should be able to:

Chapter 11

- Name the parts and functions of the digestive system.
- Describe the anatomical features of the oral cavity including the teeth.
- Describe the gross anatomy of the hard and soft palate.
- Describe the gross and microscopic anatomy of the tongue.
- Describe the gross and microscopic features of the major salivary glands.
- Describe the gross anatomy of the pharynx.
- Describe the gross and microscopic anatomy of the oesophagus.

Chapter 12

- Describe the extent of the abdominal cavity and its surface projections on to the anterior abdominal wall.
- Describe the layers of the peritoneum and their relationship with the abdominal cavity and their contained viscera.
- Describe the gross and microscopic anatomy of the stomach.
- Describe the gross and microscopic anatomy of the small intestine.
- Describe the gross and microscopic anatomy of the large intestine.

Chapter 13

- Describe the gross and microscopic anatomy of the liver.
- Describe the gross and microscopic anatomy of the extrahepatic biliary apparatus.
- Describe the gross and microscopic anatomy of the pancreas.

GLOSSARY OF TERMS

Chapter 11

- **Vestibule:** part of the oral cavity between the teeth and gums on one side and the cheek and lips on the other side
- **Pulp space:** space within the tooth that contains blood vessels and nerves along with loose connective tissue
- **Dentine:** bone-like material forming the major part of the tooth
- **Enamel:** hard covering of the dentine in the crown of the tooth
- **Cementum:** covering of the dentine in the root of the tooth
- **Periodontal membrane:** tough connective tissue that connects the cementum with the bone of the tooth socket
- **Pharyngeal plexus:** plexus of nerves that provides both motor and sensory supply to the soft palate and pharynx
- **Sulcus terminalis:** V-shaped sulcus that separates the anterior two-thirds and posterior one-third of the tongue
- **Papillae:** minute elevations on the dorsum of the tongue that usually contain taste buds
- **Frenulum:** fold of the mucous membrane that connects the tongue to the floor of the mouth
- **Pharyngobasilar fascia:** thickened submucosa of the pharynx
- **Buccopharyngeal fascia:** thickened adventitia of the pharynx
- **Nasopharynx:** part of the pharynx posterior to the nasal cavity
- **Oropharynx:** part of the pharynx posterior to the oral cavity
- **Laryngopharynx:** part of the pharynx posterior to the larynx

Chapter 12

- **Linea alba:** midline tendinous intersection formed by merging of the aponeuroses of the three muscles of the anterior abdominal wall from either side
- **Lesser sac:** portion of the peritoneal cavity behind the stomach
- **Greater sac:** the entire peritoneal cavity excluding the lesser sac
- **Omentum:** peritoneal folds attached to the stomach
- **Stomach bed:** the posterior relations of the stomach
- **Rugae:** folds seen within the stomach when it is empty
- **Mesentery:** peritoneal folds that suspend the intestine
- **Plicae circularis:** crescentic folds seen on the interior of the small intestine
- **Villi:** minute mucosal projections from the surface of the small intestine
- **Microvilli:** microscopic projections from the columnar cells lining the villi
- **Crypts of Lieberkühn:** simple tubular intestinal glands seen in the lamina propria
- **Peyer's patches:** prominent lymphatic tissue seen in the mucosa and submucosa of the ileum
- **Brunner's glands:** mucous glands seen in the submucosa of the duodenum

- **Sacculations:** pouch-like dilatations of the large intestine
- **Taeniae coli:** three bands of longitudinal smooth muscle visible on the outside of the large intestine
- **Appendices epiploicae:** peritoneal pouches of fat seen along the outer surface of the large intestine
- **Pectinate line:** line separating the upper portion of the anal canal from the remaining portion

Chapter 13

- **Falciform ligament:** peritoneal ligament connecting the liver and anterior abdominal wall
- **Ligamentum teres:** remnant of the left umbilical vein
- **Ligamentum venosum:** remnant of the ductus venosus
- **Porta hepatis:** area on the visceral surface of the liver meant for entry and exit of structures
- **Glisson's capsule:** connective tissue capsule of the liver
- **Kupffer cells:** macrophages of the liver
- **Uncinate process:** hook-like extension of the lower part of the head of the pancreas
- **Islets of Langerhans:** endocrine part of the pancreas

REVIEW QUESTIONS

1. Label the parts of the digestive system in the following figure (a-s).

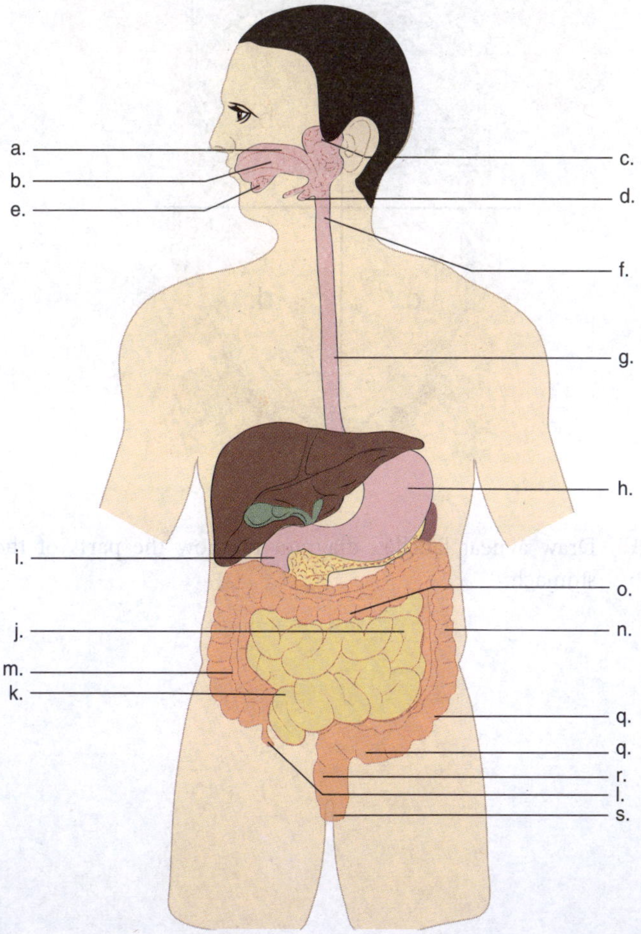

2. The four types of teeth are ______________, ______________, ______________ and ______________.
3. The number of temporary and permanent teeth are ______________ and ______________, respectively.
4. Draw a neat, labelled diagram to show the parts of a tooth.
5. The papillae of the tongue which do not contain taste buds are
   (a) Filiform
   (b) Fungiform
   (c) Foliate
   (d) Circumvallate
6. Match the following in relation to the nerve supply of the tongue. Each nerve option may be used more than once.

1. Glossopharyngeal nerve	a. Taste sensation from the anterior two-third of the tongue
2. Facial nerve	b. General sensation from the posterior one-third of the tongue
3. Lingual nerve	c. Taste sensation from the posterior one-third of the tongue
4. Vagus nerve	d. Motor supply to the muscles of the tongue
5. Hypoglossal nerve	e. General sensation from the anterior two-third of the tongue
	f. General sensation from the posterior-most part of the tongue
	g. Taste sensation from the posterior-most part of the tongue

7. Describe the gross and microscopic anatomy of the tongue.
8. Match the following in relation to the salivary glands. Each salivary gland option may be used more than once.

1. Parotid gland	a. Mucous gland
2. Submandibular gland	b. Serous gland
3. Sublingual gland	c. Mixed gland
	d. Drains by multiple ducts that open in the floor of the mouth
	e. Drains by a duct that opens in the vestibule of the mouth opposite the upper second molar tooth
	f. Drains by a duct that opens on the floor of the mouth on either side of the frenulum of the tongue

9. Describe the gross and microscopic anatomy of the major salivary glands.

10. Compare and contrast the microscopic anatomy of the salivary glands.

11. The parts of the pharynx from superior to inferior are the ______________, ______________ and ______________.

12. Match the following in relation to the parts of the pharynx. Each pharynx option may be used more than once.

1. Nasopharynx	a. Extends from C3 to C6
2. Oropharynx	b. Extends from the base of the skull to C1
3. Laryngopharynx	c. Extends from C1 to C3
	d. Contains the palatine tonsils
	e. Contains the piriform fossa
	f. Contains the opening of the auditory tube

13. Describe the gross anatomy of the pharynx.

14. Which constriction of the oesophagus is located around 37.5 cm from the incisor teeth?
(a) Pharyngo-oesophageal junction
(b) Crossing of the arch of aorta
(c) Crossing of the left bronchus
(d) Where it pierces the diaphragm

15. Describe the gross and microscopic anatomy of the oesophagus.

16. Label the abdominopelvic regions (a to i) and abdominopelvic quadrants (a to d) in the following figure.

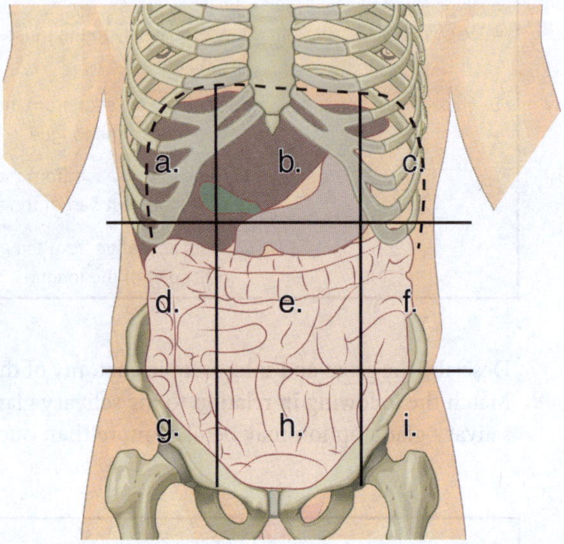

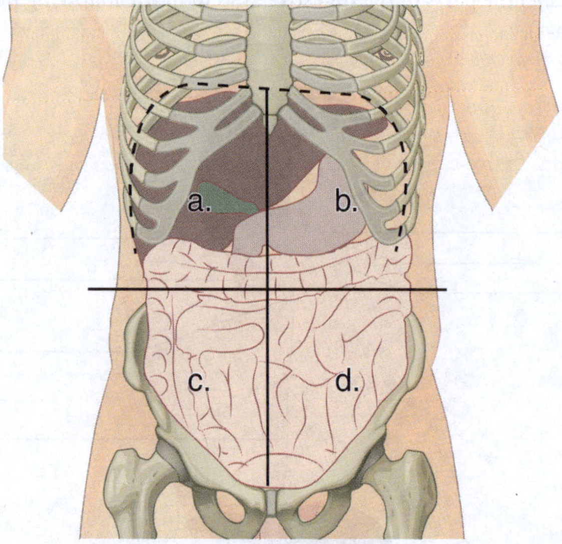

17. The two layers of the peritoneum are the ______________ and ______________ peritoneum.

18. The space between the visceral and the parietal peritoneum is called the ______________.

19. Draw a neat labelled diagram to show the parts of the stomach.

20. Label the peritoneal folds attached to the stomach in the following figure (a-d).

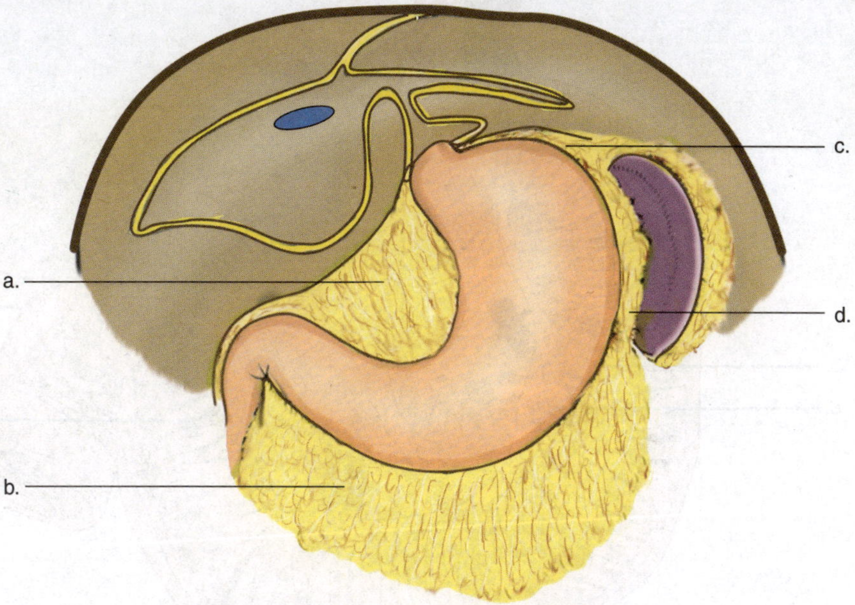

21. Label the structures forming the stomach bed in the following figure (a-g).

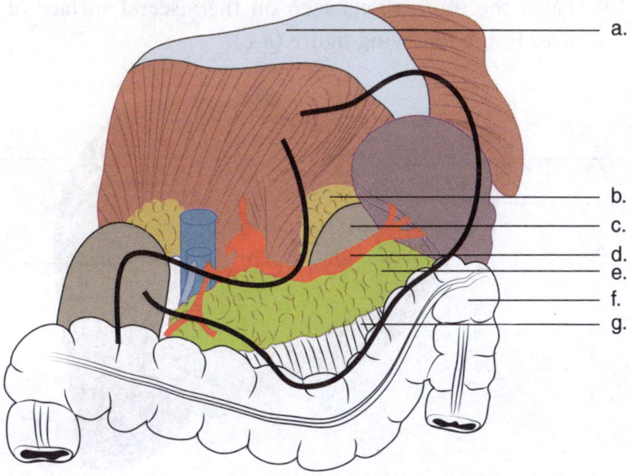

22. Describe the histology of the stomach.
23. Draw a neat labelled diagram to show the arterial supply of the stomach.
24. Draw a neat labelled diagram to show the lymphatic drainage of the stomach.
25. Compare and contrast the anatomical features of the different parts of the small intestine using a table.

26. Label the parts of the duodenum and its internal features in the following figure (a-e).

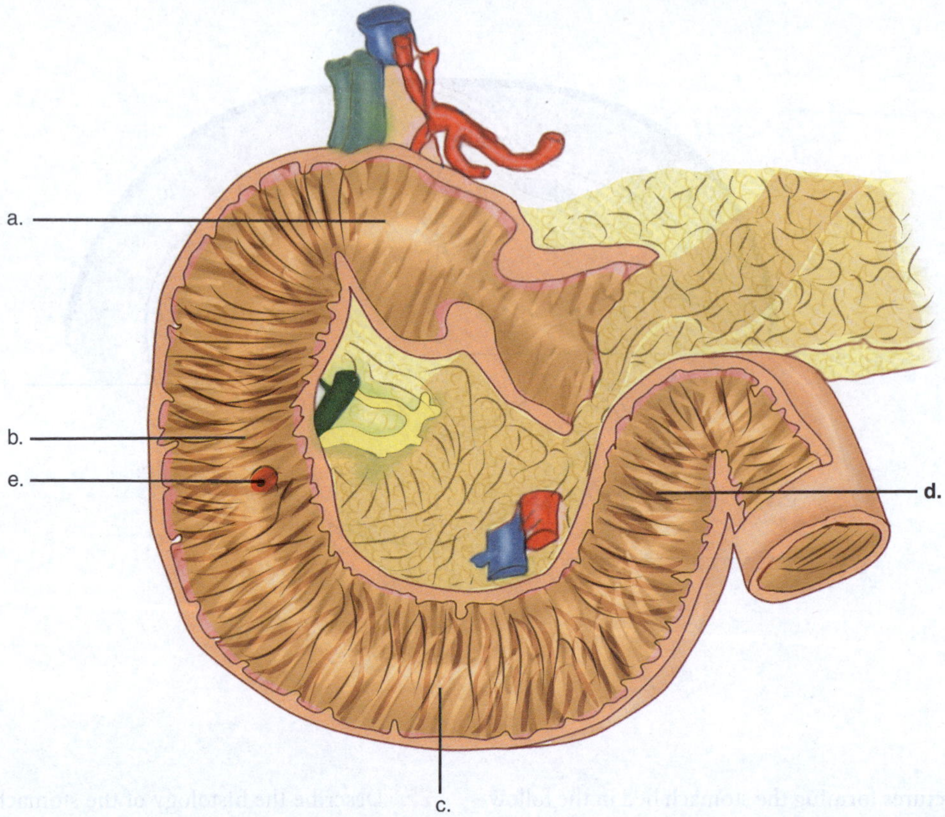

27. Describe the gross anatomy of the mesentery of the small intestine.
28. Describe the gross and microscopic anatomy of the vermiform appendix.
29. Describe the three salient anatomical features of the colon.
30. Compare and contrast the anatomical features of the small and large intestines using a table.
31. Describe the gross anatomy of the anal canal.
32. The named lobes of the liver are the ______________, ______________, ______________ and ______________ lobes.
33. The ____________ separates the right and left lobes of the liver.
34. Label the impressions seen on the visceral surface of the liver in the following figure (a-e).

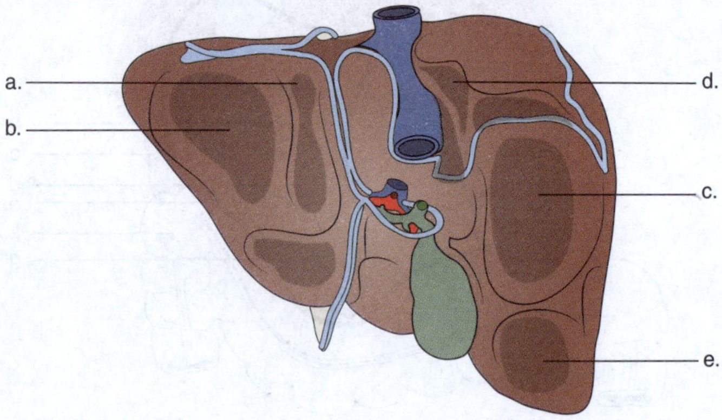

35. Draw a neat labelled diagram of the histology of the liver.
36. Describe the blood supply of the liver.
37. Draw a neat labelled diagram to show the parts of the extra-hepatic biliary apparatus.
38. The parts of the gallbladder are the ____________, ____________ and ____________.
39. Draw a neat labelled diagram of the histology of the gallbladder.
40. The parts of the pancreas are the ____________, ____________, ____________ and ____________.
41. Draw a neat labelled diagram of the histology of the pancreas.
42. Match the cells seen in the islets of Langerhans and their secretions.

1. α cell	a. Insulin
2. β cell	b. Pancreatic amylase
3. δ cell	c. Pancreatic lipase
	d. Somatostatin
	e. Glucagon

SECTION 3: WORKBOOK ANSWER KEY

The Digestive System

1. (a) Mouth; (b) Tongue; (c) Parotid gland; (d) Submandibuar gland; (e) Sublingual gland; (f) Pharynx; (g) Oesophagus; (h) Stomach; (i) Duodenum; (j) Jejunum; (k) Ileum; (l) Appendix; (m) Caecum; (n) Ascending colon; (o) Transverse colon; (p) Descending colon; (q) Sigmoid colon; (r) Rectum; (s) Anal canal
2. incisors, canines, premolars, molars
3. 20, 32
5. Correct answer: (a)
6. 1 – b, c; 2, a; 3, e; 4 – f, g; 5, d
8. 1 – b, e; 2 – c, f; 3 – a, d
11. nasopharynx, oropharynx, laryngopharynx
12. 1 – b, f; 2 – c, d; 3 – a, e
14. Correct answer: (d)
16. (a) Right hypochondriac; (b) Epigastric; (c) Left hypochondriac; (d) Right lumbar; (e) Umbilical; (f) Left lumbar; (g) Right iliac; (h) Hypogastric; (i) Left iliac (a) Right upper; (b) Left upper; (c) Right lower; (d) Left lower
17. visceral, parietal
18. peritoneal cavity
20. (a) Lesser omentum; (b) Greater omentum; (c) Gastrophrenic ligament; (d) Gastrosplenic ligament
21. (a) Diaphragm; (b) Left suprarenal gland; (c) Left kidney; (d) Splenic artery; (e) Pancreas; (f) Splenic flexure of colon; (g) Transverse mesocolon
26. (a) Superior (1st part); (b) Descending (2nd part); (c) Inferior (Horizontal or 3rd part); (d) Ascending (4th part); (e) Major duodenal papilla (Vater)
32. right, left, caudate, quadrate
33. falciform ligament
34. (a) Oesophageal impression; (b) Gastric impression; (c) Renal impression; (d) Suprarenal impression; (e) Colic impression
38. fundus, body, neck
40. head, neck, body, tail
42. 1, e; 2, a; 3, d

SECTION 4

Workbook: The Circulatory and Lymphatic System

SPECIFIC LEARNING OBJECTIVES

At the end of this chapter, the student should be able to:

Chapter 14

- Describe the structure and functions of the different types of blood vessels.
- Compare and contrast the systemic and pulmonary circulations.
- Name the arteries responsible for supplying blood to the various regions of the body.
- Describe the following arteries in detail: all parts of the aorta; subclavian artery; external carotid artery; axillary, brachial and radial arteries; femoral artery; and coeliac trunk.
- Name the veins responsible for carrying blood from the various regions of the body.
- Describe the following veins: superior and inferior vena cava, superficial veins of the limbs, axillary vein, subclavian vein, internal and external jugular veins, brachiocephalic vein and femoral vein.

Chapter 15

- Describe the gross anatomy of the pericardium.
- Describe the external features of the heart.
- Explain the blood supply of the heart and its clinical importance.

Chapter 16

- Describe the internal features of the atria and ventricles.
- Draw a neat, labelled diagram of the interior of the right atrium.
- Describe the structure of the valves of the heart.
- Describe the anatomical location of the pacemaker cells and conducting system of the heart.
- Name some common clinical conditions that affect the internal structures of the heart.

Chapter 17

- Name the structures that constitute the lymphoid tissues.
- Describe the cells found in lymphoid tissues and enumerate their functions.
- Describe the common structural features and differences between lymph nodes, spleen, thymus and tonsils.
- Name the major lymph node groups in the body.
- Describe in brief the axillary, inguinal and deep cervical lymph nodes.
- Describe the gross anatomy of the thoracic duct.

GLOSSARY OF TERMS

Chapter 14

- **Microcirculation:** arterioles with their associated capillary beds and venules
- **Tunica intima:** the inner layer of blood vessels lined by endothelium
- **Tunica media:** the middle layer of blood vessels containing smooth muscle fibres
- **Tunica adventitia:** the outer layer of blood vessels containing connective tissue
- **Systemic circulation:** high-pressure system carrying blood to and from the tissues of the body excluding the lungs
- **Pulmonary circulation:** low-pressure system carrying blood to and from the lungs for oxygenation
- **Portal circulation:** system of blood vessels that begins and ends in capillaries
- **Anastomosis:** a connection between blood vessels
- **Venae comitans:** double veins that accompany deep arteries

Chapter 15

- **Fibrous pericardium:** outer layer of the pericardium
- **Serous pericardium:** formed by outer parietal and inner serous parts separated by a pericardial cavity containing pericardial fluid
- **Pericardial sinuses:** spaces formed between prolongations of the serous pericardium over the great blood vessels of the heart
- **Endocardium:** inner layer of the heart lined by simple squamous epithelium
- **Myocardium:** middle thick muscular layer of the heart
- **Epicardium:** outer layer of the heart, otherwise called the visceral layer of serous pericardium
- **Coronary arteries:** arteries supplying the heart
- **Aortic sinuses:** spaces above the leaflets of the aortic valve from where the coronary arteries arise
- **Coronary sinus:** main vein draining blood from the heart

Chapter 16

- **Crista terminalis:** a vertical muscular ridge in the right atrium
- **Musculi pectinati:** horizontal muscular ridges extending from the crista terminalis
- **Sinus venarum:** smooth posterior part of the right atrial cavity
- **Fossa ovalis:** depression seen in the interatrial septum
- **Limbus fossa ovalis:** thickened margins of the fossa ovalis
- **Trabeculae carneae:** muscular ridges seen in the ventricles
- **Papillary muscles:** muscular pillars seen in the ventricles
- **Chordae tendineae:** fibrous cords connecting the papillary muscles and valve cusps
- **Infundibulum or conus:** smooth outflow tract of the right ventricle
- **Aortic vestibule:** smooth outflow tract of the left ventricle

Chapter 17

- **Lymphoid tissue:** connective tissue rich in lymphocytes
- **Lymphoid organs:** organs formed by dense aggregations of lymphocytes
- **Lymphocyte:** a type of white blood cell responsible for humoral and cellular immunity
- **B lymphocyte:** a type of lymphocyte responsible for humoral immunity
- **T lymphocyte:** a type of lymphocyte responsible for cellular immunity

REVIEW QUESTIONS

1. Compare and contrast the systemic and pulmonary circulation.
2. Match the following vessels to the appropriate number in order based on the direction of blood flow:

1. Venules	1
2. Capillaries	2
3. Arterioles	3
4. Elastic arteries	4
5. Large veins	5
6. Medium-sized veins	6
7. Muscular arteries	7

3. The three layers that are seen in arteries and veins in order from the inside to the outside are ________________, ________________ and ________________.
4. Compare and contrast the histology of arteries and veins.
5. Describe the gross anatomy of the arch of the aorta.
6. Label the important arteries of the upper limb in the diagram below (a-e).

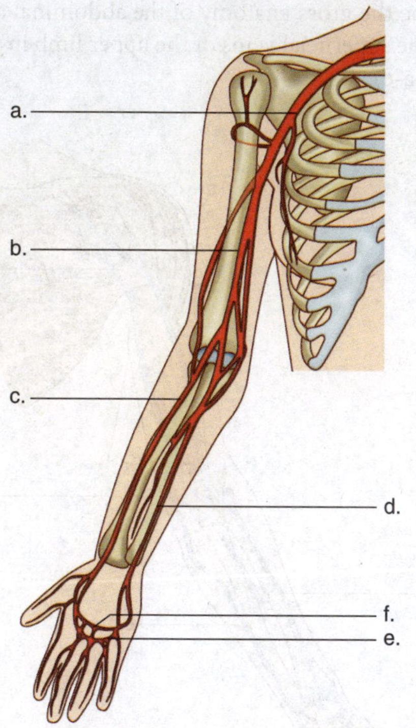

7. Describe the gross anatomy of the axillary artery.
8. Label the important arteries of the lower limb in the diagram below (a-i).

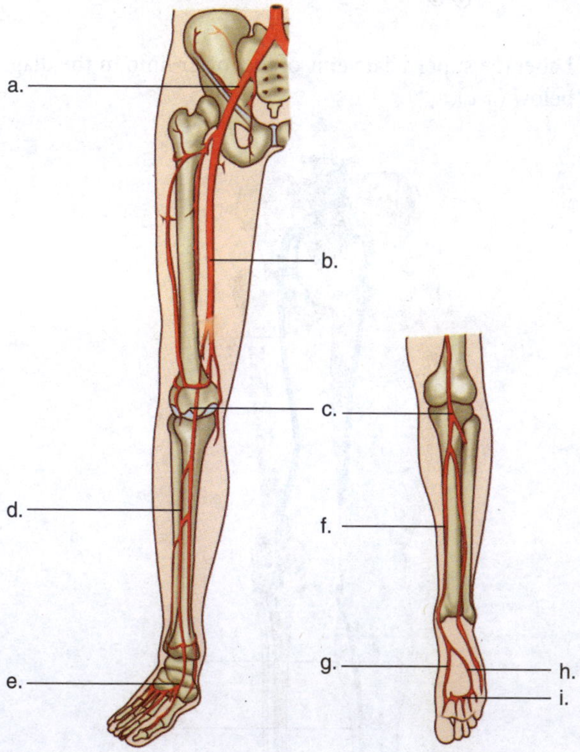

9. Describe the gross anatomy of the femoral artery.
10. Describe the gross anatomy of the internal carotid artery.
11. Describe the gross anatomy of the external carotid artery.
12. Describe the gross anatomy of the abdominal aorta.
13. Label the superficial veins of the upper limb in the diagram below (a-e).

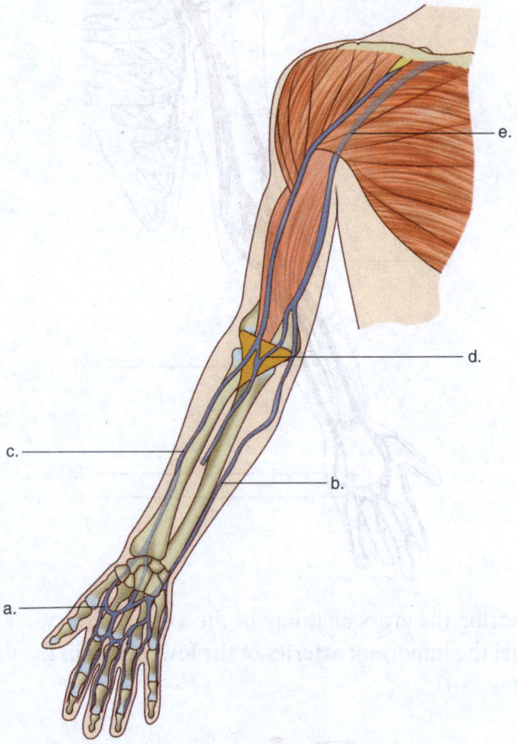

14. Label the superficial veins of the lower limb in the diagram below (a-c).

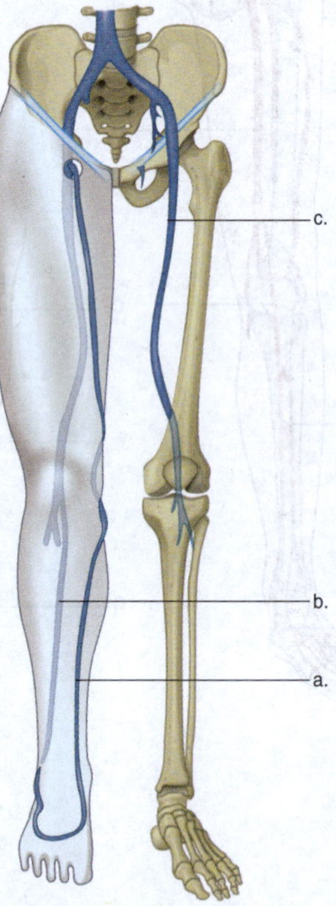

15. Describe the gross anatomy of the femoral vein.
16. Describe the gross anatomy of the portal vein.
17. Describe the gross anatomy of the inferior vena cava.
18. Describe the gross anatomy of the superior vena cava.
19. Describe the layers of the pericardium.
20. Describe the sinuses of the pericardium.
21. The three layers of the heart in order from inside to outside are the ____________, ____________ and ____________.
22. Describe the external features of the heart.
23. Match the chambers of the heart to the vessels that either enter or leave them:

1. Right atrium	a. Ascending aorta
2. Left atrium	b. Superior vena cava
3. Right ventricle	c. Pulmonary veins
4. Left ventricle	d. Pulmonary trunk

24. Describe the blood supply of the heart and its applied anatomy.
25. Match the coronary arteries with the structures supplied by them. The options on the left may be matched with more than one option on the right.

1. Left coronary artery	a. Left ventricle except for a part adjacent to the posterior interventricular sulcus
2. Right coronary artery	b. Left ventricle adjacent to the posterior interventricular sulcus
	c. Left atrium
	d. Right atrium
	e. Most of the conducting system
	f. Left bundle branch
	g. Anterior part of interventricular septum
	h. Posterior part of interventricular septum

26. Describe the anatomical features of the interior of the four chambers of the heart.

27. Label the features of the interior of the right atrium in the figure below (a-g).

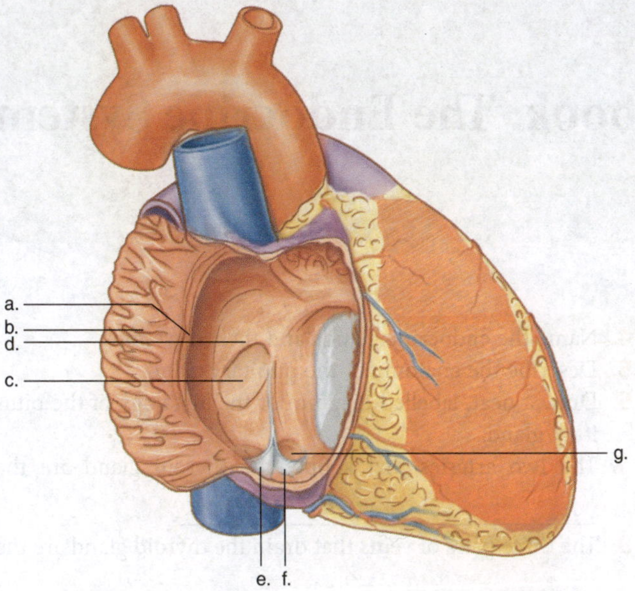

28. Describe the structure of the valves of the heart.
29. Match the valves of the heart to their correct location:

1. Tricuspid	a. Between left atrium and left ventricle
2. Mitral	b. Between left ventricle and ascending aorta
3. Aortic	c. Between right ventricle and pulmonary trunk
4. Pulmonary	d. Between right atrium and right ventricle

30. Label the parts of the conducting system of the heart in the figure below (a-f).

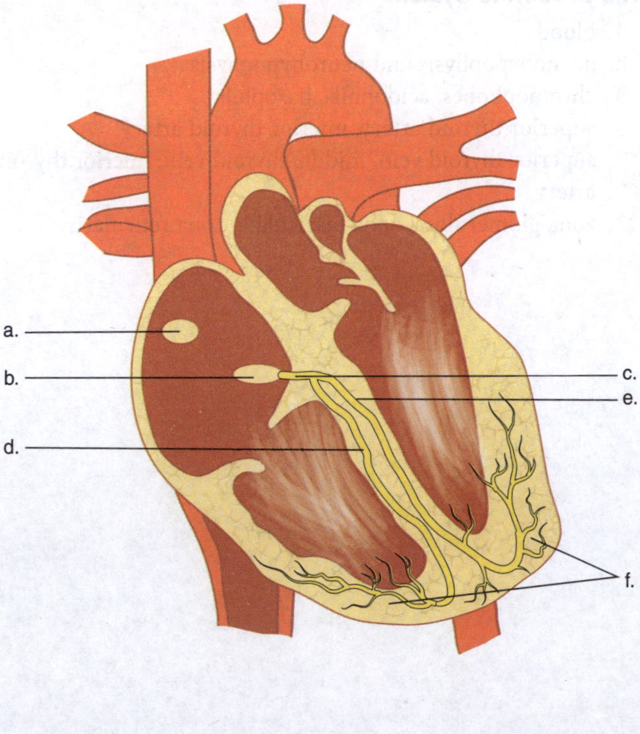

31. The predominant cell seen in lymphoid tissues is the ______________.
32. Classify lymphoid organs with suitable examples.
33. Describe the major groups of lymph nodes in the body along with their drainage areas.
34. Describe the microstructure of lymph nodes.
35. The thoracic duct begins as a continuation of the ______________ and terminates by draining into the junction of the ______________ and ______________.
36. Describe the gross anatomy of the thoracic duct.
37. Describe the microstructure of the thymus.
38. Describe the microstructure of the spleen.
39. Describe the microstructure of the palatine tonsil.
40. Match the lymphoid organs with their characteristic features:

1. Lymph node	a. Crypts
2. Thymus	b. Red and white pulp
3. Spleen	c. Hassall's corpuscles
4. Palatine tonsil	d. Medullary cords and sinuses

SECTION 4: Workbook Answer Key

The Circulatory and Lymphatic System

2. 1, 5; 2, 4; 3, 3; 4, 1; 5, 7; 6, 6; 7, 2
3. tunica intima, tunica media, tunica adventitia
6. (a) Axillary artery; (b) Brachial artery; (c) Radial artery; (d) Ulnar artery; (e) Superficial palmar arch; (f) Deep palmar arch
8. (a) External iliac artery; (b) Femoral artery; (c) Popliteal artery; (d) Anterior tibial artery; (e) Dorsalis pedis artery; (f) Posterior tibial artery; (g) Medial plantar artery; (h) Lateral plantar artery; (i) Plantar arch
13. (a) Dorsal venous network of hand; (b) Basilic vein; (c) Cephalic vein; (d) Median cubital vein; (e) Axillary vein
14. (a) Great saphenous vein; (b) Short saphenous vein; (c) Femoral vein
21. endocardium, myocardium and epicardium
23. 1 – b; 2 – c; 3 – d; 4 - a
25. 1 – a, c, f, g; 2 – b, d, e, h
27. (a) Crista terminalis; (b) Musculi pectinati; (c) Fossa ovalis; (d) Limbus fossa ovalis; (e) Valve of IVC; (f) Valve of coronary sinus; g) Opening of coronary sinus
29. 1 – d; 2 – a; 3 – b; 4 - c
30. (a) SA node; (b) AV node; (c) Bundle of His; (d) Right bundle branch; (e) Left bundle branch; (f) Purkinje fibres
31. lymphocyte
35. cisterna chyli, left internal jugular vein, left subclavian vein
40. 1 – d; 2 – c; 3 – b; 4 - a

SECTION 5

Workbook: The Endocrine System

SPECIFIC LEARNING OBJECTIVES

At the end of this chapter, the student should be able to:

Chapter 18

- Name the major endocrine organs.
- Describe the anatomy and functions of the pituitary gland, thyroid gland, adrenal gland and pancreatic islets.
- Describe in brief the anatomy and functions of the hypothalamus, parathyroid and pineal glands.

GLOSSARY OF TERMS

Chapter 18

- **Endocrine glands:** ductless glands whose secretions are poured directly into the bloodstream, for example thyroid gland
- **Endocrine tissues:** collections of endocrine cells within an organ that has other functions, for example islets of Langerhans
- **Follicle:** a central spherical space surrounded by cells

REVIEW QUESTIONS

1. Endocrine glands pour their secretions into the ______.
2. The two anatomically and functionally different parts of the pituitary gland are the ______ and ______.
3. The three types of cells that constitute the pars anterior are the ______, ______ and ______.
4. Name the endocrine glands and their secretions.
5. Describe the anatomy of the pituitary gland.
6. Draw a neat, labelled diagram of the histology of the pituitary gland.
7. The two arteries that supply the thyroid gland are the ______ and ______.
8. The three pairs of veins that drain the thyroid gland are the ______, ______ and ______.
9. Describe the anatomy of the thyroid gland.
10. Draw a neat, labelled diagram of the histology of the thyroid gland.
11. The three parts of the adrenal cortex are the ______, ______ and ______.
12. Describe the anatomy of the adrenal gland.
13. Draw a neat, labelled diagram of the histology of the adrenal gland.

SECTION 5: Workbook Answer Key

The Endocrine System

1. blood
2. adenohypophysis and neurohypophysis
3. chromophobes, acidophils, basophils
7. superior thyroid artery, inferior thyroid artery
8. superior thyroid vein, middle thyroid vein, inferior thyroid artery
11. zona glomerulosa, zona fasciculata, zona reticularis

Workbook: The Sensory Organs

SPECIFIC LEARNING OBJECTIVES

At the end of this chapter, the student should be able to:

Chapter 19

- Describe the general features of skin.
- Describe the histological features of thick skin including the layers, characteristics of each layer and other associated structures.
- Describe the histological features of thin skin as above, including hair follicles and sebaceous glands.
- Name and describe in brief the appendages of the skin.

Chapter 20

- Name the special sensory organs.
- Draw the eyeball showing the various layers.
- Describe the components of each layer in brief.
- Name the parts of the ear.
- Describe in brief each part of the ear.
- Describe the structure of a taste bud.
- Describe the structure of olfactory epithelium.

GLOSSARY OF TERMS

Chapter 19

- **Epidermis:** outer layer of the skin
- **Dermis:** inner layer of the skin
- **Stratified squamous keratinized epithelium:** the multilayered epithelium seen in the epidermis of the skin
- **Keratinocyte:** the most common cell type in the epidermis which produces keratin
- **Melanocyte:** cell responsible for pigmentation of the skin
- **Merkel cells:** sensory cells in the epidermis
- **Langerhans cells:** immune cells in the epidermis
- **Lines of Langer:** tension lines produced by collagen fibre arrangements in the dermis
- **Meissner's corpuscles:** sensory receptors in the papillary dermis that detect light touch
- **Pacinian corpuscles:** sensory receptors in the reticular dermis that respond to vibrations
- **Ruffini endings:** sensory receptors in the reticular dermis that respond to deep pressure
- **Thin skin:** skin containing hair follicles present all over the body except the palms and soles
- **Thick skin:** skin on the palms and soles without hair follicles
- **Hair:** composed of keratinized cells produced by the hair follicles
- **Sebaceous glands:** holocrine glands opening into hair follicles
- **Sweat glands:** coiled tubular glands in the dermis that open onto the surface or into hair follicles
- **Nails:** plates of hard keratin produced by the nail matrix

Chapter 20

- **Olfactory:** related to smell
- **Gustatory:** related to taste
- **Visual:** related to sight
- **Auditory:** related to hearing
- **Limbus:** junction between the sclera, cornea and iris from where aqueous humour is drained
- **Macula lutea:** small area on the retina where the cones are concentrated
- **Fovea centralis:** minute area on the macula lutea where only cones are present
- **Optic disc:** area on the retina where fibres of the optic nerve exit
- **Ora serrata:** irregular junctional line between the neural and non-neural parts of the retina
- **Canthi:** angles of the eye at the junction between the upper and lower eyelids
- **Bony labyrinth:** spaces within the petrous part of the temporal bone that contain perilymph
- **Membranous labyrinth:** a system of tube-like structures situated within the bony labyrinth that contain endolymph
- **Vestibule:** part of the bony labyrinth that contains the utricle and saccule
- **Utricle and saccule:** parts of the membranous labyrinth that are responsible for monitoring the position of the head
- **Macula:** end organ that responds to linear changes in the position of the head
- **Crista:** end organ that responds to rotational changes in the position of the head
- **Organ of Corti:** end organ of hearing
- **Taste bud:** end organ of taste
- **Papillae:** elevations on the surface of the tongue containing taste buds
- **Olfactory receptor cells:** bipolar neurons that detect odours and transmit them centrally via the olfactory nerve rootlets
- **Bowman's glands:** glands in the connective tissue underlying the olfactory epithelium that produce serous secretions

REVIEW QUESTIONS

1. The two layers of skin are the outer ______________ and inner ______________.
2. The principal cell of the epidermis is the ______________.
3. The two layers of the dermis are the ______________ layer and ______________ layer.
4. The five layers of the epidermis from deep to superficial are the______________, ______________, ______________, ______________ and ______________.
5. Draw a neat, labelled diagram showing the microscopic features of thick skin.
6. Draw a neat, labelled diagram showing the microscopic features of thin skin.
7. Name and briefly describe the derivatives of skin.
8. The three layers of the eyeball are the outer ______________ layer, middle ______________ layer and inner ______________ layer.
9. Label the parts of the eyeball in the figure below (a1-h).

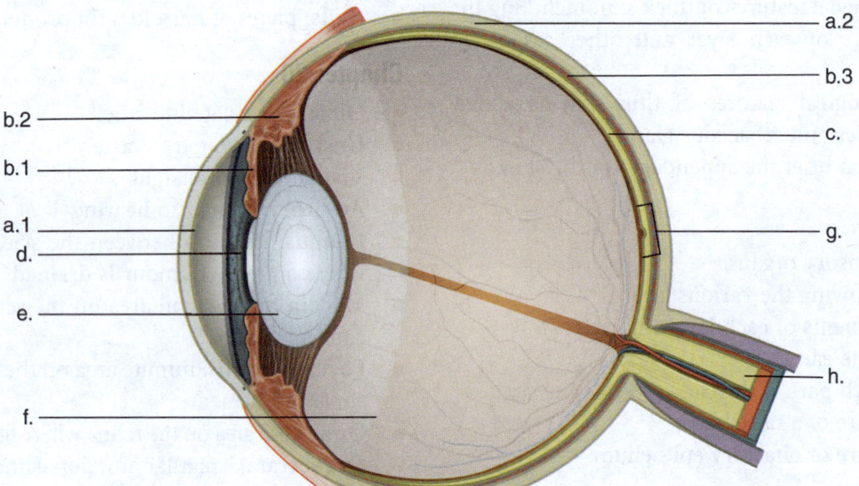

10. Draw a neat, labelled diagram of the lacrimal apparatus.
11. The three parts of the ear are the ______________, ______________ and ______________ ear.
12. The parts of the external ear include the ______________ and ______________.
13. Describe the anatomy of the middle ear.

14. Label the parts of the inner ear in the figure below (a-h).

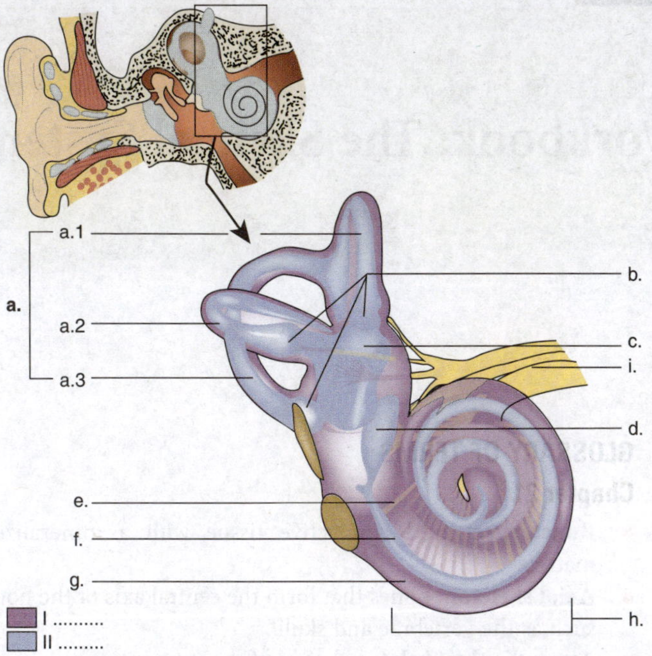

15. Two types of papillae that possess taste buds are ______________ and ______________.

16. The three nerves that carry the sensation of taste are the ______________, ______________ and ______________.

17. Describe the structure and function of taste buds.

18. The olfactory epithelium is seen lining the ______________ of the nasal cavity.

19. Describe the structure and function of olfactory epithelium.

SECTION 6: WORKBOOK ANSWER KEY

The Sensory Organs

1. epidermis, dermis
2. keratinocyte
3. papillary, reticular
4. stratum basale, stratum spinosum, stratum granuosum, stratum lucidum and stratum corneum
8. fibrous, vascular, nervous
9. (a1) Cornea; (a2) Sclera; (b1) Iris; (b2) Ciliary body; (b3) Choroid; (c) Retina; (d) Pupil; (e) Lens; (f) Vitreous body; (g) Macula; (h) Optic nerve
11. outer, middle, inner
12. auricle (pinna), external acoustic meatus (auditory canal)
14. (I) Bony labyrinth; (II) Membranous labyrinth; (a) Semicircular ducts; (a1) Anterior; (a2) Lateral; (a3) Posterior; (b) Cristae within ampullae; (c) Utricle; (d) Saccule; (e) Vestibular duct; (f) Cochlear duct; (g) Tympanic duct; (h) Cochlea; (i) Vestibulocochlear nerve
15. fungiform, circumvallate
16. facial, glossopharyngeal, vagus
18. roof

SECTION 7.1

Workbook: The Skeletal System

SPECIFIC LEARNING OBJECTIVES

At the end of this chapter, the student should be able to:

Chapter 21

- Classify the bones of the body based on their location and structure.
- Describe the general features of bone tissue.
- Compare and contrast the microstructure of compact and spongy bones.
- Describe in brief the mechanisms of bone growth and development.

Chapter 22

- Name the components of the axial skeleton.
- Describe the main anatomical features of the skull, vertebral column and bony thorax.

Chapter 23

- Name the components of the appendicular skeleton.
- Describe the main anatomical features of the skeleton of the upper limb.
- Describe the main anatomical features of the skeleton of the lower limb.

Chapter 24

- Define a joint.
- Classify joints based on their structure and function with suitable examples.
- Describe the features of a typical synovial joint.
- Classify synovial joints with suitable examples.

Chapter 25

- Name the large joints of the axial and appendicular skeleton.
- Describe the essential features of the temporomandibular, atlanto-occipital, atlantoaxial, intervertebral and sacroiliac joints.
- Describe the essential features of the shoulder, elbow and wrist joints.
- Describe the essential features of the hip, knee and ankle joints.

GLOSSARY OF TERMS

Chapter 21

- **Bone:** specialized connective tissue with a mineralized matrix
- **Axial skeleton:** bones that form the central axis of the body such as the vertebrae and skull
- **Appendicular skeleton:** bones of the extremities
- **Woven bone:** type of bone seen in the developing foetus
- **Lamellar bone:** type of bone seen in adults which is arranged in layers
- **Compact bone:** type of lamellar bone containing osteons
- **Spongy bone:** type of lamellar bone with trabeculae separated by marrow spaces
- **Osteon (Haversian system):** unit of compact bone with central Haversian canal and surrounding concentric lamellae
- **Osteoblast:** bone-forming cell
- **Osteocyte:** bone-maintaining cell
- **Osteoclast:** bone-destroying cell
- **Periosteum:** outer lining of bones
- **Endosteum:** inner lining of bones
- **Membranous ossification:** development of a bone from a membranous precursor
- **Endochondral ossification:** development of a bone from a cartilaginous precursor

Chapter 22

- **Axial skeleton:** bones that form the axis of the body and support and protect the organs of the head, neck and trunk
- **Calvaria:** part of the skull that forms the dome-like covering of the brain
- **Vertebral column:** the composite pillar-like structure formed by the cervical, thoracic, lumbar, sacral and coccygeal vertebrae enclosing the spinal cord
- **Bony thorax:** the skeletal framework of the thorax formed by the 12 pairs of ribs and sternum

Chapter 23

- **Appendages:** the upper and lower limbs
- **Appendicular skeleton:** the skeletal framework of the appendages and bones that anchor the appendages to the axial skeleton

- **Pectoral girdle:** the clavicle and scapula
- **Clavicle:** the collar bone
- **Scapula:** the shoulder blade
- **Humerus:** the arm bone
- **Radius:** the lateral bone of the forearm
- **Ulna:** the medial bone of the forearm
- **Carpal bones:** the small bones of the wrist
- **Metacarpals:** the bones of the palm
- **Phalanges:** the bones of the fingers and toes
- **Pelvic girdle:** the hip bones, sacrum and coccyx
- **Femur:** the thigh bone
- **Tibia:** the medial leg bone
- **Fibula:** the lateral leg bone
- **Tarsal bones:** the proximal bones of the foot
- **Metatarsals:** the distal bones of the foot

Chapter 24

- **Joint:** a junction between two or more skeletal elements
- **Fibrous joint:** a type of joint where fibrous connective tissue connects adjacent skeletal elements
- **Cartilaginous joint:** a type of joint where cartilage connects adjacent skeletal elements
- **Synovial joint:** a type of joint where a cavity filled with synovial fluid separates adjacent bony surfaces
- **Synarthroses:** immovable joints
- **Amphiarthroses:** partially movable joints
- **Diarthroses:** freely movable joints
- **Sutures:** fibrous joints seen between bones of the skull
- **Fontanelles:** membrane-filled gaps between bones of the skull seen in neonates
- **Gomphoses:** fibrous joints between teeth and their bony sockets
- **Syndesmoses:** fibrous joints seen in the limb bones
- **Synchondroses:** primary cartilaginous joints
- **Symphyses:** secondary cartilaginous joints
- **Uniaxial joints:** synovial joints allowing movement around one axis
- **Biaxial joints:** synovial joints allowing movements around two axes
- **Multiaxial joints:** synovial joints allowing movements around more than two axes

Chapter 25

- **Uniaxial joints:** synovial joints allowing movement around one axis
- **Biaxial joints:** synovial joints allowing movements around two axes
- **Multiaxial joints:** synovial joints allowing movements around more than two axes

REVIEW QUESTIONS

1. Bones can be classified based on ____________, ____________, ____________ and ____________.
2. Classify bones with suitable examples.
3. Match the bone to the type to which it belongs.

1. Sternum	a. Short bone
2. Femur	b. Irregular bone
3. Patella	c. Long bone
4. Vertebrae	d. Sesamoid bone
5. Tarsal bones	e. Flat bone

4. Label the essential anatomical features of a long bone in the figure below (a1-j).

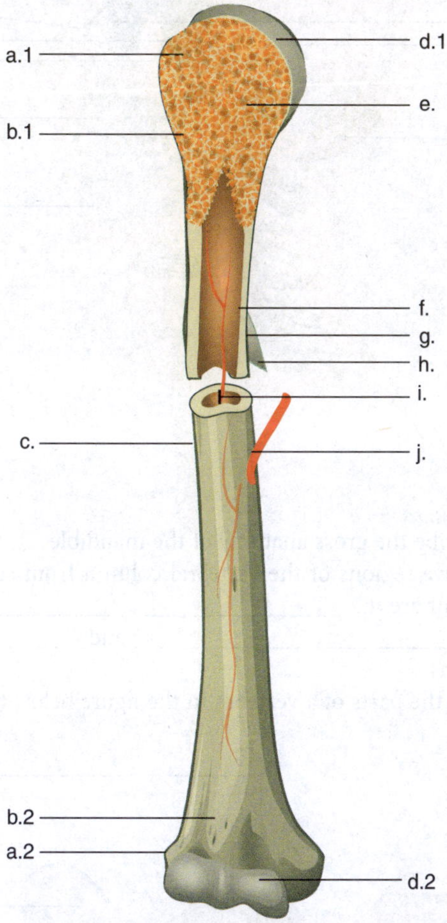

5. The four types of cells seen in bone tissue are ______, ______, ______ and ______.
6. Haversian systems are seen in ______ bone.
7. Describe the microstructure of compact bone.
8. Compare and contrast the features of compact and spongy bone.
9. The two methods of ossification of bone are ______ and ______.
10. The three parts of the axial skeleton are the ______, ______ and ______.
11. Label the parts of the skull in the figure below (a-k).

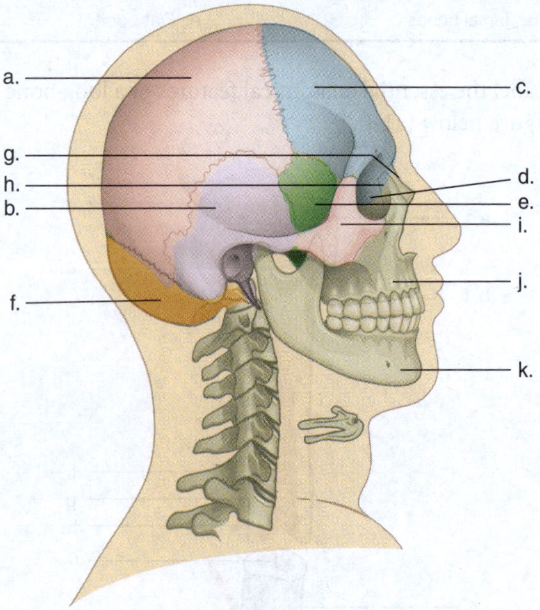

12. Describe the gross anatomy of the mandible.
13. The five regions of the vertebral column from superior to inferior are the ______, ______, ______, ______ and ______ regions.
14. Label the parts of a vertebra in the figure below (a-g).

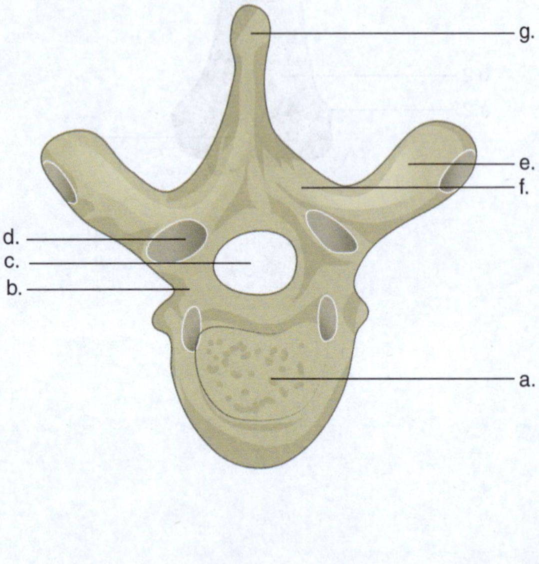

15. The three parts of the sternum from superior to inferior are the ______, ______ and ______.
16. The 3rd to 9th pair of ribs are called ______ ribs.
17. The first seven pairs of ribs are called ______ ribs.
18. Name the components of the bony thorax. Describe the parts of a typical rib.
19. Name the bones of the upper limb.
20. Name the bones forming the pectoral girdle.
21. The two ends of the clavicle are the ______ end and ______ end.
22. The three processes of the scapula are the ______, ______ and ______ process.
23. Describe the anatomical features of the humerus.
24. Describe the anatomical features of the bones of the forearm.
25. Label the carpal bones in the figure below (1-8).

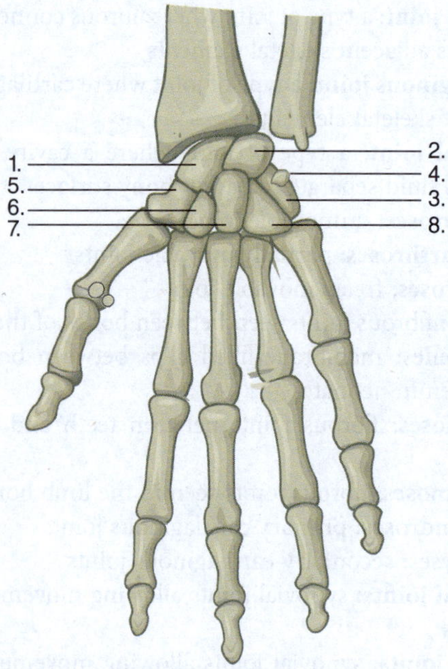

26. Name the bones of the lower limb.
27. Name the bones forming the pelvic girdle.
28. The three parts of the hip bone are the ______, ______ and ______.
29. Describe the anatomical features of the femur.
30. Describe the anatomical features of the bones of the leg.

31. Label the tarsal bones in the figure below (1-7).

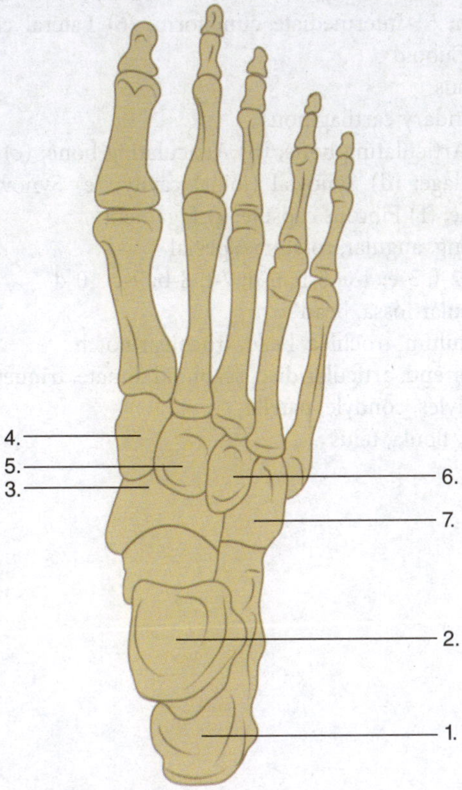

32. Define a joint. Classify joints giving examples.

33. Sutures are examples of _______________ joints.

34. Intervertebral discs are examples of _______________ _______________ joints.

35. Label the parts of a typical synovial joint in the figure below (a-g).

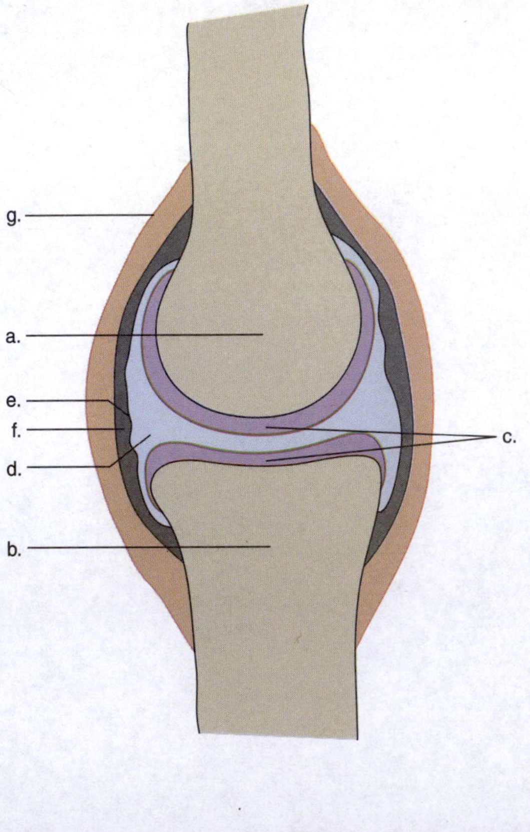

36. Describe the typical features of a synovial joint.

37. Movements that occur at synovial joints can be classified into the following four types: _______________, _______________, _______________ and _______________.

38. Classify synovial joints with examples.

39. Match the following joints with their type (each option may be used more than once):

1. Temporomandibular	a. Plane
2. Atlanto-occipital	b. Ball and socket
3. Atlantoaxial	c. Bicondylar
4. Sacroiliac	d. Hinge
5. Shoulder	e. Pivot
6. Elbow	f. Ellipsoid
7. Wrist	
8. Hip	
9. Knee	
10. Ankle	

40. The articulating parts of the temporomandibular joint are the _______________ _______________ of the temporal bone and the _______________ of the mandible.

41. Describe the movements that occur at the temporomandibular joint.

42. Describe the gross anatomy of the shoulder joint.

43. The articulating parts of the elbow joint are the _______________ and _______________ of the humerus, the _______________ of the radius and the _______________ _______________ the ulna.

44. Describe the movements that occur the elbow joint.

45. The articulating parts of the wrist joint are the _______________ _______________ of the radius and _______________ _______________ superiorly and the _______________, _______________ and _______________ bones inferiorly.

46. Describe the movements that occur the wrist joint.

47. Describe the gross anatomy of the hip joint.

48. The articulating parts of the knee joint include the _______________ of the femur, _______________ of the tibia and the _______________.

49. Describe the movements that occur the knee joint.

50. The bones that form the ankle joint include the lower ends of the _______________ and _______________ and the _______________.

51. Describe the movements that occur the ankle joint.

SECTION 7.1: Workbook Answer Key

The Skeletal System

1. position, shape, structure, development

3. 1 – e, 2 – c, 3 – d, 4 – b, 5 - a

4. a1) Proximal epiphysis; a2) Distal epiphysis; b1) and b2) Metaphyses; c) Diaphysis; d1) and d2) Articular cartilage; e) Spongy bone; f) Endosteum; g) Compact bone; h) Periosteum; i) Medullary cavity; j) Nutrient artery
5. osteogenic cells, osteoblasts, osteocytes, osteoclasts
6. compact
9. intramembranous, endochondral
10. skull, vertebral column, bony thorax
11. a) Parietal; b) Temporal; c) Frontal; d) Ethmoid; e) Sphenoid; f) Occipital; g) Nasal; h) Lacrimal; i) Zygomatic; j) Maxilla; k) Mandible
13. cervical, thoracic, lumbar, sacrum, coccyx
14. a) Body; b) Pedicle; c) Vertebral foramen; d) Superior articular facet; e) Transverse process; f) Lamina; g) Spinous process
15. manubrium, body, xiphoid process
16. typical
17. true
21. medial, lateral
22. coracoid, acromion, spinous
25. (1) Scaphoid; (2) Lunate; (3) Triquetral; (4) Pisiform; (5) Trapezium; (6) Trapezoid; (7) Capitate; (8) Hamate
28. ilium, ischium, pubi
31. (1) Calcaneus; (2) Talus; (3) Navicular; (4) Medial Cuneiform; 5) Intermediate cuneiform; (6) Lateral cuneiform; (7) Cuboid
33. fibrous
34. secondary cartilaginous
35. (a) Articulating bone; (b) Articulating bone; (c) Articular cartilage; (d) Synovial (joint) cavity; (e) Synovial membrane; (f) Fibrous capsule; g) Ligament
37. gliding, angular, rotatory, special
39. 1-c; 2-f; 3-e; 4-a; 5-b; 6-d; 7-f; 8-b; 9-c; 10-d
40. articular fossa, head
43. capitulum, trochlea, head, trochlear notch
45. lower end, articular disc, scaphoid, lunate, triquetral
48. condyles, condyle, patella
50. tibia, fibula, talus

SECTION 7.2

Workbook: The Muscular System

SPECIFIC LEARNING OBJECTIVES

At the end of this chapter, the student should be able to:

Chapter 26

- Describe the gross anatomy of the major muscle groups of the head and neck.
- Describe the gross anatomy of the major muscle groups of the upper limb.
- Describe the gross anatomy of the major muscle groups of the thorax, including the thoracoabdominal diaphragm.

Chapter 27

- Describe the gross anatomy of the major muscle groups of the abdominal wall.
- Describe the gross anatomy of the major muscle groups of the pelvis and perineum.
- Describe the gross anatomy of the major muscle groups of the lower limb.

GLOSSARY OF TERMS

Chapter 26

- **Muscles of mastication:** muscles that are responsible for chewing movements of the mandible
- **Extraocular muscles:** muscles that move the eyeball
- **Infrahyoid muscles:** muscles that extend from the sternum and larynx to the hyoid bone
- **Sternocleidomastoid muscle:** muscle of the neck that divides it into anterior and posterior triangles
- **Intercostal muscles:** muscles located in the intercostal spaces between ribs
- **Pectoral muscles:** muscles of the upper limb that arise from the front of the chest wall
- **Deltoid:** an important muscle of the shoulder region which is a common site for administration of intramuscular injections
- **Thoracoabdominal diaphragm:** the musculoaponeurotic partition between the thoracic and abdominal cavities

Chapter 27

- **Muscles of the anterior abdominal wall:** muscles that are present on the front and sides of the abdominal wall
- **Rectus sheath:** connective tissue covering of the rectus abdominis muscle formed by the aponeuroses of the other three muscles of the anterior abdominal wall
- **Linea alba:** midline structure formed by the meeting of the aponeuroses of the three muscles of the anterior abdominal wall
- **Muscles of the posterior abdominal wall:** muscles that are present behind the viscera and peritoneal cavity
- **Muscles of the pelvis:** muscles that line the walls of the pelvis and those that separate the pelvic cavity and perineum
- **Pelvic diaphragm:** muscular partition between the pelvis and perineum formed mainly by the levator ani muscle
- **Muscles of the perineum:** muscles below the pelvis in close relation to the urethra, vagina and anal canal
- **Perineal body:** fibromuscular node responsible for maintaining structural stability into which the perineal muscles are attached
- **Gluteal muscles:** muscles located in the region above the back of the thigh
- **Ligamentum patellae:** the tendon of insertion of the quadriceps femoris muscle in which the patella is located
- **Achilles tendon:** the combined tendon of insertion of the gastrocnemius and soleus muscles
- **Gluteus maximus:** a large muscle of the gluteal region into which intramuscular injections are commonly given

REVIEW QUESTIONS

7. The muscles of facial expression and the scalp are supplied by the ______________ nerve.
8. The muscles of mastication are supplied by the ______________ nerve.
9. The muscles of the tongue are supplied by the ______________ nerve.
10. The muscles of the soft palate and pharynx are supplied by the ______________ plexus.
11. The three nerves that supply the extraocular muscles are the ______________, ______________ and ______________ nerves.
12. The muscles of the larynx are supplied by the ______________ nerve.
13. Describe the gross anatomy of the sternocleidomastoid muscle.
14. Name the constrictors of the pharynx and their actions.
15. Name four muscles in the extensor compartment of the forearm. What clinical condition results if they are paralyzed?
16. Describe the gross anatomy of the deltoid muscle. Add a note on its clinical importance.

17. Describe the gross anatomy of the intercostal muscles.
18. Describe the gross anatomy of the thoracoabdominal diaphragm.
19. Label the three major openings in the thoracoabdominal diaphragm in the figure below (a to c).

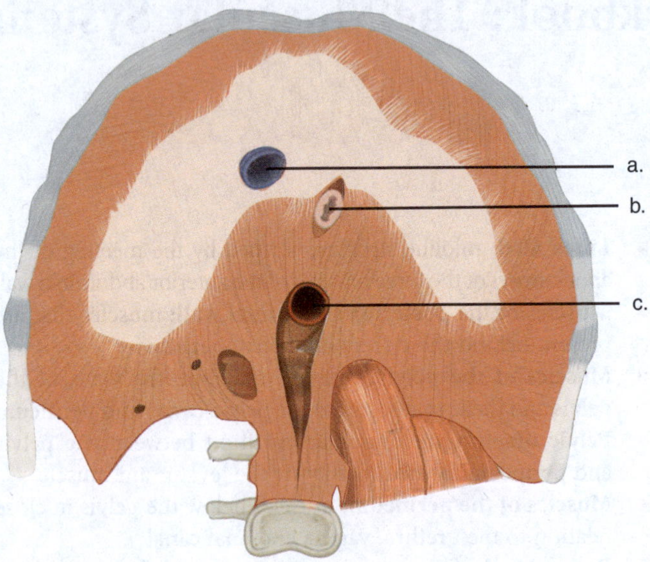

20. Match the following muscles with their action:

1. Biceps brachii	a. Extension at the elbow joint
2. Deltoid	b. Flexion at the interphalangeal joints
3. Triceps brachii	c. Abduction at the shoulder joint
4. Flexor digitorum profundus	d. Extension at the interphalangeal joints
5. Extensor digitorum	e. Flexion at the elbow joint

21. The three muscles of the anterior abdominal wall are the ______________, ______________, ______________ and ______________.
22. Describe the gross anatomy of the muscles of the anterior abdominal wall. Add a note on their clinical importance.
23. The pelvic diaphragm is formed by the ______________ muscle.
24. Describe the gross anatomy of the levator ani muscle. Add a note on its clinical importance.
25. The gluteal muscles are supplied by branches from the ______________ plexus.
26. Describe the gross anatomy of the gluteus maximus muscle. Add a note on its clinical importance.
27. The muscles of the front of the thigh are supplied by branches from the ______________ nerve.
28. The muscles of the medial side of the thigh are supplied by branches from the ______________ nerve.
29. The muscles of the back of the thigh are supplied by branches from the ______________ nerve.
30. Name the four muscles forming the quadriceps femoris. Describe the insertion of this muscle.
31. The muscles of the front of the leg are supplied by branches from the ______________ nerve.
32. What is foot drop? How is it caused?
33. The muscles of the back of the leg are supplied by branches from the ______________ nerve.
34. How is the Achilles tendon formed? What is the action of the muscles that form this tendon?
35. Match the following muscles with their action:

1. Gluteus maximus	a. Extension at the knee joint
2. Quadriceps femoris	b. Adduction at the hip joint
3. Adductor magnus	c. Plantar flexion
4. Biceps femoris	d. Extension at the hip joint
5. Extensor digitorum longus	e. Eversion of the foot
6. Peroneus longus	f. Flexion at the knee joint
7. Gastrocnemius	g. Extension of the digits

SECTION 7.2: Workbook Answer Key

The Muscular System

7. facial
8. trigeminal
9. hypoglossal
10. pharyngeal
11. oculomotor, trochlear, abducent
12. vagus
19. (a) Caval opening for IVC; (b) Oesophageal opening; (c) Aortic opening
20. 1-e; 2-c; 3-a; 4-b; 5-d
21. external oblique, internal oblique, transversus abdominis
23. levator ani
25. sacral
27. femoral
28. obturator
29. sciatic
31. deep peroneal
33. tibial
35. 1-d; 2-a; 3-b; 4-f; 5-g; 6-e; 7-c

SECTION 8

Workbook: The Excretory System

SPECIFIC LEARNING OBJECTIVES

At the end of this chapter, the student should be able to:

Chapter 28

- Name the structures that constitute the excretory system.
- Describe the functions of each part of the excretory system.
- Describe the gross anatomy, microstructure and applied anatomy of the kidney.

Chapter 29

- Describe the gross, microscopic and applied anatomy of the ureter.
- Describe the gross, microscopic and applied anatomy of the urinary bladder.
- Describe the gross and applied anatomy of the male and female urethra.

GLOSSARY OF TERMS

Chapter 28

- **Hilum:** region of the kidney along its medial border where structures enter or leave the kidney
- **Renal sinus:** cavity within the kidney that communicates with the exterior through the hilum
- **Pyramids:** well-defined areas in the medulla that drain into the renal sinus through the papillae
- **Papillae:** apices of the pyramids where they open into the renal sinus
- **Minor calyces:** relatively small spaces lined by renal fascia into which papillae open
- **Major calyces:** relatively large spaces formed by convergence of the minor calyces
- **Pelvis of ureter:** funnel-shaped, dilated origin of the ureter formed by convergence of the major calyces
- **Cortex:** peripheral darker region of the substance of the kidney
- **Medulla:** central lighter region of the substance of the kidney
- **Cortical arch:** cap of cortex around the base of a pyramid
- **Column:** extension of the cortex between adjacent pyramids
- **Medullary ray:** extension of the medulla into the cortex
- **Uriniferous tubules:** tubules formed by nephrons and collecting ducts
- **Nephron:** structural and functional unit of the kidney consisting of the renal corpuscle and renal tubule
- **Renal corpuscle:** filtration unit of the kidney containing the glomerulus and Bowman's capsule
- **Renal tubule:** tubule responsible for the selective reabsorption and concentration of the urine, consisting of a proximal tubule, loop of Henle and distal tubule
- **Mesangial cells:** connective tissue cells of the kidney
- **Juxtaglomerular apparatus:** a group of structures that is responsible for maintaining blood pressure by regulating blood flow through the glomerulus

Chapter 29

- **Pelviureteric junction:** junction between the renal pelvis and the beginning of the ureter at the lower pole of the kidney
- **Intravesical part of the ureter:** part of the ureter that courses through the wall of the bladder
- **Trigone:** triangular area in the interior of the urinary bladder that is bounded by the two ureteric orifices and the opening of the urethra
- **Internal urethral sphincter:** smooth muscle surrounding the upper portion of the urethra
- **Detrusor muscle:** smooth muscle of the urinary bladder
- **Urogenital diaphragm:** skeletal muscle covered superiorly and inferiorly by connective tissue through which the urethra passes
- **External urethral sphincter:** skeletal muscle which is part of the urogenital diaphragm which surrounds the membranous urethra

REVIEW QUESTIONS

1. Label the parts of the excretory system in the figure below (a-d).

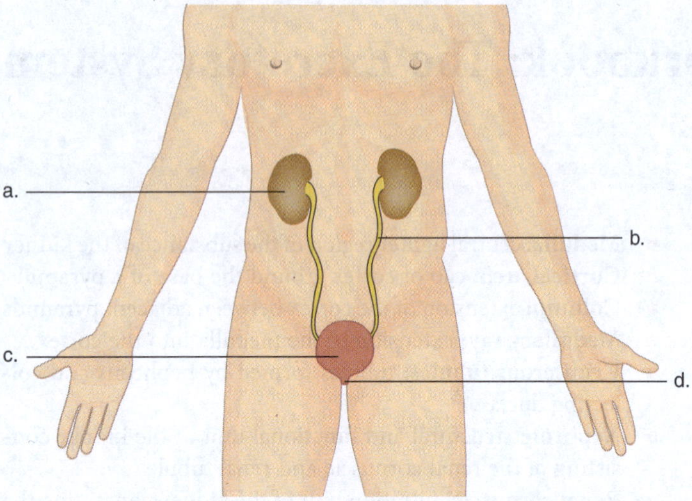

2. The four coverings of the kidney from inside to outside are the ____________, ____________, ____________, ____________ and ____________.

3. Label the posterior relations of the kidney in the figure below (a-f).

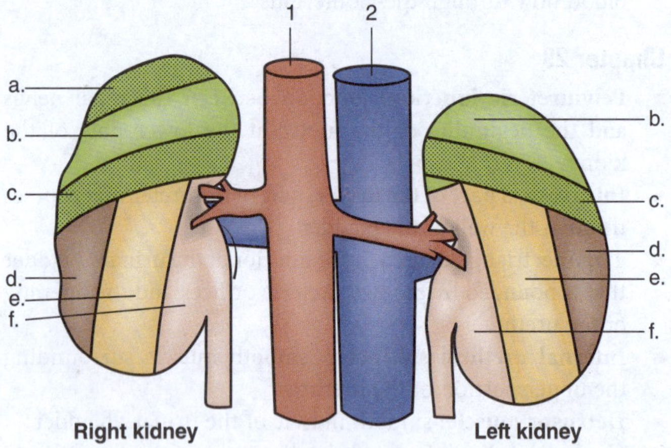

4. Label the anterior relations of the kidney in the figure below (a-j).

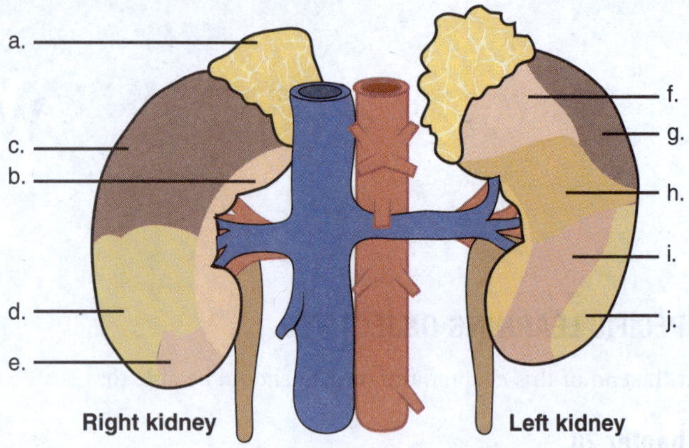

5. Describe the gross anatomy of the kidney.
6. Uriniferous tubules consist of ____________ and ____________.
7. Nephrons consist of the ____________ and ____________.
8. Describe the microscopic anatomy of the kidney.
9. Label the parts of a nephron in the figure below (1 to 3 and a to e).

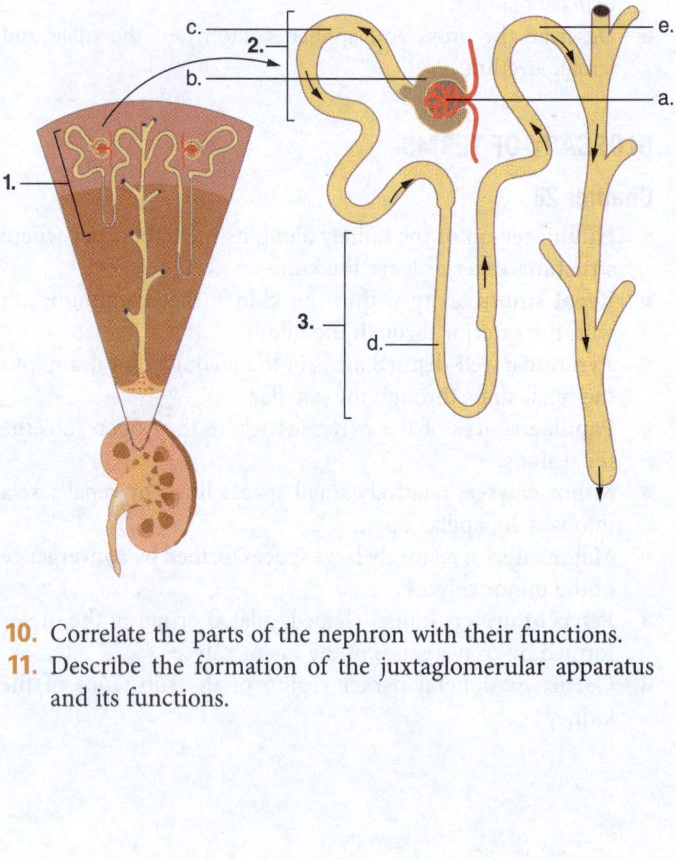

10. Correlate the parts of the nephron with their functions.
11. Describe the formation of the juxtaglomerular apparatus and its functions.

12. The parts of the ureter are the ______________, ______________ and ______________.
13. Name the sites of constriction of the ureter and their applied importance.
14. The shape of the urinary bladder is ______________ when it is empty and ______________ when it is full.
15. The inferior portion of the urinary bladder is called the ______________.
16. The smooth triangular area seen in the interior of the bladder is called the ______________.
17. Describe the gross anatomy of the urinary bladder.
18. ______________ epithelium lines the inside of the urinary bladder.
19. The smooth muscle of the bladder is called the ______________.
20. Describe the microscopic anatomy of the urinary bladder.
21. Describe the gross anatomy and functions of the trigone of the urinary bladder.
22. The parts of the male urethra are the ______________, ______________ and ______________ urethra.
23. Compare and contrast the male and female urethra.

SECTION 8: Workbook Answer Key

The Excretory System

1. (a) Kidnay; (b) Ureter; (c) Urinary bladder; (d) Urethra
2. fibrous capsule, perinephric fat, renal fascia, paranephric fat
3. (1) Aorta; (2) IVC; (a) 11th rib; (b) Diaphragm; (c) 12th rib; (d) Transversus abdominis; (e) Quadratus lumborum; (f) Psoas major
4. (a) Suprarenal gland; (b) Duodenum; (c) Liver; (d) Hepatic flexure of colon; (e) Small intestine; (f) Stomach; (g) Spleen; (h) Pancreas; (i) Jejunum; (j) Splenic flexure of colon
6. nephrons, collecting ducts
7. renal corpuscle, renal tubule
9. (1) Nephron; (2) Cortex; (3) Medulla; (a) Glomerulus; (b) Bowman's capsule; (c) PCT; (d) Loop of Henle; (e) DCT
12. abdominal, pelvic, intravesical
14. tetrahedral, ovoid
15. neck
16. trigone
18. Transitional
19. detrusor
22. prostatic, membranous, penile

Workbook: The Reproductive System

SPECIFIC LEARNING OBJECTIVES

At the end of this chapter, the student should be able to:

Chapter 30

- Name the parts of the female reproductive system.
- Describe the gross, microscopic and applied anatomy of the ovary.
- Describe the gross, microscopic and applied anatomy of the Fallopian tube.
- Describe the gross, microscopic and applied anatomy of the uterus.
- Describe the gross, microscopic and applied anatomy of the mammary gland.
- Describe the gross anatomy of the female external genitalia.

Chapter 31

- Describe the parts and functions of the male reproductive system.
- Describe the gross anatomy, histology and applied anatomy of the testis.
- Describe the gross anatomy, histology and applied anatomy of the ducts of the male reproductive system.
- Describe the gross anatomy, histology and applied anatomy of the accessory glands of the male reproductive system.

GLOSSARY OF TERMS

Chapter 30

- **Follicle:** oocyte surrounded by follicular cells
- **Zone pellucida:** glycoprotein layer surrounding the oocyte
- **Theca folliculi:** connective tissue surrounding the developing follicle
- **Cumulus oophorus:** granulosa cells surrounding the oocyte
- **Corona radiata:** granulosa cells immediately surrounding the oocyte
- **Ampulla:** part of the Fallopian tube where fertilization takes place
- **Mesosalpinx:** part of the broad ligament enclosing the Fallopian tube
- **Fundus:** uppermost part of the uterus
- **Cervix:** lower part of the uterus
- **Internal os:** opening between the body of the uterus and cervix
- **External os:** opening between the cervix and vagina
- **Isthmus:** upper part of the cervix
- **Broad ligament:** curtain-like peritoneal fold on either side of the uterus
- **Stratum basalis:** deeper part of the endometrium that is retained during menstruation
- **Stratum functionalis:** superficial part of the endometrium that is shed during menstruation
- **Fornix:** upper part of the vagina surrounding the lower part of the cervix
- **Axillary tail of Spence:** extension of breast tissue into the axilla
- **Ligaments of Cooper:** connective tissue framework of the breast

Chapter 31

- **Tunica vaginalis:** mesothelial covering of the testes
- **Tunica albuginea:** connective tissue covering of the testes
- **Tunica vasculosa:** innermost vascular covering of the testes
- **Seminiferous tubules:** tubules within the testes lined by spermatogenic and supporting cells
- **Spermatogenic cells:** cells which divide to form spermatozoa
- **Sertoli cells:** supporting cells seen within seminiferous tubules
- **Interstitial cells of Leydig:** cells seen between seminiferous tubules that secrete testosterone
- **Pampiniform plexus of veins:** plexus of veins draining the testes
- **Corpora amylacea:** calcified secretions located within prostatic acini
- **Glans penis:** the expanded distal end of the body of the penis
- **Prepuce:** fold of skin covering the glans penis
- **Bulb of the penis:** erectile tissue located in the middle of the root of the penis
- **Crura:** erectile tissue situated on either side of the bulb
- **Corpora cavernosa:** erectile tissue situated dorsolaterally within the body of the penis
- **Corpus spongiosum:** erectile tissue situated ventrally within the body of the penis
- **Buck's fascia:** fascia surrounding the circumference of the penis
- **Tunica albuginea:** connective tissue covering of the corpora cavernosa
- **Dartos:** smooth muscle of the scrotum

REVIEW QUESTIONS

1. Label the parts of the female reproductive system in the figure below (a to d).

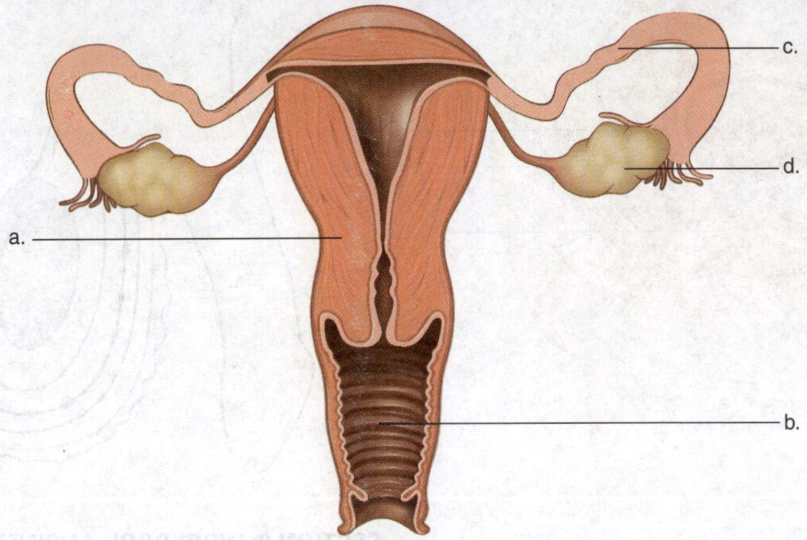

2. The four types of follicles seen in the ovary are the ______________, ______________, ______________ and ______________ follicles.
3. Following ovulation, the ruptured follicle reorganizes into a specialized endocrine structure called the ______________.
4. Describe the microscopic anatomy of the ovary.
5. Draw a neat, labelled diagram of a Graafian follicle.
6. Label the parts of the Fallopian tube in the figure below (a to d).

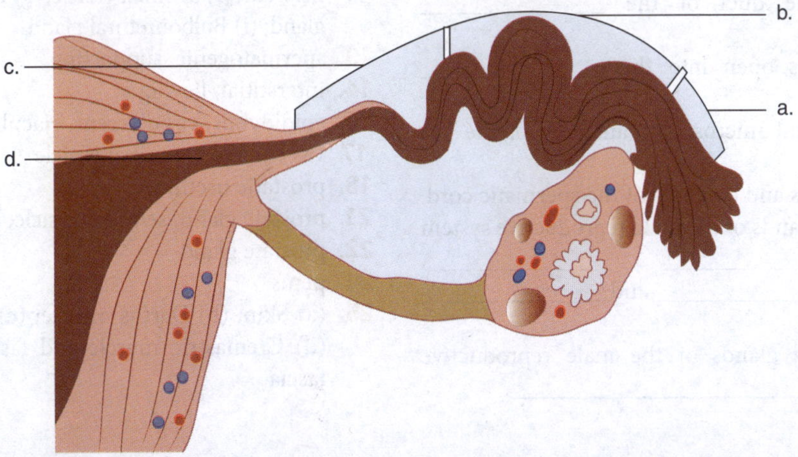

7. The three parts of the uterus are the ______________, ______________ and ______________.
8. Describe the gross anatomy of the uterus.
9. The three layers of the uterus from inside to outside are the ______________, ______________ and ______________.
10. Describe the microscopic anatomy of the uterus.
11. The breast is a modified ______________.

12. Label the parts of the male reproductive system in the figure below (a to i).

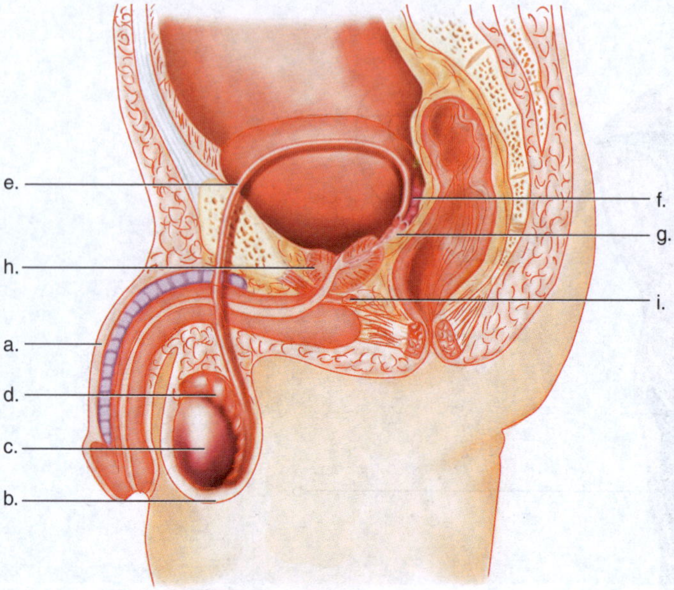

13. Seminiferous tubules are lined by ______________ and ______________ cells.
14. Between the seminiferous tubules are small clusters of eosinophilic cells called the ______________ cells of ______________.
15. Describe the gross and microscopic anatomy of the testes.
16. The duct system of the testis is formed by the ______________, ______________ ______________ and ______________ ______________.
17. The ejaculatory ducts are formed by the fusion of the ______________ and the duct of the ______________ ______________.
18. The ejaculatory ducts open into the ______________ ______________.
19. Describe the gross and microscopic anatomy of the vas deferens.
20. Describe the coverings and contents of the spermatic cord.
21. The three accessory glands of the male reproductive system are the ______________ ______________, ______________ ______________ and ______________ ______________.
22. The largest accessory glands of the male reproductive system is the ______________ ______________.
23. Describe the gross and microscopic anatomy of the prostate gland.
24. The male organ of copulation is the ______________.
25. Label the layers of the scrotum in the figure below (a to e).

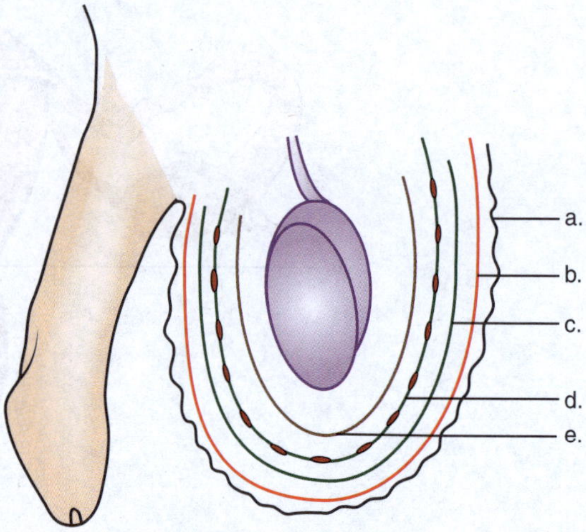

SECTION 9: WORKBOOK ANSWER KEY

The Reproductive System

1. (a) Uterus; (b) Vagina; (c) Fallopian tube; (d) Ovary
2. primordial, primary, secondary, tertiary
3. corpus luteum
6. (a) Infundibulum; (b) Ampulla; (c) Isthmus; (d) Intramural part
7. fundus, body, cervix
9. endometrium, myometrium, perimetrium
11. sweat gland
12. (a) Penis; (b) Scrotum; (c) Testis; (d) Epididymis; (e) Vas deferens; (f) Seminal vesicle; (g) Ejaculatory duct; (h) Prostate gland; (i) Bulbourethral gland
13. spermatogenic, supporting
14. interstitial, Leydig
16. epididymis, vas deferens, ejaculatory ducts
17. vas deferens, seminal vesicle
18. prostatic urethra
21. prostate gland, seminal vesicle, bulbourethral glands
22. prostate gland
24. penis
25. (a) Skin; (b) Dartos muscle; (c) External spermatic fascia; (d) Cremastric muscle and fascia; (e) Internal spermatic fascia

SECTION 10

Workbook: The Nervous System

SPECIFIC LEARNING OBJECTIVES

At the end of this chapter, the student should be able to:

Chapter 32

- Classify the nervous system.
- Name the individual parts of the nervous system.
- Classify neurons.
- Describe the structure of a typical neuron.
- Describe the structure and functions of the supporting cells of the nervous system.
- Describe the layers and structure of the meninges.
- Describe the gross anatomy of the dural venous sinuses.
- Describe the formation, flow and absorption of cerebrospinal fluid.
- Describe the salient features of the autonomic nervous system.

Chapter 33

- Describe the gross and cross-sectional anatomy of the spinal cord.
- Describe the structure of a typical spinal nerve.
- Describe the formation, important branches and distribution of the cervical, brachial, lumbar and sacral plexuses.

Chapter 34

- Name the parts of the brainstem.
- Describe the basic structure of the medulla, pons and midbrain.
- Describe the formation, course and distribution of the cranial nerves.
- Describe the gross anatomy of the cerebellum.
- Describe the gross anatomy of the fourth ventricle.

Chapter 35

- Name the parts of the forebrain.
- Describe the structure and functions of the thalamus.
- Describe the structure and functions of the hypothalamus.
- Describe the structure and functions of the basal nuclei.
- Describe the gross anatomy of the cerebrum.
- Describe the gross anatomy of the lateral and third ventricles.

GLOSSARY OF TERMS

Chapter 32

- **Grey matter:** outer layer of the cerebrum and cerebellum and inner part of the spinal cord containing neuronal cell bodies and unmyelinated neuronal processes
- **White matter:** inner layer of the cerebrum and cerebellum and outer part of the spinal cord containing myelinated neuronal processes
- **Nuclei:** collections of neuronal cell bodies within the central nervous system (CNS)
- **Ganglia:** collections of neuronal cell bodies outside the CNS
- **Tract:** collection of neuronal processes in the CNS
- **Nerve:** collection of neuronal processes outside the CNS
- **Perikaryon:** cell body of neuron
- **Nissl substance:** prominent rough endoplasmic reticulum of a neuron
- **Dendrite:** neuronal cell process carrying impulses towards the cell body
- **Axon:** neuronal cell process carrying impulses away from the cell body
- **Telodendria:** axon terminals
- **Myelin:** whitish phospholipid covering of neuronal cell processes
- **Nodes of Ranvier:** periodic gaps in the myelin sheath
- **Synapse:** site of functional contact between excitable cells
- **Dural folds:** projections of the meningeal layer of dura into the cranial cavity
- **Dural venous sinuses:** endothelial lined spaces between dural folds carrying venous blood
- **Subarachnoid space:** space between arachnoid mater and pia mater containing cerebrospinal fluid (CSF)
- **Cistern:** local expansion of the subarachnoid space
- **Arachnoid villi:** minute projections of the arachnoid mater into the dural venous sinuses

Chapter 33

- **Conus medullaris:** tapered tip of the lower end of the spinal cord
- **Cauda equina:** the lower spinal nerves that emerge from the spinal cord and resemble a horse's tail

- **Denticulate ligaments:** lateral triangular projections of the pia towards the dura that keep the spinal cord in place
- **Filum terminale:** thin strand of pia extending from the lower end of the spinal cord to the coccyx
- **Grey horns:** projections of the central grey matter of the spinal cord
- **White columns or funiculi:** subdivisions of the white matter containing tracts
- **Tract or fasciculus:** nerve fibres with a similar origin, termination and function
- **Decussation:** crossing of nerve fibres from one side to the other
- **Contralateral:** the origin and destination of pathways are on opposite sides
- **Ipsilateral:** the origin and destination of pathways are on the same side
- **Dermatome:** an area of skin supplied by a single spinal segment
- **Myotome:** all skeletal muscle fibres supplied by a single spinal segment
- **Nerve plexus:** ventral rami of spinal nerves that become interconnected to form a network and supply a particular region of the body

Chapter 34

- **Pyramid:** an elongated projection on the ventral aspect of the medulla caused by the underlying corticospinal fibres
- **Olive:** a rounded projection on the ventral aspect of the medulla caused by the underlying inferior olivary nucleus
- **Cerebellar peduncle:** connection between the brainstem and cerebellum
- **Reticular formation:** collection of neurons and nerve fibres found interspersed between the nuclei and white matter
- **Crus cerebri:** prominent ventral aspect of the midbrain caused by descending fibres from the cerebral cortex
- **Substantia nigra:** pigmented part of the midbrain containing dopaminergic neurons
- **Tegmentum:** anterior part of the midbrain
- **Tectum:** posterior part of the midbrain
- **Colliculi:** rounded projections forming part of the tectum of the midbrain
- **Vermis:** midline portion of the cerebellum connecting the two hemispheres
- **Folia:** elevated areas of the cerebellar cortex
- **Fissures:** depressed areas of the cerebellar cortex
- **Foramina of Luschka:** foramina at the lateral angles of the fourth ventricle
- **Foramen of Magendie:** median foramen at the inferior angle of the fourth ventricle

Chapter 35

- **Pulvinar:** broad, posterior end of the thalamus
- **Internal medullary lamina:** Y-shaped band of white matter within the thalamus
- **Thalamic radiation:** connection between the thalamus and cerebral cortex
- **Infundibulum:** the pituitary stalk connecting the pituitary gland to the hypothalamus
- **Median eminence:** elevation of the hypothalamus around the pituitary stalk
- **Fornix:** fibres arising from the hippocampus
- **Hypothalamo-hypophyseal portal system:** portal system connecting the capillaries around the median eminence and pituitary gland
- **Hypothalamo-hypophyseal tract:** nerve fibres extending from the hypothalamus to the posterior pituitary
- **Corpus striatum:** major component of the basal nuclei having a striated appearance
- **Caudate nucleus:** C-shaped nucleus which forms the medial component of the corpus striatum
- **Lentiform nucleus:** lens-shaped lateral component of the corpus striatum
- **Putamen:** lateral component of the lentiform nucleus
- **Globus pallidus:** medial component of the lentiform nucleus
- **Gyri:** elevations of the cerebral cortex
- **Sulci:** depressions on the cerebral cortex
- **Brodmann areas:** functional areas of the cerebral cortex
- **Homunculus:** representation of the body in the primary motor and somatosensory cortex
- **Limbic system:** forebrain structures that control visceral activity, olfaction, emotion and memory
- **Commissural fibres:** fibres that connect corresponding areas of the cerebrum
- **Association fibres:** fibres connecting areas within a hemisphere
- **Projection fibres:** fibres connecting the cerebrum with lower brain centres and the spinal cord
- **Circle of Willis:** arterial circle formed at the base of the brain by branches of the internal carotid and basilar arteries
- **Horns of the lateral ventricle:** extensions of the lateral ventricle into the frontal, occipital and temporal lobes
- **Foramen of Monro:** communications between the lateral and third ventricle on each side

REVIEW QUESTIONS

1. Structurally, the two parts of the nervous system are the ______________ and ______________ nervous system.
2. The two parts of the central nervous system are the ______________ and ______________.
3. Functionally, the two parts of the nervous system are the ______________ and ______________ nervous system.
4. Functionally, the two parts of the nervous system are the ______________ and ______________ nervous system.
5. The three parts of the brain are the ______________, ______________ and ______________.

6. Label the parts of the brain in the figure below (1 to 3 and a to f).

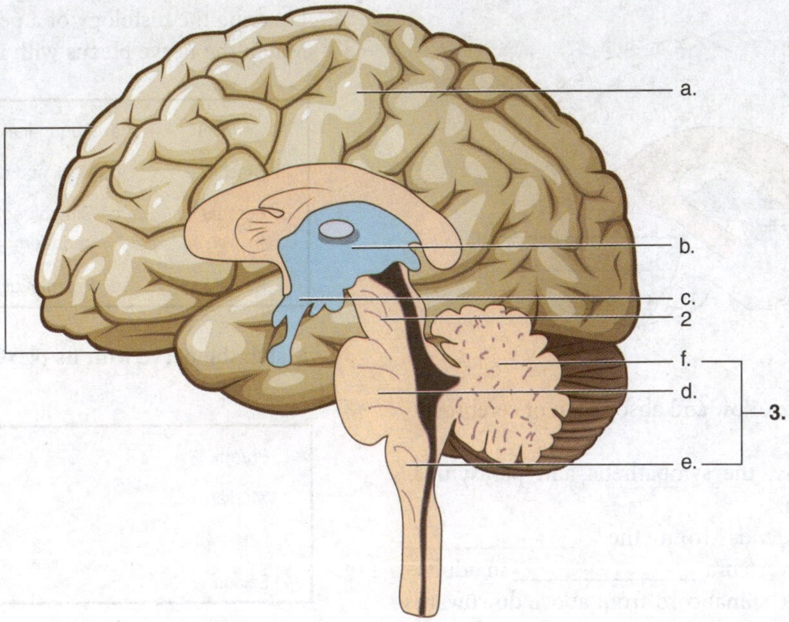

7. The two principal cell types of the nervous system are ____________ and their ____________ ____________.

8. Classify neurons with suitable examples.

9. Draw a neat, labelled diagram of a typical neuron.

10. Name the supporting cells of the nervous system and their functions.

11. From outside to inside, the three layers of meninges are the ____________ ____________, ____________ ____________ and ____________ ____________.

12. Describe the structure of the meningeal layers.

13. The four dural folds are the ____________ ____________, ____________ ____________, ____________ ____________ and ____________ ____________.

14. The space between the arachnoid mater and pia meter is called the ____________ ____________ and contains ____________ ____________.

15. Label the major dural venous sinuses in the figure below (a to g).

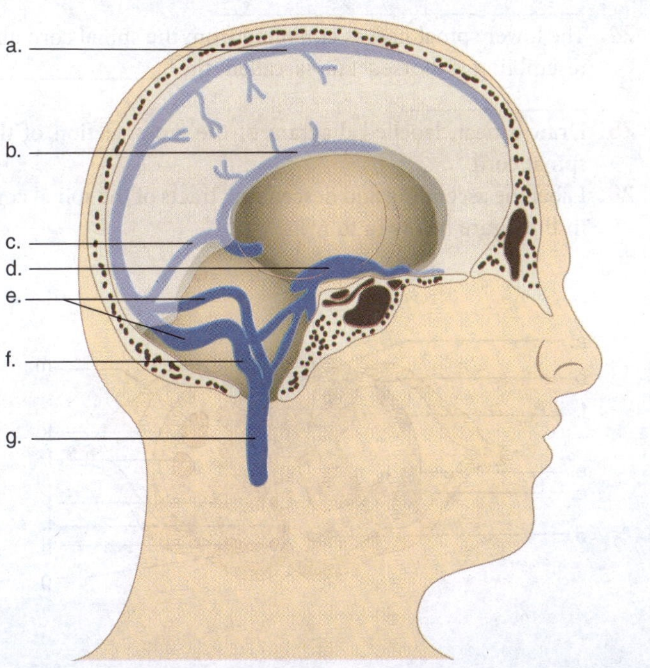

16. Classify the dural venous sinuses. Describe the gross anatomy of the cavernous sinus.
17. Label the ventricles of the brain in the figure below (a to d).

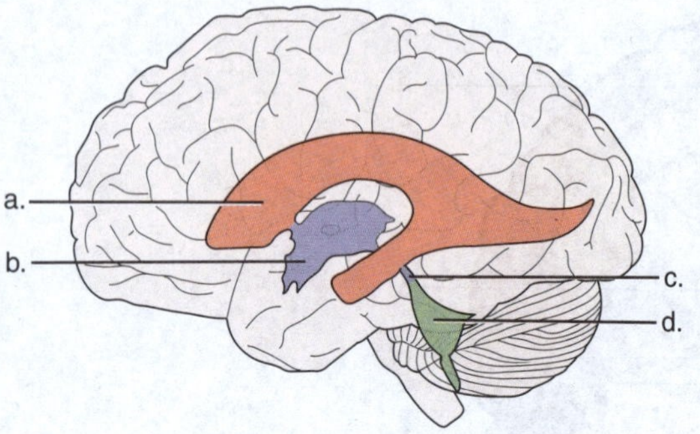

18. Describe the formation, flow and absorption of cerebrospinal fluid.
19. Compare and contrast the sympathetic and parasympathetic nervous system.
20. The spinal cord extends from the ______ ______ to vertebra ______ in adults.
21. The five regions of the spinal cord from above downwards are the ______, ______, ______, ______ and ______ regions.
22. The two enlargements of the spinal cord are the ______ and ______ enlargements.
23. The tapered tip of the spinal cord is called the ______ ______.
24. The lower spinal nerves emerging from the spinal cord and resembling a horse's tail is called the ______ ______.
25. Draw a neat, labelled diagram of the cross section of the spinal cord.
26. Label the ascending and descending tracts of the spinal cord in the figure below (a to m).

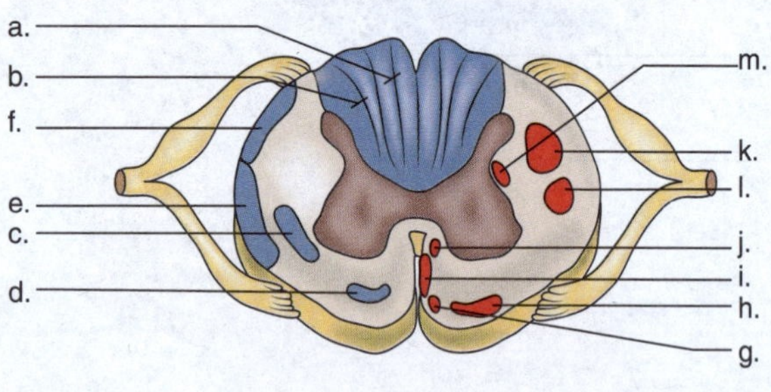

27. There are ______ pairs of spinal nerves.
28. Describe the anatomy of a typical spinal nerve.
29. A ______ is an area of skin supplied by a single spinal segment.
30. A ______ consists of all skeletal muscle fibres supplied by a single spinal segment.
31. Describe the histology of a peripheral nerve.
32. Describe the histology of a peripheral nerve.
33. Match the nerve plexus with its distribution.

1. Cervical	a. Abdominal wall, anterior thigh and genitalia
2. Brachial	b. Neck and diaphragm
3. Lumbar	c. Gluteal region, lower limb, pelvic muscles, perineum
4. Sacral	d. Pectoral girdle and upper limb

34. Match the nerve with its plexus of origin.

1. Phrenic	a. Sacral
2. Median	b. Lumbar
3. Femoral	c. Cervical
4. Sciatic	d. Brachial

35. Describe the anatomy of the brachial plexus.
36. Describe the anatomy of the sacral plexus.
37. The brainstem consists of the ______, ______ and ______.
38. Describe the anatomy of the medulla oblongata.
39. Describe the anatomy of the pons.
40. Describe the anatomy of the midbrain.
41. Match the cranial nerve with its function.

1. Olfactory (I)	a. Hearing and equilibrium
2. Optic (II)	b. Sensory supply of the face
3. Oculomotor (III)	c. Parasympathetic nerve supply to the heart and lungs
4. Trochlear (IV)	d. Movements of the tongue
5. Trigeminal (V)	e. Smell
6. Abducent (VI)	f. Pupillary constriction
7. Facial (VII)	g. Nerve supply to the superior oblique muscle
8. Vestibulocochlear (VIII)	h. Vision
9. Glossopharyngeal (IX)	i. Nerve supply to the trapezius and sternocleidomastoid
10. Vagus (X)	j. Nerve supply to the lateral rectus
11. Accessory (XI)	k. Sensory nerve supply to the pharynx
12. Hypoglossal (XII)	l. Nerve supply to the muscles of facial expression

42. The parts of the hindbrain are the ______________ ______________, ______________ and ______________.

43. Describe the gross anatomy of the cerebellum.

44. The 4th ventricle is the cavity of the ______________.

45. Describe the gross anatomy of the fourth ventricle.

46. Label the parts of the forebrain in the figure below (a to d).

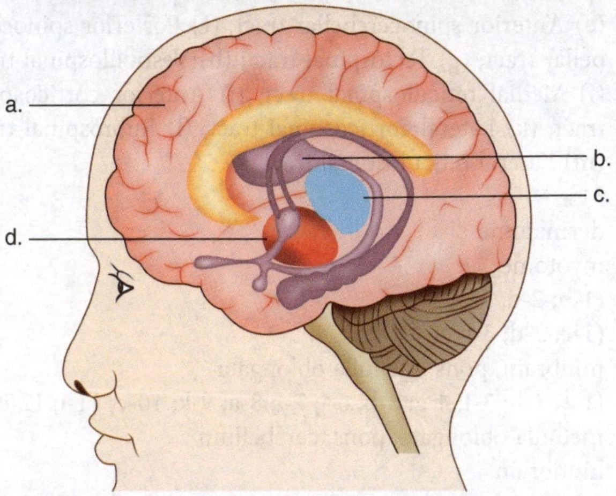

47. Describe the gross anatomy of the thalamus.

48. Describe the gross anatomy of the hypothalamus.

49. Name the components of the basal nuclei.

50. Label the lobes of the cerebrum in the figure below (a to d).

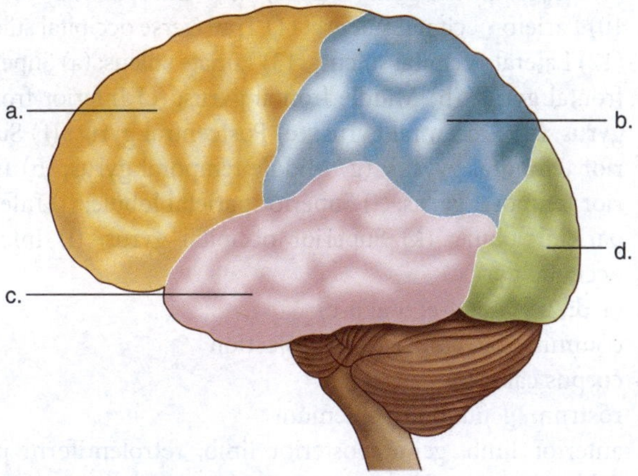

51. Label the important gyri (alphabets) and sulci (numbers) of the cerebrum in the figure below (a to l and 1 to 13).

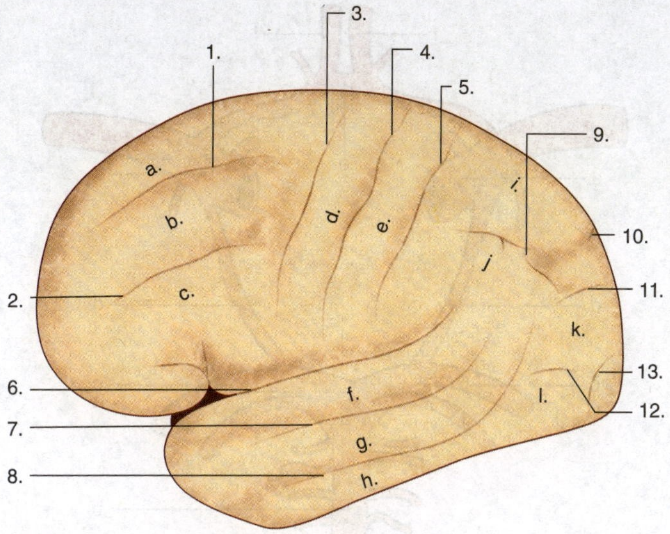

52. Match the Brodmann areas with the appropriate parts of the cerebrum.

1. Areas 3, 2, 1	a. Superior temporal gyrus
2. Area 4	b. Prefrontal cortex
3. Area 6	c. Inferior frontal gyrus
4. Area 17	d. Postcentral gyrus
5. Areas 41, 42	e. Occipital lobe
6. Areas 44, 45	f. Precentral gyrus

53. Describe the superolateral surface of the cerebrum.

54. The three types of fibres in the white matter of the cerebrum are ______________, ______________ and ______________ fibres.

55. The largest collection of commissural fibres is the ______________ ______________.

56. The four parts of the corpus callosum are the ______________, ______________, ______________ and ______________.

57. Describe the gross anatomy of the corpus callosum.

58. The five parts of the internal capsule are the ______________ ______________, ______________, ______________, ______________ ______________ and ______________.

59. Describe the gross anatomy of the internal capsule.

60. Label the arteries that form the circle of Willis in the figure below (a to f).

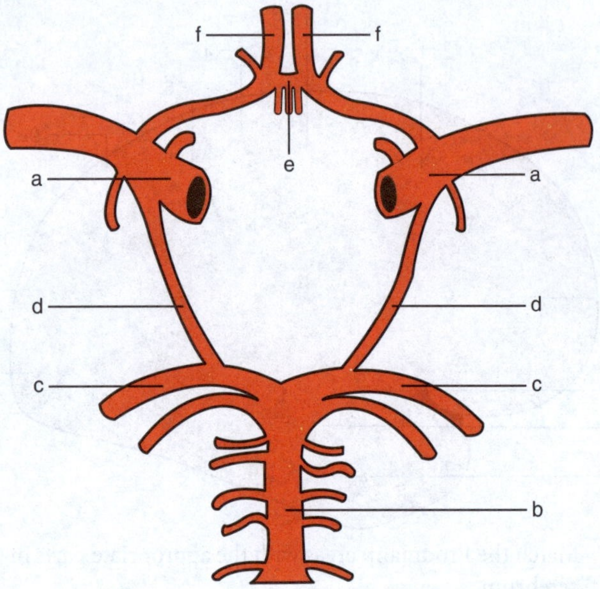

61. The four parts of the lateral ventricle are the ______________ ______________, ______________, ______________ and ______________.

62. The lateral ventricles communicate with the third ventricle on each side via the ______________ ______________.

63. Describe the gross anatomy of the lateral ventricles.

SECTION 10: WORKBOOK ANSWER KEY

The Nervous System

1. central, peripheral
2. brain, spinal cord
3. somatic, autonomic
4. somatic, autonomic
5. forebrain, midbrain, hindbrain
6. (1) Forebrain; (2) Midbrain; (3) Hindbrain; (a) Cerebrum; (b) Thalamus; (c) Hypothalamus; (d) Pons; (e) Medulla (f) Cerebellum
7. neurons, supporting cells
11. dura mater, arachnoid mater, pia mater
13. falx cerebri, tentorium cerebelli, falx cerebelli, diaphragma sellae
14. subarachnoid space, cerebrospinal fluid
15. (a) Superior sagittal sinus; (b) Inferior sagittal sinus; (c) Straight sinus; (d) Cavernous sinus; (e) Transverse sinus; (f) Sigmoid sinus; (g) Internal jugular vein
17. (a) Lateral ventricle; (b) 3rd ventricle; (c) Cerebral aqueduct; (d) 4th ventricle
21. cervical, thoracic, lumbar, sacral, coccygeal
22. cervical, lumbar
23. conus medullaris
24. cauda equina
26. (a) Faciculus gracilis; (b) Fasciculus cuneatus; (c) Lateral spinothalamic tract; (d) Anterior spinothalamic tract; (e) Anterior spinocerebellar tract; (f) Posterior spinocerebellar tract; (g) Tectospinal tract; (h) Vestibulospinal tract; (i) Medial reticulospinal tract; (j) Anterior corticospinal tract; (k) Lateral corticospinal tract; (l) Rubrospinal tract; (m) Lareral reticulospinal tract
27. 31
29. dermatome
30. myotome
33. (1-b; 2-d; 3-a; 4-c)
34. (1-c; 2-d; 3-b; 4-a)
37. midbrain, pons, medulla oblongata
41. (1-e; 2-h; 3-f; 4-g; 5-b; 6-j; 7-l; 8-a; 9-k; 10-c; 11-i; 12-d)
42. medulla oblongata, pons, cerebellum
44. hindbrain
46. (a) Cerebral cortex; (b) Basal nuclei; (c) Thalamus; (d) Hypothalamus
50. (a) Frontal; (b) Parietal; (c) Temporal; (d) Occipital
51. (1) Superior frontal sulcus; (2) Inferior frontal sulcus; (3) Precentral sulcus; (4) Central sulcus; (5) Postcentral sulcus; (6) Lateral sulcus; (7) Superior temporal sulcus; (8) Inferior temporal sulcus; (9) Intraparietal sulcus; 10) Parieto-occipital sulcus; (11) Transverse occipital sulcus; (12) Lateral occipital sulcus; (13) Lunate sulcus; (a) Superior frontal gyrus; (b) Middle frontal gyrus; (c) Inferior frontal gyrus; (d) Precentral gyrus; (e) Postcentral gyrus; (f) Superior temporal gyyrus; (g) Middle temporal gyrus; (h) Inferior temporal gyrus; (i) Superior parietal lobule; (j) Inferior parietal lobule; (k) Superior occipital gyrus; (l) Inferior occipital gyrus
52. (1-d; 2-f; 3-b; 4-e; 5-a; 6-c)
54. commissural, association, projection
55. corpus callosum
56. rostrum, genu, body, splenium
58. anterior limb, genu, posterior limb, retrolentiform part, sublentiform part
60. (a) Internal carotid artery; (b) Basilar artery; (c) Posterior cerebral artery; (d) Posterior communicating artery; (e) Anterior cerebral artery; (f) Anterior communicating artery
61. anterior horn, body, posterior horn, inferior horn
62. foramen of Munro

Index

Note: Page numbers followed by *f* indicate figures, and *t* indicate tables.